TEACHER'S EDITION

Mathematics in Action

PROGRAM OVERVIEW

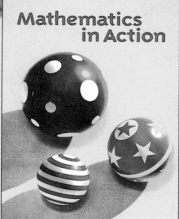

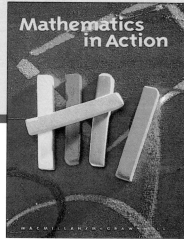

AUTHORS

Audrey L. Jackson   Richard D. Lodholz

Martin L. Johnson   Gary L. Musser

Steven L. Leinwand   Walter G. Secada

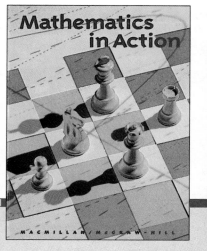

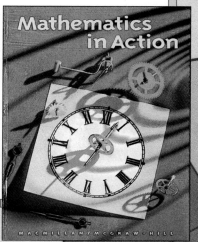

MACMILLAN/McGRAW-HILL SCHOOL DIVISION

McGRAW-HILL SCHOOL PUBLISHING COMPANY

New York • Columbus

Teaching and Learning Mathematics Has Never Been so Much Fun!

CONTENTS

AUTHORS

Audrey L. Jackson, Mathematics Specialist, Parkway School District, Missouri, specializes in developmental learning in the primary grades. She is a frequent speaker at national and regional meetings of the National Council of Teachers of Mathematics.

Dr. Martin L. Johnson, Professor of Mathematics Education at the University of Maryland, College Park, has special expertise in diagnosis and remediation in mathematics and its application to the learning of minority children. Dr. Johnson has been an advisor, consultant, and writer and is a contributor to many professional journals.

Steven J. Leinward, Mathematics Consultant for the Connecticut State Department of Education, is responsible for the development of a statewide program in mathematics. He is the author of many articles in professional journals and is a member of the Curriculum Framework Task Force of the Mathematical Sciences Education Board.

Dr. Richard D. Lodholz, Mathematics Coordinator K-12 of the Parkway School District, Missouri, supervises mathematics instruction in a nationally known, forward-looking school district. Dr. Lodholz is a member of the Board of Directors of the National Council of Teachers of Mathematics and is a frequent presenter at national and regional meetings. He has a particular expertise in the areas of estimation, mental math, and middle school.

Dr. Gary L. Musser, Professor of Mathematics at Oregon State University in Corvallis, is the author of the highly successful *Mathematics for Elementary Teachers*, published by Macmillan's College Division. Dr. Musser has taught mathematics to students from elementary schools through universities. His current research is in problem solving.

Dr. Walter G. Secada, Associate Professor of Mathematics Education at the University of Wisconsin at Madison, is a specialist in multicultural and bilingual education. He has conducted extensive research in the area of equity in mathematics education and is a consultant to school districts around the country.

CONSULTANTS

Multicultural and Educational Consultants
Rim An, Marcia Ascher, Elsie Babcock, Vicki Chan, Alejandro Gallard, Zelda Gold, Jerilyn Grignon, Earlene Hall, Susan Lair, Barbara Merino, Carol Mitchell, James R. Murphy, Gail Lowe Parrino, Yolanda Rodriguez, Claudia Zaslavsky

Assessment Consultant Michael Priestley

Cooperative Learning Consultant Liana Nan Graves

Macmillan/McGraw-Hill School Division
1221 Avenue of the Americas
New York, NY 10020
Printed in the United States of America   ISBN 0-02-109280-X / 2-2
5 6 7 8 9 WEB 99 98 97 96

Mathematics in Action

The <u>only</u> choice for students and teachers.

Take a closer look at the many resources available to make teaching mathematics easier for you!

*For a complete listing of components, see page T-16.

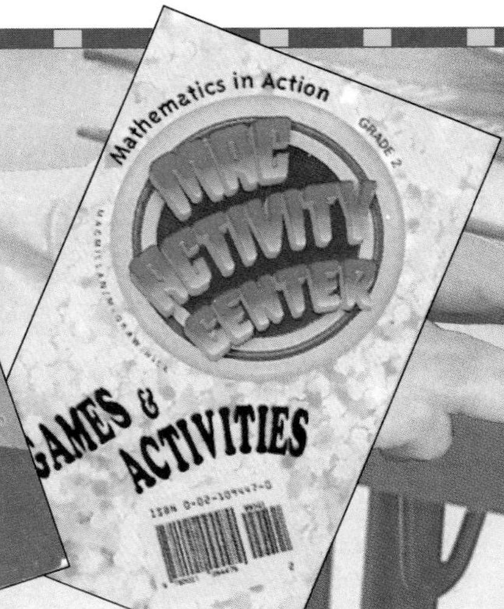

MATH SONGS

MATHEMATICS IN ACTION

I Can! MATH ACTIVITY PROGRAM

CALCULATOR WORKSHOP
BLACKLINE MASTERS & TEACHER'S EDITION
GRADE 2

Mathematics in Action

Problem of the Day

Mathematics in Action

GAMES & ACTIVITIES

MATHEMATICS IN ACTION:
MATH ANTHOLOGY
STORIES & POEMS
MACMILLAN McGRAW-HILL
GRADE 5

Active Learning Builds
Confidence

Students first encounter new concepts and skills through hands-on, high-interest activities. They deal with all new material in concrete terms, by working with manipulatives before they deal with it abstractly.

Working Together

Cooperative Learning

New concepts are introduced to students through a step-by-step activity. They work together in cooperative groups to develop these concepts, trade opinions, clarify each other's thinking, and share in the decision making process.

Versatile Manipulatives

Using graph paper, cubes, spinners, and a variety of other simple manipulatives, students connect mathematics with the real world.

Artful Questioning

Guided by carefully designed questioning sequences, students experience the satisfaction of exploring and developing an understanding of mathematical concepts individually or in a group setting.

Grade 5, pages 456–457

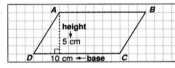

MATH CONNECTION: AREA
Area of a Parallelogram

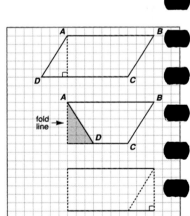

The parallelogram below has a base of 10 cm and a height of 5 cm. What is the area of the parallelogram?

WORKING TOGETHER

You can find the area of the parallelogram by doing the following activity.

Step 1 Use centimeter graph paper to draw the parallelogram described above. Label it as shown. Then cut out parallelogram ABCD.

Step 2 Fold the figure so that point D is on side DC and the fold line goes through point A.

Step 3 Unfold the paper and cut along the fold line. Fit the triangular piece on side BC to form a four-sided figure.

1. What four-sided figure did you form in Step 3?

2. What is the area of the figure you formed? How did you find the area?

3. What is the area of parallelogram ABCD?

456 Lesson 11–9

Sharing Ideas

Students discuss their various methods for calculating, discovering that there is more than one way to solve a problem.

SHARING IDEAS

Describe a method for finding the area of a parallelogram if you know its base and height.

PRACTICE

Use your method to find the area of the parallelogram.

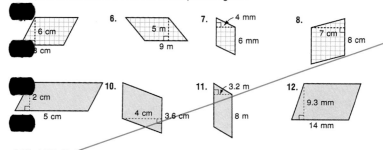

6 cm
8 cm

6. 5 m / 9 m

7. 4 mm / 6 mm

8. 7 cm / 8 cm

2 cm / 5 cm

10. 4 cm / 3.6 cm

11. 3.2 m / 8 m

12. 9.3 mm / 14 mm

Critical Thinking

Use a graph-paper model of a parallelogram to show why the area of any triangle is equal to $\frac{1}{2}$ the area of a parallelogram.

Mixed Applications

Solve. Which method did you use?

14. A sheet of glass is a parallelogram. Its base is 20 cm and its height is 45 cm. What is the area of the sheet of glass?

15. Mike has a rectangular piece of canvas 30 cm long by 45 cm wide. He cut it in half diagonally to make a triangular sail for his model boat. What is the area of the sail?

16. There are 36 members in the model-boat club. Of these, $\frac{3}{4}$ made their own boats. How many members made their own boats?

17. A garden that is a parallelogram has an area that is 18 m². The base of the parallelogram is 6 m. What is its height?

ESTIMATION
MENTAL MATH
CALCULATOR
PAPER/PENCIL

EXTRA PRACTICE, page 471

Multiplying and Dividing Fractions **457**

Practice

Built right into each lesson— enables students to apply what they've learned in a variety of ways.

Critical Thinking

Students learn that explaining and justifying their thinking is important and how a problem is solved is as important as the answer.

Mixed Applications

Presents word problems to help students review current and previous lessons.
In other lessons a mixed review section keeps students sharp by reviewing previously taught skills.

Extra Practice & Practice Plus

Offers additional practice at the end of every chapter, where it's needed most.

Fully Meets the NCTM Standards

Communication

Students communicate with each other and with their teacher to develop concepts as they question, clarify, and explain their thinking... deepening their mathematical understanding and sharpening their mathematical skills.

Reasoning

Activities are designed to exercise both mental and visual abilities... inviting students to think logically, work systematically, and thoroughly test their lessons.

Problem Solving

Whether it's counting their allowance or measuring ingredients for a recipe... students will quickly discover how mathematics relates to their everyday lives.

Connections

Language arts, music, social studies, art, and more... wherever mathematics connects with other disciplines, students are engaged in activities that make those connections clear and meaningful.

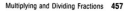

Mathematics Is
Problem Solving

Provided with high-interest, imaginative problems, students learn to reason creatively and apply skills in innovative ways that work best for the individual.

Creative Problem Solving Strategies

Students develop a highly flexible approach to problem solving and the use of problem solving strategies. The basic five-step approach— **understand, plan, try, check,** and **extend**—allows students to be truly inventive in selecting and combining those skills that are best suited to the situation (and individual) at hand.

Grade 5 , pages 242-243

UNDERSTAND
✓ PLAN
✓ TRY
CHECK
✓ EXTEND

PROBLEM SOLVING

Strategy: Finding a Pattern

Dr. Manuel is an archaeologist. He found an ancient picture made up of circles and triangles. The pattern in the picture shows 1 circle with 2 triangles, 2 circles with 4 triangles, 3 circles with 6 triangles, and so on. How many triangles will there be with 6 circles?

One way to solve the problem is to find a pattern by making a table.

Circles	1	2	3	4	5	6
Triangles	2	4	6	■	■	■

1. What is the rule for the pattern?

2. How many triangles will there be with 4 circles? with 5 circles? with 6 circles?

3. **What if** the table had looked like this? What is the rule for the pattern in this table?

Circles	1	2	3	4	5	6
Triangles	1	4	9	■	■	■

4. How many triangles would there be with 4 circles? with 5 circles? with 6 circles?

PRACTICE

Look for a pattern. Then solve the problem.

5. Dr. Manuel found a model of a temple. It was made of layers of stones. The bottom layer had 96 stones, the next layer had 88 stones, and the third layer had 80 stones. How many stones did the sixth layer have?

6. Another time he dug out a staircase. The first step was 9 inches above the ground, the second step was 18 inches above the ground, and the third step was 27 inches above the ground. How high off the ground was the eighth step?

7. Inside a temple he found a set of clay bowls that fit inside one another. The distance across the smallest bowl was 2 inches, across the next larger bowl was 6 inches, and across the third bowl was 18 inches. How many inches across was the fifth largest bowl?

8. He also discovered a pile of coins and stored them in boxes by size. He stored the smallest coins 96 to a box, the next size 48 to a box, and the next size 24 to a box. How many of the next largest coins did he store to a box?

Strategies and Skills Review

Solve. Use mental math, estimation, a calculator, or paper and pencil.

9. The archaeologists found a set of poles standing in a row. They were probably used as a primitive measuring instrument. The shortest pole was 2 inches high, the next one was 8 inches high, and the next was 32 inches high. How high was the next larger pole?

10. Dr. Johnson found an obelisk that is 78.5 feet tall. Dr. Lewis found one that is 18.25 feet tall. About how many times taller is the one Dr. Johnson found?

11. The largest standing obelisk in the world weighs 502.3 tons. The largest single block from a pyramid weighs 319.2 tons. How much more does the obelisk weigh than the block?

12. Melissa earns $7 an hour. Last week she worked 27 hours. What other information do you need in order to know whether she has earned enough money to buy a set of archaeological tools?

13. Teri's archaeology handbook has 12 chapters, each with the same number of pages. If the book is 264 pages long, how many pages are in each chapter?

14. **Write a problem** that can be solved by finding a pattern. Solve the problem. Ask others to solve your problem.

EXTRA **P**RACTICE, page 255

Dividing Whole Numbers: 2-Digit Divisors **243**

Thinking Mathematically

To help students learn to *think mathematically* and apply the skills that they've learned, they're given motivating, non-routine problems that challenge them to pursue solutions in new innovative ways.

Grade 3 pages 112-113

PROBLEM ● SOLVING

THINKING MATHEMATICALLY

ACTIVITY

TRY A TRICKY TRIANGLE

Using Number Concepts

On a sheet of paper, draw and color a triangle like the one at the right. Make the triangle larger.

Write the numbers 1, 2, 3, 4, 5, and 6 on another sheet of paper. Draw a circle around each number, then cut the numbers out. The number slips should fit inside the circles on your triangle.

1. Place one number slip on each circle. Can you place the numbers so that each side ___

To start, look for sets ___
Make a list of the set ___

1 + 2 + 6   1 + 3 ___

Now, look at your list. W ___
There are 2 ones, 2 twos, ___
Try placing these numbers ___
Then try to place the rema ___
Can you get each side to a ___

2. Now try a new puzzle.
This time make each side add up to 12.
Write down sets of three numbers that add up to 12.
How many sets can you find?

3. Look at your list.
Which numbers will you p ___
Which number ___
Wh ___

Decision Making

Students have many opportunities to work cooperatively on problems that involve tangible, real-life situations. With data to analyze and options to consider, they're on their way to becoming effective decision makers!

Grade 7, pages 266-267

COOPERATIVE LEARNING

DECISION MAKING

Problem Solving: Planning a Cable TV Show

SITUATION
The school puts on a 20-minute cable TV show every Monday morning. They have four 5-minute segments. Usually, they tape the segments in advance. Students can suggest topics they would like to have on the schedule. Then the production crew has to decide which suggestions to use for each show. Rita, Leon, and Sylvia recommended these schedules.

PROBLEM
Which schedule should the production crew use?

DATA

Cable TV SCHEDULE — SUBJECT: Planning for Today's Show

	RITA	LEON	SYLVIA
		MUSIC—Video of one of the top-ten songs for the past week	SPORTS SCENE—Announcements of sports events for the week
8:00-8:05	THE PRESIDENT SPEAKS—Student council president on upcoming events		
	THE PRINCIPAL IDEA—Interview with the principal about important school issues	SCHOOL NEWS—Student reporter presents school events (not sports) in a news format.	TALENT SEARCH—Performances by students on music emphasis for and humor
8:05-8:10		FUN FIVE—Students produce humorous skit about some aspect of school life.	LIVECAM—Crew with live camera goes into classrooms and asks students for their opinions.
	SPORTS TALK—5 coaches talk for 1 minute each about their teams and upcoming games.		
8:10-8:15		SPORTS NEWS—Student reporter presents school sports in a news format.	OUR OPINION—Students' points of view on important issues
	REVIEWS—Student reporter reviews movies, places to eat, and so on.		
8:15-8:20			

USING THE DATA

What fraction of each schedule is devoted to sports?
1. Rita's Schedule   **2.** Leon's Schedule   **3.** Sylvia's ___

What fraction of each schedule is devoted to music or performance?
4. Rita's Schedule   **5.** Leon's Schedule   **6.** Sylvi ___

What fraction of each schedule is devoted to interviews?
7. Rita's Schedule   **8.** Leon's Schedule   **9.** S ___

MAKING DECISIONS

10. Which schedule should they choose to have the most music or performance?

11. Which schedule looks as if it would be the easiest to produce ___

12. Which schedule looks as if it would be the most difficult to ___
Why?

13. *What if* the producers decide they want performances b ___
Which schedule should they avoid?

14. Which schedule would you choose? Why?

15. Would you change the order of the schedule? Why?

16. *Write a list* of other factors the producers should ___

17. Draw up your own schedule. Explain why you cho ___

Connections...
Across Disciplines, Across Cultures, Through Literature

Cultural Connections

Through various examples of art, literature, traditions, and narratives infused throughout the curriculum, students learn about the contributions made to the creation of mathematical ideas by people of all cultures. Students also see the diverse ways in which these cultures use mathematics.

Grade 5, pages 438-439

Literature Connections

Students make connections to math topics through authentic, published literature, available in the Teacher's Edition (K–2) as well as in Literature Anthologies (K–6).

Grade 2, page 185

I n the Middle East the first units of measure came from the plant world. Seeds were a popular unit of weight. The Arabic word *qirat* (KEY-raht) means the seed of the coral tree. *Qirats* were used for thousands of years to measure the weight of precious gems. Today, we say *carat*. A carat is still the unit of measure by weight for jewels. In 1913, jewelers around the world agreed that a carat would be equivalent to 200 milligrams.

Special units of we
for measuring parti
Rica a *saco de cal*
of coffee, was equ
Today, most produ
measured using t
and kilogram.

1 Why might se
unit of weigh

2 What proble
use of seeds

3

COSTA RICA
AMERICA CENTRAL

MEASURING W

AROUND THE WORLD

CHAPTER 6

Adding 2-Digit Numbers

READ ALOUD
NINETY-NINE POCKETS
By Jean Myrick

Listen to the story Ninety-Nine Pockets.

Suppose one pocket suit had 10 pockets. Tell how many pockets 10 pocket suits would have.

185

MATH CONNECTION: ALGEBRA

Algebra: Proportions

A. Joan and David made a model of their treehouse. The width and the length of one wall of the actual treehouse are 60 in. and 108 in. The corresponding length of the model is 18 in. What is the corresponding width of the model?

You can use a proportion to solve problems.

A **proportion** is a statement that two ratios are equal.

To find the model's width, you can solve the proportion by using cross products:

treehouse width → $\frac{60}{108} = \frac{n}{18}$ ← model width
treehouse length → ← model length

$108 \times n$

TRY OUT

3. $\frac{1}{4} = \frac{n}{16}$

400 Lesson

Grade 6, page 400

CURRICULUM **C**ONNECTION

Math and Music

In music, musical notes are grouped in **measures.** Rhythm in each measure is counted in units called **beats.** Here are three measures of music. They each have the same number of beats.

Quarter notes   Half notes   Whole note

MEASURE   MEASURE   MEASURE

The numbers at the left are known as the **meter signature.** The top number of the meter signature tells how many beats are in each measure. In $\frac{4}{4}$ meter, there are four beats in a measure. The bottom number tells what kind of note sounds for one beat. The 4 means a quarter note (♩) sounds for one beat in $\frac{4}{4}$ meter. So each quarter note is $\frac{1}{4}$ of a measure. A half note (♪) sounds for 2 beats. A whole note (○) sounds for 4 beats.

In $\frac{4}{4}$ meter, what fraction of a measure is a half note?

Think: There are 4 beats in a measure. A half note gets 2 beats. 2 is $\frac{1}{2}$ of 4.

So a half note is $\frac{1}{2}$ of a measure i $\frac{4}{4}$ meter.

ACTIVITIES

1. Write as many different com measure in $\frac{4}{4}$ meter as you each measure you write. Re each note.

2. Suppose the meter signature i measure? What kind of note so

372 Chapter 9

Grade 4, page 372

Technology

Calculator: Adding and Subtracting

You can use a calculator to practice your addition and subtraction facts.

Cover the display.
Press the keys shown.
Tell what the display will show.
Then check your answer.
Find each sum or difference.

1. Press
2 [+] 3 [=] _5_ [+] [-] 6 [-] 3 [=] [+] 3 [=] [C]

2. Press
1 [+] 6 [-] 2 [=]

3. Press
6 [-] 4

4. Press
4 [-] 1

5. Press
7 [+] 2

6. Press

Grade 1, page 282

Math to Math Connections

Students see how math topics relate to each other and how mathematics is relevant to real-life situations.

Curriculum Connections

Students discover that mathematics provides insights into the language arts, the fine arts, science, and social studies. Highlighting these other disciplines enriches students' understanding of mathematics.

Technology

Simulations and various other chapter activities make it easy for you to integrate computers and calculators into your program as tools for problem solving.

Chapter Organizer
Teaching Support Each Step of the Way

Chapter Organizers offer support in a time-saving, easy-to-read format. They help you provide students of every aptitude and interest with the very best mathematics experience possible.

Cultural Diversity

The contributions of other cultures to mathematics are shared with students.

Chapter Planning Guide

In this comprehensive chart (correlated to NCTM standards), you see what, when, how—*and with what options*—you'll be teaching.

Meeting the NCTM Standards

You will know precisely where and how the standards are addressed throughout the chapter.

Assessment Options–both formal and informal

Provides a method to meet every assessment need. You'll be able to learn what your students are thinking before, during, and after each concept is taught and be able to evaluate their understanding.

Meeting Individual Needs

With these activities and approaches, you can be sure that all students have equal opportunities to learn... and succeed.

Manipulatives Workshop

Summarizes the general concepts to be covered in the current chapter and recommends how to use hands-on manipulatives exercises with both individuals and groups.

Cooperative Learning Workshop

These *Workshops* help you organize and supervise cooperative learning groups, a method of instruction proven to increase student involvement.

Professional Handbook

Turn to this convenient resource for up-to-date information on Problem Solving, Communication and Reasoning, Mental Math, Estimation, Patterns, Algebra, Data Collection and Analysis, Connections, Technology, and many other major issues in mathematics education.

Lesson Plans

Easy to Follow Lesson Plans and Teaching Options

Preparations are made simpler, presentations livelier, by consistent four-page lesson plans.

At a Glance

A concise outline of lesson objectives, assignment suggestions, and teaching materials. Notes on Manipulatives and Teacher Resources make lesson planning easy.

Skills Trace

Lesson by lesson, you know where you are in the overall instructional cycle and where to turn for additional development, practice, and applications.

Meeting Individual Needs

These teaching tips help you meet the diverse needs of all students in today's math class.

Alternative Teaching Strategy
Common Error and Remediation
For Students Acquiring English
Ongoing Assessment
Cultural Diversity
Teacher to Teacher

Grade 2 TE, pages 221–222

The lesson itself is displayed on the first two pages.

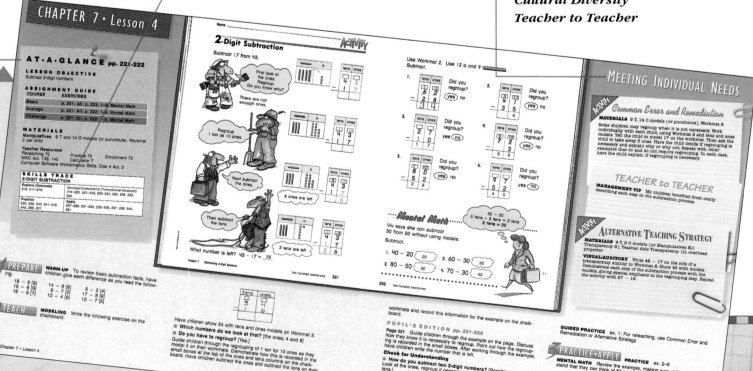

MAC Activities

They're fun for your students and convenient for you... just tear off and distribute. Only minimum supervision is required... giving you more time to work with students who need more help.

Practice, Reteaching, Enrichment

Supplements are pictured in the Teacher's Edition in a size that is **LARGE ENOUGH FOR YOU TO READ THEM EASILY!**

Problem of the Day

This handy resource is also available on a tear-off pad. These may be used to begin or end a lesson and will help students sharpen their problem solving skills.

Grade 2 TE, pages 222A–222B

The third and fourth pages organize all your follow-up activities.

Program Components

Everything you need to provide rewarding mathematical experiences for all your students.

Mathematics in Action

	K	1	2	3	4	5	6	7	8
Pupil's Edition (Consumable)	•	•	•						
Pupil's Edition (Hard Cover)				•	•	•	•	•	•
Teacher's Edition	•	•	•	•	•	•	•	•	•
Big Book and Clings	•								
Math Literature Anthology	•	•	•	•	•	•	•		
Read Aloud Cassettes	•	•	•						
Practice	•	•	•	•	•	•	•	•	•
Reteaching Activities	•	•	•	•	•	•	•	•	•
Enrichment Activities	•	•	•	•	•	•	•	•	•
Problem Solving Activities	•	•	•	•	•	•	•	•	•
Testing Program	•	•	•	•	•	•	•	•	•
Performance Assessment Activities		•	•	•	•	•	•	•	•
Critical Thinking	•	•	•	•	•	•	•	•	•
Home Involvement				•	•	•	•	•	•
Calculator Workshop			•	•	•	•	•	•	•
Computer Workshop Software	•	•	•	•	•	•	•	•	•
Teacher Aids	•	•	•	•	•	•	•	•	•
MAC Activity Pads	•	•	•	•	•	•	•	•	•
Problem of the Day Pads	•	•	•	•	•	•	•	•	•
Create-A-Kit Manipulatives	•	•	•	•	•	•	•	•	•
Posters	•	•	•	•	•	•	•	•	•
Manipulatives Kit Transparencies	•	•	•	•	•	•	•	•	•
Teacher Aids Transparencies	•	•	•	•	•	•	•	•	•
Calculator Kit		•	•	•	•	•	•	•	•
Overhead Calculator		•	•	•	•	•	•	•	•
Overhead Manipulatives			•	•	•	•	•	•	•
Cumulative Record Book		•	•	•	•	•	•	•	•
Staff Development Videos		•	•	•	•	•	•	•	•
Professional Handbook	•	•	•	•	•	•	•	•	•

I Can! Math Activity Program

A non-textbook, child-centered approach, *I Can!* follows the same Chapter Objectives as *Mathematics in Action*. Through hands-on activities you can be assured your students will make a smooth transition into third grade.

	K	1	2
Jumbo Book and Clings	•	•	•
Teacher's Guide	•	•	•
My Activity Book	•	•	•
I Can Do It! Practice Book	•	•	•
I Can Do It! TE	•	•	•
Testing Program BLM's	•	•	•
Workmats	•	•	•
Floormats	•	•	•
Literature Big Books	•	•	•
Math Literature Anthology	•	•	•
Math Songs Audio Cassette	•	•	•
Read Aloud Audio Cassette	•	•	•
Posters	•	•	•
Computer Workshop Software		•	•

To place an order or for Customer Service call:

MACMILLAN/McGRAW-HILL
1-800-442-9685

REGIONAL OFFICES

Delran, New Jersey
600 Delran Parkway
Suite 640
Delran, NJ 08075
(609) 461-2205

Norcross, Georgia
6510 Jimmy Carter Blvd.
P.O. Box 319
Norcross, GA 30071-0319
(404) 448-7997
(800) 453-2665

Irving, Texas
1320 Greenway
Suite 200
Irving, TX 75038
(214) 518-1233
(800) 882-3536

Schaumburg, Illinois
846 East Algonquin Rd.
Schaumburg, IL 60173
(708) 397-8454
(800) 428-5009

Santa Rosa, California
149 Stony Circle
Suite 210
Santa Rosa, CA 95401
(707) 579-4700

International
McGraw-Hill International
Princeton-Highstown Road
Highstown, N.J. 08520
(609) 426-5421
Fax (609) 426-7917

PUPIL'S EDITION

This section contains the following pages from the Pupil's Edition:

Table of Contents
Chapters 7-13
Picture Glossary

This section also contains teacher commentary for all lessons and Chapter Organizer pages that preview the chapter's content. In addition, Manipulatives Plus activities and Read-Aloud selections are provided for each chapter.

iii

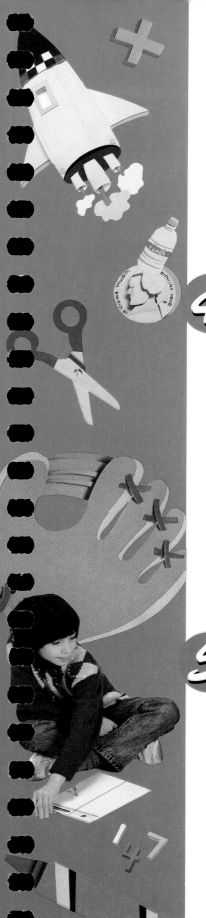

4 MONEY *Page 125*

5 MEASUREMENT *Page 151*

v

6 ADDING 2-DIGIT NUMBERS *Page 185*

LITERATURE *CONNECTION:* NINETY-NINE POCKETS

vii

Mathematics
in Action

GRADE 2 • PART 2

MACMILLAN/McGRAW-HILL SCHOOL PUBLISHING COMPANY

New York   Columbus

66 *IN CHAPTER 7, you will introduce your children to subtracting 2-digit numbers. You will also have the opportunity to explore place value, regrouping, and the algorithm for subtracting 2-digit numbers.* 99

Notes FROM THE AUTHOR

Here are some notes on the concepts presented in this chapter and how your children can apply them to solve problems.

PREREQUISITES

As with addition, your children must understand place value, know the basic subtraction facts, and be able to follow steps in order to subtract 2-digit numbers with regrouping. Some children may need remediation in these areas to achieve success in subtracting 2-digit numbers.

REGROUPING

Using ones and tens models to explore taking away enables children to understand the concept of regrouping. Encourage children to use models to work through exercises, and to discuss each step. For example:

Show 43. Take away 28.

Regroup 1 ten as 10 ones.

Take away the ones and the tens.

15

SUBTRACTING 2-DIGIT NUMBERS

Martina Johnson

SUBTRACTING 2-DIGIT NUMBERS

After children demonstrate their understanding of regrouping, introduce them to the algorithm for subtracting 2-digit numbers in the same way as the addition algorithm was introduced. Children should understand that the algorithm helps them remember what to do. They learn how to do each of the steps and understand why the algorithm works. Practicing subtracting 2-digit numbers with place-value models and without recording reinforces children's understanding of the algorithm.

Children apply their understanding of the algorithm by working through carefully structured examples such as the following.

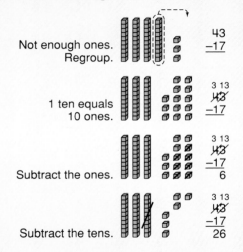

PROBLEM SOLVING

In **Problem Solving** your children (1) identify extra information to solve a problem, (2) use estimation to solve a problem, and (3) solve a problem by choosing the operation.

In **Thinking Mathematically** children use number sense and classify data. In Holiday Traffic Jam, children sort eight vehicles according to size, color, or type.

In **Decision Making** children use information to choose a prize for their class. Children analyze how many boxes of greeting cards they need to sell in order to qualify for each prize.

Mathematics and Literature

To use literature in the application of mathematics

■ Children are introduced to a story in the K–2 *Math Anthology* on page 162. By reading *A Hot Thirsty Day*, children build addition and subtraction skills and explore the concept of money.

CHAPTER PLANNING GUIDE

CHAPTER OBJECTIVES WITH STANDARDIZED TEST CORRELATIONS

A. Subtract 2-digit numbers with and without regrouping — MAT, CAT, SAT, ITBS, CTBS
B. Subtract money amounts to 99¢ — MAT, CAT, SAT, ITBS, CTBS
C. Solve problems including those that involve extra information and choosing the operation — MAT, CAT, SAT, ITBS, CTBS

SUGGESTED PACING–14 DAYS

LESSONS	NCTM STANDARDS	ASSIGNMENTS Basic/Average/Challenge	STUDENT EDITION Extra Practice/ Practice Plus	Manip. Plus	Reteach	Practice	Enrich	MAC Activities
Chapter Opener: "Using Subtraction" page 215	1, 2, 3, 4, 8							
✔ **1 Subtracting 2-Digit Numbers** page 216	1, 2, 3, 7, 8	p. 215: All; p. 216: All						
✔ **2 Regrouping Readiness** pages 217–218	1, 2, 3, 7	p. 217: 1–4; p. 218: 1–6		39, 40, 41, 42				
✔ **3 More Regrouping Readiness** pages 219–220	1, 2, 3, 7	p. 219: 1–3; p. 220: 2–3		43	69	69	69	137, 138
✔ **4 2-Digit Subtraction** pages 221–222	1, 2, 3, 8	p. 221: All; p. 222: 1–6, Mental Math			70	70	70	139, 140
5 More 2-Digit Subtraction pages 223–224	1, 2, 3, 8	p. 223: 1–4; p. 224: 1–10			71	71	71	141, 142
6 Subtraction Practice page 225	1, 2, 3, 8	p. 225: 1–4	pp. 230, 240	44	72	72	72	143, 144
7 Checking Subtraction page 226	1, 2, 3, 8	p. 226: 1–5			73	73	73	145, 146
8 PS: Identifying Extra Information pages 227–228	1, 2, 3, 8	p. 228: 1–4	p. 230		74	74	74	147, 148
✔ **9 PS: Thinking Mathematically** page 229	1, 2, 3, 9	p. 229: All						
10 PS: Using Estimation pages 231–232	1, 2, 3, 5, 6	p. 231: 1; p. 232: 1–3			75	75	75	149, 150
11 Subtracting Money page 233	1, 2, 3, 8	p. 233: 1–4	pp. 239, 240	45	76	76	76	151, 152
12 Addition and Subtraction page 234	1, 2, 3, 8	p. 234: 1–3		46	77	77	77	153, 154
13 PS: Choosing the Operation pages 235–236	1, 2, 3, 7, 8	p. 235: 1–3; p. 236: 1–4	p. 239		78	78	78	155, 156
14 PS: Decision Making page 237	1, 2, 3, 6, 8	p. 237: 1–4						

Technology: Computer page 238

Chapter Review/Test pages 241–242

Performance Assessment page 243

Cumulative Review page 245

Enrichment for All/Home Activity pages 244, 246

NATIONAL COUNCIL OF TEACHERS OF MATHEMATICS Grades K–4

1. Problem Solving
2. Communication
3. Reasoning
4. Connections
5. Estimation
6. Number Sense and Numeration
7. Concepts of Whole Number Operations
8. Whole Number Computation
9. Geometry and Spatial Sense
10. Measurement
11. Statistics and Probability
12. Fractions and Decimals
13. Patterns and Relationships

✔ Activity   👥 Cooperative Learning

MEETING the NCTM STANDARDS

Problem Solving

Strategies and Skills	• identifying extra information pp. 227–228 • using estimation pp. 231–232 • choosing the operation pp. 235–236
Applications	• **Decision Making** lesson p. 237 • **Problem of the Day** TE pp. 216, 218, 220B, 222B, 224B, 225C, 226C, 228B, 232B, 233C, 234C, 236B
Mathematical Investigations	• **Thinking Mathematically** lesson p. 229

Communication

Language	• using the language of mathematics TE pp. 217–218, 221–222, 223–224, 231–232
Oral/Written	• using cooperative learning activities pp. 216, 217, 229, 237; TE pp. 214I–214P • **Journal Writing** opportunities TE pp. 220, 222, 224, 226A, 232, 236

Reasoning

Critical Thinking	• answering questions that analyze and extend concepts pp. 215, 216, 226, 229, 235, 237, 238

Connections

To other subject areas	• Literature p. 215; Literature TE pp. 215–216

Concept Development

Concepts of Whole Number Operations	• regrouping 1 ten for 10 ones pp. 216, 217–218, 219–220; TE pp. 214I–214M
Whole Number Computation	• subtracting 2-digit numbers with and without regrouping pp. 221–222, 223–224, 225, 226; TE p. 214N • subtracting money amounts to 99¢ p. 233; TE p. 214O • adding or subtracting 2-digit numbers p. 234; TE p. 214P

ASSESSMENT OPTIONS

PERFORMANCE ASSESSMENT

Preassessment Activity

Before beginning Chapter 7, have each child bring in an empty cereal box. Children should work in pairs using two different cereal boxes. Have them write word problems using subtraction to show differences in weight, nutritional content, and so on, between their two cereal types.

Ongoing Assessment

The Ongoing Assessment cards under MEETING INDIVIDUAL NEEDS on TE pp. 220 and 224 provide criteria and questions for assessing children's understanding of the key mathematical concepts developed in the chapter.

 Journal Writing opportunities encourage children to write about mathematics. Their responses can be recorded either pictorially or in words. The journal writing opportunities on the Ongoing Assessment cards also allow you to assess children's understanding of the lessons.

In addition to the Ongoing Assessment cards, other assessment and journal writing opportunities in this chapter include:

• **CLOSE** TE pp. 222, 224, 226A, 232, 236

Performance Assessment Activity

The Performance Assessment activity on p. 243 provides an alternative to formal assessment. This activity assesses children's understanding of the key concepts of the chapter.

For performance assessment activities that are keyed to individual chapter objectives, see the *Performance Assessment* booklet.

BUILDING A PORTFOLIO

Children should be encouraged to keep a selection of their best work in portfolios. The portfolios provide a way of documenting children's growth in understanding mathematical concepts. Portfolio opportunities in this chapter include:
• **Performance Assessment** p. 243
• **Class Project** TE p. 237A

If you wish to provide additional opportunities for portfolio work, you may choose to use:
• **MAC Activities** 138, 139, 140, 141, 142, 146

You may also wish to have children include their journal writing from the Ongoing Assessment on TE pp. 220 and 224 in their portfolio.

Formal Assessment

The **Chapter Review/Test** assesses children's understanding of the concepts and skills developed in the chapter. The **Cumulative Review** assesses children's understanding of the concepts and skills developed from the beginning of the year.

You can use **Form A** or **Form B** of the **Chapter Test** found in the *Testing Program Blackline Masters and Teacher's Manual* if you wish to use a multiple-choice format to assess children's understanding of the chapter concepts and skills. You can use **Form C** if you wish to use a free-response format. Any of the forms may be used as a pretest, posttest, or for retesting.

The **COMPUTER MANAGEMENT SYSTEM**, or **CMS**, enables you to score **Forms A** and **B** of the **Chapter Test** quickly and automatically. It also prescribes learning activities based on children's test results.

For more information about Assessment, see the *Professional Handbook*.

MEETING INDIVIDUAL NEEDS

Common Error and Remediation

The Teacher's Edition notes for each Develop/Understand (Transitional/Abstract) lesson provide a common error analysis and a remediation activity. Some errors defy quick analysis and can only be identified by interviewing the child.

ALTERNATIVE TEACHING STRATEGY

Alternative Teaching Strategies appear frequently in the chapter. These strategies provide other presentations of the lessons for children who might benefit from instruction in different learning modalities: kinesthetic, visual, and/or auditory.

For Students Acquiring English (SAE)

Before beginning this chapter, review with SAE children vocabulary terms associated with subtraction and regrouping, such as **regroup, trade, model, take away, tens,** and **ones.** In doing so, use example problems that incorporate children's own experiences, and have volunteers do the talking or restate your explanations in their own words.

SAE notes appear periodically in the chapter. These notes provide suggestions for how to work with children to improve comprehension and build vocabulary.

MANIPULATIVES WORKSHOP

Tens and ones models are used in this chapter to examine subtraction of 2-digit numbers. They provide a concrete representation of the action of "taking away" and the equivalent values used in regrouping.

USING MANIPULATIVES

1. Here a child models 40 − 16.

The child uses 4 tens models to show 40.

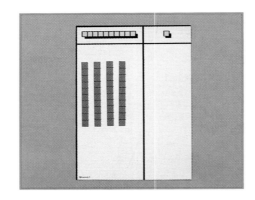

2. The child regroups 1 ten as 10 ones in order to be able to subtract 6 ones.

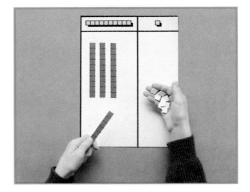

3. The child takes away 6 ones.

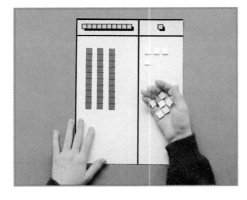

4. The child then takes away 1 ten. This leaves 2 tens and 4 ones, or 24.

MAKING MANIPULATIVES   See the Manipulatives section of the *Professional Handbook* for materials that can be used as a substitute for tens and ones models.

COOPERATIVE LEARNING WORKSHOP

GETTING STARTED

In Each Other's Shoes: Pairs and small groups need to practice cooperative skills that help them be aware that they are a team—**paying attention** to one another's needs, **comparing responses** without put-downs, **suspending judgment** when brainstorming, or **encouraging** everyone to participate. Only one skill should be assigned per lesson. When sharing ideas, each group member needs to make statements from his or her own point of view, and help the group **come to agreement** on answers the group prefers. At Close, children reflect on how well they practiced these skills. Reflection on both group process and lesson content can be entered in **group learning logs,** as simple pictures or short sentences.

IDEAS TO TRY

Rotating Pairs: In the group of four (using the pair combinations discussed in the Cooperative Learning Workshop for Chapter 6), ask the first set of pairs to do the initial modeling together, then change to the second pair combination to do the lesson sections, and the third pair combination to do the Check for Understanding. Each individual can then write or practice alone, after which a check for understanding and summarizing can be done within the entire small group. Have the first pair combinations discuss how it felt to work with a variety of children on the same lesson.

You can apply the above rotating-pairs strategy in these lessons:
7-1 *Subtracting 2-Digit Numbers* p. 216
7-2 *Regrouping Readiness* pp. 217–218
7-3 *More Regrouping Readiness* pp. 219–220

Cooperative Skills: You may begin with pairs for the Warm Up, and then combine pairs into their groups of four for the lesson. Introduce a cooperative skill such as **appreciating other's ideas** or **using "inside voices."** When you monitor the academic task, also listen for use of the cooperative skill. Place a green square on the group's work area if they are using the skill, a yellow square to remind them to use it, or a red square to indicate "Stop! What skill do you need to use right now?" Change this back to a green square when they use the skill.

You can apply the above cooperative skills in these lessons:
7-4 *2-Digit Subtraction* pp. 221–222
7-5 *More 2-Digit Subtraction* pp. 223–224
7-11 *Subtracting Money* p. 233

SEE ALSO

Cooperative Learning Tip for lessons 7-8 Problem Solving p. 228; 7-10 Problem Solving p. 232

The Cooperative Learning section of the *Professional Handbook* for additional information

ACTIVITY
INTERACTIVE BULLETIN BOARD

SETUP Cover a bulletin board with brown paper. Draw eight trees on the paper and have volunteers color the trees. Write a different 2-digit number on each tree trunk. Then cut out many apple shapes from red construction paper.

PROCEDURE 👥 Give each child an apple, and have him or her choose a tree. Have the child write on the apple an appropriate subtraction fact for that tree. Then invite the child to paste the apple on the tree.

For use before LESSON 7.2, pp. 217-218

39

REGROUPING TENS AS ONES

OBJECTIVE
Explore regrouping tens as ones.

MATERIALS
Manipulatives 3 ▣
and 20 ▣ (or square counter punchouts) per child
Teacher Resources
Teacher Aid 8

WHOLE GROUP ACTIVITY

Prepare a workmat as shown on a copy of Teacher Aid 8. Duplicate a copy for each child.

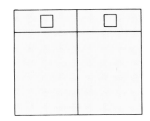

Give a workmat and 3 red and 20 blue cubes to each child.

Have children color the square at the top of the left column red and explain that this column is the tens column. Then have children color the square at the top of the right column blue and identify this column as the ones column.

Tell children to show 2 red cubes and 6 blue cubes in the columns. Read the following story aloud:

■ **You have 2 packs of stickers and 6 loose stickers. You want to give away 8 stickers. By the way, 10 stickers come in a pack. Show how to solve this problem using your cubes. How many packs of stickers and loose stickers would you have left?**

Have children share their strategies. Guide children to see that they can regroup 1 red cube as 10 blue cubes, and then take away 8 blue cubes.

EXTENDING THE ACTIVITY

Repeat the activity using the problem context of packs and loose stickers for these numbers:

1 pack 4 loose stickers. Give away 7 stickers.
  [7 loose stickers]
2 packs 7 loose stickers. Give away 9 stickers.
  [1 pack 8 loose stickers]
2 packs 1 loose sticker. Give away 5 stickers.
  [1 pack 6 loose stickers]
1 pack 5 loose stickers. Give away 6 stickers.
  [9 loose stickers]

ONGOING ASSESSMENT

✔ Are children beginning to regroup tens as ones for subtraction situations?

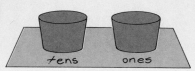

For use before LESSON 7.2, pp. 217-218

40
REGROUPING READINESS

OBJECTIVE
Explore regrouping tens as ones.

MATERIALS
Classroom Materials
counting sticks, pipe cleaners, plastic cups, oaktag, glue

PAIRS ACTIVITY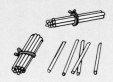

Prepare stick-holder workmats for pairs of children by gluing two plastic cups to oaktag, and then labeling them "tens" and "ones" as shown.

Assign children to work in pairs. Give each pair 29 counting sticks and 2 pipe cleaners. Tell children to count out sets of 10 sticks and wrap a pipe cleaner around each set. Explain that each stick is a ones model.

■ **What would you call a bundle of ten sticks?**
[1 tens model]

Give each pair of children a stick-holder workmat. Tell children that the cup on the right is the ones cup and the cup on the left is the tens cup.

Have children work together to model the following and tell what is left:

Show 8 ones. Take away 2 ones. [6 ones]
Show 1 ten 4 ones. Take away 3 ones. [1 ten 1 one]
Show 1 ten 7 ones. Take away 4 ones. [1 ten 3 ones]
Show 2 tens 5 ones. Take away 3 ones. [2 tens 2 ones]

Present the following regrouping situation.

Show 2 tens 6 ones. Take away 8 ones.

Have children share their strategies for solving the problem. Guide them to see that they may remove the pipe cleaner from 1 ten to make 10 ones. Then take away 8 ones.

EXTENDING THE ACTIVITY
Continue with the following regrouping problems:

2 tens 5 ones, take away 7 ones [1 ten 8 ones]
2 tens 3 ones, take away 9 ones [1 ten 4 ones]
1 ten 4 ones, take away 5 ones [9 ones]
1 ten 8 ones, take away 9 ones [9 ones]

ONGOING ASSESSMENT
✓ Are children regrouping tens as ones for subtraction situations?

41
MORE REGROUPING READINESS

OBJECTIVE
Explore regrouping tens as ones.

MATERIALS
Manipulatives 10 T and 40 O models (or punchouts), spinner for 0–9 per pair; number cube*, 2 game markers per pair (EXTENDING THE ACTIVITY only)
Teacher Resources
Teacher Aids 1, 17*

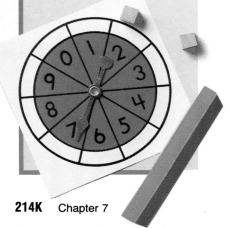

PAIRS ACTIVITY

Assign children to work in pairs. Give each pair 1 spinner for 0–9 and 10 tens and 40 ones models.

Have pairs play "Race to Zero." Each child should start with 5 tens models. Have children take turns spinning and taking away the number of ones shown.

Guide children to see that they can trade 1 ten for 10 ones and then take away the ones. Play continues until one child reaches 0.

EXTENDING THE ACTIVITY

Substitute game boards for spinners. Use Teacher Aid 1. Write a number from 1 to 9 in each space on the path. Give pairs 1 number cube and 2 markers.

Have children take turns rolling the number cube and moving their markers that number of spaces. Children should take away from the 5 tens the number of ones shown on the path. The child with the fewest models at the end of the path wins.

ONGOING ASSESSMENT
✓ Are children regrouping tens as ones for subtraction situations?

MANIPULATIVES plus • ACTIVITY •

**For use before
LESSON 7.2,
pp. 217-218**

42
REGROUPING
WITH MONEY

OBJECTIVE
Explore regrouping tens as
ones.

MATERIALS
Manipulatives 5 D and 20
P coins (or punchouts)
Teacher Resources
Teacher Aid 8

WHOLE GROUP ACTIVITY

Prepare a workmat as shown on a copy of Teacher
Aid 8. Duplicate 1 copy for each child.

Give each child 1 workmat, 5 dimes, and 20 pennies. Have children tape a dime down at the top of
the workmat's left column and a penny at the top of
the right column. Remind them that they can trade
1 dime for 10 pennies whenever they need to. Then
read these problems for children to model.

1. Carlos has 37¢. [Children place 3 dimes and 7
   pennies on their workmats.]
   He buys a stamp for 25¢. [Children take away 2
   dimes and 5 pennies.]
   How much money does Carlos have left? [12¢]
2. Clara has 34¢.
   She buys a card for 29¢.
   How much money does she have left? [5¢]
3. Walter has 40¢.
   He buys a pencil for 19¢.
   How much money does he have left? [21¢]

4. Florence has 22¢.
   She buys a plant for 15¢.
   How much money does she have left? [7¢]

EXTENDING THE ACTIVITY

Have children work with mental math for subtraction
problems involving money amounts. Read aloud
problems and challenge children to each try to
solve the problems mentally. Have individuals share
and discuss their strategies and solutions.

ONGOING ASSESSMENT

✓ Are children beginning to understand regrouping for subtraction through
the use of dimes and pennies?

**For use before
LESSON 7.3,
pp. 219-220**

43

SEPARATING
SETS

OBJECTIVE
Explore separating sets,
with and without
regrouping.

MATERIALS
Classroom Materials
number cards in each of
two colors
Manipulatives 9 T and 19
O models (or punchouts),
Workmat 2 per pair

SMALL GROUP ACTIVITY

Prepare 1 set of number cards for each small group
of four children as shown. Use two colors, such as
blue and white, for the cards.

| 62 | 73 | 85 | 91 | 58 | 27 | 36 | 49 | 38 | 24 |

Assign children to work in teams of two and have
two teams play as a group. Give each group of four
1 set of number cards. Give each team 9 tens and
19 ones models and Workmat 2.

Have one child in each pair choose a blue number
card and model the number shown on the workmat.
Have the other child in each pair choose a white
number card and take away the number shown
from the number on the workmat.

The second child in each pair says the number that
is left as tens and ones. Team members should
check the other team's answers. If correct, the team
scores one point.

Have children play the game for three rounds. The
team with the greater score wins. Rotate teams.

EXTENDING THE ACTIVITY

Have children work with mental math for subtraction
problems. Read aloud examples and challenge children to each try to mentally solve the problems.
Have individuals share and discuss their strategies
and solutions.

ONGOING ASSESSMENT

✓ Are children able to model separating sets, with and without regrouping?

**For use before
LESSON 7.6,
p. 225**

44

SUBTRACTING ON A CALCULATOR

OBJECTIVE
Subtract on a calculator.

MATERIALS
Calculator

WHOLE GROUP ACTIVITY

Give each child a calculator. Review or demonstrate the process of subtracting 2-digit numbers.

Write 82 − 58 on the chalkboard. Have children enter 82 on the calculator. Then tell them to press the − key and enter 58. Next have them press the = key and read the difference. [24]

Write the following problems on the chalkboard. Have children use their calculators to solve them.

1. Jane had 76 plants.
   Now she has 34 plants.
   How many plants did she sell? [42]
2. Louis had 92 cards.
   He also has 68 envelopes.
   How many more cards than envelopes does Louis have? [24]

Write the following sets of numbers on the chalkboard. Challenge children to find the two numbers in each row that when subtracted equal the difference in the box. Have children guess before testing.

| 64 | 29 | 33 | 50 | 21 | [50 − 29] |
| 85 | 26 | 38 | 93 | 67 | [93 − 26] |

EXTENDING THE ACTIVITY

Have children work in pairs. Have each child in a pair make up her or his own set of numbers as in the above. Have children challenge their partners to find the difference. Allow children to share with the class their strategies for solving.

ONGOING ASSESSMENT

✓ Are children able to use calculators to subtract two 2-digit numbers?

MANIPULATIVES plus ACTIVITY

For use before LESSON 7.11, p. 233

45

SUBTRACTING MONEY

OBJECTIVE
Subtract money amounts.

MATERIALS
Classroom Materials
index cards, game markers
Manipulatives number
cube*, 10 D and 10 P coins
(or punchouts) per group
Teacher Resources
Teacher Aids 1, 17*

SMALL GROUP ACTIVITY

Prepare and duplicate 1 game board per small group of three on a copy of Teacher Aid 1 as shown. Write money amounts from 25¢ to 89¢ on index cards.

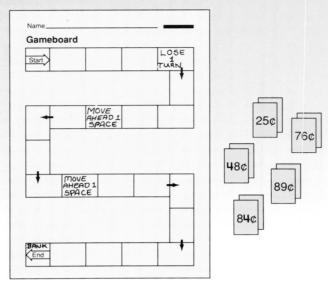

Have children play in small groups of three. Give each group 1 game board, 15 amount cards, 3 game markers, 1 number cube, 27 dimes, and 54 pennies.

Have groups play "Get to the Bank." Each player begins with a marker on *Start*. Players take turns rolling the number cube, moving that number of spaces on the game board, and taking an amount card.

Players should model the amount on the card using dimes and pennies, and then subtract 25¢ from the amount. They should regroup if they need to and say the difference as dimes and pennies.

A player may move ahead one space with a correct response, and back one space with an incorrect response. The first player to reach the bank wins.

EXTENDING THE ACTIVITY

Write money amounts from 25¢ to 89¢ in the spaces on the game board. Have players take turns modeling the amount they land on and then subtracting 25¢ from that amount, regrouping if they need to.

ONGOING ASSESSMENT

✓ Are children able to model and subtract money amounts?

MANIPULATIVES plus ACTIVITY

For use before
LESSON 7.12,
p. 234

46

ADDITION AND SUBTRACTION

OBJECTIVE
Relate addition and subtraction.

MATERIALS
Classroom Materials
addition and subtraction cards; 16 blank cards per group (EXTENDING THE ACTIVITY only)

SMALL GROUP ACTIVITY

Prepare related addition and subtraction cards as shown.

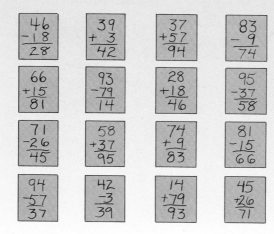

46 −18 28	39 + 3 42	37 +57 94	83 − 9 74
66 +15 81	93 −79 14	28 +18 46	95 −37 58
71 −26 45	58 +37 95	74 + 9 83	81 −15 66
94 −57 37	42 − 3 39	14 +79 93	45 +26 71

Have children play a version of the game "Concentration" in small groups of three. Give each group 1 set of 16 cards. Have children mix the cards and place them facedown in four rows of four.

Children should take turns turning over two of the cards and finding matches. A match means that the addition example can be used to check the subtraction example. Show these cards as an example.

81 −15 66	→	66 +15 81

If the cards show an addition exercise that matches a subtraction exercise, the player keeps both cards. If the cards do not match, the child turns the cards facedown again and the next child takes a turn. Play continues until all matches have been made.

EXTENDING THE ACTIVITY

Distribute 16 blank cards to each small group of three. Have children work in their groups to make their own matching addition and subtraction cards. Have them play the game using their own cards.

ONGOING ASSESSMENT

✓ Are children able to see the relationship between addition examples and their related subtraction examples?

Mathematics and Literature

Listening and Speaking

The Read-Aloud selection can be used with the Chapter 7 Opener and Lesson 7-1 on pages 215-216.

Tape 2, Side 1
Selection 1

Using Subtraction

by LEE BLAIR
from *Arithmetic in Verse and Rhyme*

I've often heard
the teacher say,
"Subtract means less,
or *take away*."
And so I'd get
great satisfaction
if I could only
do subtraction
on all of these—
yes, all of these:
    Liver,
    Spinach,
    "Quiet, please,"
    scoldings,
    early bedtime,
    rice,
    rainy Sundays,
    "Do be nice,"
    tattletales,
    big pills to take,
    sleet, and smog,
    and stomachache.
Since these all drive me
to distraction,
for them I'd always
use subtraction.

214R

AT·A·GLANCE pp. 215-216

LESSON OBJECTIVES
Explore mathematical concepts through literature.
Explore regrouping for subtraction.

ASSIGNMENT GUIDE

COURSE	EXERCISES
Basic	p. 215: All; p. 216: All
Average	p. 215: All; p. 216: All
Challenge	p. 215: All; p. 216: All

MATERIALS
Manipulatives 9 P, 4 D coins (or punchouts) per child; money amount stickers per group

Teacher Resources
Math Anthology, p. 166
Read-Aloud Cassette 2, Side 1, Selection 1

SKILLS TRACE
2-DIGIT SUBTRACTION

Explore (Concrete) 216, 217–218	Develop/Understand (Transitional/Abstract) 219–220, 221–222, 223–224, 225, 226, 233, 234
Practice 230, 239, 240, 241–242, 245, 288, 301	Apply 227–228, 231–232, 235–236, 237, 238, 244

Subtracting 2-Digit Numbers

CHAPTER 7

READ ALOUD

ARITHMETIC IN VERSE AND RHYME Selected By Allan and Leland Jacobs

 Listen to the poem <u>Using Subtraction.</u>

Tell about a problem that you would use subtraction to solve. Answers will vary.

215

Mathematics and Literature

---

① PREPARE **WARM-UP** To review regrouping dimes for pennies, write these amounts on the chalkboard and have the children give the equivalent number of pennies.

4 dimes 3 pennies = _____ pennies [43]
2 dimes 8 pennies = _____ pennies [28]
7 dimes 0 pennies = _____ pennies [70]
8 dimes 1 penny = _____ pennies [81]

② TEACH **DISCUSSING** Before reading the poem "Using Subtraction," write the word *subtract* on the chalkboard and define it for the children. Point out that usually the word *subtract* is used when discussing a math problem. Explain that subtraction can be used in a slightly different way.

PUPIL'S EDITION pp. 215-216

Page 215 Read "Using Subtraction" found on page 214Q or in *Math Anthology* to children, or play Read-Aloud Cassette 2, Side 1, Selection 1 for them.

■ **According to the poem, what does a teacher mean by subtract?** [to take away]

■ **In what way has the poet changed the meaning of the word subtraction?** [*Subtraction* usually refers to numbers; the poet is using the word to refer to getting rid of things that are bothersome.]

Have children describe a problem they could solve by using subtraction.

Page 216 ■ Working Together Assign children to work in groups of five or six. Discuss the pictures with the children.

Name _____

Subtracting 2-Digit Numbers

Working Together

Use 4 🪙 and 9 🪙 for each customer.

Use some 🪙 for the bank.

Choose 1 person to be the shopkeeper. Choose 1 person to be the banker.

Each customer must buy 1 of each sticker.
Pay the shopkeeper with pennies only.
Trade 1 dime for 10 pennies with the banker when you need to.

Pennies Please
Toy Shop

Tell how many pennies each customer has left. 4
Talk about 1 other sticker that each customer can buy.
Each customer can buy another 1-cent, 2-cent, 3-cent, or 4-cent sticker.

216   two hundred sixteen

Check for Understanding

■ **What coins must you use to buy each sticker? How many stickers must you buy?** [Only pennies can be used; one of each sticker must be purchased.]

GUIDED PRACTICE   Assign one child to be the shopkeeper, another the banker, and the rest customers. Distribute coins to each customer and give the banker enough pennies to change each customer's dimes. Give the shopkeeper stickers and tell the customers to take turns buying them.

For reteaching, use Alternative Strategy.

3 PRACTICE•APPLY   **PRACTICE**   Have children complete the activity. Have children discuss their responses within their group or as a class.

MEETING INDIVIDUAL NEEDS

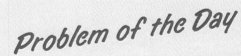

ACTIVITY
ALTERNATIVE TEACHING STRATEGY

MATERIALS 9 P, 4 D coins (or punchouts)

VISUAL Explain that you will play both banker and shopkeeper and ask one child to play the customer. Have the customer buy the stickers that cost 1¢, 2¢, and 3¢ with the 9 pennies that he or she has at the beginning of the game. Discuss why the customer cannot buy the 4¢ sticker with the remaining 3 pennies. Trade 1 dime for 10 pennies and have children count out the pennies with you. Continue until all the stickers are purchased.

CLOSE   Guide children to summarize the lesson:
■ **If you had exchanged all your dimes for pennies at one time, how many pennies would you have?** [40 pennies]

Problem of the Day

In one group, the banker ran out of pennies. The players needed to trade 5 dimes. How many pennies did the banker need to get from the teacher? [50 pennies]

AT·A·GLANCE pp. 217-218

LESSON OBJECTIVE
Explore regrouping 1 ten as 10 ones.

ASSIGNMENT GUIDE

COURSE	EXERCISES
Basic	p. 217: 1–4; p. 218: 1–6
Average	p. 217: 1–4; p. 218: 1–6
Challenge	p. 217: 1–4; p. 218: 1–6

MATERIALS
Classroom Materials rubber bands, counting sticks
Manipulatives 7 tens, 17 ones models (or punchouts), Workmat 2, spinner for 0–9* per pair

Teacher Resources
*Teacher Aid 11

SKILLS TRACE	
2-DIGIT SUBTRACTION	
Explore (Concrete) 216, 217–218	Develop/Understand (Transitional/Abstract) 219–220, 221–222, 223–224, 225, 226, 233, 234
Practice 230, 239, 240, 241–242, 245, 288, 301	Apply 227–228, 231–232, 235–236, 237, 238, 244

See **MANIPULATIVES PLUS 39–42**, pp. 214I–214L.

Name _____

Regrouping Readiness

Gail made 2 tens trains.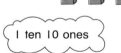
Willy needs a few cubes.

Gail took apart 1 ten train.
She regrouped 1 ten
as 10 ones.

2 tens

How many tens and
ones does Gail have?

1 ten 10 ones

Working Together

Use Workmat 2. Use a ⊙ , 19 ▢ , and 1 ▭ .

Start with 1 tens model each time.
Spin to find how many ones models to take.
Show the ten and ones on Workmat 2.

Write how many.   **Regroup 1 ten as 10 ones. Write how many.**

For Exercises 2–4 answers will vary.

1.
tens	ones
1	2

tens	ones
	12

2.
tens	ones

tens	ones

3.
tens	ones

tens	ones

4.
tens	ones

tens	ones

Macmillan/McGraw-Hill

---

1 PREPARE **WARM-UP** To review tens and ones, have children identify the tens and ones in each of the following numbers.

17 [1 ten 7 ones]
28 [2 tens 8 ones]
49 [4 tens 9 ones]
76 [7 tens 6 ones]
54 [5 tens 4 ones]
63 [6 tens 3 ones]

2 TEACH **MODELING** Have children work in pairs using Workmat 2 and tens and ones models. Tell children to show 1 ten 3 ones on the workmat. Ask a child if you can have 5 of his or her ones because you need to use them for the next example.

The child should respond that there are not enough ones.

■ **What could be done to get more ones?**

Guide children to see that if they regroup 1 ten as 10 ones, there would be enough ones to give away 5. Have children regroup 1 ten as 10 ones on their workmats.

■ **How many tens and ones do you have now?** [0 tens 13 ones]

Repeat this regrouping with 1 ten 4 ones and 1 ten 7 ones.

PUPIL'S EDITION pp. 217-218

Page 217 Guide children through the example at the top of the page.

Check for Understanding
■ **How many tens equal 10 ones?** [1 ten]

Use Workmat 2. Use 17 ▫ , and 7 ▭ .

Show 3 tens 4 ones on Workmat 2.	Regroup 1 ten as 10 ones.	How many tens and ones are there now?

3 tens 4 ones   2 tens 14 ones

Show the tens and ones models on Workmat 2.
Regroup. Write how many tens and ones.

1. 3 tens 4 ones

tens	ones
2	14

2. 5 tens 6 ones

tens	ones
4	16

3. 6 tens

tens	ones
5	10

4. 4 tens 2 ones

tens	ones
3	12

5. 7 tens 5 ones

tens	ones
6	15

6. 2 tens 7 ones

tens	ones
1	17

218   two hundred eighteen

WORKING TOGETHER Have children work in pairs. Give each pair a punchout spinner, Workmat 2, and 1 ten and 19 ones models. Read the instructions with the children.

GUIDED PRACTICE   ex. 1–4: For reteaching, use Alternative Strategy.

Page 218   Work through the example at the top of the page with the children.

PRACTICE   ex. 1–6

For Students Acquiring English (SAE)

Pair SAE children with non-SAE children for this and the next lesson. Have children work through the problems while you direct/monitor orally. Use manipulatives to demonstrate what the directions call for the children to do. For language and concept development, have SAE volunteers summarize each step in working through the problems.

ALTERNATIVE TEACHING STRATEGY

MATERIALS Workmat 2; 25 counting sticks, 2 rubber bands

VISUAL Make two tens models by putting a rubber band around ten counting sticks. Model 2 tens 5 ones on Workmat 2 using the tens bundles and single sticks for ones. Tell children that you need 8 ones but there are only 5 ones on the workmat. Explain that you will regroup 1 ten as 10 ones. Take one bundle apart and place the sticks in the ones column. Have a volunteer read the models as 1 ten 15 ones. Repeat with other numbers.

C L O S E   Guide children to summarize the lesson:
■ **If you regroup 2 tens 7 ones, how many tens and ones would you have?** [1 ten 17 ones]

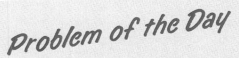

Problem of the Day

Bob has 7 packs of ten baseball cards and 4 loose cards. If he opens 1 pack, can he trade 9 cards? [Yes.]

Siena Heights College Library
1247 East Siena Heights Drive
Adrian, Michigan 49221-1796

AT·A·GLANCE pp. 219-220

LESSON OBJECTIVE
Use models to take one number away from another to find what is left.

ASSIGNMENT GUIDE

COURSE	EXERCISES
Basic	p. 219: 1–3; p. 220: 2–3
Average	p. 219: 1–3; p. 220: 2–3
Challenge	p. 219: 1–3; p. 220: 2–3

MATERIALS
Manipulatives 5 T, 15 O models (or punchouts), Workmat 2 per child

Teacher Resources
Reteaching 69
MAC Act. 137, 138
Practice 69
Teacher Aid 9
Enrichment 69

SKILLS TRACE
2-DIGIT SUBTRACTION

Explore (Concrete)	Develop/Understand (Transitional/Abstract)
216, 217–218	219–220, 221–222, 223–224, 225, 226, 233, 234
Practice 230, 239, 240, 241–242, 245, 288, 301	**Apply** 227–228, 231–232, 235–236, 237, 238, 244, 351

See **MANIPULATIVES PLUS 43**, p. 214M.

1 PREPARE **WARM-UP** To review regrouping, have children model the following by using Workmat 2 and tens and ones models. For each number, have children tell if it is possible to regroup 1 ten for 10 ones. If so, have them model the regrouping.

4 tens 1 one	[Yes; 3 tens 11 ones.]
7 ones	[No.]
8 tens	[Yes; 7 tens 10 ones.]
1 ten 2 ones	[Yes; 12 ones.]
2 tens 5 ones	[Yes; 1 ten 15 ones.]

2 TEACH **MODELING** Write 34 on the chalkboard and have children model it on Workmat 2. Then write 16 next to the 34 and tell children to take 16 away from 34. Guide children through the regrouping process.

Name _____

More Regrouping Readiness

Chita had 43 .

She sold 28 .

How many did Chita have left?

Use Workmat 2.
Use 15 ◻ and 6 ▦ .

	Show 4 tens 3 ones for the 🧁 she started with. Can you take away 8 ones? **No.** Why or why not? **There are not enough ones.**		
	Regroup 1 ten as 10 ones. How many ones do you have now? **13 ones**		
	Take away the ones and tens. How many 🧁 did Chita have left? **15**		

	Start with	**Take away**	**Do you need to regroup?**	**Number Left**
1.	tens ones: 4 2	tens ones: 1 6	(yes) / no	tens ones: 2 6
2.	tens ones: 6 0	tens ones: 2 7	(yes) / no	tens ones: 3 3
3.	tens ones: 5 3	tens ones: 3 8	(yes) / no	tens ones: 1 5

■ **Can you take 6 ones away from 4 ones? Why?** [No, because there are not enough ones.]

■ **What can you do to get more ones?** [Regroup 1 ten as 10 ones.]

Have children do the regrouping and then take 6 ones away from 14 ones. Then have them take away 1 ten and count the models to find how many are left. [18]

Repeat the activity with another pair of numbers in which regrouping is not needed.

■ **Show 47 and take away 21.**

Make sure children understand that the decision to regroup depends on the number of ones.

Show the number you start with.

Write how many tens and ones for each number.	Can you take away the ones?	Regroup if you need to. How many?	Subtract the ones. Subtract the tens. How many are left?
1. Start with 32. Take away 17. | tens	ones | | 3 | 2 | | 1 | 7 |	Take away 7 ones. Not enough ones. yes (no)		tens	ones | | 2 | 12 | | 1 | 7 |		tens	ones | | 1 | 5 |
2. Start with 43. Take away 19. | tens	ones | | 4 | 3 | | 1 | 9 |	yes (no)		tens	ones | | 3 | 13 | | 1 | 9 |		tens	ones | | 2 | 4 |
3. Start with 26. Take away 9. | tens	ones | | 2 | 6 | | | 9 |	yes (no)		tens	ones | | 1 | 16 | | | 9 |		tens	ones | | 1 | 7 |

MEETING INDIVIDUAL NEEDS

ACTIVITY Common Error and Remediation

MATERIALS place-value charts (Teacher Aid 9), 3 T, 14 O models (or punchouts), Workmat 2

Some children may regroup 1 ten but record the original number of tens. Work individually with each child. Begin by having the child model 34 on Workmat 2. Write 34 in the place-value chart. Tell the child to take away 18 and write 18 under the 34. When he or she regroups the ten as ones, have the child change the 34 on the place-value chart to 2 tens 14 ones. Tell the child to explain each step.

ONGOING ASSESSMENT

INTERVIEW (1) How can you find the answer to 23 − 12? **(2)** Do you have to regroup when you solve 43 − 25?

JOURNAL WRITING You may wish to have children record their responses in their math journals.

ACTIVITY ALTERNATIVE TEACHING STRATEGY

MATERIALS Teacher Aids Transparency 10, 3 T and 11 O models or Manipulatives Kit Transparency 9; overhead projector

VISUAL Tell children that you have 21 stamps and 7 letters to mail. Explain that you want to find out how many stamps you will have left after you put stamps on the letters. Tell children that one way to do this is to model 21 and take away 7 to find how many are left.

Model 21 on the workmat transparency. Regroup 1 ten and take away 7 ones. Have a volunteer tell how many ones are left. [14]

PUPIL'S EDITION pp. 219-220

Page 219 Guide children through the example at the top of the page.

Check for Understanding

■ **How can you tell when you will have to regroup?** [If there are not enough ones to take away]

GUIDED PRACTICE ex. 1–3: For reteaching, use Common Error and Remediation or Alternative Strategy.

Page 220 Read aloud each step at the top of the page. Have children work through ex. 1 as they show each step with models on their workmats.

3 PRACTICE·APPLY PRACTICE ex. 2–3

CLOSE Guide children to summarize the lesson:

■ **Do you have to regroup to take 15 away from 43?** [Yes.]

SPEAKING MATHEMATICALLY ■ TENS AND ONES STORIES

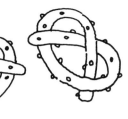

MAC Activity 137

On Your Own   Pair and Share   In a Group

Materials   punchout Workmat 2, counting sticks, rubber bands

Assign each child a partner. Have one child tell a subtraction story that includes tens and ones. Tell children that the story may or may not involve regrouping. The other child is to use counting sticks and rubber bands to model the story and arrive at the answer. Use the following as an example.

Marty had 4 packages of ten pretzels and 7 loose pretzels. If she gives 19 pretzels away, how many will she have left? [28 pretzels]

Have children reverse roles and repeat the activity.

▲
**MAC Activity 137:
Basic-to-Average**

COMPUTER ■ PROGRAMMING

MAC Activity 138

On Your Own   Pair and Share   In a Group

Materials   tens and ones models or punchouts, punchout Workmat 2, computer (optional)

Discuss with children that a program tells a computer what to do. Present the following program and discuss each line. Explain that the word *END* tells the computer to stop.

```
10      Print 27 − 19 [8]
20      Print 52 − 33 [19]
30      Print 44 − 27 [17]
40      END
```

Explain that after typing *RUN*, the computer will print the answer to each exercise. Have children use tens and ones models and Workmat 2 to find each answer and write what the screen would show. If possible, have children write and then run their own short programs using the sample program as a guide.

▲
**MAC Activity 138:
Average-to-Challenge**

RETEACHING-69

Name _____

MORE REGROUPING READINESS

Study
45 take away 28.

tens	ones
4	5
take away	
2	8

Can you take away the ones?

NO. I can't take 8 ones from 5 ones.

Regroup if you need to.

tens	ones
3	15
2	8

Subtract the ones. Subtract the tens.

tens	ones
1	7

Think: 15 ones − 8 ones
3 tens − 2 tens

Check
Use models and Workmat 2.
Show each number.

Can you take away the ones?

Regroup if you need to. How many?

Subtract the ones. Subtract the tens.

1.

tens	ones
3	4
take away	
2	7

yes (no)

tens	ones
2	14
2	7

tens	ones
	7

2.

tens	ones
3	2
take away	
1	4

yes (no)

tens	ones
2	12
1	4

tens	ones
1	8

3.

tens	ones
6	1
take away	
3	5

yes (no)

tens	ones
5	11
3	5

tens	ones
2	6

Reteaching-69

Macmillan/McGraw-Hill, MATHEMATICS IN ACTION
Grade 2, Chapter 7, Lesson 3, pages 219–220

PRACTICE-69

Name _____

MORE REGROUPING READINESS

Use models and Workmat 2. Show each number.

| Write how many tens and ones for each number. | Can you take away the ones? | Regroup if you need to. How many? | Subtract the ones. Subtract the tens. How many are left? |

1. Start with 52. Take away 39.

tens	ones
5	2
3	9

yes (no)

tens	ones
4	12
3	9

tens	ones
1	3

2. Start with 35. Take away 17.

tens	ones
3	5
1	7

yes (no)

tens	ones
2	15
1	7

tens	ones
1	8

3. Start with 23. Take away 9.

tens	ones
2	3
	9

yes (no)

tens	ones
1	13
	9

tens	ones
1	4

Practice-69

Macmillan/McGraw-Hill, MATHEMATICS IN ACTION
Grade 2, Chapter 7, Lesson 3, pages 219–220

ENRICHMENT-69

Name _____

MORE REGROUPING READINESS

On Your Own Pair and Share In a Group

TAKE IT AWAY
Use tens and ones models.
Solve.

1. Bill had 63 stamps.
He used 29 of them.
How many stamps did Bill have left? __34__

2. Ginger made 30 cookies.
She took 24 to the class party.
How many does she have left? __6__

3. Sharon saw 22 ducks on the lake.
18 ducks flew away.
How many ducks are left? __4__

4. Ron made 36 bookmarks.
He sold 27 bookmarks at the fair.
How many does he have left? __9__

5. Lara blew up 24 balloons.
She gave 22 balloons to her friends.
How many balloons does she have left? __2__

6. Bobby had 41 marbles.
He gave 9 marbles to Jack.
How many marbles does Bobby have left? __32__

Enrichment-69

Macmillan/McGraw-Hill, MATHEMATICS IN ACTION
Grade 2, Chapter 7, Lesson 3, pages 219–220

Problem of the Day

The library has 81 riddle books. The children have borrowed 28 of the books. How many are left? [53 books]

CHAPTER 7 • Lesson 4

221

AT·A·GLANCE pp. 221-222

LESSON OBJECTIVE
Subtract 2-digit numbers.

ASSIGNMENT GUIDE

COURSE	EXERCISES
Basic	p. 221: All; p. 222: 1–6, Mental Math
Average	p. 221: All; p. 222: 1–6, Mental Math
Challenge	p. 221: All; p. 222: 1–6, Mental Math

MATERIALS
Manipulatives 9 T and 14 O models (or punchouts), Workmat 2 per child

Teacher Resources
Reteaching 70   Practice 70   Enrichment 70
MAC Act. 139, 140   Calculator 7
Computer Software *Mathematics Skills:* Disk 4 Act. 3

SKILLS TRACE
2-DIGIT SUBTRACTION

Explore (Concrete) 216, 217–218	Develop/Understand (Transitional/Abstract) 219–220, 221–222, 223–224, 225, 226, 233, 234
Practice 230, 239, 240, 241–242, 245, 288, 301	Apply 227–228, 231–232, 235–236, 237, 238, 244, 351

ACTIVITY

2-Digit Subtraction

Subtract 17 from 43.

First look at the ones. Regroup. Do you know why?

There are not enough ones.

Regroup 1 ten as 10 ones.

Next subtract the ones.

6 ones are left

Then subtract the tens.

2 tens are left

What number is left? 43 − 17 = __26__

Chapter 7   Subtracting 2-Digit Numbers   two hundred twenty-one   **221**

PREPARE

WARM-UP To review basic subtraction facts, have children give each difference as you read the following.

18 − 9 [9]	14 − 6 [8]	6 − 2 [4]
15 − 6 [9]	9 − 7 [2]	17 − 8 [9]
16 − 9 [7]	10 − 4 [6]	12 − 7 [5]

TEACH

MODELING Write the following exercise on the chalkboard:

Have children show 34 with tens and ones models on Workmat 2.

■ **Which numbers do we look at first?** [the ones; 4 and 6]

■ **Do you have to regroup?** [Yes.]

Guide children through the regrouping of 1 ten for 10 ones as they model it on their workmats. Demonstrate how this is recorded in the small boxes at the top of the ones and tens columns on the chalkboard. Have children subtract the ones and subtract the tens on their

Use Workmat 2. Use 12 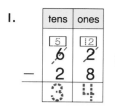 and 9 ▭▭▭▭ .
Subtract.

1.

tens	ones
⑤	⑫
̶6̶	̶2̶
− 2	8
3	4

Did you regroup?
(yes) no

2.

tens	ones
③	⑪
̶4̶	̶1̶
− 3	5
	6

Did you regroup?
(yes) no

3.

tens	ones
▢	▢
2	7
− 1	0
1	7

Did you regroup?
yes (no)

4.

tens	ones
⑥	⑫
̶7̶	̶2̶
−	3
6	9

Did you regroup?
(yes) no

5.

tens	ones
⑦	⑩
̶8̶	̶0̶
− 5	2
2	8

Did you regroup?
(yes) no

6.

tens	ones
▢	▢
9	7
− 5	2
4	5

Did you regroup?
yes (no)

Mental Math

50 − 30
5 tens − 3 tens = 2 tens
2 tens = 20

Viv says she can subtract
30 from 50 without using models.

Subtract.

1. 40 − 20 (20)   2. 60 − 30 (30)

3. 80 − 50 (30)   4. 70 − 30 (40)

ACTIVITY *Common Error and Remediation*

MATERIALS 9 T, 14 O models (or punchouts), Workmat 2

Some children may regroup when it is not necessary. Work individually with each child, using Workmat 2 and tens and ones models. Tell the child to model 17 on the workmat. Then ask the child to take away 5 ones. Have the child decide if regrouping is necessary and explain why or why not. Repeat with other examples that do and do not require regrouping. In each case, have the child explain if regrouping is necessary.

TEACHER to TEACHER

MANAGEMENT TIP My children benefited from orally describing each step in the subtraction process.

ACTIVITY **ALTERNATIVE TEACHING STRATEGY**

MATERIALS 4 T, 9 O models (or Manipulatives Kit Transparency 9), Teacher Aids Transparency 10; overhead projector

VISUAL/AUDITORY Write 42 − 17 on the side of a transparency similar to Workmat 2. Show 42 with models. Demonstrate each step of the subtraction process with the models, giving special emphasis to the regrouping step. Repeat the activity with 27 − 19.

---

workmats and record this information for the example on the chalkboard.

PUPIL'S EDITION pp. 221-222

Page 221 Guide children through the example on the page. Discuss how they know it is necessary to regroup. Point out how the regrouping is recorded in the small boxes. After working through the example, have children write the number that is left.

Check for Understanding

■ **How do you subtract two 2-digit numbers?** [Possible response: Look at the ones, regroup if necessary, subtract the ones, subtract the tens.]

Page 222 Have children use Workmat 2 and tens and ones models to complete the exercises.

GUIDED PRACTICE ex. 1: For reteaching, use Common Error and Remediation or Alternative Strategy.

3 PRACTICE•APPLY **PRACTICE** ex. 2–6

MENTAL MATH Review the example, making sure children understand that they can think of 50 and 30 as 5 tens and 3 tens.

C L O S E Guide children to summarize the lesson:

■ **How are tens and ones models used to help you subtract 2-digit numbers?** [Possible response: They are used to model the first number in the exercise. Then you take away the second number, regrouping tens as ones if necessary, to find the difference.]

SPEAKING MATHEMATICALLY ■ SUBTRACTION WORDS

MAC Activity 139

On Your Own   Pair and Share   In a Group

Read the following statements about subtracting 2-digit numbers. Have children repeat the sentence filling in the blank. Suggested responses are provided, but accept all reasonable answers.

1. To see if I need to regroup, I look at the ——. [ones]
2. If I want to take 6 ones away from 2 ones, I will need to ——. [regroup]
3. After regrouping 1 ten, I will have ——. [10 ones]
4. I always subtract the ones ——. [first]
5. I always subtract the tens —— the ones. [after]
6. When I subtract two numbers, I am finding the —— [difference or what is left]

**MAC Activity 139:
Basic-to-Average** ▶

ESTIMATION ■ COMPARE DIFFERENCES

MAC Activity 140

On Your Own   Pair and Share   In a Group

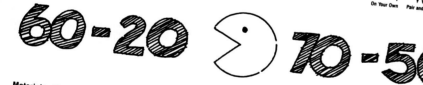

Materials Write these exercises on the chalkboard.

1. $60 - 20 \bigcirc 70 - 50$ [>]
2. $82 - 70 \bigcirc 30 - 11$ [<]
3. $52 - 10 \bigcirc 95 - 60$ [>]
4. $47 - 21 \bigcirc 81 - 40$ [<]
5. $36 - 10 \bigcirc 42 - 11$ [<]
6. $92 - 61 \bigcirc 35 - 27$ [>]
7. $65 - 12 \bigcirc 53 - 10$ [>]
8. $70 - 41 \bigcirc 95 - 15$ [<]

Have children find which side of the number sentence is greater and write < or > in the circle. Have volunteers explain how they got their answers. Encourage children to think of different ways they could arrive at an estimate.

▲
**MAC Activity 140:
Average-to-Challenge**

RETEACHING

Name _____

2-DIGIT SUBTRACTION

Study

Look at the ones.	Regroup	Subtract ones.	Subtract tens.

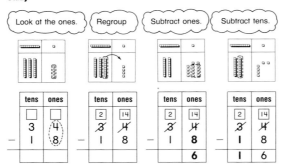

tens	ones		tens	ones		tens	ones		tens	ones
	[14]		2	[14]		2	[14]		2	[14]
3	4		3	4		3	4		3	4
− 1	8		− 1	8		− 1	8		− 1	8
							6		1	6

Check

Use models to subtract.

1.	tens	ones		tens	ones		tens	ones		tens	ones
	[4]	[12]		3	[13]		4	[14]		4	[11]
	5	2		4	3		5	4		5	1
	− 1	6		− 2	8		− 3	8		−	7
	3	6		1	5		1	6		4	4

Macmillan/McGraw-Hill, MATHEMATICS IN ACTION
Grade 2, Chapter 7, Lesson 4, pages 221–222

Reteaching-70

PRACTICE

Name _____

2-DIGIT SUBTRACTION

Use Workmat 2 and tens and ones models.
Subtract.

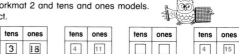

1.	tens	ones		tens	ones		tens	ones		tens	ones
	[3]	[18]		[4]	[11]					[4]	[15]
	4	8		5	1		4	4		5	5
	− 1	9		− 1	6		− 1	3		− 2	8
	2	9		3	5		3	1		2	7

2.	tens	ones		tens	ones		tens	ones		tens	ones
	[3]	[13]					[4]	[10]		[3]	[12]
	4	3		6	5		5	0		4	2
	− 3	8		− 2	2		− 3	2		− 1	7
		5		4	3		1	8		2	5

3.	tens	ones		tens	ones		tens	ones		tens	ones
	[4]	[17]		[3]	[11]		[1]	[13]		[5]	[17]
	5	7		4	1		2	3		6	7
	− 2	8		−	5		− 1	6		− 3	9
	2	9		3	6			7		2	8

4.	tens	ones		tens	ones		tens	ones		tens	ones
				[6]	[10]		[3]	[14]		[8]	[14]
	4	6		7	0		4	4		9	4
	− 2	4		− 3	2		− 2	5		− 1	8
	2	2		3	8		1	9		7	6

Macmillan/McGraw-Hill, MATHEMATICS IN ACTION
Grade 2, Chapter 7, Lesson 4, pages 221–222

Practice-70

ENRICHMENT

Name _____

2-DIGIT SUBTRACTION

On Your Own   Pair and Share   In a Group

SUBTRACTION RIDDLE
What is the biggest jewel in the world?

A	N	S	A	L
70	82	26	93	49
− 39	− 15	− 7	− 45	− 12
31	67	19	48	37

E	M	I	O	B
41	77	61	94	55
− 18	− 24	− 15	− 34	− 48
23	53	46	60	7

D	A	L	B	D
90	41	73	75	62
− 16	− 28	− 33	− 46	− 19
74	13	40	29	43

Order the answers from least to greatest.
Then write the letter under each number.

7	13	19	23	29	31	37	40
B	A	S	E	B	A	L	L

43	46	48	53	60	67	74
D	I	A	M	O	N	D

Macmillan/McGraw-Hill, MATHEMATICS IN ACTION
Grade 2, Chapter 7, Lesson 4, pages 221–222

Enrichment-70

Problem of the Day

Mrs. Reed plans to make 50 puppets for the school fair. She has already made 37. How many more does she have to make?   [13]

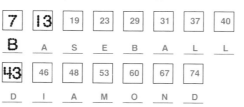

AT·A·GLANCE pp. 223-224

LESSON OBJECTIVE
Subtract 2-digit numbers.

ASSIGNMENT GUIDE

COURSE	EXERCISES
Basic	p. 223: 1–4; p. 224: 1–10
Average	p. 223: 1–4; p. 224: 1–10
Challenge	p. 223: 1–4; p. 224: 1–10

MATERIALS
Manipulatives 5 T, 13 O models (or punchouts), Workmat 2 per child

Teacher Resources
Reteaching 71
Prob. Solv. 31
Practice 71
MAC Act. 141, 142
Enrichment 71
Teacher Aid 10

SKILLS TRACE
2-DIGIT SUBTRACTION

Explore (Concrete)	Develop/Understand (Transitional/Abstract)
216, 217–218	219–220, 221–222, **223–224**, 225, 226, 233, 234
Practice 230, 239, 240, 241–242, 245, 288, 301	**Apply** 227–228, 231–232, 235–236, 237, 238, 244, 351

Name _____

More 2-Digit Subtraction

Subtract 16 from 34.

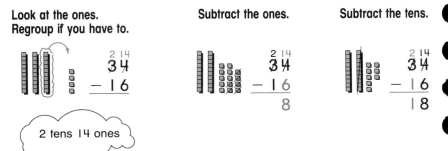

Look at the ones. Regroup if you have to.	Subtract the ones.	Subtract the tens.

2 tens 14 ones

Subtract.

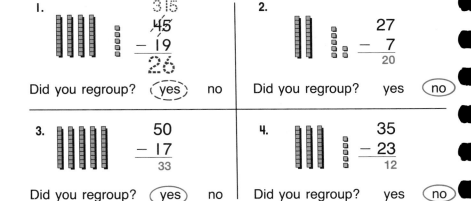

1.
$$\begin{array}{r} {}^{3}\!4\,^{1}5 \\ \cancel{4}5 \\ -\ 19 \\ \hline 26 \end{array}$$

Did you regroup? (yes) no

2.
$$\begin{array}{r} 27 \\ -\ 7 \\ \hline 20 \end{array}$$

Did you regroup? yes (no)

3.
$$\begin{array}{r} 50 \\ -\ 17 \\ \hline 33 \end{array}$$

Did you regroup? (yes) no

4.
$$\begin{array}{r} 35 \\ -\ 23 \\ \hline 12 \end{array}$$

Did you regroup? yes (no)

PREPARE

WARM-UP To review subtraction with regrouping, write the following numbers on the chalkboard.

■ **If the number 7 was subtracted from each number, would you have to regroup? 18** [No.] **24** [Yes.] **62** [Yes.] **37** [No.] **12** [Yes.] **40** [Yes.] **29** [No.]

Have children explain their reasoning.

TEACH

MODELING Write the following example on the chalkboard. Emphasize how the numbers align.

$$\begin{array}{r} 46 \\ -15 \end{array}$$

Have children use tens and ones models to model the number 46 on Workmat 2.

■ **Do you have to regroup to subtract ones?** [No, there are enough ones to take 5 ones away from 6 ones.]

After children model the subtraction of the ones, record 1 in the ones column on the chalkboard. Then have children show subtracting tens. After they model this step, record a 3 in the tens column on the chalkboard.

Repeat this procedure with an example that requires regrouping, such as 53 − 29. As children model each step of the subtraction, encourage them to discuss what they are doing and why.

PUPIL'S EDITION pp. 223-224

Page 223 Work through the example at the top of the page with the children.

Choose a number from each Pile. Subtract the number in Pile 2 from the number in Pile 1. Write your work on the lines.

Answers will vary.

Pile 1   **Pile 2**

1.
```
  810
  9̶0̶
- 46
  44
```

2.

3.

4.

5.

6.

7.

8.

Mixed Review

Add.

9. $30 + 29 =$ __59__ $47 + 33 =$ __80__ $49 + 25 =$ __74__

10.
```
   6        8       15       34       52       29
 + 9      + 8     + 27     + 36     + 40     + 34
  15       16       42       70       92       63
```

Check for Understanding

■ **If I regroup 32, how many tens and ones do I have after I regroup?** [2 tens 12 ones]

GUIDED PRACTICE   ex. 1–4: For reteaching, use Common Error and Remediation or Alternative Strategy.

Page 224   Explain to children that they will use the numbers on the blocks to make up their own exercises. Be sure they understand that they are to subtract a number in Pile 2 from a number in Pile 1.

 **PRACTICE•APPLY**   **PRACTICE**   ex. 1–10

MEETING INDIVIDUAL NEEDS

ACTIVITY   *Common Error and Remediation*

MATERIALS place-value computation boxes (Teacher Aid 10)

Some children may not be able to write a 2-digit subtraction exercise and align the digits properly. Work individually with each child. Give the child a worksheet duplicated from Teacher Aid 10. Give the child exercises such as those found on the page. Observe the child as he or she copies each exercise to make sure the digits are aligned correctly in the place-value boxes.

ONGOING ASSESSMENT
MATH JOURNAL

INTERVIEW (1) How would you find the answer to 40 − 16? (2) Would you have to regroup when you find the answer to 39 − 29? Tell why. (3) How would you solve 56 − 28?

JOURNAL WRITING You may wish to have children record their responses in their math journals.

ALTERNATIVE TEACHING STRATEGY

VISUAL Write and draw the following on the chalkboard.

```
  62
- 25
```

Work through the subtraction. Regroup tens (erase 1 ten and draw 10 ones). Cross off 5 ones and write 7 in the difference. Cross off 2 tens and write 3 in the difference. Repeat the activity to subtract 28 − 19, 34 − 9, and 50 − 12.

CLOSE Guide children to summarize the lesson:

■ **Explain how to subtract 35 from 84.** [Look at the ones, regroup, subtract the ones, and subtract the tens.]

MAC Activity 141:
Basic-to-Average

MAC Activity 141

On Your Own   Pair and Share   In a Group

MATH AND SCIENCE ■ WEATHER DIFFERENCES

Materials   weather section of a daily newspaper

Display the weather section and show children the list of high and low temperatures of the day that are recorded for various cities around the country. Using this information, have them work with a partner to write several subtraction problems. Use the following as an example:

What was the difference between yesterday's high and low temperatures in Dallas?

What was the difference between the high temperatures in Portland, Oregon and Portland, Maine?.

After the partners write their problems, have them exchange their work with another pair of children and find the answers.

MAC Activity 142:
Average-to-Challenge

LOGICAL REASONING ■ WHAT IS THE NUMBER?

MAC Activity 142

On Your Own   Pair and Share   In a Group

Materials   tens and ones models or punchout tens and ones models

Have children work in pairs to solve the following riddles. Encourage children to use models if they need help finding the number.

1. This number is more than 55 and less than 65. When I subtract 11 from it, I need to regroup. What is the number? [60]
2. This number is more than 35 and less than 45. When I subtract 12 from it I have 5 ones left. What is the number? [37]
3. This number is more than 60 and less than 70. When I subtract 42 from it, I get a zero in the difference. What is the number? [62].

Continue the activity by having children write their own riddles. Then have them exchange riddles with a partner and solve them.

Name

RETEACHING-71

MORE 2-DIGIT SUBTRACTION

Study

$$\begin{array}{r} 317 \\ \cancel{4}7 \\ -28 \\ \hline 19 \end{array}$$
I need to regroup.

$$\begin{array}{r} 36 \\ -14 \\ \hline 22 \end{array}$$
I have enough ones to subtract.

Check

Decide if you need to regroup.
Then subtract.

1. Regroup?	tens	ones
(yes) no	[5] [18] 6 − 1 **4**	8 9 **9**

2. Regroup?	tens	ones
yes (no)	4 − 2 **2**	7 4 **3**

3. Regroup?	tens	ones
yes (no)	5 − 3 **2**	6 2 **4**

4. Regroup?	tens	ones
(yes) no	[5] 6 − 4 **1**	[10] 0 9 **1**

5. Regroup?	tens	ones
(yes) no	[3] 4 − 1 **2**	[15] 5 8 **7**

6. Regroup?	tens	ones
yes (no)	3 − 1 **2**	1 0 **0**

Reteaching-71

Macmillan/McGraw-Hill, MATHEMATICS IN ACTION
Grade 2, Chapter 7, Lesson 5, pages 223–224

Name

PRACTICE-71

MORE 2-DIGIT SUBTRACTION

Subtract.

1.
$$\begin{array}{r} \cancel{5}5 \\ -38 \\ \hline 17 \end{array}$$
Did you regroup? (yes) no

2.
$$\begin{array}{r} 67 \\ -25 \\ \hline 42 \end{array}$$
Did you regroup? yes (no)

3.
$$\begin{array}{r} 63 \\ -45 \\ \hline 18 \end{array}$$
Did you regroup? (yes) no

4.
$$\begin{array}{r} 35 \\ -8 \\ \hline 27 \end{array}$$
Did you regroup? (yes) no

5.
$$\begin{array}{r} 70 \\ -43 \\ \hline 27 \end{array}$$
Did you regroup? (yes) no

6.
$$\begin{array}{r} 53 \\ -18 \\ \hline 35 \end{array}$$
Did you regroup? (yes) no

7.
$$\begin{array}{r} 42 \\ -39 \\ \hline 3 \end{array}$$
Did you regroup? (yes) no

8.
$$\begin{array}{r} 50 \\ -23 \\ \hline 27 \end{array}$$
Did you regroup? (yes) no

Practice-71

Macmillan/McGraw-Hill, MATHEMATICS IN ACTION
Grade 2, Chapter 7, Lesson 5, pages 223–224

Name

ENRICHMENT-71

MORE 2-DIGIT SUBTRACTION

On Your Own · Pair and Share · In a Group

CLEAN-UP TIME

Rags has muddy feet.
What number is under each 🐾 ?

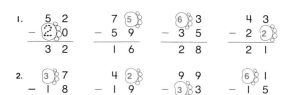

1.
$$\begin{array}{r} 52 \\ -20 \\ \hline 32 \end{array} \quad \begin{array}{r} 7\,5 \\ -59 \\ \hline 16 \end{array} \quad \begin{array}{r} 63 \\ -35 \\ \hline 28 \end{array} \quad \begin{array}{r} 43 \\ -22 \\ \hline 21 \end{array}$$

2.
$$\begin{array}{r} 37 \\ -18 \\ \hline 19 \end{array} \quad \begin{array}{r} 42 \\ -19 \\ \hline 23 \end{array} \quad \begin{array}{r} 99 \\ -33 \\ \hline 66 \end{array} \quad \begin{array}{r} 61 \\ -15 \\ \hline 46 \end{array}$$

Use the numbers on the cards.
Write 2 subtraction exercises with regrouping.
Write 2 subtraction exercises without regrouping.
Have your partner find the differences.

| 63 | 81 | 27 | 50 | 38 | 79 | 21 | 15 |

Answers will vary.

___ ___ ___ ___

Enrichment-71

Macmillan/McGraw-Hill, MATHEMATICS IN ACTION
Grade 2, Chapter 7, Lesson 5, pages 223–224

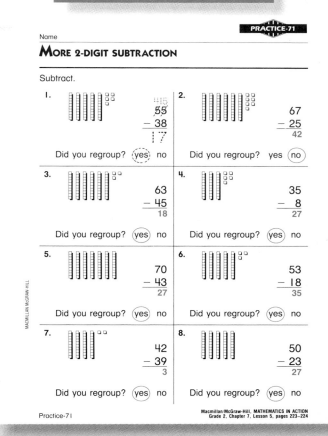

Problem of the Day

Paco has read 26 pages of a 45-page book. Judy has read 63 pages of a 78-page book. Who has the most pages left to read? [Paco; possible solution: 45 − 26 = 19; 78 − 63 = 15; 19 > 15]

CHAPTER 7 • Lesson 6

AT·A·GLANCE p. 225

LESSON OBJECTIVE
Subtract 2-digit numbers.

ASSIGNMENT GUIDE

COURSE	EXERCISES
Basic	p. 225: 1–4
Average	p. 225: 1–4
Challenge	p. 225: 1–4
Extra Practice, p. 230	Practice Plus, p. 240

MATERIALS
Manipulatives 9 T and 18 O models (or punchouts), Workmat 2 per child

Teacher Resources
Reteaching 72
MAC Act. 143, 144
Practice 72
Teacher Aid 11
Enrichment 72

SKILLS TRACE
2-DIGIT SUBTRACTION

Explore (Concrete) 216, 217–218	Develop/Understand (Transitional/Abstract) 219–220, 221–222, 223–224, 225, 226, 233, 234
Practice 230, 239, 240, 241–242, 245, 288, 301	Apply 227–228, 231–232, 235–236, 237, 238, 244, 351

See **MANIPULATIVES PLUS 44**, p. 214N.

Subtraction Practice

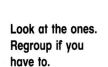

There are 86 cows.
48 of them go to the field to eat.
How many are left?

Look at the ones. Regroup if you have to.	Subtract the ones.	Subtract the tens.
$\begin{array}{r} 7\ 16 \\ 8\,6 \\ -\ 4\,8 \\ \hline \end{array}$	$\begin{array}{r} 7\ 16 \\ 8\,6 \\ -\ 4\,8 \\ \hline 8 \end{array}$	$\begin{array}{r} 7\ 16 \\ 8\,6 \\ -\ 4\,8 \\ \hline 3\,8 \end{array}$

38 cows are left.

Subtract. Use models if you need help.

1.
35	71	(40)	29	47
− 14	− 41	− 16	− 6	− 31
21	30	24	23	16

2.
76	(84)	89	(95)	83
− 42	− 67	− 82	− 36	− 21
34	17	7	59	62

3.
(91)	(70)	(51)	(53)	(92)
− 64	− 21	− 6	− 44	− 14
27	49	45	9	78

4. Ring each exercise where you regrouped.

What shape did your rings make? ____triangle____

Extra Practice, page 230 **Practice Plus,** page 240

two hundred twenty-five **225**

Macmillan/McGraw-Hill

Have children model the exercise on Workmat 2. Tell them to put the models they remove for 38 to the right of their workmat.

■ **What do the models left on the workmat show?** [the difference]
■ **What do the models you took off the workmat show?** [the number taken away]

Repeat the activity with other exercises.

PUPIL'S EDITION p. 225
Work through the example at the top of the page with the children.

Check for Understanding

■ **If you subtract 46 from 86, would you have to regroup?** [No.]

GUIDED PRACTICE ex. 1: For reteaching, use Common Error and Remediation or Alternative Strategy.

---

1 PREPARE
WARM-UP To review subtracting tens, write the following on the chalkboard. Have children solve each exercise mentally.

80 − 20 = [60]	30 − 10 = [20]
40 − 10 = [30]	70 − 30 = [40]
30 − 20 = [10]	40 − 30 = [10]
70 − 40 = [30]	80 − 60 = [20]

2 TEACH
MODELING Write the following subtraction example on the chalkboard:

$\begin{array}{r} 52 \\ -\ 38 \\ \hline \end{array}$

Common Error and Remediation

MATERIALS red and green crayons

Some children may subtract the lesser number from the greater number instead of regrouping. Work individually with each child. Write a subtraction exercise that requires regrouping, using red for the top number and green for the bottom number. Explain that a green number can be subtracted from a red number, but a red cannot be subtracted from a green. Work through each step with the child. Then write some exercises using a pencil and have the child subtract.

For Students Acquiring English (SAE)

Read the story problem aloud. Have children dramatize the story using manipulatives to solve the regrouping problem.

ACTIVITY ALTERNATIVE TEACHING STRATEGY

AUDITORY Tell children to write 72 − 57 on a sheet of paper. Have volunteers tell each step of the subtraction as the rest of the children find the difference. [15] Repeat the activity with 28 − 16, 40 − 38, and 93 − 34.

3 PRACTICE·APPLY   **PRACTICE**   ex. 2–4

CLOSE   Guide children to summarize the lesson:
- **Do you regroup when you subtract 47 − 29?** [Yes.]
- **Do you regroup when you subtract 51 − 40?** [No.]

MAC Activity 144

On Your Own   Pair and Share   In a Group

NUMBER SENSE ▪ GET TO ZERO

Materials   number cards for 0 – 9 (Teacher Aid 11), paper bags

Procedure   Have children play in groups. Give each group a bag marked *tens* that contains several number cards for 1 to 5 and a bag marked *ones* that contains several number cards for 0 to 9. Write 99 at the top of a large sheet of paper.

Tell children they will play "Get to Zero." Explain that they should take turns choosing a tens card and a ones card from the bags. The first child subtracts the number drawn from 99. Then the next child subtracts from the difference.

To Win   The first child to reach zero wins the round.

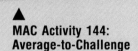

▲
MAC Activity 144:
Average-to-Challenge

MANIPULATIVES ▪ MORE PROBLEMS

MAC Activity 143

Materials   tens and ones models or punchout tens and ones models, punchout Workmat 2

Assign children to work in pairs. Give each pair of children tens and ones models and Workmat 2. Tell children they are to work together to solve the problems you will read aloud. After each problem, have a volunteer tell how each problem was solved.

1. Liz made 76 oatmeal cookies for the party. The children ate 59 of the cookies. How many cookies were left? [17]
2. Ed blew up 34 balloons for the party. The children took home 18 balloons. How many balloons were left? [16]
3. Juan served 23 glasses of lemonade at the party. He also served 19 glasses of grape drink. How many more glasses of lemonade than grape drink did he serve? [4].

To extend the activity, have each pair of children create their own problems and present them to the class to be solved.

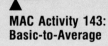

▲
MAC Activity 143:
Basic-to-Average

RETEACHING

PRACTICE

Name

RETEACHING-72

SUBTRACTION PRACTICE

Study

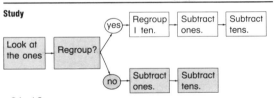

Look at the ones → Regroup? → yes → Regroup 1 ten. → Subtract ones. → Subtract tens.

Regroup? → no → Subtract ones. → Subtract tens.

36 – 12

Check

Subtract. Use models if you need help.

1.
```
  32      86      66      80      60
– 18    – 43    – 25    – 62    – 15
  14      43      41      18      45
```

2.
```
  96      54      94      33      44
– 14    – 30    – 16    – 10    – 29
  82      24      78      23      15
```

3.
```
  74      79      30      41      45
– 54    – 27    – 17    – 22    – 24
  20      52      13      19      21
```

Macmillan/McGraw-Hill, MATHEMATICS IN ACTION
Grade 2, Chapter 7, Lesson 6, page 225   Reteaching-72

Name

PRACTICE-72

SUBTRACTION PRACTICE

Subtract.
Complete the puzzle.

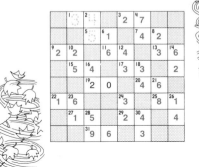

ACROSS

1. 51 – 17
3. 76 – 49
5. 81 – 30
7. 70 – 28
9. 39 – 17
11. 92 – 28
13. 51 – 15
15. 91 – 37
17. 82 – 49
19. 53 – 33
20. 70 – 24
22. 51 – 35
25. 94 – 13
27. 62 – 47
29. 43 – 19
31. 99 – 3

DOWN

2. 60 – 15
4. 97 – 23
6. 44 – 28
8. 58 – 35
10. 50 – 25
12. 70 – 27
14. 81 – 19
16. 53 – 11
18. 72 – 38
21. 83 – 15
23. 78 – 17
24. 51 – 19
26. 79 – 65
28. 98 – 39
30. 85 – 42

Macmillan/McGraw-Hill, MATHEMATICS IN ACTION
Grade 2, Chapter 7, Lesson 6, page 225   Practice-72

ENRICHMENT

Name

ENRICHMENT-72

SUBTRACTION PRACTICE

On Your Own   Pair and Share   In a Group

MAGIC SQUARES

Subtract.
Then add the differences across each row.
Add the differences down each column.
Add the differences from corner to corner.

19 − 11 = 8	56 − 55 = 1	38 − 32 = 6	15
13 − 10 = 3	27 − 22 = 5	78 − 71 = 7	15
88 − 84 = 4	49 − 40 = 9	64 − 62 = 2	15
15	15	15	15

38 − 15 = 23	57 − 41 = 16	48 − 27 = 21	60
78 − 60 = 18	43 − 23 = 20	59 − 37 = 22	60
49 − 30 = 19	66 − 42 = 24	28 − 11 = 17	60
60	60	60	60

56 − 36 = 20	79 − 66 = 13	68 − 50 = 18	51
78 − 63 = 15	47 − 30 = 17	59 − 40 = 19	51
88 − 72 = 16	36 − 15 = 21	78 − 64 = 14	51
51	51	51	51

99 − 70 = 29	37 − 15 = 22	69 − 42 = 27	78
88 − 64 = 24	47 − 21 = 26	78 − 50 = 28	78
49 − 24 = 25	96 − 66 = 30	64 − 41 = 23	78
78	78	78	78

Macmillan/McGraw-Hill, MATHEMATICS IN ACTION
Grade 2, Chapter 7, Lesson 6, page 225   Enrichment-72

Problem of the Day

Steven picked 26 apples from one tree and 34 apples from another tree. He and his classmates ate 49 apples. How many apples were left?   [11]

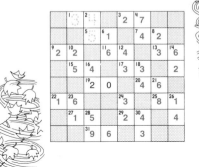

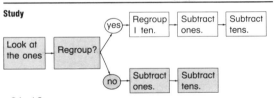

AT·A·GLANCE p. 226

LESSON OBJECTIVE
Check subtraction.

ASSIGNMENT GUIDE

COURSE	EXERCISES
Basic	p. 226: 1–5
Average	p. 226: 1–5
Challenge	p. 226: 1–5

MATERIALS
Calculator
Manipulatives 7 T and 13 O models (or punchouts), Workmat
2 per pair

Teacher Resources
Reteaching 73   Practice 73   Enrichment 73
MAC Act. 145, 146
Computer Software *Mathematics Skills:* Disk 4 Act. 4

SKILLS TRACE
2-DIGIT SUBTRACTION

Explore (Concrete)	Develop/Understand (Transitional/Abstract)
216, 217–218	219–220, 221–222, 223–224, 225, **226**, 233, 234
Practice 230, 239, 240, 241–242, 245, 288, 301	**Apply** 227–228, 231–232, 235–236, 237, 238, 244, 351

Checking Subtraction

Two science teams counted whales.
Each team has the same total.
What are the missing numbers?

Work with a partner to find out.

Whales Counted

	Team A	Team B
Total	73	
Summer	45	28
Winter		45

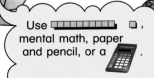

1. First find the difference.
   Then find the number that
   is missing.

$$\begin{array}{r} 73 \\ -45 \\ \hline 28 \end{array} \qquad \begin{array}{r} 28 \\ +45 \\ \hline \boxed{73} \end{array}$$

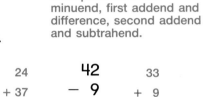

Use ▭▭▭▭▭▭ ☐,
mental math, paper
and pencil, or a 🖩.

2. Tell how the numbers you subtracted
   and added are the same.

3. Can you add to check subtraction?
   Make up your own subtraction and
   addition pairs. Use a 🖩 to find the
   differences and sums.

In their own words,
children should note that
the following numbers are
the same in the addition
and the subtraction
examples: sum and
minuend, first addend and
difference, second addend
and subtrahend.

Subtract. Add to check your answer.

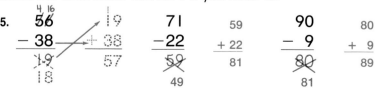

4.
$$\begin{array}{r} {}^{7\,10} \\ 8\!\!\!/0 \\ -23 \\ \hline 57 \end{array} \quad \begin{array}{r} {}^{1} \\ 57 \\ +23 \\ \hline 80 \end{array} \qquad \begin{array}{r} 61 \\ -37 \\ \hline 24 \end{array} \quad \begin{array}{r} 24 \\ +37 \\ \hline 61 \end{array} \qquad \begin{array}{r} 42 \\ -9 \\ \hline 33 \end{array} \quad \begin{array}{r} 33 \\ +9 \\ \hline 42 \end{array}$$

Check the difference. Correct it if you need to.

5.
$$\begin{array}{r} {}^{4\,16} \\ 5\!\!\!/6 \\ -38 \\ \hline \cancel{19} \\ 18 \end{array} \quad \begin{array}{r} {}^{1} \\ 19 \\ +38 \\ \hline 57 \end{array} \qquad \begin{array}{r} 71 \\ -22 \\ \hline \cancel{59} \\ 49 \end{array} \quad \begin{array}{r} 59 \\ +22 \\ \hline 81 \end{array} \qquad \begin{array}{r} 90 \\ -9 \\ \hline \cancel{80} \\ 81 \end{array} \quad \begin{array}{r} 80 \\ +9 \\ \hline 89 \end{array}$$

1 PREPARE
WARM-UP To prepare children to check subtraction, write the following on the chalkboard. Have volunteers write the sums and differences.

$$\begin{array}{r} 36 \\ -19 \\ \hline [17] \end{array} \qquad \begin{array}{r} 73 \\ -27 \\ \hline [46] \end{array} \qquad \begin{array}{r} 42 \\ -36 \\ \hline [\,6] \end{array}$$

$$\begin{array}{r} 17 \\ +19 \\ \hline [36] \end{array} \qquad \begin{array}{r} 46 \\ +27 \\ \hline [73] \end{array} \qquad \begin{array}{r} 6 \\ +36 \\ \hline [42] \end{array}$$

2 TEACH
MODELING Have children work in pairs. Give each pair ones models and Workmat 2. Tell children to model the subtraction 9 − 3. [6]

■ **What do the models you took off the workmat show?** [the number taken away]

■ **What would happen if you added 3 back to the difference?** [The sum would be the same as the number subtracted from; 9.]

PUPIL'S EDITION p. 226
Guide children through the example at the top of the page. Discuss that the chart shows the total number of whales, then the part of the total for summer and winter that each team counted. Have children relate the numbers in the chart to the examples in ex. 1.

ACTIVITY

Common Error and Remediation

MATERIALS 7 T and 13 O models (or punchouts), Workmat 2

Some children may not see the relationship between addition and subtraction of 2-digit numbers. Work individually with each child. Have the child show 7 − 4 with ones models. Then have the child add the 3 ones back to the 4 to get 7. Ask the child to describe what happened. Repeat with other numbers to 18. Then have the child do similar exercises with 2-digit numbers.

ALTERNATIVE TEACHING STRATEGY

VISUAL/AUDITORY Write the following exercises on the chalkboard.

$$\begin{array}{r} 85 \\ -19 \\ \hline [66] \end{array} \qquad \begin{array}{r} 66 \\ +19 \\ \hline [85] \end{array}$$

Tell children that they should always check their subtraction. Explain that they should add the difference to the number taken away. As you work through the examples, stress the relationship between the numbers.

 GUIDED PRACTICE ex. 1–3: Distribute calculators, ones models, tens models, and Workmat 2 to pairs. Discuss that children may choose a method: models, mental math, paper and pencil, or a calculator to find the difference and missing numbers in ex. 1. Children will use calculators in ex. 3 to subtract their own 2-digit examples, add the difference to the number they took away, and discover that addition can be used to check a difference.

Check for Understanding

■ **How can you check the difference of a subtraction example?**
[the number taken away can be added to the difference]

3 PRACTICE•APPLY

PRACTICE ex. 4–5: Discuss that the exercises in row 5 may have an incorrect difference written in. Children should add to check each difference and if the addition check does not agree with the subtraction, re-do the subtraction and check again. Children should correct the difference if they need to.

CLOSE Guide children to summarize the lesson:

■ **What should you do if the addition check does not agree with the subtraction?** [Re-do the subtraction and check again.]

**MAC Activity 145:
Basic-to-Average**
▼

CALCULATOR ■ WRITE AND SUBTRACT

MAC Activity 145

On Your Own   Pair and Share   In a Group

26
−18

Materials calculators

Have children work in pairs. Tell one child to write a 2-digit subtraction exercise. Then have the second child do the subtraction on a calculator. Tell the first child to add on the calculator to check the subtraction. Have children alternate roles.

**MAC Activity 146:
Average-to-Challenge**
▼

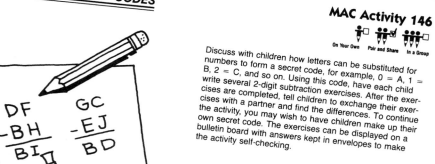

LOGICAL REASONING ■ CODES

MAC Activity 146

On Your Own   Pair and Share   In a Group

Discuss with children how letters can be substituted for numbers to form a secret code, for example, 0 = A, 1 = B, 2 = C, and so on. Using this code, have each child write several 2-digit subtraction exercises. After the exercises are completed, tell children to exchange their exercises with a partner and find the differences. To continue the activity, you may wish to have children make up their own secret code. The exercises can be displayed on a bulletin board with answers kept in envelopes to make the activity self-checking.

DF   GC
−BH   −EJ
‾BI   ‾BD

A B C D E F G H I J
0 1 2 3 4 5 6 7 8 9

RETEACHING-73

Name _____

CHECKING SUBTRACTION

Study

Look at the ones. Regroup if you need to.	Subtract the ones.	Subtract the tens.	Add to check.
$\overset{3\,13}{\cancel{4}\cancel{3}}$ $-\ 25$	$\overset{3\,13}{\cancel{4}\cancel{3}}$ $-\ 25$ $\overline{\ \ \ 8}$	$\overset{3\,13}{\cancel{4}\cancel{3}}$ $-\ 25$ $\overline{1\ 8}$	18 $+\ 25$ $\overline{43}$

I can't subtract 5 ones from 3 ones.

The sum matches the top number.

Check

Subtract. Then check the answer.

1.
45	27	33	17	60	23
-18	$+18$	-16	$+16$	-37	$+37$
$\overline{27}$	$\overline{45}$	$\overline{17}$	$\overline{33}$	$\overline{23}$	$\overline{60}$

2.
37	12	72	36	54	25
-25	$+25$	-36	$+36$	-29	$+29$
$\overline{12}$	$\overline{37}$	$\overline{36}$	$\overline{72}$	$\overline{25}$	$\overline{54}$

3.
68	43	31	15	85	18
-25	$+25$	-16	$+16$	-67	$+67$
$\overline{43}$	$\overline{68}$	$\overline{15}$	$\overline{31}$	$\overline{18}$	$\overline{85}$

4.
70	39	89	36	52	35
-31	$+31$	-53	$+53$	-17	$+17$
$\overline{39}$	$\overline{70}$	$\overline{36}$	$\overline{89}$	$\overline{35}$	$\overline{52}$

Reteaching-73

PRACTICE-73

Name _____

CHECKING SUBTRACTION

Subtract. Check your answer.

1.
73	49 ✓	47	31 ✓	60	12
-24	$+24$	-16	$+16$	-48	$+48$
$\overline{49}$	$\overline{73}$	$\overline{31}$	$\overline{47}$	$\overline{12}$	$\overline{60}$

2.
76	48	85	24	68	29
-28	$+28$	-61	$+61$	-39	$+39$
$\overline{48}$	$\overline{76}$	$\overline{24}$	$\overline{85}$	$\overline{29}$	$\overline{68}$

3.
92	48	88	38	71	19
-44	$+44$	-50	$+50$	-52	$+52$
$\overline{48}$	$\overline{92}$	$\overline{38}$	$\overline{88}$	$\overline{19}$	$\overline{71}$

4.
77	32	83	14	94	19
-45	$+45$	-69	$+69$	-75	$+75$
$\overline{32}$	$\overline{77}$	$\overline{14}$	$\overline{83}$	$\overline{19}$	$\overline{94}$

5.
97	29	75	51	56	41
-68	$+68$	-24	$+24$	-15	$+15$
$\overline{29}$	$\overline{97}$	$\overline{51}$	$\overline{75}$	$\overline{41}$	$\overline{56}$

Practice-73

ENRICHMENT-73

Name _____

CHECKING SUBTRACTION

On Your Own   Pair and Share   In a Group

SCRAPING THE SKY

SKYSCRAPERS		
Building	City	Stories
Standard Oil	Chicago	80
First Bank Tower	Toronto	72
Citicorp Center	New York	46
United California Bank	Los Angeles	62
United States Steel	Pittsburgh	64
IDS Center	Minneapolis	57
Central Trust Center	Cincinnati	27

Use the table to solve.

1. How much higher is the IDS Center than the Citicorp Center? __11__

2. How many fewer stories in the United States Steel building than in the First Bank Tower? __8__

3. How many more stories does the Standard Oil building have than the Central Trust Center? __53__

4. Mr. Green works on the 24th floor of the United California Bank. How many floors is he from the top of the building? __38__

Write your own problem.
Have your partner solve it.

Problems will vary.

_____

_____

Enrichment-73

Problem of the Day

On Monday, Barkers Bakery made 90 loaves of bread. By noon, 68 loaves were sold. A restaurant called to order 25 loaves. Could the order be filled? [No. Possible solution: $90 - 68 = 22$; $22 < 25$.]

AT·A·GLANCE pp. 227-228

LESSON OBJECTIVE
Identify extra information and solve problems.

ASSIGNMENT GUIDE

COURSE	EXERCISES
Basic	p. 228: 1–4
Average	p. 228: 1–4
Challenge	p. 228: 1–4
Extra Practice, p. 230	

MATERIALS
Manipulatives 4 T, 12 O models (or punchouts); Workmat 2 per pair

Teacher Resources
Reteaching 74   Practice 74   Enrichment 74
Prob. Solv. 32   MAC Act. 147, 148

Problem Solving

Identifying Extra Information

The Jefferson School students
voted on a space trip.
44 voted to go to the moon.
19 voted to go to Venus.
20 voted to go to Mars.
How many more students voted to go to
the moon than to go to Venus?

| **What do I want to find out?** | How many more voted to go to the moon than to go to Venus? |

| **What data do I know?** | 44 voted to go to the moon. 19 voted to go to Venus. 20 voted to go to Mars. |

| **What can I do?** | First I can cross out the data I do not need. Then I can subtract to find out how many more. |

$$\begin{array}{r} 44 \\ -\ 19 \\ \hline 25 \end{array}$$

25 more students voted to go to the moon than to go to Venus.

Macmillan/McGraw-Hill

---

1 PREPARE   **WARM-UP**   To prepare children for identifying extra information to solve problems, have them give the following sums and differences:

23 − 12 [11]	43 − 29 [14]
33 + 19 [52]	26 + 17 [43]
47 − 39 [8]	35 − 16 [19]

2 TEACH   **MODELING**   Assign children to work in pairs. Give each pair of children a workmat and tens and ones models. Explain that you will read a problem aloud and they should use the tens and ones to model the numbers in the problem.

The children voted on a sport to play. 17 voted to play baseball. 23 voted to play soccer. 12 voted to play volleyball. How many more children voted to play soccer than baseball?

■ **What numbers did you model?** [17, 23, 12]

■ **What do you want to find out?** [how many more children voted for soccer than baseball]

■ **What do you know?** [17 voted for baseball, 23 voted for soccer, and 12 voted for volleyball.]

■ **What data is not needed to solve the problem?** [The data about the 12 votes for volleyball is not needed.]

■ **What can you do to solve the problem?** [Subtract: 23 − 17 = 6.]

PUPIL'S EDITION pp. 227-228

Page 227   Have a volunteer read the problem at the top of the page. Have children respond with their own ideas.

Cross out the data you do not need.
Solve. Use models, mental math, or paper and pencil.

1. 38 spacesuits are red.
   27 spacesuits are blue.
   ~~25 spacesuits are green.~~
   How many more red than blue

   spacesuits are there? __11__ more

---

2. A space boot weighs 20 pounds.
   ~~Space boots come in 3 sizes.~~
   A helmet weighs 18 pounds.
   How much more does a space boot

   weigh than a helmet? __2__ pounds

---

3. Sy counted 25 comets.
   ~~Kara counted 44 stars.~~
   Lee counted 38 comets.

   How many comets were counted? __63__ comets

---

4. Planet X has 3 rings.
   ~~Planet Y has 7 moons.~~
   Planet X has 11 moons.
   How many rings and moons

   does Planet X have? __14__ rings and moons

228   two hundred twenty-eight

Extra Practice, page 230

TEACHER to TEACHER

COOPERATIVE LEARNING TIP 👥 After having pairs of children do the warm-up and modeling exercises, I like to ask them to work on the problems together. First they identify the extra data. Next they discuss what they need and cross out what they don't need. Then they work together to solve the problem with the remaining data. If they finish in time, they make up a problem for the other pair in their group, and swap problems. Each pair can check the work of the other pair.

For Students Acquiring English (SAE)

Have the class vote on some topic (e.g. where they would like to go on a field trip, which book they would like to read aloud next). Record the votes, then ask similar questions to those in the lesson. Focus on understanding vocabulary, such as **how many more** and **data,** and the questions used to delete extra information. Have students show how they discovered the answers.

■ **What do you know?** [You know the number of children who voted to go to the moon, to Venus, and to Mars.]

■ **What do you need to find out?** [You need to find out how many more students voted to go to the moon than to Venus.]

■ **What do you need to do?** [Cross out the information that is not needed, then make a subtraction problem with the needed data.]

Have volunteers read the example aloud.

■ **What data is not needed to solve the problem?** [votes for Mars]

■ **What did you learn?** [Possible response: Sometimes you have more data than you need to solve a problem, so you need to identify the extra information.]

Check for Understanding

■ **What if you wanted to find out how many more students voted**

to go to the moon than to Mars? How would you solve the problem? [Subtract 44 − 20 = 24. 24 more students voted for Mars.]

Page 228 Have a volunteer read the directions at the top of the page.

GUIDED PRACTICE ex. 1: Work through problem 1 with the children. Make sure they understand how to solve the problem by identifying extra information.

3 PRACTICE•APPLY PRACTICE ex. 2–4

CLOSE Guide children to summarize the lesson:

■ **How do you identify extra information in a problem?** [Possible response: Decide what you need; look for unneeded information.]

MAC Activity 147:
Basic-to-Average
▼

MAC Activity 147

CAREER–CRAFTSPERSON ▪ PUPPETS FOR SALE

On Your Own   Pair and Share   In a Group

Materials   index cards

Setup   Distribute six index cards to half of the children. Have them write the numbers 13, 26, 32, 37, 45, 21 on the index cards.

Procedure   Have each child who has a set of number cards pair up with a child who does not have cards. Tell children you will read them some problems. Explain that they are to choose the cards that show the numbers in the problems. Then they are to work together to decide what data they do not need and set that card aside. They use the remaining two cards to solve the problem.

1. One week Marla made 13 puppets. The next week she made 26 stuffed bears. The third week she made 32 clown dolls. How many more clown dolls did she make than puppets?   [19; 32 − 13 = 19]
2. Marla sold 37 puppets to a toy store. She sold 45 puppets to a department store. She sold 21 puppets to a crafts store. How many puppets did she sell to the toy store and the department store?   [82; 37 + 45 = 82]

MAC Activity 148:
Average-to-Challenge
▼

WRITING MATHEMATICS ▪ MYSTERY NUMBER

MAC Activity 148

On Your Own   Pair and Share   In a Group

Materials   counters or punchout counters, worksheet

Setup   Prepare a worksheet as shown and duplicate a copy for each child.

Procedure   Provide each child with a worksheet and 8 counters. Tell children they are going to play a game to find a mystery number. Explain to them that you will read some problems. For each problem, they are to identify the data that is not needed and place a counter over that number. Then they add or subtract and place a counter over the answer. The mystery number is the one number left uncovered.

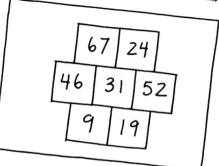

67	24	
46	31	52
9	19	

1. 24 dogs are brown. 34 dogs are white. 15 dogs are black. How many more dogs are white than black? [19; 34 − 15 = 19; place counters over 24 and 19.]
2. 38 cats are asleep. 46 cats are eating. 29 cats are playing. How many more cats are asleep than are playing?   [9; 38 − 29 = 9; place counters over 46 and 9.]
3. 24 horses pull wagons. 43 horses have riders. 31 horses are tied up. How many horses in all pull wagons and have riders?   [67; 24 + 43 = 67; place counters over 31 and 67.]

The mystery number is 52.

RETEACHING

Name _____

PROBLEM SOLVING:
IDENTIFYING EXTRA INFORMATION

Study

The children went to the zoo.
34 went by bus. ⟶ This is data you need.
27 went in cars. ⟶
12 walked. ⟶ You do not need this data. Cross it out.
How many more children
went by bus than in cars? ⟶ Subtract to find out.

34 by bus
− 27 in cars
  7 more children went by bus.

Check

Cross out the data you do not need.
Then solve.

1. Lou counted 17 parrots.   17 parrots
   ~~Gory counted 13 eagles.~~ + 25 parrots
   Marcia counted 25 parrots.   42 parrots in all
   How many parrots were counted?

2. A monkey weighs 22 pounds.   22 pounds
   An anteater weighs 14 pounds. − 14 pounds
   ~~There are 31 kinds of bats.~~   8 pounds
   How much more does the monkey
   weigh than the anteater?

3. 31 cats have stripes.   31
   19 cats have spots.   − 19
   ~~3 cats are yellow.~~   12 cats
   How many more cats have stripes than spots?

Macmillan/McGraw-Hill, MATHEMATICS IN ACTION
Grade 2, Chapter 7, Lesson 8, pages 227–228

Reteaching-74

PRACTICE

Name _____

PROBLEM SOLVING:
IDENTIFYING EXTRA INFORMATION

Cross out the data you do not need.
Then solve.

1. Matt counts 19 yellow butterflies.
   Vinnie counts 26 white butterflies.
   ~~Curt finds 13 crickets.~~
   How many more white than
   yellow butterflies were counted?   7 more

2. Jordan finds 31 maple leaves.
   ~~Nancy finds 14 oak leaves.~~
   Abe finds 29 maple leaves.
   How many maple leaves were found?   60 leaves

3. The class finds 27 birds' nests.
   ~~12 are made of sticks.~~
   22 have fallen out of the trees.
   How many are still in the trees?   5 nests

4. Jerry sees 44 ants carry leaves.
   He sees 29 ants carry sticks.
   ~~18 ants run into their ant hill.~~
   How many more ants carry
   leaves than carry sticks?   15 more

Macmillan/McGraw-Hill, MATHEMATICS IN ACTION
Grade 2, Chapter 7, Lesson 8, pages 227–228

Practice-74

ENRICHMENT

Name _____

PROBLEM SOLVING

On Your Own   Pair and Share   In a Group

ROAD SIGNS

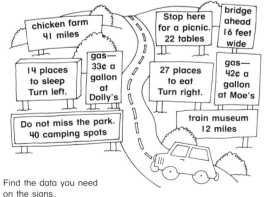

chicken farm 41 miles
Stop here for a picnic. 22 tables
bridge ahead 16 feet wide
14 places to sleep Turn left.
gas— 33¢ a gallon at Dolly's
27 places to eat Turn right.
gas— 42¢ a gallon at Moe's
Do not miss the park. 40 camping spots
train museum 12 miles

Find the data you need
on the signs.
Solve.

1. How many more miles ahead is the
   chicken farm than the train museum?   29 miles

2. How many places in all are there
   to eat and to sleep?   41 places

3. How much more does gas cost a
   gallon at Moe's than at Dolly's?   9¢ more

4. How many more camping spots
   are there than picnic tables?   18 spots

Macmillan/McGraw-Hill, MATHEMATICS IN ACTION
Grade 2, Chapter 7, Lesson 8, pages 227–228

Enrichment-74

Problem of the Day

Larry pasted 36 star stickers on paper. He drew
22 more stars.
Then he drew 14 suns.
How many more stars than suns are drawn on the
paper?   [8; 22 − 14 = 8]

AT·A·GLANCE p. 229

LESSON OBJECTIVE
Classify data.

ASSIGNMENT GUIDE

COURSE	EXERCISES
Basic	p. 229: All
Average	p. 229: All
Challenge	p. 229: All

MATERIALS
Classroom Materials paper clip, paper fastener, rubber band, pencil, pen, centimeter ruler, inch ruler, green and blue crayons
Manipulatives stickers for p. 229 per child

Teacher Resources
Crit. Think. 13

Name _____

Holiday Traffic Jam

Six children painted these holiday toys.

The children have two boxes to hold the toys.
Show different ways to sort the toys.

Answers will vary.
Children may sort by
size, color, or
type of vehicle.

▶ Talk about another way to sort the toys.
Answers will vary.

229

---

1 PLAN

AIMS AND ATTITUDES This lesson develops logical reasoning through the skill of classifying. Encourage children to verbalize their reasons for classifying as they do since some children may come up with different ways to classify other than by size, color, or kind. A child may, for example, sort the toys by number of wheels per vehicle. Stress that there are many ways to sort and praise the uniqueness of each method used.

MANAGEMENT The activity is intended for all children and has been designed for independent work. It is also appropriate for pairs of children. You may wish to prepare ahead of time the list of words used in the **EXTEND** section of this lesson.

2 GUIDE

Display a variety of classroom objects such as a paper clip, paper fastener, rubber band, pencil, crayon, pen, centimeter ruler, and inch ruler. Have each object and its use identified by the children.

■ **How can we sort these things?** [Possible responses: things used for writing, measuring, holding papers together]

Identify the pictures and have children read the directions on page 229. Have them decide upon a way to sort the toys. Then have them either use stickers or draw or write the names of the toys that should go in each box.

Then have children come up with a list of other ways to sort the toys. Have a class discussion about the different ways to sort.

For Students Acquiring English (SAE)

Define **sort** and emphasize the categories into which things are grouped. Have SAE children draw and color the toys on small, separate pieces of paper and then sort them into the boxes. To provide extra oral language practice, encourage SAE children to describe the ways they sort the toys.

3 EXTEND You might ask children to work in small groups. Provide each group with a list of the words given below or write the words on the chalkboard. The children are to make separate lists of words that may be grouped together in some way.

hat	meat	mittens	carrot
grapes	boots	sandals	coat
cherry	pants	banana	lemon
potato	scarf	bathing suit	shirt

When the lists are complete, ask a volunteer from each group to share their list with the class and tell why they grouped the words the way they did.

EXTRA PRACTICE

Extra Practice items are provided so that children may have an opportunity for further practice.

The *Additional Practice* section also provides practice you may wish to assign.

Extra Practice

Subtraction Practice, page 225

Subtract.

1.
62	85	37	93	74	58
− 45	− 48	− 19	− 76	− 27	− 31
17	37	18	17	47	27

2.
52	79	60	88	68	96
− 38	− 71	− 33	− 28	− 19	− 24
14	8	27	60	49	72

3.
75	99	85	47	66	39
− 59	− 35	− 29	− 13	− 43	− 25
16	64	56	34	23	14

Problem Solving: Identifying Extra Information, pages 227–228

Cross out the data you do not need.
Then solve.

1. Dee has 57 sheep on her farm.
   She has 38 rabbits.
   ~~Larry has 42 rabbits on his farm.~~
   How many animals does Dee have?

   __95__ animals

2. Owen used 44 blocks to build a tower.
   ~~His tower was red, blue, and yellow.~~
   Rachel used 29 blocks to build her tower.
   How many more blocks did Owen use than Rachel?

   __15__ more blocks

230 two hundred thirty

ADDITIONAL PRACTICE

p. 225 *Subtract.*

1.
81	63	79	46
− 29	− 42	− 61	− 13
[52]	[21]	[18]	[33]

2.
42	98	56	57
− 17	− 29	− 37	− 39
[25]	[69]	[19]	[18]

Subtract.

3.
97	82	61	48
− 44	− 38	− 14	− 12
[53]	[44]	[47]	[36]

4.
93	75	59	44
− 30	− 60	− 29	− 18
[63]	[15]	[30]	[26]

p. 227 *Cross out the data you do not need. Then solve.*

1. There are 76 people on Flight 904. Flight 904 leaves at 9:00. There are 37 people on Flight 821. How many more people are on Flight 904 than Flight 821? [Cross out: Flight 904 leaves at 9:00; the correct answer is: 39 more people.]

Cross out the data you do not need. Then solve.

2. Tina sold 56 tickets to Dallas. Larry sold 35 tickets to Dallas. Sam sold 48 tickets to New York. How many tickets were sold to Dallas? [Cross out: Sam sold 48 tickets to New York; the correct answer is: 91 tickets.]

CHAPTER 7 • Lesson 10

AT·A·GLANCE pp. 231-232

LESSON OBJECTIVE
Use estimation to solve problems.

ASSIGNMENT GUIDE

COURSE	EXERCISES
Basic	p. 231: 1; p. 232: 1–3
Average	p. 231: 1; p. 232: 1–3
Challenge	p. 231: 1; p. 232: 1–3

Teacher Resources
Reteaching 75
Prob. Solv. 33
Practice 75
MAC Act. 149, 150
Enrichment 75
Teacher Aid 7

Name _____

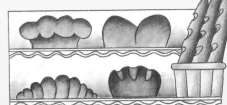

Problem Solving

UNDERSTAND / PLAN / TRY / CHECK / EXTEND

Strategy: Using Estimation

Sometimes you do not need an exact answer.

The chef needed 10 loaves of bread from the baker.
The baker made 77 loaves and sold 63 loaves.
About how many loaves did the baker have left?

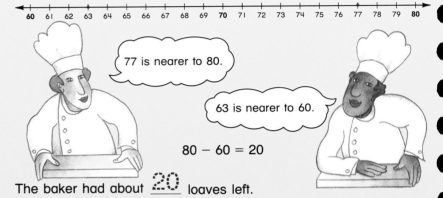

60 61 62 63 64 65 66 67 68 69 **70** 71 72 73 74 75 76 **77** 78 79 **80**

> 77 is nearer to 80.

> 63 is nearer to 60.

$$80 - 60 = 20$$

The baker had about **20** loaves left.

Did he have enough loaves left for the chef? **Yes.**

Write your estimate. Solve.

30 31 32 33 34 35 36 37 38 39 **40** 41 42 43 44 45 46 47 48 49 **50**

1. Doris needed 10 nuts to make a cake.
   She had 46 nuts.
   She used 32 nuts to make muffins.
   About how many nuts did she have left? **20** nuts

   Did she have enough nuts left for the cake? **Yes.**

Macmillan/McGraw-Hill

Chapter 7   Subtracting 2-Digit Numbers   two hundred thirty-one   **231**

---

1 PREPARE

WARM-UP To prepare children for using estimation to solve problems, write the numbers 20, 30, 40, 50, 60 on the chalkboard. Have children tell whether a given number is nearer 20, 30, 40, 50, or 60. Read aloud the following numbers.

32 [30]   58 [60]   43 [40]   19 [20]

2 TEACH

QUESTIONING Draw a number line numbered 20 through 50 on the board. Read the following:

Millie buys 38 cans of paint. She uses 21 cans to paint her garage. About how many cans are left?

■ **What do you know?** [Millie buys 38 cans and uses 21 cans.]

■ **What do you need to find out?** [about how many are left]

Remind children that finding out *about how many* means making an estimate.

■ **How do we use a number line to make an estimate?** [Find the numbers from the problem on the number line and see which numbers they are closer to, then use those numbers to solve the problem.]

Have a volunteer point to the 38 on the number line, and find whether 38 is nearer to 30 or 40.

Write 40 on the chalkboard. Then have the volunteer point to the 21 on the number line, and find whether 21 is nearer to 20 or 30.

Write 20 on the chalkboard. Write 40 − 20 = __ and have children tell the difference. [20]

■ **About how many cans of paint does Millie have left?** [about 20]

Write your estimate. Solve.

40 41 42 43 44 45 46 47 48 49 **50** 51 52 53 54 55 56 57 58 59 **60** 61 62 63 64 65 66 67 68 69 **70**

1. Tracy needed 20 boxes of
cookies for her family.
She had 62 boxes
and sold 47 boxes.
About how many boxes did she have left? __10__ boxes

Did she have enough boxes left for her family? __No.__

2. Chen needed 50 points
for a baseball mitt.
He earned 69 points.
He used 41 points for a ball.
About how many points did he have left? __30__ points

Did he have enough points for a mitt? __No.__

3. Dina needs 10 balls of
yarn to make socks.
She has 68 balls of yarn.
She uses 53 balls of yarn
for sweaters.
About how many balls of yarn

does she have left? __20__ balls of yarn.

Does she have enough balls of yarn

left for socks? __Yes.__

MEETING INDIVIDUAL NEEDS

TEACHER to TEACHER

COOPERATIVE LEARNING TIP 👥 When pairs do estimation exercises, I have them make up problems for one another and check and coach each other. Explaining their strategies aloud to someone else helps them clarify their thinking about the problem. I also encourage them to use a calculator to find the answer so that they can compare it with their estimates. They then exchange problems with another pair. I switch partners across pairs for coaching and checking answers.

TEACHER to TEACHER

ESTIMATION TIP As their number sense develops by using the number line, many of my children are able to generalize the rules for rounding to the nearest ten: If the digit in the ones place is less than 5, round down; if it is 5 or greater, round up.

PUPIL'S EDITION pp. 231-232

Page 231   Have a volunteer read the problem at the top of the page.

■ **What do you know?** [The chef needed 10 loaves of bread. The baker made 77 loaves and sold 63 loaves.]

■ **What do you need to find out?** [how many loaves are left]

■ **What do you need to do?** [Use the number line to find the nearest 10 for each number. Subtract to find about how many loaves are left.]

Work through the example with the children. Encourage children to explain other ways to solve this problem.

Check for Understanding

■ **What if the chef needed 20 loaves, and the baker made 82 loaves and sold 68. Would there be enough loaves for the chef?** [No. Since 80 − 70 = 10, there would only be about 10 loaves left.]

GUIDED PRACTICE   ex. 1: Work through problem 1 with the children.

Page 232   Have a volunteer read the directions at the top of the page.

**PRACTICE·APPLY**   **PRACTICE**   ex. 1–3

CLOSE   Guide children to summarize the lesson:

■ **How can you use estimation to solve problems?** [Find the nearest 10 on a number line for each number in a problem. Decide what you need to find out. This will help you when you subtract or add.]

**MAC Activity 149:
Basic-to-Average**

▼

MAC Activity 149

On Your Own Pair and Share In a Group

ESTIMATION ▪ IS THREE ENOUGH?

Materials metric measuring tapes (Teacher Aid 7)

Procedure Assign children to work in groups of three. Provide each group with a metric measuring tape. Explain to children that you will read them some problems. They are to use their tapes as a number line to solve the problems.

1. Miguel needs 23 centimeters of string to tie up a box. He cuts a piece of string that measures 62 centimeters. About how much string does he have left? [about 40 cm; 60 − 20 = 40]
2. Diane needs 17 socks to make sock puppets. Someone gives her 48 socks. About how many extra socks does she have? [about 30; 50 − 20 = 30]

Continue the activity with similar problems.

MENTAL MATH ▪ YES AND NO

MAC Activity 150

On Your Own Pair and Share In a Group

**MAC Activity 150:
Average-to-Challenge** ▶

Explain to children that you will read some problems. Have them estimate the answers. You may wish to time the children and make the activity a contest to see who can answer in the shortest time. Children may receive points for quickness as well as for correctness.

1. Mark needs 20 gallons of gasoline to get to the next town. He put 38 gallons in his truck. Then he used 23 gallons to run errands. Does he have enough gasoline left to drive to the next town? [Yes, 40 − 20 = 20.]
2. Vera needs 30 apples to make pies. She buys 54 apples. Her family eats 13. Are there enough apples left? [Yes; 50 − 10 = 40; 40 > 30.]

Continue the activity with similar problems.

PLEASANTVIEW 20 miles

RETEACHING-75

Name _____

PROBLEM SOLVING STRATEGY: USING ESTIMATION

Study

Ken needed 10 carrots for a salad.
He bought 38 carrots.
He used 22 carrots in a cake.
Does he have enough carrots left for the salad?

20 21 22 23 24 25 26 27 28 29 30 31 32 33 34 35 36 37 38 39 40

(22 is closer to 20)   (38 is closer to 40)

Subtract. $40 - 20 = 20$

Ken has about 20 carrots left.
He has enough carrots for a salad.

Check

Write your estimate. Solve.

1. Kathy needs 30 spoons for the picnic.

   She has 73 spoons.   about **70**

   She gives 51 spoons to her sister.   about **50**

   About how many spoons does she have left?   **20**

   Does she have enough spoons left for the picnic?   **no**

2. Max needs 20 nails to make a birdhouse.

   He buys 68 nails.   about **70**

   He uses 27 nails to make a shelf.   about **30**

   About how many nails does he have left?   **40**

   Does he have enough nails left for the birdhouse?   **yes**

Reteaching-75   Macmillan/McGraw-Hill, MATHEMATICS IN ACTION
                                 Grade 2, Chapter 7, Lesson 10, pages 231–232

PRACTICE-75

Name _____

PROBLEM SOLVING STRATEGY: USING ESTIMATION

Write your estimate. Solve.

30 31 32 33 34 35 36 37 38 39 **40** 41 42 43 44 45 46 47 48 49 **50** 51 52 53 54 55 56 57 58 59 **60**

1. Lee needs 10 rolls to make sandwiches.
   She had 51 rolls.
   Her dog ate 32 of the rolls.   **20** rolls
   About how many rolls are left?
   Are there enough rolls for sandwiches?   **yes**

2. Gary needed 20 pine cones.
   He collected 58 pine cones.
   31 pine cones were too small.   **30** cones
   About how many pine cones were left?
   Does Gary have enough pine cones?   **yes**

3. Fran needs 40 yards of cloth for a curtain.
   She had 51 yards of cloth.
   She uses 33 yards for costumes.
   About how many yards does she have left?   **20** yards
   Does she have enough cloth left for the   **no**
   curtain?

4. Nicky needs 30 feet of wire for a fence.
   He brings home 47 feet of wire.
   He uses 39 feet of wire for a dog pen.   **10** feet
   About how many feet of wire are left?
   Is there enough wire left for the fence?   **no**

Practice-75   Macmillan/McGraw-Hill, MATHEMATICS IN ACTION
                                 Grade 2, Chapter 7, Lesson 10, pages 231–232

ENRICHMENT-75

Name _____

PROBLEM SOLVING

On Your Own   Pair and Share   In a Group

THE PATH TO RICHES

Find the correct path to the treasure chest.
Look at the subtraction example on each key.
Estimate the difference and choose that path.
All you can take with you is a ⌨ .

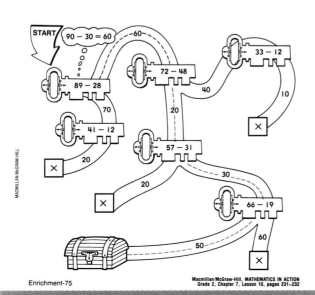

Enrichment-75   Macmillan/McGraw-Hill, MATHEMATICS IN ACTION
                                 Grade 2, Chapter 7, Lesson 10, pages 231–232

Problem of the Day

Wendell needs 20 different crayon colors to draw a picture. He picks out 33 colors. He gives 12 crayons to Marcia. Will Wendell be able to draw his picture?   [Yes; $30 - 10 = 20$.]

AT·A·GLANCE p. 233

LESSON OBJECTIVE

Subtract money amounts.

ASSIGNMENT GUIDE

COURSE	EXERCISES
Basic	p. 233: 1–4
Average	p. 233: 1–4
Challenge	p. 233: 1–4
Extra Practice, p. 239	Practice Plus, p. 240

MATERIALS

Manipulatives 18 P and 7 D coins (or punchouts), Workmat 2 per child

Teacher Resources
Reteaching 76   Practice 76   Enrichment 76
MAC Act. 151, 152

SKILLS TRACE
2-DIGIT SUBTRACTION

Explore (Concrete) 216, 217–218	Develop/Understand (Transitional/Abstract) 219–220, 221–222, 223–224, 225, 226, 233, 234
Practice 230, 239, 240, 241–242, 245, 288, 301	Apply 227–228, 231–232, 235–236, 237, 238, 244

See **MANIPULATIVES PLUS 45**, p. 2140.

Name _____

Subtracting Money

The children are having a yard sale.
Iris buys a ball.
She pays with a half dollar.
How much change does Iris get?

$$\begin{array}{r} \overset{4\ \ 10}{\cancel{5}\cancel{0}}¢ \\ -\ 28¢ \\ \hline 22¢ \end{array}$$

(change)

Subtract.

1.
45¢	33¢	50¢	68¢	21¢	36¢
− 12¢	− 7¢	− 20¢	− 64¢	− 19¢	− 17¢
33¢	26¢	30¢	4¢	2¢	19¢

2.
72¢	39¢	84¢	40¢	57¢	54¢
− 25¢	− 19¢	− 38¢	− 24¢	− 39¢	− 9¢
47¢	20¢	46¢	16¢	18¢	45¢

3.
95¢	66¢	70¢	58¢	87¢	47¢
− 78¢	− 27¢	− 18¢	− 19¢	− 23¢	− 18¢
17¢	39¢	52¢	39¢	64¢	29¢

Solve.

4. Olga buys a whistle.
She pays with a quarter.
How much is Olga's change? __8¢__

$$\begin{array}{r} 25¢ \\ -\ 17¢ \\ \hline 8¢ \end{array}$$

Extra Practice, page 239 *Practice Plus,* page 240

two hundred thirty-three   **233**

Macmillan/McGraw-Hill

---

1 PREPARE

WARM-UP To review money amounts, remind children that there are 10 pennies in 1 dime. Then write these amounts on the chalkboard. Have children show each amount and tell how much each set of coins is worth.

2 dimes 3 pennies [23¢]
7 dimes 8 pennies [78¢]
3 dimes 9 pennies [39¢]
6 dimes 7 pennies [67¢]
4 dimes 5 pennies [45¢]
1 dime   6 pennies [16¢]

2 TEACH

MODELING Remind children that pennies can be thought of as ones and dimes can be thought of as tens. Write the following exercise on the chalkboard and then tell the story.

$$\begin{array}{r} 75¢ \\ -52¢ \end{array}$$

Mark had 75¢. He bought a poster for 52¢. How much money did he have left? [23¢]

Have children model the money amounts on their workmats.

■ **Do you need to regroup? Why?** [No; because 2 pennies can be taken away from 5 pennies.]

ACTIVITY

Common Error and Remediation

MATERIALS 2 D and 13 P coins (or punchouts), 2 T and 13 O models (or punchouts)

Some children may not understand the relationship between money amounts and whole numbers. Show the following exercises:

$$23 \\ -14 \over [\ 9]$$ $$23¢ \\ -14¢ \over [\ 9¢]$$

Have the child use tens and ones models to show 23, and dimes and pennies to show 23¢. Have the child subtract, one step at a time.

For Students Acquiring English (SAE)

Explain **yard sale.** Have children role-play putting price tags on various classroom items. "Shoppers" should practice getting **change.**

ACTIVITY

ALTERNATIVE TEACHING STRATEGY

MATERIALS 13 P and 7 D coins (or punchouts)

VISUAL Display 7 dimes and 3 pennies on a table. Explain that you need 29¢ to pay for a purchase. Tell children that you want to find how much money you would have left. Exchange 1 dime for 10 pennies, take away 9 pennies and 2 dimes and count the money left. Write 73¢ − 29¢ on the chalkboard. Tell children that another way to find how much you would have left is to subtract. Work through the subtraction.

Repeat the procedure with another exercise in which regrouping is needed. Make sure children understand that subtracting money is no different than the subtraction they have been doing.

PUPIL'S EDITION p. 233

Guide children through the example at the top of the page.

Check for Understanding

■ **If you had 50¢ and bought a toy boat for 33¢, how much change would you get?** [17¢]

GUIDED PRACTICE ex. 1: Remind children to write a cent sign for each difference. For reteaching, use Common Error and Remediation or Alternative Strategy.

3 PRACTICE•APPLY PRACTICE ex. 2–4

CLOSE Guide children to summarize the lesson:

■ **Why can you use dimes and pennies as models when you subtract?** [because 10 pennies equal 1 dime]

**MAC Activity 151:
Basic-to-Average**
▼

MAC Activity 151

On Your Own   Pair and Share   In a Group

ESTIMATION ▪ WHICH IS CLOSER?

Write the following problems on the chalkboard. Have children estimate to find the answers.

1. Which is closer to 25¢?
   97¢ − 47¢   59¢ − 30¢ [√] 70¢ − 33¢
2. Which is closer to 50¢?
   60¢ − 20¢   98¢ − 39¢   89¢ − 37¢ [√]
3. Which is closer to 50¢?
   82¢ − 21¢   68¢ − 19¢ [√] 75¢ − 15¢

To extend the activity, have children find the difference that is farthest from the given amount.

**MAC Activity 152:
Average-to-Challenge**
▼

MAC Activity 152

On Your Own   Pair and Share   In a Group

CALCULATOR ▪ SUBTRACTING MONEY

$ .98
− .74

Materials calculators

Give each child a calculator and assign children to work in pairs. Write the following exercises on the chalkboard. Guide children through the first exercise. Remind them to put a decimal point in front of each number. Have children read the differences.

$.98	$.36	$.42	$.84	$.99
−.74	−.29	−.15	−.28	−.55
[$.24]	[$.07]	[$.27]	[$.56]	[$.44]

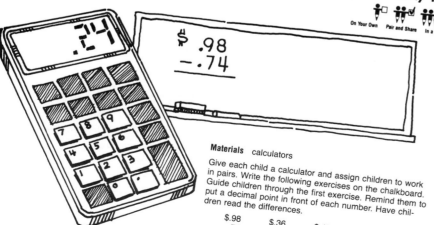

Name _____

SUBTRACTING MONEY

Study

tens	ones		dimes	pennies		tens	ones		dimes	pennies
3	9		3	9		³⁄₄	¹²⁄₂		³⁄₄	¹²⁄₂
− 1	6		− 1	6		− 2	7		− 2	7
2	3		2	3		1	5		1	5

        23   23¢   15   15¢

Check

Subtract.

1.
71¢	47¢	30¢	49¢	62¢
− 26¢	− 19¢	− 12¢	− 17¢	− 28¢
45¢	28¢	18¢	32¢	34¢

2.
46¢	27¢	72¢	84¢	60¢
− 39¢	− 8¢	− 25¢	− 76¢	− 43¢
7¢	19¢	47¢	8¢	17¢

3.
51¢	32¢	55¢	74¢	56¢
− 20¢	− 17¢	− 39¢	− 40¢	− 37¢
31¢	15¢	16¢	34¢	19¢

4.
36¢	41¢	27¢	53¢	62¢
− 19¢	− 25¢	− 8¢	− 28¢	− 46¢
17¢	16¢	19¢	25¢	16¢

Name _____

SUBTRACTING MONEY

Subtract.

1.
35¢	42¢	50¢	63¢	70¢	74¢
− 17¢	− 9¢	− 22¢	− 29¢	− 43¢	− 58¢
18¢	33¢	28¢	34¢	27¢	16¢

2.
43¢	56¢	40¢	65¢	79¢	62¢
− 23¢	− 37¢	− 24¢	− 7¢	− 29¢	− 18¢
20¢	19¢	16¢	58¢	50¢	44¢

3.
83¢	54¢	70¢	52¢	41¢	90¢
− 41¢	− 45¢	− 39¢	− 13¢	− 27¢	− 35¢
42¢	9¢	31¢	39¢	14¢	55¢

Solve.

4. Mark has 34¢ in his bank.
He spends 19¢ on a top.
How much money does he
have left?   15¢

34¢
− 19¢
15¢

5. Tara has 90¢ in her bank.
She buys a pin for 53¢.
How much money does
Tara have left in her bank? 37¢

90¢
− 53¢
37¢

Name _____

SUBTRACTING MONEY

On Your Own   Pair and Share   In a Group

GRANDMOTHER'S JOURNAL

Allison's grandmother let Allison read
her journal. She read about a day
long ago.

> July 30, 1941
>
> Today I went to the fair.
> Dad gave me 75¢ to start.
> I spent 15¢ for a ticket.
> Then I spent 8¢ for a
> lemonade. A merry-go-
> round ride cost 5¢.
> I bought lunch for 19¢.
> I spent 10¢ on the
> Ferris wheel. Then I
> found a quarter.
> What a great day!

Use the information in the
journal to complete.

How much to start?   **75¢**

The ticket cost?   15¢

How much left?   60¢

The lemonade cost?   8¢

How much left?   52¢

The merry-go-round?   5¢

How much left?   47¢

Lunch cost?   19¢

How much left?   28¢

The Ferris wheel?   10¢

How much left?   18¢

Found a quarter.   25¢

How much money at
the end of the day?   43¢

Problem of the Day

Lloyd went to the toy store with a half dollar. He
bought a balloon for 19¢. On his way out, he saw
a toy plane for 37¢. Did he have enough left to
buy the plane? [No. Possible solution:
50¢ − 19¢ = 31¢; 31¢ < 37¢.]

AT·A·GLANCE p. 234

LESSON OBJECTIVE
Add and subtract 2-digit numbers.

ASSIGNMENT GUIDE

COURSE	EXERCISES
Basic	p. 234: 1–3
Average	p. 234: 1–3
Challenge	p. 234: 1–3

Teacher Resources
Reteaching 77   Practice 77   Enrichment 77
MAC Act. 153, 154   Teacher Aid 1, 17

SKILLS TRACE
2-DIGIT SUBTRACTION

Explore (Concrete) 216, 217–218	Develop/Understand (Transitional/Abstract) 219–220, 221–222, 223–224, 225, 226, 233, 234
Practice 230, 239, 240, 241–242, 245, 288, 301	Apply 227–228, 231–232, 235–236, 237, 238, 244, 351

See **MANIPULATIVES PLUS 46**, p. 214P.

Addition and Subtraction

Ed and Hal are shopping in the art store.

How much do the two markers cost?	How many more pencils are in the large box?
44¢ + 39¢ 83¢	40 − 25 15

Add or subtract.

1.
37	62	50	25	94¢	27¢
+ 12	+ 28	− 19	+ 68	− 66¢	+ 47¢
49	90	31	93	28¢	74¢

2.
42	58	33	67	72¢	81¢
− 11	+ 7	− 8	− 28	+ 19¢	− 3¢
31	65	25	39	91¢	78¢

Solve.

3. Ed bought a small box of pencils. He gave the clerk 75¢.

   What is his change? 8¢

   75¢
   − 67¢
   8¢

■ **How are these exercises alike and how are they different?** [The numbers are the same, but the operation is different.]

Work through the exercises with the children. Have them explain why regrouping is necessary in the subtraction and why it is not necessary in the addition.

■ **Why is it always important to look at the operation sign before doing an exercise?** [The sign tells what operation should be performed.]

PUPIL'S EDITION p. 234

Guide children through the examples at the top of the page. Point out the operation used in each.

Check for Understanding

■ **Should you add or subtract to find 25 minus 12?** [subtract]

PREPARE   **WARM-UP**   To prepare children to complete mixed exercise sets, have them give the sums and differences for the following.

9 + 8 [17]	9 − 8 [1]
4 + 1 [5]	4 − 1 [3]
10 + 3 [13]	10 − 3 [7]
50 + 20 [70]	50 − 20 [30]

TEACH   **DISCUSSING**   Write the following exercises on the chalkboard.

63   63
+15   −15

Common Error and Remediation

MATERIALS red crayon

Some children may forget to look at the operation sign when doing mixed practice. Work individually with each child. Provide addition and subtraction exercises. Then have him or her say which operation will be performed before beginning each exercise. Have the child ring the operation sign in red and solve the problem.

For Students Acquiring English (SAE)

Read the story problems aloud and have children role-play them. Assign a "narrator" to verbalize the operations involved.

ALTERNATIVE TEACHING STRATEGY

VISUAL/AUDITORY Read the following exercises and have children write each in vertical form. Before children find the sums and differences, have volunteers read each exercise. Have children check their papers to see if they have written the correct operation sign.

47	70	84	62	43
+13	−13	+ 9	− 7	−26
[60]	[57]	[93]	[55]	[17]

GUIDED PRACTICE ex. 1: For reteaching, use Common Error and Remediation or Alternative Strategy.

3 PRACTICE•APPLY **PRACTICE** ex. 2–3

C L O S E Guide children to summarize the lesson:

■ **What two operations did you use for this lesson?** [addition and subtraction]

MAC Activity 154

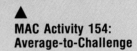

On Your Own · Pair and Share · In a Group

NUMBER SENSE ▪ ADD OR SUBTRACT?

Have children solve the following oral problems. After each problem, call on a volunteer to give the answer to the problem and tell how it was solved.

1. Ross collected 23 baseball cards. Simon collected 18 baseball cards. How many more cards did Ross collect than Simon? [5; subtract]
2. Dorrie collected 18 charms. She gave 6 of them to her sister. How many charms does she have left? [12; subtract]
3. Jeff collected 16 model cars. He collected 23 model planes. How many models does he have in all? [39; add]
4. Mary collected 27 stickers. Twelve of the stickers are hearts. How many stickers are not hearts? [15; subtract]

▲ MAC Activity 154:
Average-to-Challenge

NUMBER SENSE ▪ *ADDITION/SUBTRACTION RACE*

MAC Activity 153

On Your Own · Pair and Share · In a Group

Materials game board (Teacher Aid 1), game markers, number cubes (Teacher Aid 17)

Setup Write 2-digit addition and subtraction exercises in the squares of the game board on Teacher Aid 1. Duplicate a copy for each group.

Procedure Assign children to work in groups and give each group a game board, game markers, and a number cube. Children are to take turns rolling the cube and moving their marker that number of spaces. When they land in a square, they find the sum or difference for the exercise. If the answer is correct, they stay in the square. If the answer is wrong, they move back a space.

To Win The first child to get to the end of the path wins the game.

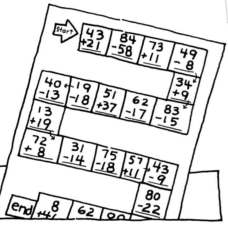

▲ MAC Activity 153:
Basic-to-Average

Name _____

ADDITION AND SUBTRACTION

Study

Add.	Subtract.	Add.	Subtract.
29 + 16 45	29 − 16 13	44 + 27 71	44 − 27 17

Check

Add or subtract.

1.
81	51	13	84	54
− 60	+ 17	+ 66	− 29	− 16
21	68	79	55	38

2.
63	77	47	97	35
+ 27	− 34	+ 26	− 46	+ 14
90	43	73	51	49

3.
36	69	99	43	73
+ 18	− 13	− 19	+ 21	− 36
54	56	80	64	37

Reteaching-77

Name _____

ADDITION AND SUBTRACTION

20 balloons 39¢	15 hats 75¢	25 favors 60¢	12 horns 59¢

Add or subtract.

1.
44	30	64	96	73
− 29	+ 18	+ 12	− 14	− 37
15	48	76	82	36

2.
94	41	38	66	56
− 15	− 22	+ 13	− 25	+ 21
79	19	51	41	77

Solve.

3. Ben bought 20 balloons and 12 horns. How much did he spend? __98¢__

4. Sara bought 15 hats and 20 balloons. How many more balloons than hats did she get? __5__

5. Sam bought 25 favors. He gave the clerk 75¢. What was his change? __15¢__

Practice-77

Name _____

ADDITION AND SUBTRACTION

On Your Own   Pair and Share   In a Group

PLUS-MINUS GAME

Play this game with your friends.

START	86 + 5 91	61 − 35 26	25 + 35 60	82 − 24 58	51 + 24 75	Move ahead 1 space.
						90 − 85 5
56 − 37 19	43 + 29 72	75 − 16 59	Move back 1 space.	17 + 34 51	63 − 48 15	26 + 72 98
56 − 31 25	Plus-Minus Game Rules. 1. Three or more players. 2. Roll a number cube. Move that many spaces. 3. Find the sum or difference mentally. 4. If correct, stay in the space until next turn. If incorrect, move back 1 space.					
26 + 27 53						
58 + 25 83	Take another turn!	72 − 21 51	37 + 16 53	84 − 48 36	98 − 15 83	END

 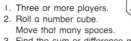

Enrichment-77

Problem of the Day

Sharon bought a book for 49¢ and a pen for 29¢. She gave the clerk 80¢. Did she get any change? [Yes; 2¢.]

235 Chapter 7 • Lesson 13

AT·A·GLANCE pp. 235-236

LESSON OBJECTIVE
Choose the operation to solve problems.

ASSIGNMENT GUIDE

COURSE	EXERCISES
Basic	p. 235: 1–3; p. 236: 1–4
Average	p. 235: 1–3; p. 236: 1–4
Challenge	p. 235: 1–3; p. 236: 1–4
Extra Practice, p. 239	

MATERIALS
Manipulatives 7 T, 17 O models (or punchouts), Workmat 2 per child

Teacher Resources
Reteaching 78   Practice 78   Enrichment 78
Prob. Solv. 34   MAC Act. 155, 156

Name _____

Problem Solving

Strategy: Choosing the Operation

Skip had 56 balloons at his party.
27 balloons did not pop.
How many balloons popped?

Should you add or subtract to solve the problem?

$$56 \qquad 56$$
$$\underline{+\ 27} \qquad \underline{-\ 27}$$

Subtract.
You should subtract. The answer 29 shows the number taken away.

Solve. Use models, mental math, or paper and pencil.

1. Meg has 47 candles.
   19 of them are blue.

   How many candles are not blue? __28__ candles

   _____

2. Grace brought 64 records.
   Ryan brought 29 records.

   How many records did they bring? __93__ records

   _____

3. There are 72 party plates in the pack.
   18 of the plates were used.

   How many plates were left? __54__ plates

Macmillan/McGraw-Hill

---

1 PREPARE

WARM-UP To prepare children for choosing the operation to solve a problem, have them give the following sums and differences.

52 + 27 [79]	63 − 38 [25]
19 + 45 [64]	72 − 24 [48]
33 + 37 [70]	89 − 56 [33]

2 TEACH

DISCUSSING Read aloud the following problem.

Gloria has a photo album that holds 55 photos. She has 39 photos in the album. How many more photos can she put in the album?

Discuss with children how they would decide to solve the problem.

■ **What do you know?** [Gloria has 39 photos in an album that holds 55 photos.]

■ **What do you need to find out?** [how many more photos she can put in the album]

■ **What do you do to find how many more?** [Subtract; 55 − 39 = 16 photos.]

PUPIL'S EDITION pp. 235-236

Page 235 Have a volunteer read the problem at the top of the page.

■ **What do you know?** [Skip had 56 balloons; 27 balloons did not pop.]

■ **What do you need to find out?** [how many balloons popped]

Use addition or subtraction to solve.

1. The children bought 32 cups
   at the party store.
   They bought 28 plates.
   How many cups and plates did they buy?

   __60__ cups and plates

2. The party store has 73 toy yo-yos.
   19 of them are blue.
   How many are not blue?

   __54__ are not blue

3. The package has 36 large balloons.
   It has 15 small balloons.
   How many balloons does the
   package have?

   __51__ balloons

4. The store has 73 party hats.
   It has 47 party masks.
   How many more hats
   than masks does it have?

   __26__ more hats

Extra Practice, page 239

TEACHER to TEACHER

MANIPULATIVES TIP My children benefit from using tens and ones models to help them choose the operation to solve a problem. They are better able to visualize the situation and decide whether their answer makes sense.

For Students Acquiring English (SAE)

Using real balloons, party plates, and candles, demonstrate the meaning of the negative (**did not pop, are not blue**). This concept may be difficult for SAE children. Pair SAE and non-SAE students to read problems aloud.

Discuss the question and the choices for solving the problem. Guide children to see that they can use subtraction to find out how many balloons popped. Have a volunteer demonstrate the process with tens and ones models.

■ **What did you learn?** [Possible response: Sometimes you need to decide if you can add or subtract to solve a problem.]

Encourage children to explain other ways to solve this problem.

Check for Understanding

■ **What if Skip had 27 balloons that popped, then another 29 balloons that popped? How many balloons would have popped?** [27 + 29 = 56]

GUIDED PRACTICE ex. 1–3: Work through problem 1 with the children. Make sure they understand how to solve the problem by choosing the operation.

Page 236 Have a volunteer read the directions at the top of the page.

3 PRACTICE•APPLY PRACTICE ex. 1–4

C L O S E Guide children to summarize the lesson:

■ **How do you know if you should add or subtract to solve a problem?** [Possible response: You read the question and decide whether you need to join two groups or take some away from one group to solve the problem.]

**MAC Activity 155:
Basic-to-Average** ▼

MAC Activity 155

On Your Own　Pair and Share　In a Group

MATH AND CONSUMERS ■ WHAT A BARGAIN!

Materials department store ads

Setup Select pages from department store ads that show prices as 2-digit numbers under $100, for example, gloves on sale for $22, down from an original price of $28. Collect enough pages for each pair of children to have one or two, or duplicate two or three pages.

Procedure Assign children to work in pairs. Provide each pair with a page or two from a store bulletin. Give each pair two or three problems to solve from each page. For example:

1. I see gloves on this page that are on sale for $22. Find the price the gloves were before they went on sale. Tell me how much you can save. [$6]

2. Here are some slippers for $24. Tell me how much you will spend if you buy two pairs. [$48]

3. Here is a sweater for $38. Here is a shirt for $16. How much money will you spend if you buy both items? [$54]

After children are finished, discuss the answers and what operations they used.

MAC Activity 156

On Your Own　Pair and Share　In a Group

WRITING MATHEMATICS ■ UP OR DOWN

Materials index cards

Setup Prepare game cards by writing data on a set of cards. On one side of each card, write two 2-digit numbers such as 73 and 19. On the other side of each card, write a word, such as players, cups, bicycles, or shoes. Also prepare a set of four cards with the words addition or subtraction.

Procedure Have children play in small groups. Give each group a set of at least seven of each type of card. Explain to children that they will make up word problems using the information on both cards. For example, if a child chooses a cups card and a subtraction card, the child will use the numbers on the card to make up a problem such as: "There were 73 cups on the shelf. I used 29 cups. How many cups were still on the shelf?" If the child uses the cards correctly, he or she scores one point. The first child in the group to solve the problem correctly then selects two new cards.

To Win The child with the most points at the end of 20 minutes is the winner.

73 19	CUPS
14 25	shoes
addition	subtraction

▲ **MAC Activity 156:
Average-to-Challenge**

RETEACHING

Name

PROBLEM SOLVING STRATEGY: CHOOSING THE OPERATION

Study

Luis had 24 toy robots.
He put 17 robots in a box.
How many were not in the box?

Do you add or subtract?

Understand	Plan	Try
Luis had 24 robots. He put 17 in a box.	Subtract the 17 robots in the box.	24 robots − 17 robots in the box 7 robots not in the box

Check

Complete the exercise.
Write + or − to show addition or subtraction.

1. Teresa had 32 race cars.
   14 are red.
   How many are not red?
   __18__ are not red

   32
   ···· 14
   18

2. Barry had 63 books on one shelf.
   He had 27 books on another shelf.
   How many books are on both shelves?
   90 ____ books

   63
   + 27
   90

3. Marta had 68 toy horses.
   She picked 29 to sell at the fair.
   How many horses were left?
   39 ____ horses

   68
   − 29
   39

Macmillan/McGraw-Hill, MATHEMATICS IN ACTION
Grade 2, Chapter 7, Lesson 13, pages 235–236

Reteaching-78

PRACTICE

Name

PROBLEM SOLVING STRATEGY: CHOOSING THE OPERATION

Use addition or subtraction to solve.

1. The art room has 28 chairs.
   The music room has 52 chairs.
   How many chairs are in both rooms?
   __80__ chairs

2. The art class has 19 students.
   The music class has 42 students.
   How many more music students
   than art students are there?
   __23__ students

3. In the music room are 33 horns.
   16 of them are trumpets.
   How many are not trumpets?
   __17__ are not trumpets

4. The art class made 46 paper tigers.
   Then they made 28 paper lions.
   How many paper animals did they make?
   __74__ paper animals

5. The school band has 64 members.
   36 members are girls.
   How many members are boys?
   __28__ boys

Macmillan/McGraw-Hill, MATHEMATICS IN ACTION
Grade 2, Chapter 7, Lesson 13, pages 235–236

Practice-78

ENRICHMENT

Name

PROBLEM SOLVING

On Your Own   Pair and Share   In a Group

BIKE FOR SALE

Use addition or subtraction. Solve.

1. Brian bought a bicycle.
   He gave the clerk $50.
   He got $8 back in change.
   How much did the bicycle cost?
   $ __42__

2. Tony wanted to buy Brian's
   new bicycle.
   Brian sold the bicycle to Tony
   for $14 more than he paid at
   the store.
   How much money did Tony spend?
   $ __56__

3. Tony bent a wheel on the
   bicycle.
   He sold the bicycle to Janie
   for $29 less than he paid
   for it.
   How much money did Tony get?
   $ __27__

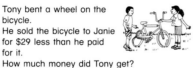

4. Janie fixed the wheel.
   She won a big race on the
   bicycle.
   A friend wanted to buy
   the bike.
   Janie said she would not
   sell it unless she got $55
   more than she paid.
   How much does the bicycle cost now?
   $ __82__

Macmillan/McGraw-Hill, MATHEMATICS IN ACTION
Grade 2, Chapter 7, Lesson 13, pages 235–236

Enrichment-78

Problem of the Day

A farmer had 43 cows. She sold all but 27 cows.
How many cows did the farmer have left?   [She
had 27 cows left after she sold the others.]

CHAPTER 7 • Lesson 14

AT·A·GLANCE p. 237

LESSON OBJECTIVE
Make decisions using information.

ASSIGNMENT GUIDE

COURSE	EXERCISES
Basic	p. 237: 1–4
Average	p. 237: 1–4
Challenge	p. 237: 1–4

Teacher Resources
Crit. Think. 14   Prob. Solv. 35

Decision Making

Problem Solving: Choosing a Prize

EARN PRIZES FOR YOUR CLASSROOM!

Sell 35 boxes to earn this prize.

Sell greeting cards. Price: $2.00 a box

Sell 50 boxes to earn this prize.

Sell 70 boxes to earn this prize.

Sell 95 boxes to earn this prize.

Students in your class are selling greeting cards.

Answers will vary.

1. Which prize do you think would be the best

   for your class? Why? _____

   _____

2. Suppose each student in your class sells
   1 box of cards. How many more boxes
   would you need to sell to earn this prize? _____

3. How many boxes do you think you could sell?
   List the people who might buy the cards.

   _____   _____

   _____   _____

 4. Talk with a partner about the prize you chose.
   How did you make your decisions?

Chapter 7   Subtracting 2-Digit Numbers   two hundred thirty-seven   **237**

---

1 PREPARE   **WARM-UP**   To review subtracting 2-digit numbers, write the following on the chalkboard.

68	79	25	46	99	57
−23	−44	−13	−35	−88	− 7
[45]	[35]	[12]	[11]	[11]	[50]

Have children find the differences. Continue with other exercises as needed.

2 TEACH   **DISCUSSING**   Define the word *prize* for the children. Explain that it is something that is won in a contest or a game. Discuss with children what kinds of activities or contests usually offer prizes. Have children discuss the times they won a prize. Encourage them to tell what they did to win the prize and tell

what they won as a prize. Then make a list of prizes that children would like to win.

PUPIL'S EDITION p. 237

Identify the prizes and number of boxes at the top of the page that must be sold.

Check for Understanding

■ **What do you win if 35 boxes of cards are sold?** [musical instruments]

■ **Imagine that you have sold 62 boxes of cards. How many more boxes of cards would you need to sell in order to win the sports equipment?** [33]

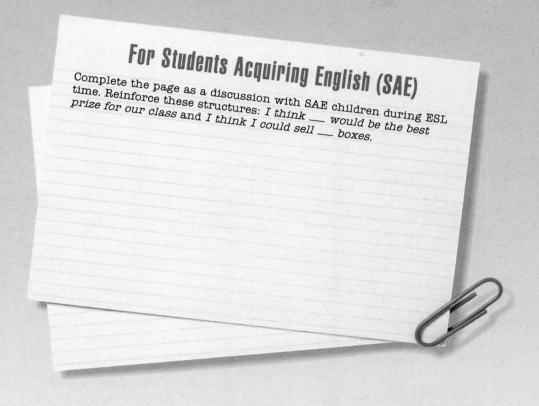

For Students Acquiring English (SAE)

Complete the page as a discussion with SAE children during ESL time. Reinforce these structures: *I think ___ would be the best prize for our class* and *I think I could sell ___ boxes.*

3 PRACTICE•APPLY

Have children complete ex. 1–4. Call on volunteers to tell how they decided which prize would be best for their classroom, how many boxes of cards they would need to sell in order to win the prize, and strategies for selling that number of boxes of cards.

CLOSE Guide children to summarize the lesson:

■ **What should you do before choosing a prize for the class?**
[Decide which prize would be best for the class.]

CLASS PROJECT

Materials chart paper

Have children work in small groups to plan a contest. Tell them to decide on the kind of contest, contest rules, and the prizes that would be given to the winners of the contest. Assign one group member to record the group's ideas on chart paper.

When groups have completed the project, have one member from each group report the group's information. If possible, have children participate in each other's contests.

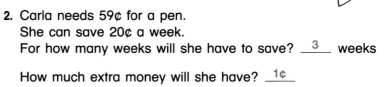

Technology

AT·A·GLANCE p. 238

OBJECTIVE
Use computer spreadsheets to solve problems involving addition and subtraction patterns of money.

MATERIALS
Computer
Manipulatives 10 P coins (or punchouts) per pair

Teacher Resources
Computer Software *Computer Workshop:* MONEY

Computer Spreadsheet: Money

Jerry needs 85¢ to buy a book.
He can save 15¢ a week.
For how many weeks will he have to save?

You can use a computer to find the answer.

At the Computer
Run the program MONEY.

Jerry can save 85¢ in ___6___ weeks. He will have ___5___ ¢ extra.

1. What if Jerry saved 12¢ a week? ___8___ weeks

   How much extra money would he have? __11¢__

2. Carla needs 59¢ for a pen.
   She can save 20¢ a week.
   For how many weeks will she have to save? ___3___ weeks

   How much extra money will she have? __1¢__

3. José needs 75¢ for a pad.
   He can save 10¢ a week.
   For how many weeks will he have to save? ___8___ weeks

   How much extra money will he have? __5¢__

4. Use your own data. You show how much
   money is needed. Show how much is saved
   each week. Have your partner find for how
   many weeks you will have to save. Take turns.

 5. Talk about how a computer can help you solve problems.
   Possible answer: A computer can make a chart to show my data and
   238   two hundred thirty-eight   rule. I can use the chart to help solve problems.

PREPARE **WARM-UP** To prepare children to use computer spreadsheets to solve problems involving addition and subtraction patterns have them give the following sums and differences.

1. 15¢ + 15¢ [30¢]
2. 42¢ − 30¢ [12¢]
3. 12¢ + 12¢ + 12¢ [36¢]
4. 40¢ − 36¢ [4¢]

TEACH **MODELING** Assign children to work in pairs and give each pair a set of coins. Read the following

José needs 9¢ for an eraser.
He saves 2¢ a week.
For how many weeks will he have to save?

Have children work together to try to solve the problem.

■ **What strategy did you use to solve the problem?** [Possible response: Make sets of 2 pennies, then count how many twos are enough for the amount needed.]

■ **For how many weeks would José have to save? Why?** [5 weeks; because 4 weeks produces only 8¢]

■ **Would José have saved any extra money? How much?** [Yes; 1¢.]

Discuss all strategies children tried.

For Students Acquiring English (SAE)

Introduce **spreadsheets** by relating them to **tables**. Elicit why tables are useful; ask children to name a situation in which they might use a table. Read the problems on page 238 aloud. Give SAE children opportunities to pronounce **spreadsheets**. To help SAE children with the data, distribute coins or punchout coins to use in completing the addition and subtraction.

PRACTICE•APPLY

Read the problem at the top of the page with the children.

■ **Can you use the same strategies for this problem?** [Yes.]

Explain that they can use a computer spreadsheet to help them solve the problem. A computer spreadsheet organizes numbers in rows and columns and adds or subtracts the numbers.

AT THE COMPUTER Have children work in pairs using the computer program MONEY. Guide children as necessary in interpreting the spreadsheet on the screen. Be sure they understand that they are to type in the amount of money needed and the amount of money to be saved each week. Point out that money amounts are shown in cents. Remind children that if they have 100¢ or more, they should change the cents to dollars and cents. Have children use the data to solve the example problem.

For ex. 1, tell children to type in the new amount of money to be saved each week and keep the amount of money needed the same. For ex. 2 and 3, have them type in both amounts. Children then take turns making up similar problems and solving them and discussing how the computer helps them.

C L O S E Guide children to summarize the lesson:

■ **What is the computer doing when it shows you the total amount of money saved at the end of each week?** [skip counting or adding]

■ **What is the computer doing when it shows you the difference between the amount of money needed and the amount saved?** [subtracting]

CHAPTER 7

Subtracting Money, page 233 . . . .

Subtract.

1.
34¢	55¢	77¢	61¢	43¢	82¢
−19¢	−41¢	−39¢	−25¢	−28¢	−56¢
15¢	14¢	38¢	36¢	15¢	26¢

2.
65¢	46¢	86¢	59¢	73¢	97¢
−27¢	−18¢	−72¢	−30¢	−44¢	−79¢
38¢	28¢	14¢	29¢	29¢	18¢

3.
95¢	67¢	43¢	88¢	79¢	90¢
−81¢	−48¢	−25¢	−35¢	−62¢	−49¢
14¢	19¢	18¢	53¢	17¢	41¢

Problem Solving: Choosing the Operation, pages 235–236 . . . .

Solve.

1. Norm ate 24 grapes. Tod ate 19 grapes. How many grapes did the two boys eat?

   __43__ grapes

2. Debbie had 65 buttons in her button box. She gave 18 buttons to Stacy. How many buttons did Debbie have left?

   __47__ buttons

Macmillan/McGraw-Hill

ADDITIONAL PRACTICE

p. 233 *Subtract.*

1.
24¢	61¢	73¢	46¢
−14¢	−29¢	−37¢	−31¢
[10¢]	[32¢]	[36¢]	[15¢]

2.
84¢	99¢	52¢	39¢
−38¢	−26¢	−18¢	−19¢
[47¢]	[73¢]	[34¢]	[20¢]

p. 235 *Solve.*

1. Sally hopped on her left foot 45 times. She hopped on her right foot 61 times. How many more times did Sally hop on her right foot? __[16]__ more times

Solve.

2. Steve clapped his hands 23 times. Maria clapped her hands 36 times. How many times did they clap hands in all? __[59]__ times

Practice Plus

Key Skill: Subtraction, page 225 . . . .

Subtract.

1.	32 − 17 15	48 − 23 25	86 − 67 19	54 − 31 23	69 − 19 50
2.	77 − 46 31	51 − 27 24	98 − 25 73	66 − 33 33	40 − 16 24	83 − 55 28
3.	53 − 26 27	31 − 8 23	74 − 26 48	95 − 48 47	57 − 19 38	21 − 10 11

Key Skill: Subtracting Money, page 233 . . . .

Subtract.

1.	27¢ − 18¢ 9¢	31¢ − 26¢ 5¢	44¢ − 27¢ 17¢	63¢ − 29¢ 34¢	97¢ − 59¢ 38¢	80¢ − 41¢ 39¢
2.	49¢ − 22¢ 27¢	74¢ − 59¢ 15¢	89¢ − 39¢ 50¢	56¢ − 37¢ 19¢	65¢ − 48¢ 17¢	92¢ − 15¢ 77¢
3.	38¢ − 29¢ 9¢	52¢ − 13¢ 39¢	84¢ − 68¢ 16¢	67¢ − 43¢ 24¢	75¢ − 27¢ 48¢	99¢ − 11¢ 88¢

CHAPTER 7

PRACTICE *PLUS*

Practice Plus is provided to supply additional practice for the two key skills in this chapter.

Key Skills
Page 225: Subtraction Practice
Page 233: Subtracting Money

The *Additional Practice* also provides practice you may wish to assign for key skills in this chapter.

ADDITIONAL PRACTICE

p. 225 *Subtract.*

1.	46 − 23 [23]	87 − 42 [45]	96 − 39 [57]	71 − 33 [38]
2.	56 − 45 [11]	90 − 48 [42]	69 − 26 [43]	74 − 18 [56]

3.	83 − 48 [35]	76 − 51 [25]	57 − 18 [39]	90 − 55 [35]
4.	39 − 12 [27]	84 − 36 [48]	67 − 41 [26]	95 − 45 [50]
5.	73 − 17 [56]	41 − 27 [14]	59 − 36 [23]	92 − 68 [24]

p. 233 *Subtract.*

1.	49¢ − 28¢ [21¢]	98¢ − 43¢ [55¢]	35¢ − 15¢ [20¢]	62¢ − 47¢ [15¢]
2.	71¢ − 19¢ [52¢]	84¢ − 40¢ [44¢]	69¢ − 34¢ [35¢]	56¢ − 27¢ [29¢]

AT·A·GLANCE pp. 241-242

OBJECTIVE
Review/test the concepts and skills presented in Chapter 7.

7A. Subtract 2-digit numbers with and without regrouping.
7B. Subtract money amounts to 99¢.
7C. Solve problems including those that involve identifying extra information and choosing the correct operation.

Teacher Resources
Testing Program, pp. 73–78

Name _____

Chapter Review/Test

Language and Mathematics
Choose the correct word.

1. When you subtract 47 − 28, you must

   _____regroup_____ I ten as 10 ones.

2. After you subtract the ones, you

   subtract the _____tens_____ .

regroup
tens

Concepts and Skills
Subtract. Use models if you need help.

3. Did you regroup?

$$\begin{array}{r} 45 \\ -18 \\ \hline 27 \end{array}$$ (yes) no

4. Did you regroup?

$$\begin{array}{r} 53 \\ -45 \\ \hline 8 \end{array}$$ (yes) no

5. $$\begin{array}{r} 78 \\ -36 \\ \hline 42 \end{array}$$ yes (no)

6. $$\begin{array}{r} 94 \\ -43 \\ \hline 51 \end{array}$$ yes (no)

7. $$\begin{array}{r} 64 \\ -27 \\ \hline 37 \end{array}$$ (yes) no

8. $$\begin{array}{r} 82 \\ -34 \\ \hline 48 \end{array}$$ (yes) no

9. $$\begin{array}{r} 31 \\ -13 \\ \hline 18 \end{array}$$ (yes) no

10. $$\begin{array}{r} 59 \\ -48 \\ \hline 11 \end{array}$$ yes (no)

Macmillan/McGraw-Hill

Chapter 7   Subtracting 2-Digit Numbers   two hundred forty-one   **241**

USING THE CHAPTER REVIEW/TEST
The Chapter Review/Test may be used as a review to survey children's knowledge and understanding of the chapter material. Or it may be used as a test to formally assess children's understanding of the concepts and skills taught in the chapter. If used as a test, you may wish to assign one or more of the resources listed in *Reinforcement and Remediation* on p. 242 after reviewing children's test results.

If the Chapter Review/Test is used as a review, you may wish to have children work in pairs to complete it. Then, you can use the Chapter Tests—Forms A, B, and C—provided in the *Testing Program Blackline Master and Teacher's Manual* for testing purposes. Any of these forms may be used for pretesting, posttesting, or retesting.

A performance assessment activity for the key concept in this chapter is provided on page 243.

Subtract.

11.
45¢	34¢	80¢	92¢	57¢	83¢
− 26¢	− 12¢	− 55¢	− 3¢	− 34¢	− 38¢
19¢	22¢	25¢	89¢	23¢	45¢

12.
72	60	45	89	29	56
− 28	− 32	− 6	− 66	− 5	− 48
44	28	39	23	24	8

Problem Solving

Cross out the data you do not need. Then solve.

13. Ashley has 46 books.
~~He read 20 of the books.~~
Evan has 28 books.
How many more books does Ashley have than Evan?

___18___ more books

Solve.

14. Beverly makes a chain with 77 paper clips.
Yuri makes a chain with 49 paper clips.
How many more paper clips does
Beverly have than Yuri?

___28___ more paper clips

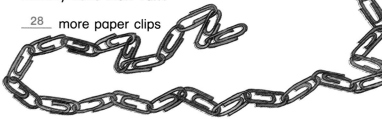

15. Beverly takes 25 paper clips off her chain.
How many paper clips are now on her chain?

___52___ paper clips

242 two hundred forty-two

CHAPTER REVIEW / TEST

MEETING INDIVIDUAL NEEDS

Reinforcement and Remediation

CHAP. OBJ.	TEST ITEMS	PUPIL'S EDITION pp.			TEACHER'S EDITION pp.	TEACHER RESOURCES	
		Lesson	Extra Practice	Practice Plus	Alt. Teaching Strategy	Reteaching	Practice
7A	1–10, 12	217–226	230	240	218, 220, 222, 224, 225A, 226A 233A	69, 70, 71, 72, 73	69, 70, 71, 72, 73
7B 7C	11 13–15	233–234 227–228, 235–236	239 230 239	240		76, 77 74, 78	76, 77 74, 78

For Students Acquiring English (SAE)

Before beginning the Chapter Review/Test with SAE children, scan the pages for any unfamiliar vocabulary that should be pretaught. You may wish to pair or group SAE children with non-SAE children. You may also wish to repeat some of the activities and techniques for SAE children that were suggested earlier in this chapter.

CHAPTER 7

AT·A·GLANCE p. 243

OBJECTIVE
Assess whether children can subtract 2-digit numbers (with and without regrouping), including money values, in a problem.

MATERIALS
Manipulatives 2 Q, 1D, 2 N, 5 P coins (or punchouts) per pair

Teacher Resources
Performance Assessment booklet, pp. 30–32

For Students Acquiring English (SAE)

Before beginning the performance assessment with SAE children, scan the page for any unfamiliar vocabulary that should be pretaught. You may wish to pair or group SAE children with non-SAE children. You may also wish to repeat some of the activities and techniques for SAE children that were suggested earlier in this chapter.

Performance Assessment

Work with a partner.

Look at the items for sale.
You have 75¢ to spend.
You can buy an item at a time until there
is not enough money to buy another item.

Write each item in the table.
Use coin models if you want.

Items Bought	Cost	Amount left

Macmillan/McGraw-Hill

You may put this page in your

PERFORMANCE ASSESSMENT

USING PERFORMANCE ASSESSMENT
The Performance Assessment activity may be used to informally assess children's understanding of the key concept(s) of the chapter. Additional assessment activities and Math Journal Options are provided in the *Performance Assessment* booklet.

Performing the Activity
Assign children to work in pairs. Provide coin models for them to use. (You may wish to act as a banker for coin exchanges.) Have them choose items to buy, then figure how much money they have left after each purchase. Have children record their findings individually.

Evaluation Guidelines
Use these criteria to help determine the holistic score for each child. The holistic scoring scale can be found in the Teacher's Reference Section.

- How do children decide what to buy?
- Do children estimate costs to see how much money they will have left?
- Can children subtract 2-digit numbers with or without regrouping?

[Example Response: Toy car, 29¢ (46¢ left)]

If children do not have a full understanding of the key concept(s), you may wish to use the Alternative Teaching Strategies or the MAC Activities within the chapter.

 You may wish to have children put their final revised work in their portfolios.

A formal assessment of the concepts and skills taught in this chapter is provided on pages 241–242.

Enrichment For All

Patterns in Addition and Subtraction

Think about tens and ones.
Talk about the pattern in this table.

+	6
4	10
14	20
24	30
34	40

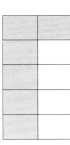

Complete each table.

1.

+	8
2	10
12	20
22	30
32	40

2.

+	5
3	8
13	18
23	28
33	38

3.

−	7
9	2
19	12
29	22
39	32

4.

−	9
16	7
26	17
36	27
46	37

5. Make your own table to
show a pattern.
Answers will vary.

AT·A·GLANCE p. 244

OBJECTIVE
Identify patterns in addition and subtraction.

ASSIGNMENT GUIDE

COURSE	EXERCISES
Basic	p. 244: 1–5
Average	p. 244: 1–5
Challenge	p. 244: 1–5

MATERIALS
Manipulatives   4 T, 16 O models (or punchouts) per child

For Students Acquiring English (SAE)

Before SAE children fill in the tables in ex. 1–4, make sure they
understand that they will add to complete ex. 1–2 and subtract to
complete ex. 3–4. Guide them in using the tens and ones models.
Pair SAE and non-SAE children to complete ex. 5 together.

---

1 PREPARE   **WARM-UP**   To prepare children to identify patterns
in addition and subtraction, have them start at 10
and count by tens to 50. Continue the activity, starting at 5; 4; 3.

2 TEACH   **MODELING**   Have children study the table at the
top of the page. Point out that 6 is added to each
number in the left column. Then have them use models to add.

■ **What pattern do you see in the numbers on the left? on the
right?** [Each number is 10 more in both cases.]

■ **What pattern would you see if you added 4 ones to each number on the left?** [the same pattern; 10 more]

■ **What pattern would you see if you subtracted 2 ones from
each number on the left?** [the same pattern; 10 more]

3 PRACTICE·APPLY   Have children complete ex. 1–5. For
ex. 1–4, volunteers identify patterns
and discuss the tables they made for ex. 5.

CLOSE   Guide children to summarize the lesson:

■ **If the numbers on the left side of a table increased by fives,
what pattern would the numbers show on the right side?** [the
same pattern]

CHAPTER 7

AT·A·GLANCE p. 245

OBJECTIVE
Review and maintain previously learned concepts and skills.

Name _____

Cumulative Review

Fill in the ◯ to answer each question.

1.

$$6 + 2$$

10	8	6	4
◯	●	◯	◯

2.

$$9 + 8$$

17	15	12	1
●	◯	◯	◯

3. What is the temperature?

10°C	20°C	30°C	40°C
◯	◯	●	◯

4.

$$14 + 12$$

36	26	22	2
◯	●	◯	◯

5.

$$12¢ + 19¢$$

31¢	22¢	21¢	7¢
●	◯	◯	◯

6.

$$75¢ - 62¢$$

3¢	13¢	14¢	23¢
◯	●	◯	◯

7. Thorne read a book for 36 minutes. Carolyn read a book for 18 minutes. How many more minutes did Thorne read than Carolyn?

- ◯ 54 minutes
- ◯ 44 minutes
- ◯ 22 minutes
- ● 18 minutes

Macmillan/McGraw-Hill

USING THE CUMULATIVE REVIEW
The Cumulative Review is presented in a multiple-choice format to provide practice in taking a standardized test. It gives children an opportunity to review previously learned skills. An answer sheet, similar to those used when taking standardized tests, can be found in the *Testing Program Blackline Masters and Teacher's Manual.*

The table that follows correlates the review items to the lesson pages on which the skills are taught.

Review Items	Text Pages	Review Items	Text Pages
1	34	5	203
2	107–108	6	233–234
3	160	7	235–236
4	191–195		

Testing Program Blackline Masters
In addition to the Cumulative Review in the Pupil's Edition, there are quarterly Cumulative Tests and an End-Year Test. These tests are multiple choice and provide additional opportunities for children to practice taking standardized tests.

Cumulative Tests measure children's performance on major skills and concepts taught during the previous quarters. The **End-Year Test** measures children's performance on major skills and concepts taught throughout the year.

Home Activity

Your child has been learning to subtract 2-digit numbers. You can use this game to help your child practice this skill.

Players:
2

Materials:
paper and pencils

Directions:
1. Each player thinks of a number between 9 and 99.

2. Both players subtract the smaller number from the larger.

3. Make sure both differences are the same.

Variations:
1. Instead of players thinking of a number in step 1, cut out numbers from a calendar or write 2-digit numbers on small cards. Put the numbers in a bag or box, and have each player choose one.

2. Make up riddles, like the following, and ask your child to solve them.
   a. Subtract the number of days in a week from the number of days in this month.
   b. Subtract the number of letters in your whole name from 85.
   c. Subtract 17 from the number of pennies in a quarter.

AT·A·GLANCE p. 246

OBJECTIVE
Give family members an opportunity to share in their child's mathematics learning.

For Students Acquiring English (SAE)

Before assigning this Home Activity to SAE children, find out if someone at home will be able to work with them in English. If not, prepare them to complete the activity independently at home. Explain the directions of the activity and ask SAE children to restate them so you can check comprehension. Scan the page and preteach any difficult vocabulary or phrases that they may not know. If you feel that an SAE child will need extra help with the activity, you might assign that child a non-SAE partner and arrange a time for them to work on the activity in or out of school.

USING THE ACTIVITY

Have children look at the page. Explain that the page has a game that an adult in the family can help them complete. Read the page with the children, making sure that they understand what needs to be done. Tell children that they will do this page at home.

> **❝IN CHAPTER 8, you will introduce your children to time. You will also have the opportunity to develop concepts of time, explore telling time with analog and digital clocks, and explore calendars.❞**

Notes
FROM THE AUTHOR

Here are some notes on the concepts presented in this chapter and how your children can apply them to solve problems.

DEVELOPING CONCEPTS of TIME

Help your children gain understanding of time concepts. Children develop these concepts gradually, and like adults, they can find it difficult to estimate how long it takes to do something. Children's perceptions of time also vary by how much the activity being considered is enjoyed. Participating in timed activities helps them develop their concept of time.

TELLING TIME

Encourage children to understand that time is a way of assigning numbers to specific parts of the day. Children use both analog and digital clocks and compare their characteristics.

Walter G. Secada

TIME

Children review and practice telling time to the hour and half hour. Work with a demonstration clock helps children who need reteaching of this skill, and all children will enjoy making their own paper-plate clocks.

As children explore time to the quarter hour and five-minute intervals, help them relate these times to their own activities and experiences.

CALENDARS

Children extend their understanding of time on a clock to time on a calendar. Encourage children to recognize their familiarity with the calendar and the days of the week. Introduce the months of the year to children who may not be familiar with them. The activity of reading a daily calendar to find the day and the date helps children learn the months of the year.

PROBLEM SOLVING

In **Problem Solving** your children (1) work backward to solve a problem and (2) solve a problem by using number sense.

In **Thinking Mathematically** children use number sense to determine elapsed time. In Party Time, children plan which activities to include during a two and one-half hour party.

In **Decision Making** children use two sets of information about time to schedule a class trip to a farm. They decide which activities they would choose and at what time they would schedule each activity.

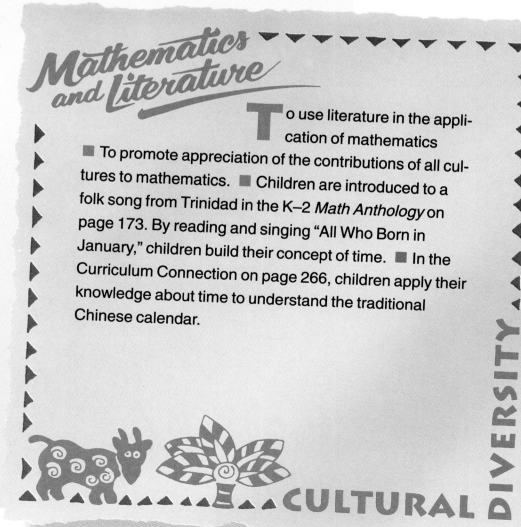

Mathematics and Literature

To use literature in the application of mathematics ■ To promote appreciation of the contributions of all cultures to mathematics. ■ Children are introduced to a folk song from Trinidad in the K–2 *Math Anthology* on page 173. By reading and singing "All Who Born in January," children build their concept of time. ■ In the Curriculum Connection on page 266, children apply their knowledge about time to understand the traditional Chinese calendar.

CULTURAL DIVERSITY

CHAPTER PLANNING GUIDE

CHAPTER OBJECTIVES
WITH STANDARDIZED TEST CORRELATIONS

A. Tell time to the hour and half hour on digital and analog clocks   MAT, CAT, SAT, ITBS

B. Tell time to the quarter hour and five-minute intervals on digital and analog clocks   MAT, CAT, SAT, ITBS

C. Read a calendar   MAT, CAT, SAT, CTBS

D. Solve problems including those that involve using number sense

SUGGESTED PACING-14 DAYS

LESSONS	NCTM STANDARDS	ASSIGNMENTS Basic/Average/Challenge	STUDENT EDITION Extra Practice/ Practice Plus	ADDITIONAL RESOURCES Manip. Plus	Reteach	Practice	Enrich	MAC Activities
Chapter Opener: *Clocks and More Clocks* page 247	1, 2, 3, 4, 10	p. 247: All						
✔ **1 Time** page 248 👥	1, 2, 3, 10	p. 248: All						
✔ **2 Hour** pages 249–250 👥	1, 2, 3, 10	p. 249: All; p. 250: 1–9	p. 254	47, 48, 49	79	79	79	157, 158
3 Half Hour pages 251–252	1, 2, 3, 10	p. 251: 1–4; p. 252: 1–5	pp. 254, 268	50	80	80	80	159, 160
✔ **4 PS: Thinking Mathematically** page 253 👥	1, 2, 3, 10	p. 253: All						
5 PS: Working Backward pages 255–256	1, 2, 3, 10	p. 256: 1–5			81	81	81	161, 162
6 Quarter Hour pages 257–258	1, 2, 3, 10	p. 257: 1–5; p. 258: 2–6, Reasoning			82	82	82	163, 164
✔ **7 Five Minutes** pages 259–260 👥	1, 2, 3, 10	p. 259: 1–4; p. 260: 2–3, Reasoning	pp. 267, 268	51, 52	83	83	83	165, 166
8 Calendar pages 261–262	1, 2, 3, 10	p. 261: 1–6; p. 262: 2–5	p. 267		84	84	84	167, 168
9 PS: Using Number Sense pages 263–264	1, 2, 3, 6	p. 263: 1–3; p. 264: 1–5	p. 267		85	85	85	169, 170
10 PS: Decision Making page 265 👥	1, 2, 3, 10	p. 265: 1–3						

Curriculum Connection: Social Studies page 266 CC

Chapter Review/Test pages 269–270

Performance Assessment page 271

Cumulative Review page 273

Enrichment for All/Home Activity pages 272, 274

NATIONAL COUNCIL OF TEACHERS OF MATHEMATICS Grades K–4

1. Problem Solving
2. Communication
3. Reasoning
4. Connections
5. Estimation
6. Number Sense and Numeration
7. Concepts of Whole Number Operations
8. Whole Number Computation
9. Geometry and Spatial Sense
10. Measurement
11. Statistics and Probability
12. Fractions and Decimals
13. Patterns and Relationships

✔ Activity   👥 Cooperative Learning   CC Cultural Connection

MEETING the NCTM STANDARDS

Problem Solving

Strategies and Skills
- working backward pp. 255–256
- using number sense pp. 263–264

Applications
- **Decision Making** lesson p. 265
- **Problem of the Day** TE pp. 248, 250B, 252B, 256B, 258B, 260B, 262B, 264B

Mathematical Investigations
- **Thinking Mathematically** lesson p. 253

Communication

Language
- using the language of mathematics TE pp. 249–250, 251–252, 257–258

Oral/Written
- using cooperative learning activities pp. 248, 249–250, 253, 259–260, 265, 266; TE pp. 246I–246N
- **Journal Writing** opportunities TE pp. 248, 250, 253A, 260, 262, 264

Reasoning

Critical Thinking
- answering questions that analyze and extend concepts pp. 247, 248, 257, 263, 265

Connections

To other subject areas
- Literature p. 247, Social Studies p. 266; Literature TE pp. 247–248, 259, 261–262

To all cultures
- song from Trinidad, "All Who Born in January," *Math Anthology* p. 173
- Chinese calendar p. 266

Concept Development

Measurement
- exploring the concept of time p. 248
- telling time to the hour and half hour on digital and analog clocks pp. 249–250, 251–252; TE pp. 246I–246L
- telling time to the quarter hour and five minute intervals on digital and analog clocks pp. 257–258, 259–260; TE pp. 246M–246N
- reading a calendar pp. 261–262

ASSESSMENT OPTIONS

PERFORMANCE ASSESSMENT

Preassessment Activity

Before beginning Chapter 8, display an analog clock to children. Have them read the time for various intervals, including hour, half hour, quarter hour, and five minutes. Have children give real-life examples of time duration, for example, the number of times they can write their name in one minute.

Ongoing Assessment

The Ongoing Assessment cards under MEETING INDIVIDUAL NEEDS on TE pp. 250 and 262 provide criteria and questions for assessing children's understanding of the key mathematical concepts developed in the chapter.

MATH JOURNAL *Journal Writing* opportunities encourage children to write about mathematics. Their responses can be recorded either pictorially or in words. The journal writing opportunities on the Ongoing Assessment cards also allow you to assess children's understanding of the lessons.

In addition to the Ongoing Assessment cards, other assessment and journal writing opportunities in this chapter include:

• **CLOSE** TE pp. 248, 253A, 262, 264

Performance Assessment Activity

The Performance Assessment activity on p. 271 provides an alternative to formal assessment. This activity assesses children's understanding of the key concepts of the chapter.

For performance assessment activities that are keyed to individual chapter objectives, see the *Performance Assessment* booklet.

BUILDING A PORTFOLIO

Children should be encouraged to keep a selection of their best work in portfolios. The portfolios provide a way of documenting children's growth in understanding mathematical concepts. Portfolio opportunities in this chapter include:
• **Performance Assessment** p. 271
• **Class Project** TE p. 265A

If you wish to provide additional opportunities for portfolio work, you may choose to use:
• **MAC Activities** 159, 164, 170

You may also wish to have children include their journal writing from the Ongoing Assessment on TE pp. 250 and 262 in their portfolio.

Formal Assessment

The **Chapter Review/Test** assesses children's understanding of the concepts and skills developed in the chapter. The **Cumulative Review** assesses children's understanding of the concepts and skills developed from the beginning of the year.

You can use **Form A** or **Form B** of the **Chapter Test** found in the *Testing Program Blackline Masters and Teacher's Manual* if you wish to use a multiple-choice format to assess children's understanding of the chapter concepts and skills. You can use **Form C** if you wish to use a free-response format. Any of the forms may be used as a pretest, posttest, or for retesting.

The **COMPUTER MANAGEMENT SYSTEM**, or **CMS**, enables you to score **Forms A** and **B** of the **Chapter Test** quickly and automatically. It also prescribes learning activities based on children's test results.

For more information about Assessment, see the *Professional Handbook*.

Common Error and Remediation

The Teacher's Edition notes for each Develop/Understand (Transitional/Abstract) lesson provide a common error analysis and a remediation activity. Some errors defy quick analysis and can only be identified by interviewing the child.

ALTERNATIVE TEACHING STRATEGY

Alternative Teaching Strategies appear frequently in the chapter. These strategies provide other presentations of the lessons for children who might benefit from instruction in different learning modalities: kinesthetic, visual, and/or auditory.

For Students Acquiring English (SAE)

Syntactical structures for telling time may differ in other languages. For example, the equivalent of *10 minutes after 3* in Spanish is *the 3 and 10*. Provide many opportunities throughout the day for SAE children to practice telling time in English—both orally and in writing. Personal daily journals will be good diagnostically and will allow children to build confidence. The journals might include the times of favorite meals and television programs.

SAE notes appear periodically in the chapter. These notes provide suggestions for how to work with children to improve comprehension and build vocabulary.

MANIPULATIVES WORKSHOP

Analog and digital clocks are used in this chapter to investigate concepts of time. They provide two ways to represent time in hours and minutes.

USING MANIPULATIVES

Here a child uses an analog clock to show 4:00.

The child moves the hour hand to the 4 and the minute hand to the 12.

The child then moves the clock hands to show quarter after four.

The child shows the same time on a digital clock. It says 4:15.

MAKING MANIPULATIVES   See the Manipulatives section of the *Professional Handbook* for materials that can be substituted for analog and digital clocks.

COOPERATIVE LEARNING WORKSHOP

GETTING STARTED

Getting Back on Track: You can now form groups for distributing specific abilities or to assure that linguistic minorities or personality types are evenly spread. The class can develop a **"happy talk" list** of phrases they want to foster during the lesson, such as "That's a good idea!" and "Nice drawing!" Be sure to model these phrases and even provide picture reminders. After the modeling, children need time to discuss what they should say and do during the lesson.

When you monitor the groups and discover that some are having difficulties with interruptions, try allowing only the child holding an object (**"the mike"**) to talk. If someone dominates the discussion, pass out three **talk tokens** to each child. Each time a statement is made, the speaker places a token in the center of the group. Tokens are then redistributed when all have been used. When Checking for Understanding, have the children also check whether they practiced the cooperative skill.

IDEAS TO TRY

Team-Building Structures: When studying time, groups can invent names for themselves that are time related: The Super Speeders, The Hickory Dickory Clocks, or The Calendar Kids. They can agree on appropriate symbols and construct them out of paper or make clothes-hanger mobiles.

Apply time concepts by having group members talk about which exercises will take the group a longer or a shorter time to complete. Afterward, have them show on a model clockface how long it actually took them. During reflection, the group can list all the ways they spent the time and whether they want to do things differently next time.

You can apply the above team-building structures in these lessons:
8-1 *Time* p. 248
8-2 *Hour* pp. 249–250
8-3 *Half Hour* pp. 251–252

Threes or Fours? Dividing the class by fours occasionally results in a group of three if numbers are uneven. **Roles** or **jobs** for each child will help ensure participation so that no one is left out. For groups of four, add the role of facilitator. This person models for the group the use of one of the following skills: **clarifying the problem, checking for agreement or understanding,** or **explaining reasoning.** Roles rotate for each new lesson so all can model the skill. At Close, the facilitator writes the group's conclusions on both the lesson content and the cooperative skill.

You can apply the above grouping ideas in these lessons:
8-6 *Quarter Hour* pp. 257–258
8-7 *Five Minutes* pp. 259–260

SEE ALSO

Cooperative Learning Tip for lessons 8-5 Problem Solving p. 256; 8-9 Problem Solving p. 264; 8-10 Decision Making p. 265A

The Cooperative Learning section of the *Professional Handbook* for additional information

---

ACTIVITY
INTERACTIVE BULLETIN BOARD

SETUP Cover a bulletin board with white background paper. Write the days of the school week across the top. Then list the school hours down the side of the board.

PROCEDURE 👥 Tell children that they are going to help you plan this week's school schedule. Read the times with the children. Have them identify any routine times, such as lunch, gym, recess, art class, and so on. Write the activities next to the appropriate times. Then complete the weekly schedule with the children.

Encourage children to refer to the schedule during the week.

Our Weekly Schedule

	Monday	Tuesday	Wednesday	Thursday	Friday
9:00	Reading	Reading	Reading	Reading	Reading
9:30	Reading	Reading	Reading	Reading	Reading
10:00	Math	Math	Math	Math	Math
10:30	Math	Math	Math	Math	Math
11:00	Social Studies	Science	Spelling Bee		
11:30	Social Studies	Science	Spelling Bee		
12:00	Lunch	Lunch	Lunch	Lunch	Lunch
12:30	Lunch	Lunch	Lunch	Lunch	Lunch
1:00	Gym				
1:30	Gym				
2:00	Art		Art		
2:30	Art	Gym	Art		
3:00	Free Play	Gym			
3:30	Dismissal				

For use before LESSON 8.2, pp. 249-250

47

HOUR

OBJECTIVE
Explore time to the hour.

MATERIALS
Classroom Materials
paper plates, paper
fasteners, hour hands and
minute hands cut from
oaktag, assorted crayons
and markers;
demonstration clock
Manipulatives 1 analog
clock face punchout per
group

WHOLE GROUP ACTIVITY

Display a demonstration clock and review telling
time to the hour. Be sure children can identify the
hour and minute hands. Show 1 o'clock on the
clock.

■ **What time is it when the minute hand points
to the 12 and the hour hand points to the 1?** [1
o'clock]

Turn the minute hand once around the clock and
ask what time the clock shows. [2 o'clock] Continue
until you reach 12 o'clock.

SMALL GROUP ACTIVITY

Assign children to work in groups. Give each group
3 paper plates, 3 paper fasteners, 3 hour hands
and 3 minute hands cut from oaktag, 1 set of crayons and markers, and 1 punchout clockface.

Tell children that they will design their own clock
faces. Have children use the punchout clockface as
a model for drawing marks around the outside of
the clock. Then have children decorate their clocks.

Have volunteers display their clockfaces. Assign
each child a time to the hour and have children set
their clocks to that time. Then have children order
themselves to show the times in order.

EXTENDING THE ACTIVITY

Call out times to the hour at random and have each
child take a turn showing the time on her or his
clock.

ONGOING ASSESSMENT

✓ Can children read and show time to
the hour? Are they able to replicate a
clock face?

For use before LESSON 8.2, pp. 249-250

48

SEQUENCE EVENTS

OBJECTIVES
Sequence events.
Make a time schedule.

MATERIALS
Classroom Materials
demonstration clock

WHOLE GROUP ACTIVITY

Work with children to establish a time schedule for the next day.

■ **What subjects do we study each day?** [Record answers on the chalkboard. Answers will vary.]

Tell children what time you will begin teaching each subject and write it on the chalkboard.

■ **What other things happen during the day?** [Record answers on the chalkboard. Answers will vary and may include recess or lunch.]

Write a time for each of these events.

Draw a grid for a time schedule on the chalkboard.

Write in the start of the school day on the schedule. Then have volunteers tell what to write next on the chart, based on the time each event occurs.

When the schedule has been completed, ask questions based on the information it contains, for example: "Which subject is taught earlier in the day, reading or mathematics?"

EXTENDING THE ACTIVITY

Provide children with a time schedule grid similar to the one on the chalkboard. Have children complete it for the time after school until bedtime.

ONGOING ASSESSMENT

✓ Can children sequence events of the day and make a time schedule?

For use before LESSON 8.2, pp. 249-250

49
NUMBER LINE
CLOCK

OBJECTIVE
Relate a clock to a number line.

MATERIALS
Classroom Materials
strips of 24-inch-long oaktag, paper fasteners, scissors

WHOLE GROUP ACTIVITY

Prepare three oaktag strips as shown.

1	2	3	4	5	6	7	8	9	10	11	12

5	10	15	20	25	30	35	40	45	50	55	60

5	10	15	20	25	30	35	40	45	50	55	60
1	2	3	4	5	6	7	8	9	10	11	12

Show children the 1–12 strip.

■ **What does this line look like?** [Children may recognize it as a number line.]

Have the class count using the number line.

Then show children the 5–60 strip. Have children count by fives on the number line.

Gather children around you as you display the combined 5–60 and 1–12 number line. Cut the strip into sections as shown. Attach each section with a fastener and bend the pieces to form a circle.

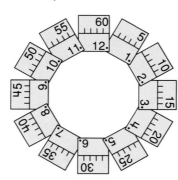

■ **What does this line look like now?** [a clock]

Have the class count on from *1 o'clock* to *12 o'clock* on the clock number line. Then have the class count by 5s from *5 minutes* to *60 minutes* on the clock.

EXTENDING THE ACTIVITY

Detach the fastener holding the 12 to the 1 on the clock. Have each child explore making a circle using the number line.

ONGOING ASSESSMENT

✔ Are children beginning to recognize the units that make up a clock?

MANIPULATIVES plus ACTIVITY

For use before LESSON 8.3, pp. 251-252

50
HALF HOUR

OBJECTIVES
Explore duration.
Explore time to the half hour.

MATERIALS
Classroom Materials
table games, demonstration clock
Manipulatives 1 analog clock face punchout per pair

PAIRS ACTIVITY

Display the demonstration clock and review the concept of time to the half hour.

- **How many minutes in an hour?** [60]
- **How many minutes in a half hour?** [30]

Have pairs of children choose a table game to play for a half hour.

Before they begin, distribute a clock punchout to each pair and have them set it to the starting time of the game. Ask them to write the number of rounds or turns they think they would complete in a half hour.

Time children and tell them when a half hour is up. Have them change their clock faces to show the current time. Tell children to compare their estimates to the actual number of rounds they played.

Ask children if the half hour seemed long or short and have them tell why.

- **Can you think of a situation in which time seems to go very slowly?** [Possible responses: waiting for the bell to ring for lunch or to go home; waiting for a younger brother or sister]

- **Can you think of a situation in which time seems to go very quickly?** [Possible responses: when you have a half hour until bedtime; during your favorite television show; during lunchtime]

Discuss that the duration of a half hour is always the same, even though it may not seem that way because of our activities.

EXTENDING THE ACTIVITY

Have children work with their clock faces to show a time and then move the minute hand 30 minutes ahead to show time passing.

ONGOING ASSESSMENT

✓ Are children beginning to recognize the duration of a half hour?

MANIPULATIVES plus ACTIVITY

For use before LESSON 8.7, pp. 259-260

51 MINUTES

OBJECTIVE
Explore time in minutes.

MATERIALS
Classroom Materials
clock with a second hand; one-minute timer (EXTENDING THE ACTIVITY only)

WHOLE GROUP ACTIVITY

Ask children how long they think a minute is. Explain to children that you will look at your watch or the clock and time one minute. Challenge children to indicate when they think one minute has passed by raising their hands.

Following the activity, display a clock with a second hand and have children observe its movement. Have the class count off seconds from 1 to 60 by using any popular method; for example, 1 Mississippi, 2 Mississippi, 3 Mississippi, ...

PAIRS ACTIVITY

Assign children to work in pairs. Present all or some of the following activities, one at a time.

■ **How many times can you write the numbers 1 to 10 in one minute?**

■ **How many times can you jump in one minute?**

■ **How many times can you write the alphabet in one minute?**

Before each activity, have children write an estimate for the activity. Keep the time for one minute as one child in each pair carries out the activity and the other child keeps count. Have children switch roles. Then have them compare their estimates to their actual accomplishments.

EXTENDING THE ACTIVITY

Throughout the year, allow children to take turns keeping time with a one-minute timer. Have children time regular classroom activities, such as a 5-minute break, the time it takes for a child to go to the office and come back to the classroom, the time it takes to dismiss the class, and so on.

ONGOING ASSESSMENT

✓ Are children beginning to recognize the duration of a minute?

MANIPULATIVES plus ACTIVITY

**For use before
LESSON 8.7,
pp. 259-260**

52

FIVE MINUTES

OBJECTIVE
Explore time in 5-minute
intervals.

MATERIALS
Classroom Materials
clock with a second hand,
yarn, hole punch, 2 sets of
number cards for 9–18; 5-
minute timer (EXTENDING
THE ACTIVITY only)
Manipulatives 1 analog
clock face punchout per
child; 1 spinner for 0–9 per
small group of three

WHOLE GROUP ACTIVITY 🕐
Display a clock with a second hand and have children observe as the hand goes around once and
review this as one minute.

■ **How many minutes will it take for the second
hand to go around 5 times?** [5 minutes]

SMALL GROUP ACTIVITY 🕐 👥
Present the following games, one at a time. Explain
to children that they will play each game for 5 minutes. After each game, discuss whether the 5 minutes seemed long or short.

Spin for Minutes
Assign children to play in small groups of three.
Give each child a clockface punchout. Give each
group a 0–9 spinner. Have children set their clocks
at 12:00. Players should take turns spinning the
spinner and moving the minute hand on the clockface that number of minutes. Players should move
the hour hand as appropriate. The player who advances the minute hand the farthest after 5 minutes
wins.

Addition Relay
Use yarn, a hole punch, and number cards to make
2 flip books for the numbers 9–18. Separate the
class into 2 teams. Divide each team in half and
have teammates in each half line up facing each
other with about 10 feet separating teammates.
Give a flip book to the first child on each team.

Call out an addition fact for 9 to 18. The child holding the flip book should display the sum on the flip
book. When a correct sum is shown, the child runs
to the opposite side and hands the flip book to the
teammate standing at the front of the line, then
goes to the end of that line. The team that completes the relay first wins.

EXTENDING THE ACTIVITY
Throughout the year, have children take turns keeping time with a 5-minute timer. Have them time
classroom activities, such as a 5-minute break, 5-
minute work time, 5-minute errand, and so on.

ONGOING ASSESSMENT
✓ Are children beginning to recognize
the duration of 5 minutes?

Mathematics and Literature

Listening and Speaking

The Read-Aloud selection can be used with the Chapter 8 Opener and Lesson 8-1 on pages 247-248.

**Tape 2, Side 1
Selection 2**

CLOCKS
AND MORE CLOCKS

By Pat Hutchins

•

The illustrations in this book picture the Clockmaker holding out a large pocket watch for Mr. Higgins to see as he checks the time on each clock. You will need to explain this to your children as you read the word "Look" when spoken by the Clockmaker. If an instructional clock is available, you may wish to read the story a second time, moving the hands of the clock to show the progression of time.

•

One day Mr. Higgins found a clock in the attic. It looked very splendid standing there. "How do I know if it's correct?" he thought.

So he went out and bought another which he placed in the bedroom.

"Three o'clock," said Mr. Higgins. "I'll see if the other clock is right."

He ran up to the attic, but the clock said one minute past three. "How do I know which one is right?" he thought.

So he went out and bought another which he placed in the kitchen. "Ten minutes to four, I'll check the others."

He ran up to the attic. The attic clock said eight minutes to four. He ran down to the bedroom. The bedroom clock said seven minutes to four.

"I still don't know which one is right," he thought.

So he went out and bought another which he placed in the hall.

"Twenty minutes past four," he said, and ran up to the attic. The attic clock said twenty-three minutes past four.

He ran down to the kitchen. The kitchen clock said twenty-five minutes past four.

He ran up to the bedroom. The bedroom clock said twenty-six minutes past four.

"This is no good at all," thought Mr. Higgins.

And he went to the Clockmaker.

"My hall clock says twenty minutes past four, my attic clock says twenty-three minutes past four, my kitchen clock says twenty-five minutes past four, my bedroom clock says twenty-six minutes past four, and I don't know which one is right!" said Mr. Higgins.

So the Clockmaker went to the house to look at the clocks.

The hall clock said five o'clock. "There's nothing wrong with this clock," said the Clockmaker. "Look!"

The kitchen clock said one minute past five.

"There!" shouted Mr. Higgins. "Your watch said five o'clock."

"But it is one minute past now!" said the Clockmaker. "Look!"

The bedroom clock said two minutes past five. "Absolutely correct!" said the Clockmaker. "Look!"

The attic clock said three minutes past five. "There's nothing wrong with this clock either," said the Clockmaker. "Look!"

"What a wonderful watch!" said Mr. Higgins.

And he went out and bought one. And since he bought his watch all his clocks have been right.

AT·A·GLANCE pp. 247-248

LESSON OBJECTIVES
Explore mathematical concepts through literature.
Explore the concept of one minute.

ASSIGNMENT GUIDE

COURSE	EXERCISES
Basic	p. 247: All; p. 248: All
Average	p. 247: All; p. 248: All
Challenge	p. 247: All; p. 248: All

MATERIALS
Classroom Materials a clock with second hand

Teacher Resources
Math Anthology, pp. 167–168
Read-Aloud Cassette 2, Side 1, Selection 2

SKILLS TRACE

TIME	
Explore (Concrete) 248	Develop/Understand (Transitional/Abstract) 249–250, 251–252, 257–258, 259–260, 261–262
Practice 254, 267, 268, 269–270, 273, 301, 308	Apply 253, 255–256, 263–264, 265, 266, 272, 285

Mathematics and Literature

Time

CHAPTER 8

READ ALOUD
Clocks and More Clocks

CLOCKS AND MORE CLOCKS
By Pat Hutchins

Listen to the story Clocks and More Clocks.

Tell why Mr. Higgins thought something was wrong with his clocks. He did not know that each clock's hands moved as he walked from clock to clock.

247

---

1 PREPARE **WARM-UP** To review the concept of a minute, have children close their eyes. Tell them to raise their hands when they think a minute has passed. Using a watch or clock with a second hand, call "time" when 60 seconds have passed. Poll children to see who thought a minute was longer and who thought a minute was shorter.

2 TEACH **DISCUSSING** Before reading the story *Clocks and More Clocks,* ask children to think about where they have seen clocks. Discuss what might happen if all the clocks in school showed different times. Explain that in this story, they will learn how a man named Mr. Higgins tried to solve his problem with his clocks.

PUPIL'S EDITION pp. 247-248

Page 247 Read *Clocks and More Clocks* found on pages 246O–246P or in *Math Anthology* to children, or play Read-Aloud Cassette 2, Side 1, Selection 2 for them.

■ **What did Mr. Higgins discover in his attic?** [a beautiful old clock]

■ **How did Mr. Higgins check to see if the time on the attic clock was correct?** [He bought another clock, put it in his bedroom, and then compared the times on the two clocks.]

Discuss the problem on the page. Guide children to see that time passed as Mr. Higgins walked from room to room.

Page 248 ■ **Working Together** Discuss the activity shown in each picture with the children. Then read the directions aloud.

ACTIVITY

Time

Working Together

How many times can you do each of these things in one minute?
First guess. Then test by timing.

Clap your hands.	Write your first name.	Hop.

Alexander
Alexander
Alexa

Answers will vary.

Guess ____ times **Guess** ____ times **Guess** ____ times

Timed ____ times **Timed** ____ times **Timed** ____ times

Count to 10.	Draw a circle.	Say the alphabet.

1, 2, 3 . . .

A, B, C . . .

Guess ____ times **Guess** ____ times **Guess** ____ times

Timed ____ times **Timed** ____ times **Timed** ____ times

Talk about things you do that take about one minute. Answers will vary.

Check for Understanding

■ **What do you do first before you are timed on each activity?** [Make a guess about how many times you can do the activity in one minute.]

GUIDED PRACTICE Review the first picture with the children and have them make a guess about how many times they can clap their hands in one minute. Then time the children as they count and clap their hands. Have them record the number of claps and compare the number to their estimates.

For reteaching, use Alternative Strategy.

3 PRACTICE•APPLY

PRACTICE Continue to work with the whole class and time each activity. Then have children compare their guesses with their timed results.

MEETING INDIVIDUAL NEEDS

For Students Acquiring English (SAE)

When discussing this and other chapter opener pages, ask children to locate specific details in the photograph. This technique will improve comprehension and build vocabulary. If necessary, simplify the wording of the questions. Correct errors tactfully; model correct responses in a natural, unexaggerated manner.

ACTIVITY ALTERNATIVE TEACHING STRATEGY

MATERIALS watch with a second hand

AUDITORY Assign children partners to help them keep track of the number of repetitions of each activity. While you time the activity, one child does the activity while the partner counts the number of repetitions. Have children switch roles and repeat the activity. After each activity, have them compare their guess with their timed performance. Encourage them to use this information when making their next guess.

C L O S E Guide children to summarize the lesson:

■ **What do you do every day that takes about a minute?** [Answers will vary; possible responses: brushing teeth, washing face, making bed, sharpening pencil]

Problem of the Day

After school, Sophie washed her hands, did the dishes, went to the library, read a book, signed out a library book, and went home for dinner. Which things took about a minute? [washing her hands, signing out a library book]

AT·A·GLANCE pp. 249-250

LESSON OBJECTIVE
Tell time to the hour.

ASSIGNMENT GUIDE

COURSE	EXERCISES
Basic	p. 249: All; p. 250: 1–9
Average	p. 249: All; p. 250: 1–9
Challenge	p. 249: All; p. 250: 1–9
Extra Practice, p. 254	

MATERIALS
Classroom Materials demonstration clock, digital clock
Manipulatives digital and analog clockface and punchouts per pair

Teacher Resources
Reteaching 79   Practice 79   Enrichment 79
MAC Act. 157, 158   Teacher Aid 17

SKILLS TRACE

TIME	
Explore (Concrete) 248	Develop/Understand (Transitional/Abstract) 249–250, 251–252, 257–258, 259–260, 261–262
Practice 254, 267, 268, 269–270, 273, 301, 308	Apply 253, 255–256, 263–264, 265, 266, 272, 285

See *MANIPULATIVES PLUS 47–49*, pp. 246I–246K.

MANIPULATIVES plus ACTIVITY

---

1 PREPARE
WARM-UP To prepare children for time to the hour, write the following patterns on the chalkboard. Have children complete each pattern. Then have them skip-count by fives to 60.

5, 10, __, __, 25 [15, 20]
25, __, __, 40, 45 [30, 35]
__, __, 50, __, 60 [40, 45, 55]

2 TEACH
MODELING Display a demonstration **analog clock.** Help children identify the short hand as the **hour hand** and the long hand as the **minute hand.** Explain that each of the 12 numbers on the clock stands for a different **hour** and the small marks between the numbers stand for **minutes.** Point to and count the minutes by fives to 60 with the children.

Name _____

ACTiViTY

Hour

One **hour** is 60 minutes.

7 o'clock

Working Together

Use an 🕐 and a 📱 .
   analog clock   digital clock
Show a time in two ways.
Say the time.
Take turns.

I move the hour hand to show a time.

I show the same time.

Count by fives to 60 to show an hour.

Chapter 8   Time

249

Show 4:00 on the clock. Name the time with the children.

- **Where is the hour hand?** [on the 4]
- **Where is the minute hand?** [on the 12]

Display a **digital clock** and set it for 4:00. Discuss how the clocks are the same and different. Point out the colon and the 2 zeros. Explain that the colon separates the hour from the minutes. Finally ask children to show the following times on both of their punchout clocks: 2:00, 10:00, and 6:00.

PUPIL'S EDITION pp. 249-250

Page 249 Discuss the example at the top of the page.

WORKING TOGETHER Have children work with partners to show times on their clocks.

Write each time in two ways.

1.

__10__ o'clock

__10:00__

2.

__3__ o'clock

__3:00__

3.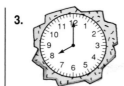

__8__ o'clock

__8:00__

4.

__1__ o'clock

__1:00__

5.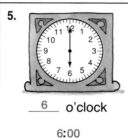

__6__ o'clock

__6:00__

6.

__12__ o'clock

__12:00__

Draw the hour hand and the minute hand.
Write the time. For Exercises 7–9 answers will vary.

7. About what time do you wake up?

__:__

8. About what time do you eat lunch?

__:__

9. About what time do you leave school?

__:__

Extra Practice, page 254

ACTIVITY

ALTERNATIVE TEACHING STRATEGY

MATERIALS digital clock punchout, bell; demonstration clock

AUDITORY/VISUAL Tell children that some clocks have bells or chimes that ring to tell the hour. Ring a bell six times and have children count aloud. Show 6:00 on the demonstration clock. Review the position of the hands. Repeat with the digital clock. Ring the bell to signal other times as children count aloud. Have volunteers set the clocks to show the times.

ONGOING ASSESSMENT

 MATH JOURNAL

OBSERVATION Determine whether children tell time correctly in the activity on p. 249.

INTERVIEW Display a demonstration clock showing 4:00. **(1) What time does the clock show? (2) Show me where the hands would be at 12:00; at 7:00.**

JOURNAL WRITING You may wish to have children record their responses in their math journals.

ACTIVITY

Common Error and Remediation

MATERIALS clockface punchout, number cube (Teacher Aid 17)

Some children may not be able to tell time to the hour. Work individually with each child, using an analog clockface and a number cube. Tape the minute hand to the 12 and set the hour hand at 12. Have the child roll a number cube and count off the number shown on the cube as hours, for example, 1:00, 2:00, 3:00. As each hour is said, the child should move the hour hand. Reset the hour hand to 12 and repeat the activity.

Check for Understanding
Show 5:00 on a digital clock.

■ **Show this time on your clockface.** [Children show 5:00.]

Page 250 Have children read the directions.

GUIDED PRACTICE Work through ex. 1 with the children. For re-teaching, use Common Error and Remediation or Alternative Strategy.

3 PRACTICE·APPLY **PRACTICE** ex. 2–9: Be sure children understand they are to show the times when they get up, eat lunch, and leave school. Remind them to draw the hour hand shorter than the minute hand.

C L O S E Guide children to summarize the lesson:

■ **How do you show 3:00 on a clockface?** [Put the minute hand on the 12 and the hour hand on the 3.]

■ **How do you show 3:00 on a digital clock?** [Show a 3 to the left of the colon and 2 zeros to the right.]

MAC Activity 158

On Your Own   Pair and Share   In a Group

MATH AND MUSIC ▪ *HICKORY, DICKORY, DOCK*

Materials   punchout clockfaces

Review the words and the tune for the nursery rhyme "Hickory, Dickory, Dock." Have children work in small groups to compose new verses with different times. Use the following as an example.

> Hickory, dickory, dock.
> The mouse ran up the clock.
> The clock struck two.
> The mouse hid in a shoe.
> Hickory, dickory, dock.

Have each group use a punchout clock to model the time in each of its verses.

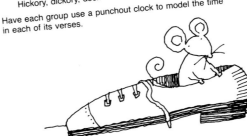

▲
MAC Activity 158:
Average-to-Challenge

MANIPULATIVES ▪ *HUMAN CLOCK*

MAC Activity 157

On Your Own   Pair and Share   In a Group

Materials   chalk, large number cards for 1-12, strips of crepe paper

Take children to an open area and draw the outline of a large clockface with chalk. Make 12 X's around the inside perimeter of the circle and 1 X in the center. Distribute number cards for 1 to 12 to twelve children, one to each child. Have them stand on the X's to represent the numbers on the dial. Have another child stand on the center X holding two strips of crepe paper that represent clock hands.

Then call on two volunteers to pretend to be the hour hand and the minute hand. Have them decide on a time. Each child holds the appropriate strip of crepe paper. The "hour hand" child stands on a number and the "minute hand" child stands on the 12. Have the rest of the children "read" the time on the human clock. Give each child an opportunity to be part of the human clock.

▲
MAC Activity 157:
Basic-to-Average

RETEACHING

Name

HOUR

Study

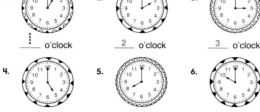

hours minutes

4 o'clock

Check

Write each time.

1. ____ o'clock

2. __2__ o'clock

3. __3__ o'clock

4. __5__ o'clock

5. __8__ o'clock

6. __10__ o'clock

7. 9:00

8. 7:00

9. 11:00

Reteaching-79

Macmillan/McGraw-Hill, MATHEMATICS IN ACTION
Grade 2, Chapter 8, Lesson 2, pages 249–250

PRACTICE

Name

HOUR

Match the clocks.

1.

1:00   6:00   11:00   4:00

Draw the hour hand and the minute hand.
Write the time.

2. 7 o'clock   7:00

3. 3 o'clock   3:00

4. 10 o'clock   10:00

5. 8:00   __8__ o'clock

6. 5:00   __5__ o'clock

7. 9:00   __9__ o'clock

Practice-79

Macmillan/McGraw-Hill, MATHEMATICS IN ACTION
Grade 2, Chapter 8, Lesson 2, pages 249–250

ENRICHMENT

Name

HOUR

On Your Own   Pair and Share   In a Group

TIME TO MOVE

Show the time on each clock.
Answer the question.

FLIGHT	TO	DEPARTS
123	Boston	7:00
557	New York	1:00
738	Tucson	2:00

1. The bus leaves at 6:00.   The bus ride lasts 1 hour.   What time does the bus arrive?   7:00

2. The plane leaves at 2:00.   The plane ride lasts 3 hours.   What time does the plane arrive?   5:00

3. The boat leaves at 9:00.   The boat ride lasts 3 hours.   What time does the boat arrive?   12:00

4. The helicopter leaves at 11:00.   The helicopter ride lasts 2 hours.   What time does the helicopter arrive?   1:00

Enrichment-79

Macmillan/McGraw-Hill, MATHEMATICS IN ACTION
Grade 2, Chapter 8, Lesson 2, pages 249–250

Problem of the Day

Shady Hill School begins the school day at 9:00.
The children go home at 4:00. How many hours
are the children in school? [7 hours]

AT·A·GLANCE pp. 251-252

LESSON OBJECTIVE
Tell time to the half hour.

ASSIGNMENT GUIDE

COURSE	EXERCISES
Basic	p. 251: 1–4; p. 252: 1–5
Average	p. 251: 1–4; p. 252: 1–5
Challenge	p. 251: 1–4; p. 252: 1–5
Extra Practice, p. 254	Practice Plus, p. 268

MATERIALS
Classroom Materials demonstration clock, digital clock
Manipulatives clockface and digital clock punchouts per child

Teacher Resources
Reteaching 80   Practice 80   Enrichment 80
Prob. Solv. 36   MAC Act. 159, 160

SKILLS TRACE

TIME	
Explore (Concrete) 248	**Develop/Understand (Transitional/Abstract)** 249–250, 251–252, 257–258, 259–260, 261–262
Practice 254, 267, 268, 269–270, 273, 301, 308	**Apply** 253, 255–256, 263–264, 265, 266, 272, 285

See **MANIPULATIVES PLUS 50**, p. 246L.

---

1 PREPARE **WARM-UP** To review ordering numbers, write the following numbers on the chalkboard. Have children say the number that comes just after each number as you read it aloud.

3 [4] 7 [8] 5 [6] 8 [9] 11 [12]

2 TEACH **MODELING** Show 2:00 on a demonstration clock. Have children do the same on their punchout clockfaces. Then move the minute hand to the 6, counting by fives. Ask children to count with you. Move, or note the movement of, the hour hand to halfway between 2 and 3. When you reach 6, read the time as 2:30. Explain that 2:30 means that it is one **half hour,** or thirty minutes, after 2:00. Have children use their punchout digital clocks to show 2:30.

Name _____

Half Hour

One **half hour** is 30 minutes.
You can count by fives to 30 to show a half hour.

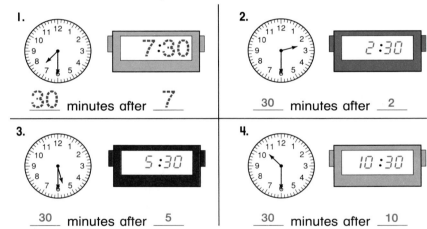

9 o'clock

▶ 30 minutes **after** 9
▶ nine-thirty
▶ half past nine

9:00   9:30

Look at the hour hand on each clock. Where does it point? Why?

Children should note that at 9:30 the hour hand moved to point halfway between 9 and 10.

Write the time in two ways.

1. 7:30
_30_ minutes after _7_

2. 2:30
_30_ minutes after _2_

3. 5:30
_30_ minutes after _5_

4. 10:30
_30_ minutes after _10_

■ **What does the number before the colon tell you?** [the hour]
■ **What does the number after the colon tell you?** [how many minutes]

Ask volunteers to show other times to the hour and to the half hour on both types of punchout clocks. Call on other children to say each time using the correct terms. Then have volunteers write the times on the chalkboard.

PUPIL'S EDITION pp. 251-252

Page 251 Direct children's attention to the clock pictured at the top left of the page. Have children count by fives to 60 as they read the numbers around the clock. Remind them that there are 60 minutes in an hour. Then using the clock pictured at the top right, have children

DR. SY ENCE SHOW

T.V. LISTINGS	
2:30 TOON TIME	4:00 MAGIC FUN
3:00 DR. SY ENCE	4:30 NUMBER CIRCUS
3:30 KID COOKS	5:30 RACE THE CLOCK

Write the time.
Ring the name of the TV show that is on.

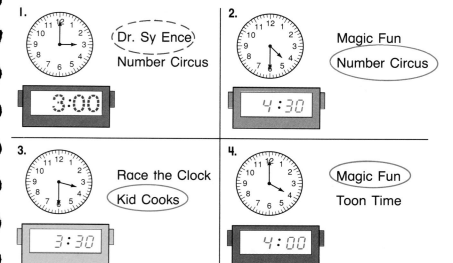

1.
(Dr. Sy Ence)
Number Circus

3:00

2.
Magic Fun
(Number Circus)

4:30

3.
Race the Clock
(Kid Cooks)

3:30

4.
(Magic Fun)
Toon Time

4:00

Mixed Review ▰▰▰▰▰▰▰▰▰▰▰▰▰▰▰▰▰▰▰▰▰▰▰

Add. Did you have to regroup? Ring *yes* or *no*.

5.
$\begin{array}{r} 25 \\ + 36 \\ \hline 61 \end{array}$ (yes) no

$\begin{array}{r} 51 \\ + 29 \\ \hline 80 \end{array}$ (yes) no

$\begin{array}{r} 36 \\ + 62 \\ \hline 98 \end{array}$ yes (no)

Extra Practice, page 254 *Practice Plus*, page 268

ALTERNATIVE TEACHING STRATEGY

MATERIALS colored chalk

VISUAL/KINESTHETIC Draw a large clockface on the chalkboard with marks to indicate minutes. Have children count the marks to establish that there are 60 minutes in an hour. Use chalk to shade the right half of the clockface. Have children count the marks on the right half to establish the minutes in a half hour. Draw a minute hand pointing to 12, then ask a volunteer to draw the hour hand to show 8:00. Repeat with other times.

TEACHER to TEACHER

MANAGEMENT TIP My children benefited from hearing the time throughout the day, i.e., "It is 2 o'clock, time for art."

ACTIVITY *Common Error and Remediation*

MATERIALS paper plates, paper fasteners, oaktag, crayons, scissors

Some children may not grasp the concept of a half hour. Work individually with each child. Have the child make a clock with a paper plate and hands cut from oaktag. Before attaching the hands with a paper fastener, have the child draw a line down the middle of the paper plate and color the right side with a crayon. Read aloud the following times and have the child show each one on the clock, counting by fives while moving the minute hand: 1:00, 1:30; 9:00, 9:30; 10:00, 10:30; 4:00, 4:30; 2:00, 2:30.

count by fives to 30. Point out the shaded portion of the clock, and explain that there are 30 minutes in a half hour.

Discuss how the position of the hour hand changes from 9 to halfway between 9 and 10.

Check for Understanding

■ **Where does the hour hand point when it is 5:30?** [between 5 and 6]

GUIDED PRACTICE ex. 1–4: For reteaching, use Common Error and Remediation or Alternative Strategy.

Page 252 Discuss the TV schedule at the top of the page with the children. Call on volunteers to read each listing aloud.

3 PRACTICE·APPLY **PRACTICE** ex. 1–5

C L O S E Guide children to summarize the lesson:
■ **How do you show 8:30 on a clockface?** [Put the minute hand on the 6 and the hour hand between the 8 and the 9.]

MAC ACTIVITY CENTER

**MAC Activity 159:
Basic-to-Average**
▼

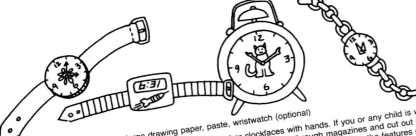

MAC Activity 159

On Your Own   Pair and Share   In a Group

MATH AND CONSUMERS ▪ MY WATCH

Materials   magazines, scissors, large drawing paper, paste, wristwatch (optional)

Discuss with children that wristwatches can be either digital or clockfaces with hands. If you or any child is wearing a watch, display it, and ask children to describe it. Then have children look through magazines and cut out pictures of different types of clocks and watches. Call on volunteers to discuss their pictures based on the features of the watches. For example, children might find pictures of watches that show dates and/or seconds, or have more than one face.

Then assign children to work with a partner and sort their pictures into categories. When sorted, have children paste their pictures on a large sheet of paper and write a sentence identifying the category.

**MAC Activity 160:
Average-to-Challenge** ▶

MATH AND HEALTH ▪ SLEEP TIME

MAC Activity 160

On Your Own   Pair and Share   In a Group

Materials   drawing paper, crayons, punchout clockfaces

Discuss the idea that as people grow older they need less sleep. Invite the school nurse to talk to the class about the average amount of sleep needed by infants, children, adolescents, and adults. If such a visit is inconvenient, present the following information.

infants	12 to 16 hours of sleep
children	9 to 12 hours of sleep
adolescents	8 to 10 hours of sleep
adults	6 to 9 hours of sleep

Have children use their punchout clocks to show what time they go to bed and what time they get up each morning. Ask them to write the time to the nearest hour or half hour. Demonstrate how children can use their punchout clockfaces to find the total amount of time they sleep. Tell them to compare this time to the average sleep requirements for children.

As an extension of the activity, children may also interview their family members and draw clocks showing their average amounts of sleep each night.

RETEACHING

Name _____

HALF HOUR

RETEACHING-80

Study

8 o'clock
8:00

eight-thirty
8:30

Check

Write the time.

1.
 1:00
 1:30
 2:00
 2:30

2.
 9:30
 10:00
 10:30
 11:00

3.
 4:30
 12:30
 7:00
 5:30

Macmillan/McGraw-Hill, MATHEMATICS IN ACTION
Grade 2, Chapter 8, Lesson 3, pages 251–252

Reteaching-80

PRACTICE

Name _____

HALF HOUR

PRACTICE-80

Write the time in two ways.

1. __3__ o'clock
3:00

 2. __30__ minutes after __3__
3:30

3. __30__ minutes after __7__
7:30

4. __30__ minutes after __12__
12:30

5. __9__ o'clock
9:00

6. __30__ minutes after __4__
4:30

Draw the minute hand to show the time.

7.
two-thirty

8.
half past 8

9.
30 minutes after 10

Macmillan/McGraw-Hill, MATHEMATICS IN ACTION
Grade 2, Chapter 8, Lesson 3, pages 251–252

Practice-80

ENRICHMENT

Name _____

HALF HOUR

ENRICHMENT-80

On Your Own Pair and Share In a Group

IT'S ABOUT TIME

Read each story with a partner.
Write *early*, *late*, or *on time*.

1. The school bus comes
at [8:00].
Pam gets to the corner

at
Pam is **on time**.

2. Gym class starts
at [10:30].
Rick gets to the gym

at
Rick is ___early___

3. Reading starts
at [1:30].
Toby opens her book

at
Toby is ___late___

4. The swim team meets
at [4:00].
Robin gets to the pool

at
Robin is ___early___

Answers will vary for 5 and 6.

5. My family eats dinner
at [:].
I get home at

I am _____.

6. My bedtime is
at [:].
Last night I went to
bed at

I was _____.

Macmillan/McGraw-Hill, MATHEMATICS IN ACTION
Grade 2, Chapter 8, Lesson 3, pages 251–252

Enrichment-80

Problem of the Day

The scouts were meeting at thirty minutes past eight for a bike hike. Ron got to the meeting place at 9:00. Dan got there at 8:30. Joe got there at 8:00. Which scout was early for the hike? [Joe] Which scout was late for the hike? [Ron] Which scout was on time? [Dan]

AT·A·GLANCE p. 253

LESSON OBJECTIVE
Determine elapsed time.

ASSIGNMENT GUIDE

COURSE	EXERCISES
Basic	p. 253: All
Average	p. 253: All
Challenge	p. 253: All

MATERIALS
Classroom Materials demonstration clock (optional)
Manipulatives analog clock punchout per child

Teacher Resources
Crit. Think. 15

Name _____

party time

Plan a party that starts at 2:00
and ends at 4:30.

What We Will Do	From	To
Puppet Show		
Answers will vary.		

Choices of Things to Do	How Long They Last
Magic Show	60 Minutes
Puppet Show	30 Minutes
Balloon Game	60 Minutes
Lunch	30 Minutes
Clown Show	60 Minutes
Dance	30 Minutes
Card Game	30 Minutes

253

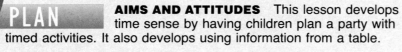

1 PLAN

AIMS AND ATTITUDES This lesson develops time sense by having children plan a party with timed activities. It also develops using information from a table.

You can encourage a sense of independence among children by telling them that they may choose any activities they wish in planning the party, so long as the party ends at 4:30.

MANAGEMENT The activity is intended for all children and has been designed for independent work. It is also appropriate for pairs of children.

You may wish to prepare ahead of time a sheet of blank clockfaces for each child to use in the **EXTEND** section of this lesson.

2 GUIDE

Ask children to model various times using a punchout analog clock.

■ **Show 10:00 on your clock.**
■ **What time will it be in 30 minutes? Show the time on your clock.** [10:30]
■ **Your clock shows 10:30. What time will it be in 60 minutes?** [11:30]
■ **What time does school end? Show the time on your clock.** [3:00]
■ **What time will it be 60 minutes later? Show the time on your clock.** [4:00]

Repeat the activity for other times, asking similar questions.

For Students Acquiring English (SAE)

For extra practice with elapsed time, use the format on page 253 to have the class plan a school day. Set up heterogeneous groups. Write on the chalkboard a list of activities for the day and the time allowed for each of the activities. Direct each group to make a new schedule for the day and share it with the class.

Read with children the directions and chart on page 253. Ask questions about the chart so that you are sure children know how to use it.

■ **Is it possible to do all the activities at this party?** [No.]

■ **Why not?** [The party ends at 4:30.]

Point out to children that the first activity has already been planned and that it ends at 2:30. They are to continue planning the party and draw the times on the remaining clocks. Remind them that the party must end at 4:30.

Allow children who may have difficulty drawing the hands on the clockfaces to model the times on a demonstration clock.

3 EXTEND Provide each child with a sheet of blank clockfaces and let them repeat the activity using the table on page 253. This time, children should plan another party that begins at 11:00 and ends at 1:30.

CHAPTER 8

Extra Practice

Hour, pages 249–250 . . . .

Write each time in two ways.

I.

__2__ o'clock

`2 : 00`

2.

__5__ o'clock

`5 : 00`

3.

__11__ o'clock

`11 : 00`

Half Hour, pages 251–252 . . . .

Write each time in two ways.

I.

__30__ minutes after __3__

__3:30__

2.

__30__ minutes after __7__

__7:30__

3.

__30__ minutes after __12__

__12:30__

4.

__30__ minutes after __6__

__6:30__

254 two hundred fifty-four

ADDITIONAL PRACTICE

p. 249 Show children a large demonstration clock for these activities.

Write each time in two ways.

1.   [4] o'clock
[4:00]

2.   [8] o'clock
[8:00]

3.    [3] o'clock
[3:00]

4.   [10] o'clock
[10:00]

p. 251 *Write each time in two ways.*

1. [30] minutes after [2]
[2:30]

2. [30] minutes after [5]
[5:30]

3. [30] minutes after [1]
[1:30]

4. [30] minutes after [4]
[4:30]

CHAPTER 8 • Lesson 5

Problem Solving

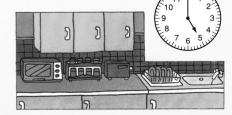

Strategy: Working Backward

Lee took the turkey out of
the oven at 5:00.
It took 4 hours to cook.
What time did she put the
turkey in the oven?

What do I know?

It is 5:00.
The turkey took
4 hours to cook.

**What do I need
to find out?**

What time did she
put the turkey in
the oven?

What can I do?

Use the clock
to work backward.
Start with 5.
4, 3, 2, 1.

She put the turkey in the oven
at 1:00.

Macmillan/McGraw-Hill

Chapter 8   Time

two hundred fifty-five **255**

---

1 PREPARE **WARM-UP** To prepare children for working backward to solve problems, have them count backward from 12 to 3, 6 to 1, 11 to 4, and 7 to 5.

2 TEACH **MODELING** Assign children to work in pairs. Give each pair of children a punchout clockface. Explain that you will read a problem aloud and they should use the clock to model the time in the problem.

Jeff helped David fix his bicycle. They worked for 3 hours. They finished at 6:00. What time did they start?

■ **What time did you show on your clocks?** [6:00]

■ **What do you know about the time the boys worked?** [They worked for 3 hours. They finished at 6:00.]

■ **What do you need to find out?** [what time they started working]
■ **What can you do to find out what time it was 3 hours earlier than 6:00?** [Count back 3 hours on the clock.]
■ **What time did they start?** [3:00]

PUPIL'S EDITION pp. 255-256

Page 255 Have a volunteer read the problem at the top of the page.

■ **What do you know?** [Mom took the turkey out of the oven at 5:00. It took 4 hours to cook.]

■ **What do you need to find out?** [You need to find out what time Mom put the turkey in the oven.]

■ **What do you need to do?** [Use the clock to count backward 4 hours from 5:00.]

Solve.

1. The movie ended at 7:00.
   It was 2 hours long.
   What time did the movie start?

   5:00

2. Every Saturday Lee works at
   the bakery for 3 hours.
   He finishes work at 12:00.
   What time does he begin working?

   9:00

3. Charles took an ice-skating lesson.
   It ended at 11:00.
   It lasted for 2 hours.
   What time did the lesson start?

   9:00

4. The football game began at 1:00.
   It lasted for 3 hours.
   What time did the game end?

   4:00

5. The Explorer Club hiked
   along the trail for 5 hours.
   They reached the end of the
   trail at 6:00.
   What time did they begin hiking?

   1:00

256 two hundred fifty-six

For Students Acquiring English (SAE)

Scan the pages for vocabulary that may be new to SAE children. Introduce new words by using visuals, gestures, and body movements to convey meaning. Ask questions frequently to check comprehension. Demonstrate with a real clock how to work backward to find the time. Allow students to use paper clocks to complete the lesson.

TEACHER to TEACHER

MANIPULATIVES TIP My children benefit from using the clocks to count backward. They are better able to visualize the amount of time that passes.

TEACHER to TEACHER

COOPERATIVE LEARNING TIP My students like to work in groups of two pairs to develop the reasoning for working backward. First both pairs work with their partners to solve the problems in the text. Next one partner makes up a new problem and the second partner develops a working-backward strategy with the first partner's help. They then switch roles. Finally each pair poses a problem to the other pair, who must solve it with this method. Each pair then checks the strategy and conclusions of the other pair.

Have children use their clocks to count backward. Work through the example problem.

■ **What did you learn?** [Possible response: You can work backward to solve a problem.]

Encourage children to explain other ways to solve this problem.

Check for Understanding

■ **What if Mom took the turkey out of the oven at 7:00 and it took 5 hours to cook? What time would she have put the turkey in the oven?** [2:00]

Page 256 Read the problems with the children as necessary.

GUIDED PRACTICE ex. 1: Work through problem 1 with the children. Make sure they understand how to solve the problem by working backward.

3 PRACTICE•APPLY PRACTICE ex. 2–5

CLOSE Guide children to summarize the lesson:

■ **How do you know when you can work backward to solve a problem?** [Possible response: When you know the ending number or time, you can solve the problem by working backward to find the starting number or time.]

MAC Activity 162
On Your Own Pair and Share In a Group

WRITING MATHEMATICS ▪ *WHAT IS THERE TO DO?*

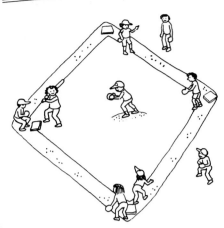

Materials   punchout clockfaces

Procedure   Discuss with children what activities they like to do on a Saturday, such as playing baseball, riding a bicycle, or reading a book. Have children estimate in hours how long each activity might take. List five to ten activities and the times they require on the chalkboard. Give each child a clockface.

Tell children that they are to plan a day that ends at 5:00. Have them write this time on a sheet of paper. Then have them select activities from the list on the chalkboard and copy them on their paper. Tell children to list the starting time next to each activity based on the times on the list.

After they are finished, discuss with the children how many activities they were able to plan in a day. Be sure children understand that they will not be able to fit in everything, and that some children had to start their day earlier in order to do what they had planned.

▲
**MAC Activity 162:
Average-to-Challenge**

MATH AND LANGUAGE ARTS ▪ *WHAT IS THE TIME?*

MAC Activity 161
On Your Own Pair and Share In a Group

Materials   punchout clockfaces

Procedure   Separate the class into small groups. Give each group a punchout clockface. Write a list on the chalkboard of school activities that take 1 hour, 2 hours, and 3 hours. Write the activities in the order in which they happen and the amount of time each one takes.

Then have children model the time school is over on their clocks. Have them work backward on their clocks to find and write the time each activity starts. Have children check each other's clockfaces to be sure they all show the same time.

▲
**MAC Activity 161:
Basic-to-Average**

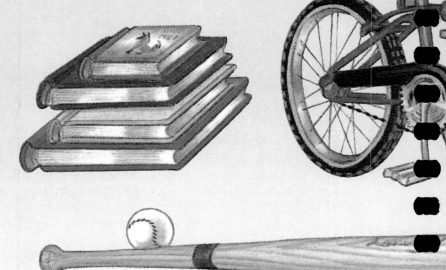

RETEACHING

Name

PROBLEM SOLVING STRATEGY: WORKING BACKWARD

Study

The baseball team played for 3 hours.
The game ended at 8:00.
When did the game begin?

Start at 8:00.

Count back 3 hours.

The game began at 5:00.

Check

Count back to solve.

1. Jake and his father were out shopping for 2 hours. They got home at 3:00. What time did they leave home?

   1:00

   Start here.

2. Neal worked on his airplane model for 4 hours. He finished the model at 7:00. What time did he start working?

   3:00

3. Elena worked in her garden for 3 hours. She stopped at 5:00. When did she start working?

   2:00

Reteaching-81

PRACTICE

Name

PROBLEM SOLVING STRATEGY: WORKING BACKWARD

Solve.

1. The swim team practiced for 3 hours. They finished at 1:00. What time did they start? 10:00

2. Miguel delivers newspapers. It takes him 2 hours. This morning he finished at 8:00. What time did he begin? 6:00

3. Myrna works in the library for 4 hours on Saturday. She goes home at 12:00. What time does she start? 8:00

4. Tom had a music lesson. It ended at 11:00. It lasted for 2 hours. What time did the lesson start? 9:00

5. Corey rode his bike for 5 hours. He stopped at 9:00. What time did he start? 4:00

Practice-81

ENRICHMENT

Name

PROBLEM SOLVING

On Your Own   Pair and Share   In a Group

TIME GOES BY

Mr. Clock Watcher plans his day to the exact hour.
Today he did 5 things between breakfast and dinner.
He had dinner at 7:00.
What time did he **start** each activity?
Use the clock to help you find the times.

Mr. Clock Watcher finished breakfast.

8:00   He spent 1 hour cleaning the house.

9:00   He worked in the garden for 3 hours.

12:00   It took him 1 hour to make and eat lunch.

1:00   He worked 4 hours in the garage fixing his car.

5:00   It took him another 2 hours to make dinner.

Mr. Clock Watcher goes to bed 4 hours after dinner. What time does he go to bed?

11:00

Enrichment-81

Problem of the Day

Rhonda has a science project that will take her 5 hours to do. She has to be finished by 6:00. What time should she start her project to make sure she will finish on time?   [1:00; work backward 5 hours from 6:00 to 1:00. She could start any time before 1:00.]

LESSON OBJECTIVE
Tell time to the quarter hour.

ASSIGNMENT GUIDE

COURSE	EXERCISES
Basic	p. 257: 1–5; p. 258: 2–6, Reasoning
Average	p. 257: 1–5; p. 258: 2–6, Reasoning
Challenge	p. 257: 1–5; p. 258: 2–6, Reasoning

MATERIALS
Classroom Materials demonstration clock, digital clock
Manipulatives clockface and digital clock punchouts per child

Teacher Resources
Reteaching 82   Practice 82   Enrichment 82
Prob. Solv. 38   MAC Act. 163, 164

SKILLS TRACE

TIME	
Explore (Concrete) 248	Develop/Understand (Transitional/Abstract) 249–250, 251–252, 257–258, 259–260, 261–262
Practice 254, 267, 268, 269–270, 273, 301, 308	Apply 253, 255–256, 263–264, 265, 266, 272, 285

Name _____

Quarter Hour

5 o'clock

5:00

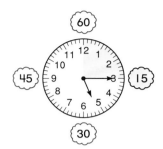

▶ 15 minutes after 5

▶ five-fifteen

▶ quarter after 5

5:15

Write the time.

1.
__15__ minutes after __5__
5:15

2.
__30__ minutes after __12__
12:30

3.
__15__ minutes after __9__
9:15

4.
__15__ minutes after __6__
6:15

5. Talk about what you can do in 15 minutes. Answers will vary.
What takes more than 15 minutes to do? Answers will vary.

Chapter 8   Time   two hundred fifty-seven **257**

PREPARE   **WARM-UP**   To review times to the hour and half hour, display a demonstration clock and lead children in counting five-minute intervals around the clock. Write these times on the chalkboard and have volunteers set the clock to show each time.

2:00, 2:30   10:00, 10:30
7:00, 7:30   12:00, 12:30
8:00, 8:30   3:00, 3:30

TEACH   **MODELING**   Show 8:00 on the demonstration clock. Have children model this time on their punch-out clockfaces. Move the minute hand to 8:15. Explain that the hand has moved one-quarter of the way around the clock. Move, or note movement of, the hour hand to a little past the 8. Have children move the hands on their clocks to this new position as they count off by fives.

■ **How many minutes did you count?** [15 minutes]

Explain that the clock now shows a **quarter after** 8, or 15 minutes after 8. Write the time 8:15 on the chalkboard and have it read aloud. Repeat this procedure with several other times to the quarter hour.

PUPIL'S EDITION pp. 257-258

Page 257   Have children use their punchout clocks as you guide them through the example at the top of the page.

Check for Understanding

■ **Where is the minute hand when it is 15 minutes after 6?**
[on the 3]

Draw the minute hand.

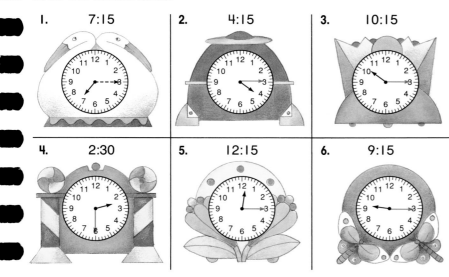

1. 7:15
2. 4:15
3. 10:15
4. 2:30
5. 12:15
6. 9:15

···· Reasoning ····

Read the list below.
Write the place where Grandpa
should be at each time.

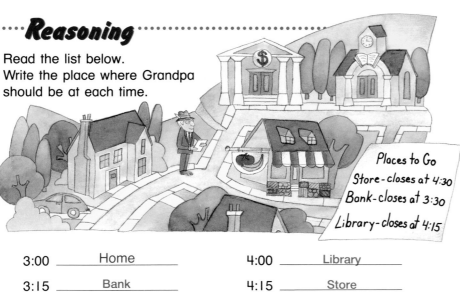

Places to Go
Store - closes at 4:30
Bank - closes at 3:30
Library - closes at 4:15

3:00 _____Home_____ 4:00 _____Library_____

3:15 _____Bank_____ 4:15 _____Store_____

GUIDED PRACTICE ex. 1–5: For reteaching, use Common Error
and Remediation or Alternative Strategy.

Page 258 Guide children through ex. 1.

3 PRACTICE•APPLY **PRACTICE** ex. 2–6

REASONING You may want to have children work in groups to complete the activity.

CLOSE Guide children to summarize the lesson:

■ **If the hour hand is just past the 12 and the minute hand is on
the 3, what time is it?** [12:15]

ACTIVITY Common Error and Remediation

MATERIALS paper circles, crayons, demonstration clock

Some children may confuse half hour and quarter hour. Work
individually with each child. Give the child two paper circles.
Have the child fold one circle in half and color the right half,
then fold the other circle in quarters and color the upper right
quarter. Set 8:30 on the clock. Show how the first circle matches
the position of the minute hand. Reset the clock to 8:15; compare
a quarter hour with the second circle. Repeat with other times.

For Students Acquiring English (SAE)

Provide extra oral practice of the different ways of saying the
quarter hour. Pair SAE children with non-SAE children. Less
literate SAE children should indicate their responses for their
partners to write.

ACTIVITY ALTERNATIVE TEACHING STRATEGY

MATERIALS red and blue chalk, red and blue crayons

VISUAL Draw three clock faces on the chalkboard showing
9:00, 9:15, and 9:30. Use red chalk for the hour hands and blue
for the minute hands. Have children write each time. Tell them
to use red crayons for the hours and blue for the minutes. Repeat
with other series of times.

MAC Activity 163:
Basic-to-Average ▼

MANIPULATIVES ▪ CLOCK BINGO

MAC Activity 163

On Your Own   Pair and Share   In a Group

4:15	8:15	9:15	1:15
2:15	12:15	3:15	10:15

10:15	12:15	11:15	2:15
3:15	4:15	6:15	8:15

Materials oaktag, marking pens, demonstration clock, markers or chips

Setup Cut out 6″ x 12″ pieces of oaktag. Make eight sections on each bingo-type card, two rows of four boxes.

Procedure Give each player a bingo card. Have players write a different time to the quarter hour in each box, such as 4:15, 8:15, 12:15, 3:15. Remind children that they should not look at each other's boards.

Assign a child to be the caller. The caller sets the demonstration clock to show times to the quarter hour and then calls out the time. The players who have a match on their card will cover it with a chip.

To Win The first player to cover a horizontal row wins the game.

MAC Activity 164:
Average-to-Challenge ▼

MATH AND LANGUAGE ARTS ▪ TIME BOOK

MAC Activity 164

On Your Own   Pair and Share   In a Group

I get out of school at 2:15.

I have piano lessons at 4:30.

I eat dinner at 6:00.

Materials construction paper, crayons

Distribute a sheet of construction paper and crayons to each child. Tell children that they are going to make a time book. Have them fold the paper in half vertically to make little booklets. Explain that on each of the four pages they are to draw a picture of a clock and to show the time. Then have them write a sentence telling what they usually do at that time of day or night. Some children may wish to add pictures illustrating each activity.

RETEACHING-82

Name

QUARTER HOUR

Study

9:00   9:15

Check

Ring the correct time.

1. 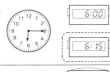 5:00 / **6:15**

2. 10:15 / 10:30

3. 9:30 / 9:00

4. 2:00 / 2:15

5. 11:30 / 11:15

6. 9:00 / 9:15

Macmillan/McGraw-Hill, MATHEMATICS IN ACTION
Grade 2, Chapter 8, Lesson 6, pages 257–258

Reteaching-82

PRACTICE-82

Name

QUARTER HOUR

Write the time.

1.  **8** o'clock
   8:00

2.   **15** minutes after **8**
   8:15

3. **15** minutes after **6**
   6:15

4. **15** minutes after **9**
   9:15

5. **30** minutes after **2**
   2:30

6. **15** minutes after **5**
   5:15

Draw the minute hand.

7. ten-fifteen

8. 15 minutes after 7

9. quarter past 11

Macmillan/McGraw-Hill, MATHEMATICS IN ACTION
Grade 2, Chapter 8, Lesson 6, pages 257–258

Practice-82

ENRICHMENT

ENRICHMENT-82

Name

QUARTER HOUR

On Your Own   Pair and Share   In a Group

SHOW TIME

Six Screen Cinema			
1. Dogs, Dogs, Dogs	3:15	4. The Red Jacket	2:30
2. The Last Dragon	5:30	5. Heidi	5:00
3. Sam's Kids	4:15	6. Big Wish	3:30

Work with a partner to find the answers.

1. Which movie is shown first?
   The Red Jacket

2. Which movie is shown last?
   The Last Dragon

3. The movie "Sam's Kids" lasts 2 hours. What time does it end?
   6:15

4. The movie "Dogs, Dogs, Dogs" lasts 1 hour 15 minutes. What time does it end?
   4:30

5. Marcy is to meet her mom at 5:00. The movie "Big Wish" lasts 1 hour 30 minutes. Will Marcy be out in time?
   yes

6. Tom leaves his house at 4:15. It takes him a quarter hour to get to the theatre. What is the first movie he could see?
   Heidi

Macmillan/McGraw-Hill, MATHEMATICS IN ACTION
Grade 2, Chapter 8, Lesson 6, pages 257–258

Enrichment-82

Problem of the Day

It takes Pia 15 minutes to wash a window. She has eight windows to wash. If she starts at 9:00, what time will she finish the job? [11:00]

AT·A·GLANCE pp. 259-260

LESSON OBJECTIVE
Tell time at five-minute intervals.

ASSIGNMENT GUIDE

COURSE	EXERCISES
Basic	p. 259: 1–4; p. 260: 2–3, Reasoning
Average	p. 259: 1–4; p. 260: 2–3, Reasoning
Challenge	p. 259: 1–4; p. 260: 2–3, Reasoning
Extra Practice, p. 267	Practice Plus, p. 268

MATERIALS
Classroom Materials demonstration clock, digital clock
Manipulatives analog and digital clockface punchouts per pair

Teacher Resources
Reteaching 83   Practice 83   Enrichment 83
MAC Act. 165, 166   Calculator 8
Math Anthology, pp. 170–172

SKILLS TRACE

TIME	
Explore (Concrete) 248	Develop/Understand (Transitional/Abstract) 249–250, 251–252, 257–258, 259–260, 261–262
Practice 254, 267, 268, 269–270, 273, 301, 308	Apply 253, 255–256, 263–264, 265, 266, 272, 285

See **MANIPULATIVES PLUS 51–52**, pp. 246M–246N.

1 PREPARE **WARM-UP** To review telling time, show the following times on a demonstration clock.

5:15, 7:30, 9:15, 6:30

Have children say the time in various ways; for example, 5:15, 15 minutes after 5, and a quarter after 5.

2 TEACH **DRAMATIZING** Have children stand and raise their right hands. Tell them that the hand is the minute hand and that it is in the twelve o'clock position. Demonstrate how to move the "minute" hand in five-minute intervals to make a complete circle showing one hour. Have children repeat the activity.

Show 4:00 on a demonstration clock. As children move their hands, have them skip-count the minutes by five as you move the hands of

---

Five Minutes

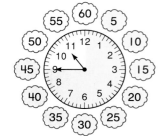

 45 minutes after 10

You can count minutes by fives.

Look at the hour hand on each clock.
Where does it point? Why?
The hour hand moves from 10 to 11.

Working Together

Use an 🕐 and a ▦ .
Show the time on both clocks.

	Show	Count by fives. Show	Write the time.
1.	4:00	4:15	15 minutes after 4
2.	12:00	12:20	20 minutes after 12
3.	3:00	3:35	35 minutes after 3
4.	5:00	5:45	45 minutes after 5

Macmillan/McGraw-Hill

the clock to show the time in five-minute intervals. Repeat by beginning at other hours.

PUPIL'S EDITION pp. 259-260

Page 259 Guide children through the examples at the top of the page. Have them use their clockfaces as they count off minutes by fives. Discuss how the hour hand advances on the four clockfaces. Have children predict where the hour hand would be at 15 minutes after 10:45. [pointing to 11]

Check for Understanding

■ **What time is it when the hour hand is almost on the 7 and the minute hand is on the 10?** [6:50]

WORKING TOGETHER Have children work with a partner using analog and digital clockfaces.

Use a 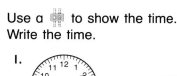 to show the time.
Write the time.

1.

5 minutes later

`4:10`   `4:15`

2.

10 minutes later

`8:30`   `8:40`

3.

5 minutes earlier

`10:15`   `10:10`

····· *Reasoning* ·····

Read the schedule.

COUNTY FAIR

5:15 Sack Race	6:10 Pet Show
5:40 Watermelon Eating Contest	7:20 Barbecue

FINISH

1. Write the time.

4:55

The Sack Race begins
in about

10 minutes   (20 minutes)

2. Write the time.

7:05

The Pet Show just ended.
It took about

35 minutes   (55 minutes)

· ·

260 two hundred sixty

Extra Practice, page 267 *Practice Plus,* page 268

ALTERNATIVE TEACHING STRATEGY

MATERIALS analog clockface per child; Teacher Aids
Transparency 8, overhead projector

VISUAL/KINESTHETIC Move the hands of a clockface on the
overhead transparency to show 4:00. Have children show 4:00
on their clockfaces and identify the positions of the hour and
minute hands. Repeat with these times: 4:05, 4:10, 4:15, and so
on.

For Students Acquiring English (SAE)

Pair SAE children with non-SAE children for Working Together.
Write the daily class schedule on the chalkboard. Provide extra
oral practice with **later** and **earlier,** which may be difficult for
SAE children. For Reasoning, define **sack race** and **pet show** to
make the problems more comprehensible.

ACTIVITY *Common Error and Remediation*

MATERIALS drawing paper; analog and digital clockfaces (or
punchouts)

Some children may not be able to read times at five-minute
intervals. Work individually with each child. Tape an analog
clockface to a sheet of paper and label the five-minute intervals
around the clock perimeter. Have the child skip-count by fives
while moving the minute hand around the dial. Then show
various times on a digital clock and have the child show the
same time on the analog clockface.

GUIDED PRACTICE ex. 1–4: For reteaching, use Common Error
and Remediation or Alternative Strategy.

Page 260 Guide children through ex. 1.

*Mathematics
and Literature*

3 PRACTICE•APPLY **PRACTICE** ex. 2–3

REASONING Read the schedule for the children. Explain that for
each problem, they are to find the times based on the clock and the
schedule.

Read *Maxie* to the class. As you read, pause whenever a specific time
is mentioned. Have a volunteer write the time on the chalkboard as
the others make their clockfaces show it. At the end of the story, discuss the importance of Maxie's routines to everyone around her.

C L O S E Guide children to summarize the lesson:
■ **Pretend it is now 5:20. What time would it be in 10 minutes?**
[5:30]

■ **Pretend it is now 7:30. What time would it be in 5 minutes?**
[7:35]

MAC Activity 166

MATH AND SCIENCE ■ ALL DAY LONG

On Your Own   Pair and Share   In a Group

Materials   drawing paper

Tell children that the sun rises and sets a few minutes later or earlier each day depending upon the season of the year. Explain that the longest day of the year is usually on or near June 21 and that the shortest day is usually on or near December 21. Days and nights are about equal in length on or around March 21 and September 21.

Provide information about sunrise and sunset for a specific day from the weather section of a daily newspaper. Round it to the nearest five-minute interval. Then using this information, have children draw clocks to show when the sun rises and when it sets. Then ask children to use their clocks to calculate the number of hours and minutes of daylight.

`7:07`   `6:27`

▲
**MAC Activity 166:
Average-to-Challenge**

LOGICAL THINKING ■ *WHAT IS THE TIME?*

MAC Activity 165

On Your Own   Pair and Share   In a Group

Materials   punchout clockfaces

Have children work in pairs. Explain that one child is to set a punchout clockface, keeping it hidden from the other child. Then the first child describes the position of the hands and asks a question; for example, "The minute hand points to the 5. The hour hand is between the 12 and the 1. What is the time?" The second child gives the answer. Then have children reverse roles and repeat the activity.

▲
**MAC Activity 165:
Basic-to-Average**

RETEACHING-83

Name

FIVE MINUTES

Study

7:00   7:05   7:10

Check

Match the time on the clocks.

1.

| 2:15 | 2:00 | 2:45 | 2:05 | 2:35 |

Write the time.

| 6:15 | 9:35 | 11:20 | 1:50 | 4:30 |

Reteaching-83

Macmillan/McGraw-Hill, MATHEMATICS IN ACTION
Grade 2, Chapter 8, Lesson 7, pages 259–260

PRACTICE-83

Name

FIVE MINUTES

Write the time.

1. __5__ minutes after __2__
2:05

5 minutes earlier
2:00

2. __10__ minutes after __4__
4:10

10 minutes later
4:20

3. __15__ minutes after __8__
8:15

15 minutes later
8:30

4. __30__ minutes after __10__
10:30

30 minutes earlier
10:00

5. __55__ minutes after __3__
3:55

10 minutes earlier
3:45

6. __10__ minutes after __9__
9:10

30 minutes later
9:40

Practice-83

Macmillan/McGraw-Hill, MATHEMATICS IN ACTION
Grade 2, Chapter 8, Lesson 7, pages 259–260

ENRICHMENT-83

Name

FIVE MINUTES

On Your Own   Pair and Share   In a Group

TIME OUT

Time yourself doing each thing.
Write the time you start.
Write the time you stop.
Find how long each thing took.

8:02

8:28

I began breakfast at 8:02. I finished at 8:28. From 8:02 to 8:28 is 26 minutes.

| | | Time Started. | Time Finished. | How Long? |
Answers will vary.

1. Getting dressed ___:___ ___:___ _____

2. Brushing teeth ___:___ ___:___ _____

3. Making bed ___:___ ___:___ _____

4. Going to school ___:___ ___:___ _____

5. Eating lunch ___:___ ___:___ _____

6. Coming home ___:___ ___:___ _____

Enrichment-83

Macmillan/McGraw-Hill, MATHEMATICS IN ACTION
Grade 2, Chapter 8, Lesson 7, pages 259–260

Problem of the Day

Tim practices the horn for 45 minutes beginning at 2:40. Pam practices the drum for 20 minutes beginning at 3:05. Who finishes practicing first?
[They both finish at 3:25.]

AT·A·GLANCE pp. 261-262

LESSON OBJECTIVES
Read and understand information on a calendar.
Use a calendar to solve problems.

ASSIGNMENT GUIDE

COURSE	EXERCISES
Basic	p. 261: 1–6; p. 262: 2–5
Average	p. 261: 1–6; p. 262: 2–5
Challenge	p. 261: 1–6; p. 262: 2–5
Extra Practice, p. 267	

MATERIALS
Classroom Materials large calendar for the current month

Teacher Resources
Reteaching 84   Practice 84   Enrichment 84
MAC Act. 167, 168

SKILLS TRACE

TIME	
Explore (Concrete) 248	Develop/Understand (Transitional/Abstract) 249–250, 251–252, 257–258, 259–260, 261–262
Practice 254, 267, 268, 269–270, 273, 301, 308	**Apply** 253, 255–256, 263–264, 265, 266, 272, 285

Calendar

Months of a Year

1. How many days are in a week? **7** days

2. How many months are in a year? **12** months

3. How many days are in June? **30** days

4. How many days are in September? **30** days

5. Which month has the fewest days?

_____ February _____

6. Which is the second month of the year?

_____ February _____

Macmillan/McGraw-Hill

1 PREPARE

WARM-UP To prepare children for using information on a calendar, have children count in order by ones from 1 to 31. Then ask a child to choose a number from 1 to 20, such as 11. Call on another volunteer to say the number that comes just after 11. [12] Call on a third volunteer to say the number that comes just after 12, and so on. Continue with other numbers and other volunteers.

2 TEACH

DISCUSSING Display this month's calendar or draw a large calendar on chart paper. Have the days of the week read aloud. Point to dates randomly and have those read aloud. Record children's birthdays or special class events for that month. Then ask questions about the information on the calendar, such as:

■ **How many days is it until we go to the zoo (or some other class trip)?**
■ **What day will (child's name) celebrate her birthday?**
■ **When will the class go to the Special Assembly?** [Answers will vary.]

PUPIL'S EDITION pp. 261-262

Page 261 Discuss the display at the top of the page with the children. Have the names of the months of the year read aloud.

Check for Understanding
■ **Which is the first month of the year?** [January]
■ **Which is the last month of the year?** [December]

Solve.

November

Sun.	Mon.	Tues.	Wed.	Thurs.	Fri.	Sat.
				1	2	3
4	5	6	7	8	9	10
11	12	13	14	15	16	17
18	19	20	21	22	23	24
25	26	27	28	29	30	

1. Adam has a piano lesson once a week on Monday. How many lessons will he have in November?

   __4__ lessons

2. Nia's birthday is on November 8. She will have a party on the Saturday after her birthday. On what date will she have a party?

   November __10__

3. The next to last Thursday in November is Thanksgiving. What date is that?

   November __22__

4. Write a calendar for this month. Check students' answers.

Sun.	Mon.	Tues.	Wed.	Thurs.	Fri.	Sat.

5. Write three questions about your calendar. Have a partner solve them. Answers will vary.

Use your own paper.

Extra Practice, page 267

MEETING INDIVIDUAL NEEDS

ACTIVITY *Common Error and Remediation*

MATERIALS large calendar for the current month

Some children may have difficulty reading a calendar. Work individually with each child. Ask the child to point to the 15th on the calendar and name the day of the week on which the 15th occurs. Repeat for other dates. Then name a day of the week and ask the child to tell you the dates listed on the calendar for that day.

ONGOING ASSESSMENT MATH JOURNAL

INTERVIEW Provide the current month's calendar. **(1) What day of the week is [month] 8th? (2) How would you find the date of the second Monday in [month]? (3) How many Fridays are there in [month]?**

JOURNAL WRITING You may wish to have children record their responses in their math journals.

ACTIVITY ALTERNATIVE TEACHING STRATEGY

MATERIALS index cards

KINESTHETIC Write the names of the months on cards, a different name on each card. Prepare a set of number cards from 1 to 31. Have volunteers arrange the cards for the names of the months in order. Then have them arrange the number cards under one month in numerical order.

GUIDED PRACTICE ex. 1–6: For reteaching, use Common Error and Remediation or Alternative Strategy.

Page 262 Discuss the calendar shown at the top of the page. Have ex. 1 read aloud. Explain how children can find the answer. [by counting the number of Mondays in the month]

3 PRACTICE•APPLY **PRACTICE** ex. 2–5

CLOSE Guide children to summarize the lesson:

■ **What are some of the ways people can use a calendar?** [possible responses: to plan ahead; to record events, holidays, and birthdays]

MATH AND PHYSICAL EDUCATION ▪ PIN THE CALENDAR

MAC Activity 167

On Your Own   Pair and Share   In a Group

Materials   calendar pages, stickers

Setup   Take the children to the gym or an open area. Tape four calendar pages in a row across a wall at the average child's height. Assign children to four teams and give each child a small sticker. Mark a starting line for each team. Have each team line up behind the starting line and directly across from a calendar.

Procedure   Tell children that you will say a number aloud. Then the first team member will run to the team's calendar, place the sticker on that date, and then run back to the end of the team's line. If the sticker is placed correctly, the team scores one point. The team member who runs back to the line first scores 2 points for his or her team. After each round, record the scores or appoint a scorekeeper.

To Win   The team with the most points at the end of the game is the winner.

MAC Activity 167:
Basic-to-Average ▶

MATH AND CONSUMERS ▪ A SHOPPING TRIP

MAC Activity 168

On Your Own   Pair and Share   In a Group

Materials   current month's calendar page

Give each child a copy of a calendar page for this month. Tell children to pretend that they are going on a shopping trip. Explain that you will read some problems aloud and they will use their calendars to find the answers. [Answers will depend on the month being used.]

1. You buy a present for your mom on Sunday. The salesperson tells you it will be delivered eight days later. On what day will it be delivered? [Monday]

2. A sale begins on the second Thursday of the month. What is the date?
   The sale lasts three days. When is the sale over?

3. The toy store has sale days every Tuesday of this month. How many sale days are there?

Continue the activity with similar problems.

▲
MAC Activity 168:
Average-to-Challenge

RETEACHING-84

Name

CALENDAR

Study

October						
Sunday	Monday	Tuesday	Wednesday	Thursday	Friday	Saturday
	1	2	3	4	5	6
7	8	9	10	11	12	13
14	15	16	17	18	19	20
21	22	23	24	25	26	27
28	29	30	31			

September comes before October.

November comes after October.

Check

1. How many days are in October? __31__

2. How many Mondays in October? __5__

3. How many Fridays in October? __4__

4. How many days in a week? __7__

5. October is the tenth month. Which is the ninth month? __September__

6. Is your birthday in October? __Answers will vary.__

Macmillan/McGraw-Hill, MATHEMATICS IN ACTION
Grade 2, Chapter 8, Lesson 8, pages 261–262

Reteaching-84

MACMILLAN McGRAW-HILL

PRACTICE-84

Name

CALENDAR

June						
May						
April						
March						
February						
January						
S	M	T	W	T	F	S
	1	2	3	4	5	6
7	8	9	10	11	12	13
14	15	16	17	18	19	20
21	22	23	24	25	26	27
28	29	30	31			

December						
November						
October						
September						
August						
July						
S	M	T	W	T	F	S
	1	2	3	4	5	6	7
8	9	10	11	12	13	14
15	16	17	18	19	20	21
22	23	24	25	26	27	28
29	30	31				

1. How many months in a year? __12__

2. How many Sundays in July? __5__

3. The children are having a picnic. on the Fourth of July. What day is the picnic? __Wednesday__

4. Jenna's birthday is on the third Tuesday in January. On what date is her birthday? __January 16__

Macmillan/McGraw-Hill, MATHEMATICS IN ACTION
Grade 2, Chapter 8, Lesson 8, pages 261–262

Practice-84

MACMILLAN McGRAW-HILL

ENRICHMENT-84

Name

CALENDAR

On Your Own   Pair and Share   In a Group

A BUSY MONTH
Color the dates.

-))) blue))) first day of school, September 4
-))) red))) piano lesson, September 20
-))) green))) science club, second Wednesday
-))) yellow))) party, Saturday after the first day of school
-))) purple))) dentist, day after science club

September						
Sunday	Monday	Tuesday	Wednesday	Thursday	Friday	Saturday
						1
2	3	4 b	5	6	7	8 y
9	10	11	12 g	13 p	14	15
16	17	18	19	20 r	21	22
23/30	24	25	26	27	28	29

1. What is the last day of summer vacation? __September 3__

2. What date comes after September 30? __October 1__

Macmillan/McGraw-Hill, MATHEMATICS IN ACTION
Grade 2, Chapter 8, Lesson 8, pages 261–262

Enrichment-84

MACMILLAN McGRAW-HILL

Problem of the Day

Barbara left for her vacation on July 7. She came back on July 18. How long was she away on her vacation? [11 days]

AT·A·GLANCE pp. 263-264

LESSON OBJECTIVE
Use number sense to solve problems.

ASSIGNMENT GUIDE

COURSE	EXERCISES
Basic	p. 263: 1–3; p. 264: 1–5
Average	p. 263: 1–3; p. 264: 1–5
Challenge	p. 263: 1–3; p. 264: 1–5
Extra Practice, p. 267	

MATERIALS
Classroom Materials calendar, clock

Teacher Resources
Reteaching 85   Practice 85   Enrichment 85
Prob. Solv. 39   MAC Act. 169, 170

Name _____

 Problem Solving

Strategy: Using Number Sense

Doris is going to sleep.
About how long will she sleep?

 8 minutes?   8 hours?   8 days?

 Which is the correct unit? Why?
Hours; the other units are too large or too small.
Will Doris sleep for 8 hours or 80 hours? Why?
8 hours; healthy people do not sleep for 80 hours in one night.

Ring about how long.

1. Nat is going to walk his dog.
   About how long will the walk take?

   (10 minutes)   10 hours   10 days

2. Carol is going to school for the day.
   About how long will she be in school?

   1 hour   (8 hours)   20 hours

3. Dwight's family is taking a vacation.
   About how long will they be gone?

   14 minutes   14 hours   (14 days)

Macmillan/McGraw-Hill

---

1 PREPARE **WARM-UP** To prepare children for using number sense to solve problems, ask them whether they would estimate these activities in minutes, hours, days, or months:

vacation [weeks or months]   painting a room [hours]
getting dressed [minutes]   going camping [days]

2 TEACH **VISUALIZING** Display a calendar and a clock and discuss the units of time each measures. Ask children to imagine the scene described in the following problem.

Phil is helping his mother make dinner. She shows Phil how to cook the chicken. Then Phil sets the table and makes a salad. About how long does Phil work, 1 minute, 1 hour, or 1 day?

■ **Is 1 minute a sensible answer? Why?** [No; it would take longer than 1 minute to do everything Phil does.]

■ **Is 1 hour a sensible answer? Why?** [Yes; Phil might be able to do everything in 1 hour.]

PUPIL'S EDITION pp. 263-264

Page 263 Have a volunteer read the problem at the top of the page. Discuss the pictures and the time choices.

■ **What do you know?** [Doris is going to sleep.]

■ **What do you need to find out?** [You need to find out whether Doris will sleep about 8 minutes, 8 hours, or 8 days.]

Ring about how long.

1. Tina is eating lunch.
About how long will it take?

(35 minutes)   35 days   35 months

2. Ray is playing in a football game.
About how long will the game take?

2 minutes   (2 hours)   2 days

3. Dino is showing his younger
brother how to brush his teeth.
About how long do they brush?

(3 minutes)   43 minutes   83 minutes

4. The summer season is beginning.
About how long will summer last?

3 hours   3 days   (3 months)

5. Doreen is tying her shoes.
About how long will it take?

(1 minute)   21 minutes   101 minutes

Extra Practice, page 267

MEETING INDIVIDUAL NEEDS

TEACHER to TEACHER

COOPERATIVE LEARNING TIP 👫 My class enjoys adopting time-related group names and making symbols to fit the names. For instance, a group might name itself "The Speedy Foursome" and decide that their symbol will be a clock with wings. To insure that children develop **interdependence** when making the symbols, I require that they all agree on one **group product** for the symbol and decide how it will be made before their materials manager gets the materials. If a mobile is the design, each group member can make a different time symbol to hang over the group.

For Students Acquiring English (SAE)

Review the vocabulary **minutes, hours,** and **days** using visuals of activities that would use those units. Use the structure **About how long will _____ take?** orally with children.

■ **What do you need to do?** [Think of the amounts of time you sleep and decide which estimate makes the most sense.]

■ **How do people usually measure the amount of time they sleep during the night?** [in hours]

Discuss the questions on the page. Discuss why minutes and days are not sensible estimates.

■ **What did you learn?** [Possible response: When you make an estimate to solve a problem, you must think about whether it is sensible.]

Encourage children to explain other ways to solve this problem.

Check for Understanding

■ **What if Doris was washing her face and hands? Which amount of time would be the best estimate of about how long it would take her to get ready: 8 minutes, 8 hours, or 8 days?** [8 minutes]

GUIDED PRACTICE   ex. 1–3: Work through problem 1 with the children. Make sure they understand how to solve the problem by using number sense.

Page 264   Have a volunteer read the directions at the top of the page. Discuss the pictures and help children identify the activities.

3 PRACTICE•APPLY   PRACTICE   ex. 1–5

CLOSE   Guide children to summarize the lesson:

■ **How do you make a sensible estimate of time to solve a problem?** [Possible response: You use what you know and think about how long an activity would take.]

MAC ACTIVITY CENTER

MAC Activity 169:
Basic-to-Average
▼

MAC Activity 169

On Your Own   Pair and Share   In a Group

MATH AND SOCIAL STUDIES ■ WORK TIME

Materials punchout clockfaces, calendar pages, counters or punchout counters

Procedure Assign children to work in pairs. Give each pair of children a punchout clockface, a calendar page from any month, and 14 counters. Tell children that you will read them some problems. Explain that they are to work together to make an estimate to solve each problem. Then they are to move the clock hands to model the number of minutes or hours, or place counters on the calendar page to show the number of days. If they think an activity will take one or more months, they should place that many counters at the top of the calendar page.

1. Sylvia delivers mail every day. She walks to each house on her route and puts the mail in the mailbox. About how long does her daily delivery take, 3 minutes, 3 hours, or 3 days?   [3 hours]
2. Janine plants a garden. About how long does she have to wait for her vegetables to grow, 2 minutes, 2 days, or 2 months?   [2 months]

Continue the activity with similar problems.

MAC Activity 170:
Average-to-Challenge
▼

SPEAKING MATHEMATICALLY ■ A PICTURE IN TIME

MAC Activity 170

On Your Own   Pair and Share   In a Group

Materials drawing materials, index cards

Setup Prepare time cards by writing different amounts of time on index cards, such as 8 minutes, 5 days, 4 hours, 1 month. Prepare enough cards for each child to have at least 2 cards.

Procedure Put the time cards facedown on a table. Have each child choose at least two cards. Then have children draw a picture showing themselves or someone else doing a work or fun activity that takes about the amount of time shown on each card. For example, if a child picks "3 hours," he or she might draw a picture of someone playing baseball or football. Before children begin working, discuss ideas for different activities.

When children have finished, have them show and tell about their pictures. After each presentation, have volunteers estimate about how long the activity in the picture takes.

RETEACHING

PROBLEM SOLVING STRATEGY: USING NUMBER SENSE

Study

Larry is sharpening some pencils.
About how long will it take?

I day is too long	I hour is still too long	I minute is about how long it takes to sharpen pencils.

Check

Ring about how long.

1. Penny is making sandwiches.
   About how long will it take?

   (10 minutes)   10 hours

2. Tiffany's family is on a camping trip.
   About how long will they be gone?

   4 months   (4 days)

3. John is playing in a baseball game.
   About how long will the game last?

   2 days   (2 hours)

PRACTICE

PROBLEM SOLVING STRATEGY: USING NUMBER SENSE

Ring about how long.

1. George is changing his shoes.
   About how long will it take him?

   25 minutes   60 minutes   (2 minutes)

2. Lorna and her friends are going swimming.
   About how long will they be gone?

   2 months   (2 hours)   2 days

3. The winter vacation is beginning.
   About how long will it last?

   14 minutes   14 hours   (14 days)

4. Alvin is starting a summer job.
   About how long will he be working?

   3 hours   3 days   (3 months)

5. Hanna is washing her dog.
   About how long will it take her?

   I minute   (I hour)   I month

6. Tasha is setting the table.
   About how long will it take her?

   (10 minutes)   I day   I month

ENRICHMENT

PROBLEM SOLVING

A TIME FOR EVERYTHING
How long?
Write **minutes, hours, days,** or **months.**

fall season

3 months

taking a walk

30 minutes

raking leaves

2 hours

summer season

3 months

playing catch

I hour

growing tomatoes

3 months

taking off shoes

I minute

eating lunch

40 minutes

Problem of the Day

It took Lenore about 10 minutes to oil the gears on her bicycle. She washed the bicycle for 20 minutes, polished it for 30 minutes, and took a ride for an hour. How many hours did she spend working on and riding her bicycle?   [2 hours; 10 + 20 + 30 = 60 minutes, or 1 hour; 1 + 1 = 2 hours]

AT·A·GLANCE p. 265

LESSON OBJECTIVE
Make decisions about information.

ASSIGNMENT GUIDE

COURSE	EXERCISES
Basic	p. 265: 1–3
Average	p. 265: 1–3
Challenge	p. 265: 1–3

MATERIALS
Classroom Materials TV schedules

Teacher Resources
Crit. Think. 16   Prob. Solv. 40

Name _____

Decision Making

Problem Solving: Planning a Class Trip

Activity	1st Session	2nd Session
Apple Picking	12:30–1:00	1:30–2:00
Pony Rides	12:00–12:30	2:00–2:30
Hay Ride	1:00–2:00	2:00–3:00
Tractor Pull	12:00–1:00	1:00–2:00
Lunch	12:30–1:00	1:00–1:30
Cow Milking	12:00–1:00	2:00–3:00

Your class is taking a trip to a farm.
You will be at the farm from 12:00 until 3:00.
Each activity will be done at two different times.

1. What activities would you like to do
   at the farm? Make a list. Answers will vary.

   Use your own paper.

2. List each activity you will have time to do.
   Write the time you will do it.

   _____   _____

   _____   _____

   _____   _____

   _____   _____

 3. Talk about your list with a partner.
   Will you do any of the activities at the same time?

Chapter 8   Time   two hundred sixty-five   **265**

 **PREPARE**   **WARM-UP** To review time concepts, ask children
the following questions.

■ **How many minutes are in 1 hour?** [60 minutes]

■ **How many minutes are in a half hour?** [30 minutes]

■ **If you started reading at 3:00 and read for 15 minutes, what
time would it be when you stopped reading?** [3:15]

TEACH   **DISCUSSING** Distribute copies of TV schedules to
the children, or display a schedule. Discuss the information that is found on a TV schedule. Explain that people use TV
schedules so they know what television programs are on, when programs air, and on which channels to find specific programs.

Then have volunteers name their favorite TV shows and the times of
the shows. List their responses on the chalkboard. Have children use
the information to plan what they would watch if they were allowed to
watch TV for two hours.

PUPIL'S EDITION p. 265

Read the schedule at the top of the page with the children.

Check for Understanding

■ **How long is each apple-picking session?** [one-half hour]

■ **Would you be able to go on the hay ride, eat lunch, and participate in the tractor pull? Explain.** [Yes; lunch is from 12:30–1:00, the
tractor pull is from 1:00–2:00, and the second session for the hay ride
is from 2:00–3:00.]

TEACHER to TEACHER

COOPERATIVE LEARNING TIP Children might plan ways to raise money for a class trip by working in small groups. Each group member brings to class information on costs for some aspect of the trip. The small group reports its findings in a community meeting and a class list is compiled. I help children focus on ways they might earn the money. The small groups meet again to brainstorm and choose a plan. When the final decision is made, each group contributes to raising the money. The groups also plan the activities for the trip and the time it will take to do them.

For Students Acquiring English (SAE)

Point out the illustrations on the page to make sure that SAE children understand the activities. Have children act out those activities that are not shown in the illustrations.

3 PRACTICE·APPLY Have children complete ex. 1–3. Call on volunteers to tell the activities they would like to do and at what times, and then explain their decisions.

CLOSE Guide children to summarize the lesson:

■ **What should you do before you plan a class trip?** [Decide in which activities to participate, the times these activities take place, and the length of each activity.]

CLASS PROJECT

Materials chart paper

Have children work in pairs to plan another class trip. Tell children to decide where they would like to go, the activities that are available there, and the times and lengths of the activities. Distribute chart paper to each pair and have them record their schedule on a chart.

When partners have completed their project, have them, in turn, display and read their schedules. Have the rest of the class decide on the activities they would like to do.

Curriculum Connection

Math and Social Studies

Phillip was born in the
Year of the Hare.
On his Chinese calendar,
the year was 4685.
On his American calendar,
the year was 1987.

Every year in the Chinese calendar has a number
and an animal name. There are 12 different animals.
They form a pattern that repeats every 12 years.
When Phillip is 12, it will be the Year of the Hare again.

1. What is the animal for 1994? _____dog_____

2. What animal year was it when Phillip was 3? _____horse_____

3. When is the next Year of the Hare? _____1999/4697_____

Working Together

Find the year when you were born.   Check students'
Write the number for that Chinese calendar year. answers.
Make up Chinese calendar questions
your partner can answer.

WARM-UP   Ask volunteers to tell the years they
were born as you write them on the chalkboard. Ask
children for other key years they may know such as the year they
began school or the year a sibling was born. Save this list for use later
in the lesson.

Before using the page, explain that the calendar we use in the United
States is not the same one that people use in other parts of the world.
The way months and years are named and counted and the dates of
certain events may vary.

DISCUSSING   Read the opening paragraph together. Explain that Cheng's birth year is given in
two different numbers, because the Chinese began counting years before the people who use the western (or Gregorian) calendar did.

Be sure children understand that the circle-shaped picture is a special
type of chart that shows how the Chinese calendar cycle works. Help
them find the Year of the Hare on the chart by asking:

■ **What is another word for hare?** [rabbit]

■ **What does the circle-shaped picture show?** [the 12 Chinese animal years]

■ **Which way do the years go in the chart?** [clockwise, the way the
clock hands move]

■ **What do the numbers mean under each picture?** [The greater
number is the year as the Chinese count, the other number is the year
as western calendar users count.]

CULTURAL DIVERSITY

THE CHINESE CALENDAR

Chinese folklore says the traditional calendar began with the year 1 [the western year 2698 B.C.] when Huang Ti, a mythical ruler, devised a plan so farmers would know when to plant and harvest their crops. By tradition, each animal of the calendar represents characteristics that people born during that year hope to possess—the Hare is gentle and lucky, and the Snake is sensible and elegant. Today, the Chinese calendar is used to determine the Chinese New Year, other traditional holidays and celebrations, and to plan social events.

BIBLIOGRAPHY

Behrens, June. *Gung Hay Fat Choy*. Chicago: Childrens Press, 1982.

3 PRACTICE•APPLY

Have children answer the questions. To help them answer Question 2, ask:

■ **How can you figure out the year when Cheng was 3?** [Add 3 to 1987; count three years past the Year of the Hare.]

WORKING TOGETHER Divide the class into pairs. Partners can work together and help each other figure out the Chinese years and animals for the western years they have chosen. Refer children who have trouble creating a set of years to the list developed at the beginning of the lesson, or provide a list of events of general interest, such as local festivals or new buildings. Encourage partners to make up questions for each other to solve, such as: *What year comes after The Year of the Dog?*

C L O S E Guide children to summarize the lesson:
■ **What happens after the twelfth year in the Chinese calendar?** [The animal names repeat in the same order.]

EXTRA PRACTICE

Extra Practice items are provided so that children may have an opportunity for further practice.

The Additional Practice section also provides practice you may wish to assign.

Five Minutes, pages 259–260

Write the time.

1.

   11:05

2.

   2:40

3.

   6:25

Calendar, pages 261–262

1. What date is the third Saturday of this month?

   _____ January 18 _____

2. How many Mondays are in this month?

   _____ 4 _____

· **JANUARY** ·						
Sun	Mon	Tues	Wed	Thurs	Fri	Sat
				1	2	3	4
5	6	7	8	9	10	11
12	13	14	15	16	17	18
19	20	21	22	23	24	25
26	27	28	29	30	31	

Problem Solving: Using Number Sense, pages 263–264

Ring about how long.

1. Wendy will brush her teeth. About how long will it take?

   (about 10 minutes)   about 10 hours   about 10 days

2. Sal will write his name. About how long will it take?

   (about 1 minute)   about 30 minutes   about 60 minutes

Macmillan/McGraw-Hill

Chapter 8   Time   two hundred sixty-seven   **267**

ADDITIONAL PRACTICE

p. 259 Show children a large demonstration clock.

Write the time.

1. [12:25]

2. [3:50]

p. 261 Show children any month from this year's calendar. Have them answer these questions.

1. What is the first day of this month? _____

2. What date is the fourth Friday of this month? _____

3. How many Saturdays are in this month?

   _____

p. 263 *Ring how long each takes.*

1. Jan will take a picture.   [about 1 minute] about 30 minutes

2. Hal will set the table.   about 2 hours [about 2 minutes]

3. Sandy will rake the leaves.   [about 1 hour] about 5 minutes

Practice Plus

Key Skill: Half Hour, page 252 . . . .

Write each time in two ways.

1.

__30__ minutes after __11__

__11:30__

2.

__30__ minutes after __4__

__4:30__

3.

__30__ minutes after __1__

__1:30__

4.

__30__ minutes after __8__

__8:30__

Key Skill: Five Minutes, page 260 . . . .

Write the time.

1.

10 minutes earlier

12:25   12:15

2.

5 minutes later

9:05   9:10

268   two hundred sixty-eight

PRACTICE PLUS

Practice Plus is provided to supply additional practice for the two key skills in this chapter.

Key Skills
Page 252: Half Hour
Page 260: Five Minutes

The *Additional Practice* also provides practice you may wish to assign for key skills in this chapter.

ADDITIONAL PRACTICE

p. 252   Use a demonstration clock.

Write each time in two ways.

1.   [30] minutes after [12]
[12:30]

2.   [30] minutes after [9]
[9:30]

p. 260   Use a demonstration clock.

Write the time.

1.    [3] : [10]   **5 min. later** [3] : [15]

2.   [6] : [05]   **5 min. later** [6] : [10]

3.   [2] : [15]   **5 min. later** [2] : [20]

4.   [9] : [35]   **5 min. earlier** [9] : [30]

CHAPTER 8

AT·A·GLANCE pp. 269-270

OBJECTIVE
Review/test the concepts and skills presented in Chapter 8.

8A. Tell time to the hour and half hour on digital and analog clocks.
8B. Tell time to the quarter hour and five-minute intervals on digital and analog clocks.
8C. Read a calendar.
8D. Solve problems including those that involve using number sense.

Teacher Resources
Testing Program, pp. 79–90

Name _____

Chapter Review/Test

Language and Mathematics

Choose the correct words.

1. One ____half hour____ is the same as 30 minutes.

2. 60 minutes is the same as 1 ____hour____.

3. 8:20 means twenty minutes ____after____ eight o'clock.

| hour |
| half hour |
| after |

Concepts and Skills

Draw the minute hand.

4.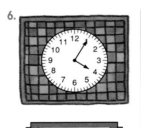

5.

Write the time.

6. 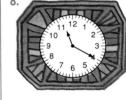   7.   8.

6. 4 : 05

7. 7 : 30

8. 11 : 20

Macmillan/McGraw-Hill

USING THE CHAPTER REVIEW/TEST

The Chapter Review/Test may be used as a review to survey children's knowledge and understanding of the chapter material. Or it may be used as a test to formally assess children's understanding of the concepts and skills taught in the chapter. If used as a test, you may wish to assign one or more of the resources listed in *Reinforcement and Remediation* on p. 270 after reviewing children's test results.

If the Chapter Review/Test is used as a review, you may wish to have children work in pairs to complete it. Have them talk about something they do after school that takes more than 1 hour. Then, you can use the Chapter Tests—Forms A, B, and C—provided in the *Testing Program Blackline Master and Teacher's Manual* for testing purposes. Any of these forms may be used for pretesting, posttesting, or retesting.

A performance assessment activity for the key concept in this chapter is provided on page 271.

Write the time.

9.

6 : 15

10.

9 : 35

11.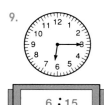

3 : 10

	MAY					
Sunday	Monday	Tuesday	Wednesday	Thursday	Friday	Saturday
		1	2	3	4	5
6	7	8	9	10	11	12
13	14	15	16	17	18	19
20	21	22	23	24	25	26
27	28	29	30	31		

12. Which month is shown? _____May_____

13. On what day is May 16? _____Tuesday_____

14. How many Mondays are in the month? __5__

Problem Solving

Ring about how long.

15. Alex and Hector went to the movies.
About how long were they there?

about 2 minutes   (about 2 hours)   about 2 days

16. Edith and Zoe made a castle in the sandbox.
About how long did it take to make the castle?

(about 1 hour)   about 15 hours   about 30 hours

MEETING INDIVIDUAL NEEDS

Reinforcement and Remediation

CHAP. OBJ.	TEST ITEMS	PUPIL'S EDITION pp.			TEACHER'S EDITION pp.	TEACHER RESOURCES	
		Lesson	Extra Practice	Practice Plus	Alt. Teaching Strategy	Reteaching	Practice
8A	1–2, 4–5, 7	249–252	254	268	250, 252	79, 80	79, 80
8B	3, 6, 8–11	257–260		268	258, 260	82, 83	82, 83
8C	12–14	261–262	267		262	84	84
8D	15–16	255–256, 263–264	267			81, 85	81, 85

For Students Acquiring English (SAE)

Before beginning the Chapter Review/Test with SAE children, scan the pages for any unfamiliar vocabulary that should be pretaught. You may wish to pair or group SAE children with non-SAE children. You may also wish to repeat some of the activities and techniques for SAE children that were suggested earlier in this chapter.

CHAPTER 8

AT·A·GLANCE p. 271

OBJECTIVE
Assess whether children can tell time (to 5-minute intervals) and apply concepts of time in a problem setting.

MATERIALS
Manipulatives analog, digital clockface punchouts per pair

Teacher Resources
Performance Assessment booklet, pp. 33–35

For Students Acquiring English (SAE)

Before beginning the performance assessment with SAE children, scan the page for any unfamiliar vocabulary that should be pretaught. You may wish to pair or group SAE children with non-SAE children. You may also wish to repeat some of the activities and techniques for SAE children that were suggested earlier in this chapter.

Performance Assessment

Work with a partner.

What is your morning schedule in school?
Write your schedule up until lunchtime.
Show the times on both clocks.

Use an and a ⬚ if you want.

Our Morning Schedule

Time		What We Do
(clock)	⬚ : ⬚	
(clock)	⬚ : ⬚	
(clock)	⬚ : ⬚	
(clock)	⬚ : ⬚	
(clock)	⬚ : ⬚	

Macmillan/McGraw-Hill

You may put this page in your Portfolio

USING PERFORMANCE ASSESSMENT
The Performance Assessment activity may be used to informally assess children's understanding of the key concept(s) of the chapter. Additional assessment activities and Math Journal Options are provided in the *Performance Assessment* booklet.

Performing the Activity
Assign children to work in pairs. Provide analog and digital clockfaces for use. Have children work together to determine their morning schedule. Let them fill in what time each class period begins until lunchtime. Children should record their findings individually.

Evaluation Guidelines
Use these criteria to help determine the holistic score for each child. The holistic scoring scale can be found in the Teacher's Reference Section.

- Does the child's schedule show number sense in terms of the length of each class period?
- Do children write the schedule in consecutive order?
- Can the child illustrate each time on the clockfaces?

[Example Response: Math begins at 8:45.]

If children do not have a full understanding of the key concept(s), you may wish to use the Alternative Teaching Strategies or the MAC Activities within the chapter.

You may wish to have children put their final revised work in their portfolios.

A formal assessment of the concepts and skills taught in this chapter is provided on pages 269–270.

Enrichment For All

A.M. and P.M.

Each day, the hour hand goes around the clock twice.
The times before 12 noon are A.M.
The times after 12 noon are P.M.

Still Sleeping	Breakfast	Lunch	Dinner	Bedtime

6:00 A.M.	8:00 A.M.	12 noon	6:00 P.M.	8:00 P.M.

Write A.M. or P.M.

1.

A.M.

2.

A.M.

3.

P.M.

4.

P.M.

AT·A·GLANCE p. 272

OBJECTIVE
Identify and write A.M. or P.M.

ASSIGNMENT GUIDE

COURSE	EXERCISES
Basic	p. 272: 1–4
Average	p. 272: 1–4
Challenge	p. 272: 1–4

MATERIALS
Manipulatives   1 analog clock punchout per child

For Students Acquiring English (SAE)

Read the page aloud to SAE children, referring to the five activities and times of day on a large demonstration clock. Explain and demonstrate unknown key vocabulary. SAE children may have difficulty distinguishing between A.M. and P.M. Provide additional practice by linking certain times of day with habitual activities. Ask questions, such as *What do you usually do at 7 P.M.?*, and model correct responses. Be sure children include A.M. or P.M. in their responses.

---

1 PREPARE

WARM-UP   To prepare children for identifying time as A.M. or P.M., have them name school activities that they do in the morning and in the afternoon.

2 TEACH

MODELING   Give each child a punchout analog clock. Call on a volunteer to read the information at the top of the page. Explain that A.M. is the hours between 12 midnight and 12 noon; P.M. is the hours between 12 noon and 12 midnight. Have children study the clocks and model the times shown. Discuss the activities and the time of day.

■ **What part of the day is A.M.?** [the morning, or before noon]
■ **What part of the day is P.M.?** [the afternoon and evening]

3 PRACTICE·APPLY

Have children complete ex. 1–4. Ask them to think about which part of the day each activity would occur.

CLOSE   Guide children to summarize the lesson:

■ **If lunch started at 12 noon, would you be finished at 1 A.M. or 1 P.M.? Write the answer on paper.** [1 P.M.]

AT·A·GLANCE p. 273

OBJECTIVE
Review and maintain previously learned concepts and skills.

Name _____

Cumulative Review

Fill in the ◯ to answer each question.

1.

$$\begin{array}{r} 10 \\ -\ 4 \\ \hline \end{array}$$

5	6	7	8
◯	●	◯	◯

2. Compare.

$$24 \bigcirc 76$$

+	=	<	>
◯	◯	●	◯

3.

$$\begin{array}{r} 12 \\ +\ 6 \\ \hline \end{array}$$

20	18	16	6
◯	●	◯	◯

4. What amount is shown?

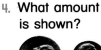

42¢	37¢	32¢	27¢
◯	●	◯	◯

5.

$$\begin{array}{r} 94 \\ -45 \\ \hline \end{array}$$

59	51	49	41
◯	◯	●	◯

6. What time is shown?

5:05	4:05	4:00	1:20
◯	●	◯	◯

7. Brock practiced the piano for 20 minutes on Monday.
He practiced for 35 minutes on Tuesday. How many minutes did he practice altogether?

●	55 minutes
◯	45 minutes
◯	35 minutes
◯	20 minutes

Macmillan/McGraw-Hill

Chapter 8   Time   two hundred seventy-three   **273**

USING THE CUMULATIVE REVIEW

The Cumulative Review is presented in a multiple-choice format to provide practice in taking a standardized test. It gives children an opportunity to review previously learned skills. An answer sheet, similar to those used when taking standardized tests, can be found in the *Testing Program Blackline Masters and Teacher's Manual*.

The table that follows correlates the review items to the lesson pages on which the skills are taught.

Review Items	Text Pages	Review Items	Text Pages
1	38	5	221–225
2	75–76	6	259–260
3	191–195	7	259–260
4	129–130		

Testing Program Blackline Masters

In addition to the Cumulative Review in the Pupil's Edition, there are quarterly Cumulative Tests and an End-Year Test. These tests are multiple choice and provide additional opportunities for children to practice taking standardized tests.

Cumulative Tests measure children's performance on major skills and concepts taught during the previous quarters. The **End-Year Test** measures children's performance on major skills and concepts taught throughout the year.

Home Activity

Your child has been learning about time. Here is an activity you can do together to strengthen your child's understanding of time.

Materials:
pencil
watch or clock

Directions:
Plan activities for a "perfect morning" or a "perfect afternoon" together. After you have decided what activities to include, talk about when your schedule will begin and how long each activity will take. Try to work in intervals of an hour, half hour, or fifteen minutes. Make up a schedule for your perfect time together.

A Perfect Morning

Start Time	Activity

A Perfect Afternoon

Start Time	Activity

AT·A·GLANCE p. 274

OBJECTIVE
Give family members an opportunity to share in their child's mathematics learning.

For Students Acquiring English (SAE)

Before assigning this Home Activity to SAE children, find out if someone at home will be able to work with them in English. If not, prepare them to complete the activity independently at home. Explain the directions of the activity and ask SAE children to restate them so you can check comprehension. Scan the page and preteach any difficult vocabulary or phrases that they may not know. If you feel that an SAE child will need extra help with the activity, you might assign that student a non-SAE partner and arrange a time for them to work on the activity in or out of school.

USING THE ACTIVITY

Have children look at the page. Explain that the page has an activity that an adult in the family can help them complete. Read the page with the children, making sure that they understand what needs to be done. Tell children that they will do this page at home.

Previewing
CHAPTER 9

UNDERSTANDING NUMBERS to 1,000

"IN CHAPTER 9, you will be introducing your children to numbers to 1,000. You will also have the opportunity to explore place value, reading and writing 3-digit numbers, counting and order, and comparing 3-digit numbers."

Notes
FROM THE AUTHOR

Here are some notes on the concepts presented in this chapter and how your children can apply them to solve problems.

PLACE VALUE

Your children build on their knowledge of 2-digit numbers to understand 3-digit numbers. Using place-value models helps children use regrouping to understand the concept of hundreds, tens, and ones, and the relationship of the units. Children begin by counting ones, and regrouping 10 ones as 1 ten. Then they count tens and regroup 10 tens as 1 hundred. They then count hundreds.

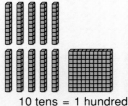

10 ones = 1 ten   10 tens = 1 hundred

Through modeling children come to understand that 1 ten is the same as 10 ones, and 10 ones is the same as 1 ten. They also learn that 1 hundred is the same as 100 ones or 10 tens.

Participating in activities and games allows children to explore larger numbers and to become comfortable with hundreds, tens, and ones before they read and write the numbers.

Steve Leinwand

READING and WRITING 3-DIGIT NUMBERS

Children use models to represent 3-digit numbers, write how many hundreds, tens, and ones, and write the numbers in standard form.

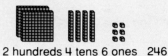

2 hundreds 4 tens 6 ones   246

They also write how many hundreds, tens, and ones for a given number. For example:

9 hundreds 7 tens 2 ones   <u>972</u>

309 <u>3</u> hundreds <u>0</u> tens <u>9</u> ones

COUNTING and ORDER

Help children use patterns to think about the order of numbers. Children learn that in counting either 2-digit or 3-digit numbers by ones, the tens digit stays the same while the ones digit increases from 0–9.

90, 91, 92, 93, 94, 95, 96, 97, 98, 99, 100
390, 391, 392, 393, 394, 395, 396, 397, 398, 399, 400

COMPARING 3-DIGIT NUMBERS

Your children share models and work in pairs or groups to compare 3-digit numbers. They extend their understanding of place value by comparing and showing numbers that are 1 more (or less), 10 more (or less), and 100 more (or less) than a given number.

PROBLEM SOLVING

In **Problem Solving** your children (1) make a list to solve a problem and (2) review problem-solving strategies they have previously learned.

In **Thinking Mathematically** children use logical reasoning to sequence events. In Pick a Path, children draw a path that shows the order in which a child will run errands.

In **Decision Making** children read and use information to write details about a recycling drive in a school paper.

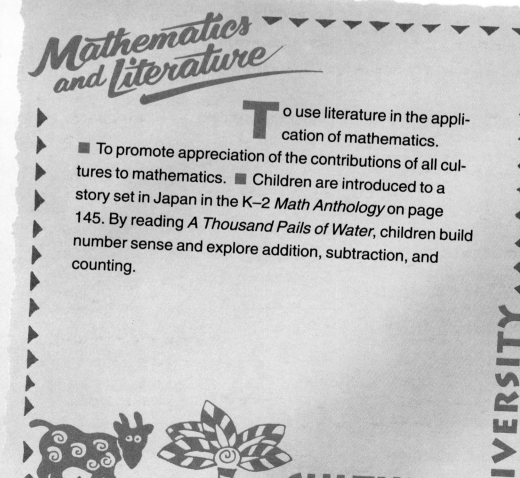

Mathematics and Literature

To use literature in the application of mathematics. ■ To promote appreciation of the contributions of all cultures to mathematics. ■ Children are introduced to a story set in Japan in the K–2 *Math Anthology* on page 145. By reading *A Thousand Pails of Water*, children build number sense and explore addition, subtraction, and counting.

CULTURAL DIVERSITY

CHAPTER 9 • ORGANIZER

CHAPTER PLANNING GUIDE

A. Read and write 3-digit numbers for hundreds, tens, and ones — MAT, CAT, SAT, ITBS, CTBS

B. Read, write, and order numbers to 1,000 — MAT, CAT, SAT, ITBS, CTBS

C. Compare numbers to 1,000 — MAT, CAT, SAT, ITBS, CTBS

D. Solve problems including those that involve making a list

SUGGESTED PACING-10 DAYS

LESSONS	NCTM STANDARDS	ASSIGNMENTS Basic/Average/Challenge	STUDENT EDITION Extra Practice/ Practice Plus	Manip. Plus	Reteach	Practice	Enrich	MAC Activities
Chapter Opener: *Two Hundred Rabbits* page 275	1, 2, 3, 4, 6	p. 275: All						
✔ 1 Understanding Numbers to 1,000 page 276	1, 2, 3, 6	p. 276: All						
✔ 2 Hundreds, Tens, and Ones pages 277–278	1, 2, 3, 6	p. 277: All; p. 278: 2–8		53				
✔ 3 More Hundreds, Tens, and Ones pages 279–280	1, 2, 3, 6	p. 279: 1–3; p. 280: 2–5, Reasoning			86	86	86	171, 172
✔ 4 Place Value pages 281–282	1, 2, 3, 6	p. 281: 1–5; p. 282: 2–6, 8–12, Estimation	pp. 286, 296	54	87	87	87	173, 174
5 PS: Making a List pages 283–284	1, 2, 3, 11	p. 283: 1; p. 284: 1–4	p. 286		88	88	88	175, 176
✔ 6 PS: Thinking Mathematically page 285	1, 2, 3, 9	p. 285: All						
7 Ordering to 1,000 pages 287–288	1, 2, 3, 6	p. 287: 1–5; p. 288: 1–10	pp. 295, 296	55	89	89	89	177, 178
✔ 8 Comparing Numbers to 1,000 pages 289–290	1, 2, 3, 6	p. 289: 1–2; p. 290: 1–7	p. 295	56	90	90	90	179, 180
9 PS: Strategies Review pages 291–292	1, 2, 3, 5, 8, 11	p. 291: 1–2; p. 292: 1–5			91	91	91	181, 182
10 PS: Decision Making page 293	1, 2, 3, 6	p. 293: All						

Technology: Calculator page 294

Chapter Review/Test pages 297–298

Performance Assessment page 299

Cumulative Review page 301

Enrichment for All/Home Activity pages 300, 302

NATIONAL COUNCIL OF TEACHERS OF MATHEMATICS Grades K–4

1. Problem Solving
2. Communication
3. Reasoning
4. Connections
5. Estimation
6. Number Sense and Numeration
7. Concepts of Whole Number Operations
8. Whole Number Computation
9. Geometry and Spatial Sense
10. Measurement
11. Statistics and Probability
12. Fractions and Decimals
13. Patterns and Relationships

✔ Activity   Cooperative Learning

MEETING the NCTM STANDARDS

Problem Solving

Strategies and Skills
- making a list pp. 283–284
- strategies review pp. 291–292

Applications
- **Decision Making** lesson p. 293
- **Problem of the Day** TE pp. 276, 278, 280B, 282B, 284B, 288B, 290B, 292B

Mathematical Investigations
- **Thinking Mathematically** lesson p. 285

Communication

Language
- using the language of mathematics TE pp. 287–288

Oral/Written
- using cooperative learning activities pp. 276, 277–278, 279–280, 285, 287–288, 289–290, 293; TE pp. 274I–274L
- **Journal Writing** opportunities TE pp. 276, 280, 284, 290

Reasoning

Critical Thinking
- answering questions that analyze and extend concepts pp. 275, 276, 277, 278, 285, 294

Connections

To other subject areas
- Literature p. 275; Literature TE pp. 275–276, 287, 289

To all cultures
- Japanese story, *A Thousand Pails of Water*, Math Anthology p. 145

Concept Development

Number Sense and Numeration
- reading and writing 3-digit numbers for hundreds, tens, and ones pp. 281–282; TE p. 274J
- reading and writing numbers through 1,000 pp. 276, 277–278, 279–280; TE p. 274I
- ordering numbers through 1,000 pp. 287–288; TE p. 274K
- comparing numbers through 1,000 pp. 289–290; TE p. 274L

ASSESSMENT OPTIONS

PERFORMANCE ASSESSMENT

Preassessment Activity

Before beginning Chapter 9, have children use place-value models to show the number 153. Assess children's knowledge of the hundreds model. Have them tell how many ones, tens, and hundreds there are in 153. Then have them model, read, and write numbers that are greater than and less than 153.

Ongoing Assessment

The Ongoing Assessment cards under MEETING INDI-VIDUAL NEEDS on TE pp. 280 and 290 provide criteria and questions for assessing children's understanding of the key mathematical concepts developed in the chapter.

 Journal Writing opportunities encourage children to write about mathematics. Their responses can be recorded either pictorially or in words. The journal writing opportunities on the Ongoing Assessment cards also allow you to assess children's understanding of the lessons.

In addition to the Ongoing Assessment cards, other assessment and journal writing opportunities in this chapter include:

• **CLOSE** TE pp. 276, 284, 290

Performance Assessment Activity

The Performance Assessment activity on p. 299 provides an alternative to formal assessment. This activity assesses children's understanding of the key concepts of the chapter.

For performance assessment activities that are keyed to individual chapter objectives, see the *Performance Assessment* booklet.

BUILDING A PORTFOLIO

Children should be encouraged to keep a selection of their best work in portfolios. The portfolios provide a way of documenting children's growth in understanding mathematical concepts. Portfolio opportunities in this chapter include:
• **Performance Assessment** p. 299
• **Class Project** TE p. 293A

If you wish to provide additional opportunities for portfolio work, you may choose to use:
• **MAC Activities** 172, 176, 179, 180, 182

You may also wish to have children include their journal writing from the Ongoing Assessment on TE pp. 280 and 290 in their portfolio.

Formal Assessment

The **Chapter Review/Test** assesses children's understanding of the concepts and skills developed in the chapter. The **Cumulative Review** assesses children's understanding of the concepts and skills developed from the beginning of the year.

You can use **Form A** or **Form B** of the **Chapter Test** found in the *Testing Program Blackline Masters and Teacher's Manual* if you wish to use a multiple-choice format to assess children's understanding of the chapter concepts and skills. You can use **Form C** if you wish to use a free-response format. Any of the forms may be used as a pretest, posttest, or for retesting.

The **COMPUTER MANAGEMENT SYSTEM**, or **CMS**, enables you to score **Forms A** and **B** of the **Chapter Test** quickly and automatically. It also prescribes learning activities based on children's test results.

For more information about Assessment, see the *Professional Handbook*.

Common Error and Remediation

The Teacher's Edition notes for each Develop/Understand (Transitional/Abstract) lesson provide a common error analysis and a remediation activity. Some errors defy quick analysis and can only be identified by interviewing the child.

ALTERNATIVE TEACHING STRATEGY

Alternative Teaching Strategies appear frequently in the chapter. These strategies provide other presentations of the lessons for children who might benefit from instruction in different learning modalities: kinesthetic, visual, and/or auditory.

For Students Acquiring English (SAE)

Practice oral counting of numbers greater than 100, so that SAE children will internalize the oral pattern of the numbers. Introduce hundreds, tens, and ones models and have SAE children learn the vocabulary.

SAE notes appear periodically in the chapter. These notes provide suggestions for how to work with children to improve comprehension and build vocabulary.

MANIPULATIVES WORKSHOP

Hundreds, tens, and ones models are used in this chapter to explore greater numbers and number concepts. They provide a concrete representation of ones, tens, hundreds, and the relationships among them.

USING MANIPULATIVES

Here a child compares two numbers.

The child uses 3 hundreds, 2 tens, and 6 ones to model 326.

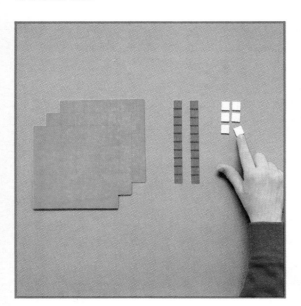

The child then uses 2 hundreds, 3 tens, and 6 ones to model 236.

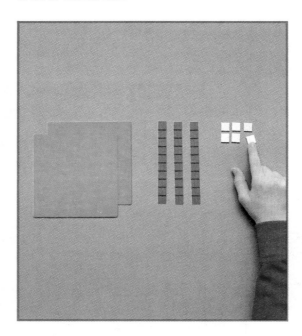

The child compares the number of hundreds in each model. Because 3 hundreds is more than 2 hundreds, 326 is greater than 236.

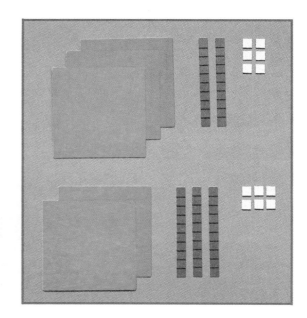

MAKING MANIPULATIVES See the Manipulatives section of the *Professional Handbook* for materials that can be used as a substitute for hundreds, tens, and ones models.

COOPERATIVE LEARNING WORKSHOP

GETTING STARTED

Positive Interdependence: Children are now capable of setting and achieving **group goals,** supporting team and community spirit, and learning **role responsibilities** in the small group. When they achieve a goal, they should receive recognition from the community as well as from the teacher. These achievements can be entered in the **group learning log** and the **class album.**

In addition they should be learning effective problem-solving strategies and skills: **clarifying** the problem; **checking** the group for alternatives or for agreement on a solution; **explaining** strategies, reasons, and methods to others; and **evaluating** the best method to solve a particular problem. Solving their interpersonal problems and using **conflict resolution** helps them to hone these skills, so don't be too quick to step in with solutions to their difficulties.

IDEAS TO TRY

Reflecting Together: Teachers often ask how to find time for reflecting on group interaction. Try (1) **integrating reflection** of group process with reflection on lesson content, and (2) using **small group learning logs** which include both types of reflection. Loose-leaf notebooks are good for entering individual sheets from each group member. When children discuss ideas and conclusions, have them also share how their interaction went, how it can be improved, and have them write suggestions. When Checking for Understanding, also have them check that everyone understands the cooperative skill assigned. During Close, write down group suggestions. Have the group's recorder enter the reflection sheets in the learning log each day.

You can apply the above reflection strategies in these lessons:
9-1 *Understanding Numbers to 1,000* p. 276
9-2 *Hundreds, Tens, and Ones* pp. 277–278
9-3 *More Hundreds, Tens, and Ones* pp. 279–280

Teacher Monitoring: Observing the small groups at work will help you assign children to heterogeneous groups of four that are mixed with respect to gender, ethnicity, and facility with mathematics or logical reasoning. Keep these groups together at least a week or two now so they can develop good problem-solving patterns and become proud of displaying their work and presenting it to other groups. If one child in a group has difficulty with a particular type of work, remind the entire group that we are all good at certain things, and suggest the others search for ways to make understanding easier.

You can apply the above monitoring strategies in these lessons:
9-4 *Place Value* pp. 281–282
9-7 *Ordering to 1,000* pp. 287–288
9-8 *Comparing Numbers to 1,000* pp. 289–290

SEE ALSO

Cooperative Learning Tip for lessons 9-5 Problem Solving p. 284; 9-9 Problem Solving p. 292

The Cooperative Learning section of the *Professional Handbook* for additional information

---

ACTIVITY
INTERACTIVE BULLETIN BOARD

SETUP Cover a bulletin board with blue construction paper. Give each child three index cards and have him or her write a different number from 600 through 1,000 on each card.

PROCEDURE Collect the cards, and have children work together to arrange the cards in numerical order. Help children tack the cards in order on the bulletin board. Call on children to read the numbers aloud.

53

HUNDREDS, TENS, AND ONES

OBJECTIVE
Explore grouping based on a given set of rules.

MATERIALS
Manipulatives 24 blue-square, 24 yellow-square, and 12 red-square counter punchouts, number cube per pair
Teacher Resources
Teacher Aid 15

PAIRS ACTIVITY

Assign children to play "Red/Yellow/Blue" in pairs. Give each pair 1 number cube, 24 blue squares, 24 yellow squares, 12 red squares, and 2 workmats duplicated from Teacher Aid 15.

▢	▢	▢

Have each pair put a blue square at the top of the right column, a yellow square at the top of the middle column, and a red square at the top of the left column on the workmat.

Write the following trading rules on the chalkboard.

■ 6 blues equal one yellow

■ 6 yellows equal one red

■ There cannot be more than six squares in a column at one time.

Children should take turns rolling the number cube and putting that number of blue squares on the

workmats. Players should follow the trading rules. At the end of each turn, players must read the number shown; as in 1 yellow, 2 blues or 1 red, 4 blues. The first player to get 6 red squares wins.

EXTENDING THE ACTIVITY

Change the rules of the game to base ten so ten blues equal one yellow and ten yellows equal one red. The first player to get 1 red square wins.

ONGOING ASSESSMENT

✓ Are children able to represent numbers by grouping by 6s and by 10s?

MANIPULATIVES plus ACTIVITY

For use before LESSON 9.4, pp. 281-282

54
PLACE VALUE

OBJECTIVES
Identify the place of a digit.
Identify the value of a digit.

MATERIALS
Manipulatives 5 H, 5 T, and 9 O models (or punchouts), Workmat 3 per child
Teacher Resources Teacher Aid 9 (EXTENDING THE ACTIVITY only)

WHOLE GROUP ACTIVITY

Distribute 5 hundreds, 5 tens, and 9 ones models and Workmat 3 to each child. Tell children to model the number 246 on the workmat.

- **How many ones are in 246?** [6]
- **How many tens are in 246?** [4]
- **How many hundreds are in 246?** [2]

Draw a place-value chart on the chalkboard and write 246 in it.

hundreds	tens	ones
2	4	6

Point to the 2 in the chart and explain that the 2 is in the **hundreds place** and it has a value of 200. Have children verify this by pointing to the two models on their workmats.

- **In what place is the digit 4?** [tens]
- **What is the value of 4 in 246?** [40]
- **In what place is the digit 6?** [ones]
- **What is the value of 6 in 246?** [6]

Repeat the activity with the numbers 624 and 462.

EXTENDING THE ACTIVITY

Distribute copies of Teacher Aid 9 to children. Have children fold their papers so only the four 3-digit place-value charts show. Read the following numbers and have children model them and record the digits on a place-value chart.

1 in the hundreds place, 3 in the tens, 7 in the ones
2 in the hundreds place, 5 in the tens, 1 in the ones
4 in the hundreds place, 2 in the tens, 5 in the ones
1 in the hundreds place, 4 in the tens, 7 in the ones

ONGOING ASSESSMENT

✓ Are children able to identify the place of a digit and the value of a digit?

MANIPULATIVES plus ACTIVITY

For use before LESSON 9.7, pp. 287-288

55 ORDERING

OBJECTIVES
Order numbers to 1,000.
Count on from various numbers.

MATERIALS
Teacher Resources
Teacher Aid 2

WHOLE GROUP ACTIVITY

Duplicate ten copies of the hundred chart on Teacher Aid 2. Label nine of the charts 100, 200, . . ., 900.

Separate children into ten groups. Give each group a hundred chart. Read the labels 100 to 900 with children. Then have groups line up in order.

Call out the following numbers, one at a time. For each number have the group that has that number of hundreds say the next ten numbers. For example, call out the number 235. Have the first group count on from 235 to 245.

320 225 680 480 965 750 140 510

870 29 328 237 653 438 927 718

173 549 862

Assign groups to different hundred charts and repeat the activity.

EXTENDING THE ACTIVITY

Use numbers that require counting from one group of hundreds to the next. Have one group begin the counting and the next group continue.

97 195 296 398 493 597 694 792 895

ONGOING ASSESSMENT

✔ Are children beginning to order numbers to 1,000 and count on from larger numbers?

MANIPULATIVES plus ACTIVITY

For use before LESSON 9.8, pp. 289-290

56 COMPARING NUMBERS

OBJECTIVE
Explore comparing numbers.

MATERIALS
Classroom Materials oaktag, small beanbags
Manipulatives 1 number cube, 9 H, 9 T, 9 O models (or punchouts), Workmat 3 per group

SMALL GROUP ACTIVITY

Make 1 game board of 3-digit numbers per small group of three as shown.

216	651	825	328
367	734	259	475
699	347	502	298
584	873	790	462

Assign children to play in small groups of three. Give each group 1 game board, 1 beanbag, 9 hundreds, 9 tens, 9 ones models, and Workmat 3.

Players should take turns throwing the beanbag onto the game board, reading the number shown and modeling the number with hundreds, tens, and ones. Then the player adds 1 ten and tells the number that is ten more than the original number.

After two rounds, change the rules to have players take away 1 ten and tell the number that is ten less than the original number.

Repeat the game for hundreds as follows:

■ add 1 hundred and tell the number that is one hundred more than the original number
■ take away 1 hundred and tell the number that is one hundred less

EXTENDING THE ACTIVITY

Give each group one more beanbag. Have groups toss both beanbags, read the numbers shown, then tell which number is greater and which number is less.

ONGOING ASSESSMENT

✓ Are children able to model and compare larger numbers?

READ ALOUD

TWO HUNDRED RABBITS
By Lonzo Anderson and Adrienne Adams

Mathematics and Literature

Listening and Speaking

The Read-Aloud selection can be used with the Chapter 9 Opener and Lesson 9-1 on pages 275-276.

Tape 2, Side 1
Selection 3

Two Hundred Rabbits

BY LONZO ANDERSON AND ADRIENNE ADAMS

The narrator of this story is a rabbit. This does not become readily apparent until near the end of the story, when an illustration in the book shows the rabbit scampering out from under the king's throne. You may need to stop reading at this point to explain this fact to your children, or you may wish to have them use the context clues to discover it for themselves.

In my travels I came to the land of Jamais and stopped on a hill to look at the valley below.

A forest was in the middle of the view, and on one side of it stood the king's castle, surrounded by a moat full of water.

On the other side of the forest was a cottage made of stone and wood, with straw for a roof.

Someone was working in the garden near the cottage.

I love vegetables, especially lettuce, so I went down for a closer look.

The someone was a young boy. He whistled and sang as he worked.

His garden was the neatest and prettiest I had ever seen.

"Hmm," I said to myself. "This boy is really special. Great things are going to happen to him."

I decided to stop here in my travels for a while. It would be fun, as long as I could keep out of sight and just watch.

The garden had a good fence around it, so I stayed outside; but when the boy cleaned out his lettuce bed he threw over enough lettuce to fill me up, and after dark I ate it.

Early the next morning the boy set out through the forest toward the king's castle, carrying his lunch. I hustled along, keeping near him without his noticing me.

When he came out of the forest it was hard for me to follow him without being seen; but if he had looked around at me, I could have pretended to be on my way somewhere else.

The boy came to the castle moat. The guard stopped him at the drawbridge.

"What do you want?" he demanded.

"Isn't this the Festival Day at the castle?"

"It is," the guard replied, stiff as his staff.

"I wish to entertain the king," the boy said, "and maybe he will give me a steady job."

"Oh?" The guard raised an eyebrow. "And what can you do to entertain the king?"

"I can stand on my head longer than almost anybody."

"The king would not be amused," the guard said.

"I can skate faster than . . ."

"In *summer?*" The guard raised his other eyebrow.

"I can swim . . ."

The guard was shaking his head.

"Then what *do* people do to entertain the king?" the boy asked.

"Some sing," the guard said.

The boy went into the forest to practice singing. He sang, and the birds all flew out of the forest in horror. Even I felt like stopping up my ears.

"Oh, this will never do!" I said to myself. "If only he could think of something better!"

The boy went again to the guard and asked, "What else do people do to entertain the king?"

"Some play musical instruments," the guard said.

The boy ran home for his fiddle and went into the forest to practice playing. The squirrels and chipmunks and foxes and wolves all came to scold him, but I kept as quiet as I could. I was still panting from running to keep up with him.

"Oh, this is not good," I said to myself. I could hear the sounds of the festival at the castle. "If only he could think of a fine idea before it is too late!"

The boy took his fiddle home, then scampered once more to the guard.

"What else do people do?" he asked, out of breath.

"Some juggle," the guard said.

The festival was almost half over. The boy did not stop to listen to the happy roar in the courtyard. He hurried into the forest to practice juggling.

He juggled with sticks and stones and old pine cones, but they all slipped through his hands or fell on his head. The birds and animals watched him and sneered and jeered.

He sat down on a log. My heart ached for him, he looked so discouraged. Soon the festival would be over, and he would have lost his chance to entertain the king.

Suddenly, an old woman was standing there.

The boy jumped up and bowed.

"You look sad," the old woman said.

He smiled. "I didn't mean to," he said. "Won't you sit down and rest?"

"Thank you, I think I will," the old woman said.

They sat together on the log.

"You do have troubles, though," she said.

He sighed. "Life is more difficult than I ever thought, when it comes to making my way in the world."

"Tell me about it," she said.

As he told her, he shared his sausages with her. He gave her more than half. I could see his eyes as he looked at her thin, old face; he thought she was starving.

"But," she said when he had finished his story, "the best way to catch the king's attention is to show him something that no one else has in all the world."

"Yes," the boy said, "but what?"

"Do you know how to make a slippery-elm slide whistle?" the old woman asked.

"Why, yes," he said. "Doesn't everyone?"

"Let me see you do it," she said.

He found a slippery-elm tree. It had many twigs of the right size and smoothness for a whistle, but one in particular wriggled, as if to catch his eye, while all the others kept still.

He cut the enchanted twig with his sheath knife and made it the right length.

The old woman was watching him like a hawk. She nodded approvingly as he cut and notched and sliced and tapped until it was finished.

"What a clever boy!" I said to myself. Never had I seen a whistle like this.

"Blow it," the old woman said.

He blew, and by sliding the lower part of the twig up and down inside the slippery bark as he blew into the mouthpiece, he was able to play a tune.

At the sound all the rabbits that lived in the forest came running, and crowded about him.

"A magic whistle!" the boy cried, and I danced for joy.

"Blow it again," the old woman said.

He blew, and the rabbits lined up like soldiers.

There were twenty rows of them, ten in each row but the last. In the last row there were only nine.

"Tch-tch!" the old woman said. "How annoying. A hundred and ninety-nine rabbits. They don't come out even. I'm sorry."

"But what does it matter? This is wonderful!"

The boy looked at the rabbits, and they looked at him as if they were ready to follow him anywhere.

"Atten-*tion!*" he cried.

The rabbits stood straight up, like soldiers.

"Forward, *march!*"

The rabbits marched through the forest toward the king's castle, the boy leading them with short steps so as not to leave them behind. He played a bouncy little tune on his whistle, nodding and bowing his thanks to the old woman.

I was so excited I was shivering. What a wonderful thing it was, that rabbit parade! But oh, was it too late for the festival? How I hoped the boy would be in time!

Out of the forest the rabbits went marching. They were having such fun I was tempted to march with them. But I was a stranger there, and the old woman's magic was not for me.

The festival was not over yet. Some people were coming out of the courtyard, but others were going in.

The king looked out of his window and saw the marvelous marching rabbits. He called to invite them to cross the drawbridge, and they did. And so did I, losing myself in the crowd.

The king came down from his room and sat on his courtyard throne to review the parade.

In the excitement I crawled under the throne from behind, to keep out of the way and have a good view.

"Halt!" the king shouted suddenly.

The boy stopped the parade and the marching tune.

"That last row!" the king said crossly. "It doesn't come out even!"

"True, Your Majesty," the boy said, bowing.

"Well, it looks silly," the king complained. "It looks ragged. *Away with those last nine rabbits!*"

"But, Your Majesty," the boy said, "that would break their hearts!"

"Hmph," the king said. "I suppose it would. Hmmm . . . *Then get another rabbit!*"

"But Your Majesty," the boy said, "there is not one other rabbit in our whole forest."

"Oh," His Majesty said, scowling. He cocked his head and thought, while I held my breath, waiting.

Then, "*Away with all of you!*" he roared.

Now I had no choice. How could I just sit there and not help?

I popped out from under the king's throne and took my place in the last row of rabbits.

That made everything all right.

The boy smiled. He took up his tune where he had left off, and gave the signal to march. We paraded in front of the king, who clapped his hands and cried:

"This will make my court the most popular court in the whole world!"

Oh, well. I was tired of traveling anyway.

AT·A·GLANCE pp. 275-276

LESSON OBJECTIVES
Explore mathematical concepts through literature.
Explore larger numbers.

ASSIGNMENT GUIDE

COURSE	EXERCISES
Basic	p. 275: All; p. 276: All
Average	p. 275: All; p. 276: All
Challenge	p. 275: All; p. 276: All

MATERIALS
Manipulatives 10 T, 10 H models (or punchouts) per child; spinner for 1–5 (or punchout) per pair

Teacher Resources
Math Anthology, pp. 174–178
Read-Aloud Cassette 2, Side 1, Selection 3

SKILLS TRACE
NUMBERS TO 1,000

Explore (Concrete) 276, 277–278	Develop/Understand (Transitional/Abstract) 279–280, 281–282, 287–288, 289–290
Practice 286, 295, 296, 297–298, 331, 361, 389	Apply 283, 284, 291–292, 293, 294, 300

CHAPTER 9

Understanding Numbers to 1,000

READ ALOUD

TWO HUNDRED RABBITS
By Lonzo Anderson and Adrienne Adams

Listen to the story Two Hundred Rabbits.

Tell how many rabbits were in each row. 10
Tell what was different about the last row.
The last row needed 1 more rabbit to make 10.

Mathematics and Literature

---

1 PREPARE
WARM-UP To review counting by tens, give each child a tens model. Call groups of up to ten children to the front of the room. Have them stand in a line and count off by tens as they hold up their models. Repeat the activity until all children have had a turn.

2 TEACH
DISCUSSING Before reading the story *Two Hundred Rabbits,* ask children to recall parades they have seen. Discuss how the musicians and marchers usually line up in straight rows. You may wish to have children line up in a parade formation of four or five across, and march as you play a tune. Ask children which they think would look better in a parade: rows with the same number of marchers or rows with different numbers of marchers. Encourage them to explain why they think as they do.

PUPIL'S EDITION pp. 275-276

Page 275 Read *Two Hundred Rabbits* found on pages 274M–274N or in *Math Anthology* to children, or play Read-Aloud Cassette 2, Side 1, Selection 3 for them.

■ **Who tells the story *Two Hundred Rabbits*?** [a rabbit who is visiting the area]

■ **What does the boy want to do?** [entertain the king on Festival Day]

■ **Why does the king tell the boy and his rabbits to leave?** [He thinks the parade looks ragged because there is one rabbit missing.]

■ **How is this problem solved?** [The visiting rabbit joins the parade and fills the one empty space in the row.]

Discuss the directives on the page.

Name _____

Understanding Numbers to 1,000

Working Together

Use 10 ▭▭▭ for each player and a 🕐 .

Show the rows in a parade.
Spin to find how many rows
of tens models to show.

Take turns spinning until you
each get to 10 tens exactly.

Complete.

__10__ rows   __10__ tens   100

🔲 hundreds model

Use a 🔲 and some ▭▭▭ .

Show one hundred in two different ways.

▶ If ten tens is one hundred, how much is twenty tens? two hundred
Use models to show it.

276   two hundred seventy-six

Page 276 ■ Working Together   Assign each child a partner. Give each pair a spinner and give each child 10 tens models. Discuss the pictures with the children and read the directions aloud.

Check for Understanding

■ **How many marchers does a tens model show?** [10 marchers]

GUIDED PRACTICE   Have each child take a turn spinning and showing tens.

For reteaching, use Alternative Strategy.

PRACTICE•APPLY   **PRACTICE**   Have children complete the page.

CLOSE   Guide children to summarize the lesson:

ACTIVITY

ALTERNATIVE TEACHING STRATEGY

MATERIALS 20 T, 2 H models (or punchouts) per pair, spinner for 1–5

VISUAL Give half the children 20 tens models, and the other half 2 hundreds models. Spin the spinner and have children holding tens put that number in front of them. Continue until they have 10 tens models lined up. Then have them trade these models for a hundreds model. Continue spinning until another 10 models have been lined up. Have children trade for another hundreds model. Have those with tens models count by tens. Have those with hundreds models count by hundreds.

■ **How would you use models to show the parade of rabbits at the end of the story?** [Line up 20 rows of tens models or show 2 hundreds models.]

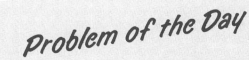

Problem of the Day

A band has ten marchers in each row. How many marchers are there in 7 rows? in 10 rows? in 12 rows? [70 marchers, 100 marchers, 120 marchers]

AT·A·GLANCE pp. 277-278

LESSON OBJECTIVE
Explore hundreds, tens, and ones.

ASSIGNMENT GUIDE

COURSE	EXERCISES
Basic	p. 277: All; p. 278: 2–8
Average	p. 277: All; p. 278: 2–8
Challenge	p. 277: All; p. 278: 2–8

MATERIALS
Manipulatives 2 H, 20 T, 20 O models (or punchouts), spinner for 0–9 (or punchout), Workmat 3 per pair

SKILLS TRACE
NUMBERS TO 1,000

Explore (Concrete)	Develop/Understand (Transitional/Abstract)
276, 277–278	279–280, 281–282, 287–288, 289–290
Practice	**Apply**
286, 295, 296, 297–298, 331, 361, 389	283, 284, 291–292, 293, 294, 300

See **MANIPULATIVES PLUS 53**, p. 274I.

1 PREPARE **WARM-UP** To prepare children to regroup tens as hundreds, write the following on the chalkboard. Have children regroup the ones and identify the number of tens and ones in each number.

1. 26 ones [2 tens 6 ones]
2. 40 ones [4 tens 0 ones]
3. 77 ones [7 tens 7 ones]
4. 19 ones [1 ten 9 ones]
5. 6 ones [0 tens 6 ones]
6. 82 ones [8 tens 2 ones]

2 TEACH **MODELING** Using Workmat 3 and hundreds, tens, and ones models, demonstrate regrouping ones for tens. Display 12 ones and ask a volunteer to count them.

Name _____

ACTIVITY

Hundreds, Tens, and Ones

You can regroup ones as tens.
You can regroup tens as hundreds.

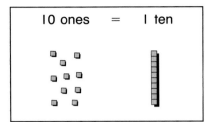

10 ones	=	1 ten

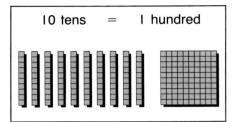

10 tens	=	1 hundred

Working Together

Use some  ,  ,  and a  .

Spin to find how many ones to take.
Take turns spinning for ones.

Regroup 10 ones as 1 ten whenever you can.

Regroup 10 tens as 1 hundred whenever you can.

Take turns until each of you has collected 1 hundred.

▶ Talk about how many ones there are in 1 hundred. There are 100 ones in 1 hundred.

Macmillan/McGraw-Hill

Chapter 9   Understanding Numbers to 1,000   two hundred seventy-seven   **277**

■ **Do you have enough ones to regroup as 1 ten?** [Yes.]
As you make the exchange, reinforce that 10 ones equal 1 ten.

Then display 10 tens models and have children count by tens as you hold up each model.
■ **How many tens equal 100?** [10 tens]
As you exchange the 10 tens models for 1 hundreds model, explain that 10 tens equal 1 hundred.

PUPIL'S EDITION pp. 277-278

Page 277 Discuss the display at the top of the page with the children.

Check for Understanding
■ **How many tens do you need to regroup for 1 hundred?** [10 tens]

Use Workmat 3. Use 20 ▭ and 2 ▦.
Show the number of tens on Workmat 3.
Regroup 10 tens as 1 hundred. Write how many.

1. 11 tens [Regroup.] __1__ hundred __1__ ten

2. 12 tens [Regroup.] __1__ hundred __2__ tens

3. 13 tens [Regroup.] __1__ hundred __3__ tens

4. 14 tens [Regroup.] __1__ hundred __4__ tens

5. Talk about the pattern you see.
   Possible answer: The number of tens increases by 1 each time.

Regroup. How many?

6. 20 tens [Regroup.] __2__ hundred __0__ tens

Mixed Review

Complete.

7. 4 tens 6 ones = __46__   8. 6 tens 7 ones = __67__

278   two hundred seventy-eight

CHAPTER 9 • Lesson 3

AT·A·GLANCE pp. 279-280

LESSON OBJECTIVE
Read and write 3-digit numbers.

ASSIGNMENT GUIDE

COURSE	EXERCISES
Basic	p. 279: 1–3; p. 280: 2–6, Reasoning
Average	p. 279: 1–3; p. 280: 2–6, Reasoning
Challenge	p. 279: 1–3; p. 280: 2–6, Reasoning

MATERIALS
Manipulatives Workmat 3 per child; 5 H, 10 T, 10 O models and 3 spinners for 0–9 (or punchouts) per pair

Teacher Resources
Reteaching 86   Practice 86   Enrichment 86
Prob. Solv. 41   MAC Act. 171, 172   Teacher Aid 11

SKILLS TRACE
NUMBERS TO 1,000

Explore (Concrete) 276, 277–278	Develop/Understand (Transitional/Abstract) 279–280, 281–282, 287–288, 289–290
Practice 286, 295, 296, 297–298, 331, 361, 389	Apply 283, 284, 291–292, 293, 294, 300

---

1 PREPARE   **WARM-UP**   To review regrouping tens as hundreds, write the following on the chalkboard. Have children regroup and identify how many hundreds and tens.

1. 18 tens [1 hundred 8 tens]
2. 10 tens [1 hundred 0 tens]
3. 14 tens [1 hundred 4 tens]
4. 20 tens [2 hundreds 0 tens]
5. 21 tens [2 hundreds 1 ten]

2 TEACH   **MODELING**   Provide children with hundreds, tens, and ones models and Workmat 3. Have children place 2 hundreds models in the hundreds column.

■ **What number have you modeled?** [200]

ACTIVITY

More Hundreds, Tens, and Ones

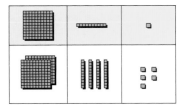

hundreds	tens	ones
2	4	5

245

Working Together

Use Workmat 3. Use 9 ▫ , 9 ▬ , 9 , and 3 .
You spin each spinner.
Your partner uses models to show the number.

hundreds   tens   ones

Write how many.   Write the number.

1.

hundreds	tens	ones
4	0	3

403

2.

hundreds	tens	ones

_____

For Exercises 2–3, answers will vary.

3.

hundreds	tens	ones

_____

Macmillan/McGraw-Hill

Tell children to leave the 2 hundreds in place on their workmats and place 9 tens and 5 ones on their workmats.

■ **How many hundreds, tens, and ones are on your mats now?** [2 hundreds, 9 tens, 5 ones]

■ **What number has 2 hundreds 9 tens 5 ones?** [295]

Have children place 5 more ones models on their workmats. Guide them in regrouping the 10 ones for 1 ten and the 10 tens for 1 hundred. Have children identify the number of hundreds, tens, and ones, and read the number. [3 hundreds, 0 tens, 0 ones; 300] Repeat the activity, building to 400 and 500.

PUPIL'S EDITION pp. 279-280

Page 279   Discuss the display at the top of the page.

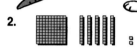

Write how many. Write the number.

1.
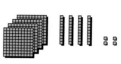

hundreds	tens	ones
1	2	3	123

2.
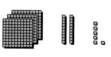

hundreds	tens	ones
1	5	2	152

3.

hundreds	tens	ones
3	2	6	326

4.

hundreds	tens	ones
5	0	4	504

5.

hundreds	tens	ones
4	4	4	444

6.

hundreds	tens	ones
2	6	5	265

Reasoning

Write the numbers.

 100   200   300

Write the next six numbers in the pattern.

400   500   600   700   800   900

Check for Understanding

■ What number is shown with 4 hundreds, 3 tens, and 8 ones? [438]

WORKING TOGETHER Give pairs of children three spinners and 9 of each model. Make sure children understand that one spinner is for hundreds, the second is for tens, and the third is for ones.

GUIDED PRACTICE ex. 1–3: For reteaching, use Common Error and Remediation or Alternative Strategy.

Page 280 Do ex. 1 with the children.

MEETING INDIVIDUAL NEEDS

ACTIVITY

Common Error and Remediation

MATERIALS 9 H, 9 T, 9 O models (or punchouts), Workmat 3, 3 sets of number cards for 0–9 (Teacher Aid 11)

Some children may have difficulty reading or writing 3-digit numbers. Work individually with each child. Say a 3-digit number. Have the child model the number on Workmat 3. Then have him or her place number cards below the models. Finally, have the child write the number on a sheet of paper.

ONGOING ASSESSMENT

OBSERVATION Determine whether children model and write numbers correctly in the activity on p. 279.

INTERVIEW (1) What number has 3 hundreds 8 tens 7 ones? Write the number. **(2)** Write 294. What number is this? Tell how you know.

JOURNAL WRITING You may wish to have children record their responses in their math journals.

ACTIVITY

ALTERNATIVE TEACHING STRATEGY

MATERIALS Teacher Aids Transparency 11, 2 H, 3 T, 7 O models (or punchouts) or Manipulatives Kit Transparencies 8, 9, overhead projector

VISUAL Place Teacher Aids Transparency 11 on an overhead projector. Place 2 hundreds, 3 tens, and 7 ones models on the workmat transparency. As children identify the number of hundreds, tens, and ones, record this information in a place-value box on the chalkboard. Then write the number as 237. Repeat with other numbers.

3 PRACTICE·APPLY **PRACTICE** ex. 2–6

REASONING Have children read the numbers they have written next to the models. Then have them continue the pattern.

CLOSE Guide children to summarize the lesson:

■ If your three spinners each showed a 7, what number would you get? [777]

MAC Activity 171:
Basic-to-Average

MAC Activity 171

On Your Own   Pair and Share   In a Group

CALCULATOR ▪ NUMBER PUNCH-IN!

Materials calculators, number cards 0–9 (Teacher Aid 11)

Procedure Assign children to work in pairs. Give each pair of children a calculator and number cards for 0 to 9. Explain that they are going to take turns entering 3-digit numbers into a calculator. Tell children they should begin by turning all the number cards face down on the table and mixing them up. Then one child selects 3 cards and keeps them hidden from view. He or she then arranges the cards to form a 3-digit number and reads off the number of hundreds, tens, and ones.

As the number is read, the second child enters it on the calculator. Have children compare the calculator display and the number cards to confirm if the number has been entered correctly. The second child erases the number and then continues for 4 more turns. Then children reverse roles.

MAC Activity 172:
Average-to-Challenge ▶

LOGICAL REASONING ▪ GUESS THE NUMBER

MAC Activity 172

On Your Own   Pair and Share   In a Group

Have children make up a riddle for a mystery 3-digit number. Explain that they should give 3 clues, 1 for each digit in the number. Write the following example on the chalkboard.

My hundreds digit is 1 greater than my tens digit. My tens digit is 3 less than my ones digit. My ones digit is 6. What is my number? [436]

Once children have completed their riddles, have them exchange them with a partner who will find the mystery number.

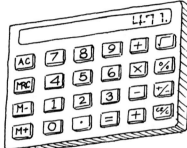

6 ones
6 - 3 = 3
3 + 1 = 4
436

RETEACHING

Name _____

MORE HUNDREDS, TENS, AND ONES

Study

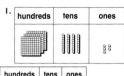

3 hundreds 2 tens 6 ones

hundreds	tens	ones	
3	2	6	326

Check

Write how many. Write the number.

1.

hundreds	tens	ones	
2	3	4	234

2.
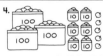

hundreds	tens	ones	
1	5	8	158

3.

hundreds	tens	ones	
4	4	3	443

4.

hundreds	tens	ones	
3	6	5	365

PRACTICE

Name _____

MORE HUNDREDS, TENS, AND ONES

Write how many. Write the number.

1.
hundreds	tens	ones

hundreds	tens	ones	
3	4	5	345

2.
hundreds	tens	ones

hundreds	tens	ones	
2	1	7	217

3.
hundreds	tens	ones

hundreds	tens	ones	
4	2	9	429

4.
hundreds	tens	ones

hundreds	tens	ones	
3	0	4	304

5.
hundreds	tens	ones

hundreds	tens	ones	
5	3	6	536

6.
hundreds	tens	ones

hundreds	tens	ones	
2	6	1	261

ENRICHMENT

Name _____

MORE HUNDREDS, TENS, AND ONES

On Your Own   Pair and Share   In a Group

FOREIGN MONEY

The people on the planet Squirt have unusual money.

5 🐚 = 1 🍊   5 🍊 = 1 ⭐

Match money amounts of equal value.

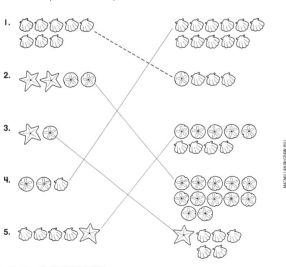

Problem of the Day

The town library plans to give bookmarks to the 358 children who entered the summer reading game. There are 100 bookmarks in a pack. Are 3 packs of bookmarks enough? [No. Possible solution: 3 packs = 300; 300 < 358.]

CHAPTER 9 • Lesson 4

AT·A·GLANCE pp. 281-282

LESSON OBJECTIVE
Identify the value of a digit in a 3-digit number.

ASSIGNMENT GUIDE

COURSE	EXERCISES
Basic	p. 281: 1–5; p. 282: 2–6, 8–12; Estimation
Average	p. 281: 1–5; p. 282: 2–6, 8–12; Estimation
Challenge	p. 281: 1–5; p. 282: 2–6, 8–12; Estimation
Extra Practice, p. 286	Practice Plus, p. 296

MATERIALS
Manipulatives 7 H, 7 T, 9 O models (or punchouts), Workmat
3 per child

Teacher Resources
Reteaching 87   Practice 87   Enrichment 87
MAC Act. 173, 174   Teacher Aids 11, 15

SKILLS TRACE
NUMBERS TO 1,000

Explore (Concrete) 276, 277–278	Develop/Understand (Transitional/Abstract) 279–280, 281–282, 287–288, 289–290
Practice 286, 295, 296, 297–298, 331, 361, 389	Apply 283, 284, 291–292, 293, 294, 300

See **MANIPULATIVES PLUS 54**, p. 274J.

Place Value

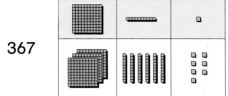

367

hundreds	tens	ones
3	6	7

How many hundreds? __3__ hundreds   value → 300

How many tens? __6__ tens   value → 60

How many ones? __7__ ones   value → 7

Use models to show	Write how many.	How many?	Value

1. 521

hundreds	tens	ones
5	2	1

__5__ hundreds   500

2. 438

hundreds	tens	ones
4	3	8

__3__ tens   30

3. 369

hundreds	tens	ones
3	6	9

__9__ ones   9

4. 704

hundreds	tens	ones
7	0	4

__7__ hundreds   700

5. 170

hundreds	tens	ones
1	7	0

__7__ tens   70

Chapter 9   Understanding Numbers to 1,000   two hundred eighty-one   **281**

PREPARE   **WARM-UP**   To prepare children for understanding the value of each place in a 3-digit number, read the following. Have children say the numbers aloud.

1. 3 hundreds [300]
2. 3 tens [30]
3. 3 ones [3]
4. 9 hundreds [900]
5. 9 tens [90]
6. 9 ones [9]

TEACH   **DISCUSSING**   Write the number 428 on the chalkboard and have it read aloud. Have a volunteer use hundreds, tens and ones to model the number on Workmat 3. Have

another child enter the number on a place-value chart drawn on the chalkboard.

hundreds	tens	ones
4	2	8

■ **How many hundreds are in the hundreds place?** [4 hundreds]
■ **How many tens are in the tens place?** [2 tens]
■ **How many ones are in the ones place?** [8 ones]
Explain that each number has a value depending on its place.
■ **What is the value of 4 hundreds?** [400]
■ **What is the value of 2 tens?** [20]

Write the number.

1. 5 hundreds   0 tens   2 ones   **502**

2. 9 hundreds   5 tens   8 ones   _958_

3. 1 hundred   2 tens   4 ones   _124_

4. 5 hundreds   3 tens   1 one   _531_

5. 0 hundreds   8 tens   3 ones   _83_

6. 3 hundreds   9 tens   0 ones   _390_

Write how many.

7. 309   _3_ hundreds   _0_ tens   _9_ ones

8. 67   _0_ hundreds   _6_ tens   _7_ ones

9. 467   _4_ hundreds   _6_ tens   _7_ ones

10. 236   _2_ hundreds   _3_ tens   _6_ ones

11. 589   _5_ hundreds   _8_ tens   _9_ ones

12. 690   _6_ hundreds   _9_ tens   _0_ ones

···· *Estimation* ··

Ring about how many.

1. about 3 kernels

    about 30 kernels

    (about 300 kernels)

2. (about 6 apples)

    about 60 apples

    about 600 apples

3. about 2 grapes

    (about 20 grapes)

    about 200 grapes

MEETING INDIVIDUAL NEEDS

Common Error and Remediation

MATERIALS 7 H, 7 T, 9 O models (or punchouts), Workmat 3

Some children may have difficulty understanding the concept of the value of a digit. Work individually with each child. Begin by having the child model these numbers, one below the other, on Workmat 3: 200, 40, and 6. Then have the child combine the models for 40 and 6 to show 46, and 200 and 46 to show 246. Have the child read and write the numbers at each stage of the activity. Repeat with other numbers.

TEACHER to TEACHER

MANIPULATIVES TIP My children benefited from combining models to form 3-digit numbers.

ALTERNATIVE TEACHING STRATEGY

MATERIALS 4 H, 6 T, 2 O models (or punchouts), Workmat 3

VISUAL Have children work in pairs. Tell one child to use hundreds, tens, and ones models to model the number 462 on Workmat 3. Have the other child model the numbers 400, 60, and 2 on the workmat. Ask how many hundreds they have [4], how many tens [6], and how many ones. [2] Ask what would happen if the numbers 400, 60, and 2 were combined. [The number would be 462.] Have children combine the models.

■ **What is the value of 8 ones?** [8]

To show that a digit's place determines its value, analyze the numbers 284 and 842 in a similar way. Guide children in comparing the value of each digit for all three numbers.

PUPIL'S EDITION pp. 281-282

Page 281 Discuss the display at the top of the page with the children.

Check for Understanding

■ **What is the value of the hundreds, the tens, and the ones digits in the number 645?** [600, 40, 5]

GUIDED PRACTICE ex. 1–5: Have children use models to show each number on Workmat 3 before writing the numbers and their values.

For reteaching, use Common Error and Remediation or Alternative Strategy.

Page 282 Read the directions for the two exercise sets. Then do ex. 1 and 7 with the children.

3 PRACTICE·APPLY   **PRACTICE** ex. 2–6; 8–12

ESTIMATION After children have completed the exercises, have them explain their reasoning for each estimate.

CLOSE Guide children to summarize the lesson:

■ **What is the value of the digit 5 in the number 518?** [500] **In the number 805?** [5] **In the number 158?** [50]

MAC Activity 174

LOGICAL REASONING ▪ BUILD A NUMBER

On Your Own   Pair and Share   In a Group

Materials   sets of number cards for 0–9 (Teacher Aid 11), place-value workmats (Teacher Aid 15), small boxes or paper bags

Place 1 set of number cards for 0 to 9 in a box or bag. Distribute a place-value workmat and a set of number cards to each child. Tell children that they are going to draw 3 number cards, one at a time. After each draw, they are to place the number card in either the hundreds, tens, or ones place on their place-value workmat. Explain that their goal is to build the greatest number from the 3 digits. Tell children that once they have placed a digit, they cannot move it.

After several rounds of play, children should begin to develop a strategy that involves the value of the digits. Encourage those who build the greatest number to explain their thinking.

To further extend the activity, challenge children to play with the goal of building the smallest number.

hundreds	tens	ones
8	4	2

▲
MAC Activity 174:
Average-to-Challenge

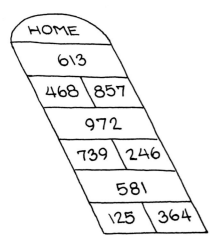

MATH AND PHYSICAL EDUCATION ▪ HOPSCOTCH

MAC Activity 173

On Your Own   Pair and Share   In a Group

Materials   chalk or masking tape, beanbags

Setup   Using chalk, draw a hopscotch game board on the classroom floor, playground, or gym floor. Write a 3-digit number in each box.

Procedure   Tell children that this game is a variation of "Hopscotch." Direct each child to toss a beanbag, and give the place value of each digit in the number on which the beanbag lands. For example, if the beanbag lands on 972, he or she should say "nine hundreds, seven tens, two ones." If the beanbag lands on a line, the child tosses again. Each child hops and jumps over the board to get to "Home." If a child steps on a line, or jumps in the box that has the beanbag, or reads the number incorrectly, he or she must wait until everyone else has had a turn before trying again. Continue the game until everyone has successfully reached "Home."

▲
MAC Activity 173:
Basic-to-Average

Reteaching

RETEACHING-87

Name _____

PLACE VALUE

Study

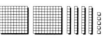

2 hundreds = 200
4 tens   = 40
5 ones = 5
         245

hundreds	tens	ones
2	4	5

Check

Write the number.

1.

   __2__ hundreds = __200__

   __1__ tens   = __10__

   __3__ ones = __3__

2.

   __3__ hundreds __2__ tens __1__ ones

3. 723 __7__ hundreds __2__ tens __3__ ones

   942 __9__ hundreds __4__ tens __2__ ones

Reteaching-87

Macmillan/McGraw-Hill, MATHEMATICS IN ACTION
Grade 2, Chapter 9, Lesson 4, pages 281–282

Practice

PRACTICE-87

Name _____

PLACE VALUE

Write the number.

1. 2 hundreds 4 tens 6 ones __246__

2. 7 hundreds 2 tens 0 ones __720__

3. 6 hundreds 9 tens 9 ones __699__

4. 9 hundreds 6 tens 1 one __961__

5. 0 hundreds 5 tens 3 ones __53__

6. 5 hundreds 0 tens 7 ones __507__

Write how many.

7. 438 __4__ hundreds __3__ tens __8__ ones

8. 172 __1__ hundreds __7__ tens __2__ ones

9. 85 __0__ hundreds __8__ tens __5__ ones

10. 310 __3__ hundreds __1__ tens __0__ ones

11. 804 __8__ hundreds __0__ tens __4__ ones

Practice-87

Macmillan/McGraw-Hill, MATHEMATICS IN ACTION
Grade 2, Chapter 9, Lesson 4, pages 281–282

Enrichment

ENRICHMENT-87

Name _____

PLACE VALUE

On Your Own Pair and Share In a Group

NUMBER CARDS

Write as many different numbers as you can.
Compare your list with your partner's list.
Use these number cards.

1. [6][7][5]
   675
   657
   765
   756
   567
   576

2. [4][2][8]
   428
   482
   248
   284
   842
   824

3. [1][3][9]
   139
   193
   319
   391
   913
   931

4. [5][3][2]
   532
   523
   352
   325
   253
   235

5. [1][6][8]
   168
   186
   618
   681
   816
   861

6. [4][0][9]
   409
   490
   904
   940
   94
   49

Enrichment-87

Macmillan/McGraw-Hill, MATHEMATICS IN ACTION
Grade 2, Chapter 9, Lesson 4, pages 281–282

Problem of the Day

Mark modeled 608 with place-value models. Did he show more hundreds models or more ones models? [more ones models]

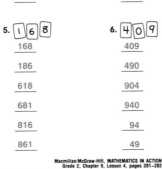

AT·A·GLANCE pp. 283-284

LESSON OBJECTIVE
Make a list to solve problems.

ASSIGNMENT GUIDE

COURSE	EXERCISES
Basic	p. 283: 1; p. 284: 1–4
Average	p. 283: 1; p. 284: 1–4
Challenge	p. 283: 1; p. 284: 1–4
Extra Practice, p. 286	

MATERIALS
Classroom Materials index cards

Teacher Resources
Reteaching 88
MAC Act. 175, 176

Practice 88
Teacher Aid 11

Enrichment 88

Name _____

Problem Solving

Strategy: Making a List

Sara lost her ticket.
She does not remember her seat number.
She remembers some things about the number.

> It had two digits.
> The two digits were different.
> The digits were either 2, 6, or 9.

> We can make a list.

Start with	Possible Numbers
2	26, 29
6	62, 69
9	92, 96

Make a list to show all the possible numbers.

1. Max forgot his room number.
   He remembers these things.
   It had two digits.
   They were different.
   The digits were either 1, 4, or 9.

Start with	Possible Numbers
1	14, 19
4	41, 49
9	91, 94

---

① PREPARE   **WARM-UP**   To prepare children for making a list to solve problems, have them make the greatest and the least numbers possible from the following digits:

3, 6 [63, 36]	5, 1, 7 [751, 157]
4, 9 [94, 49]	3, 9, 2 [932, 239]
7, 1 [71, 17]	4, 6, 2 [642, 246]

② TEACH   **MODELING**   Assign children to work in pairs. Give each pair three index cards. Explain that you will read a problem aloud and they should write each number in the problem on an index card.

Alletta is planning to visit a friend, but she does not remember the address. She knows the address has two different digits. The dig-

its were either 7, 1, or 3. How many different 2-digit numbers could be made from these three digits?

■ **What numbers did you write on the cards?** [7, 1, and 3]

Explain to children that in order to find out all the possible numbers, they should start with one digit and make different combinations with the other digits. Have children start with the index card with the number 7 on it and use the 1 and 3 cards to model different 2-digit numbers. As children make these combinations, write them on the chalkboard. [71, 73]

Then have children make combinations starting with the 1 and starting with the 3. Record all numbers on the chalkboard. [17, 13; 37, 31]

■ **How many possible numbers are there in all?** [6]

Give children a clue that the address is greater than 15 and less than 20. Have them tell you what the number is. [17]

These children forgot their locker numbers.
Make a list to show all the possible numbers.

Each locker number has digits that are different.

1. It has two digits.
The digits are 2, 4, or 8.

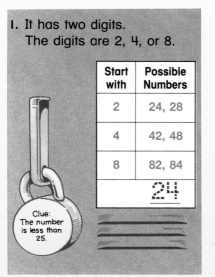

Start with	Possible Numbers
2	24, 28
4	42, 48
8	82, 84
	24

Clue:
The number is less than 25.

2. It has two digits.
The digits are 1, 2, or 8.

Start with	Possible Numbers
1	12, 18
2	21, 28
8	81, 82
	18

Clue:
The number is between 15 and 20.

3. It has two digits.
The digits are 3, 5, or 6.

Start with	Possible Numbers
3	35, 36
5	53, 56
6	63, 65
	65

Clue:
The number is greater than 64.

4. It has two digits.
The digits are 1, 2, or 3.

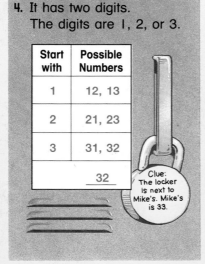

Start with	Possible Numbers
1	12, 13
2	21, 23
3	31, 32
	32

Clue:
The locker is next to Mike's. Mike's is 33.

Extra Practice, page 286

MEETING INDIVIDUAL NEEDS

TEACHER to TEACHER

COOPERATIVE LEARNING TIP I find that a simultaneous round-robin structure is a good way for groups of four to generate and check lists. Each group member has a separate piece of paper on which is written a problem that requires making a list. Each person writes one number (or idea), then passes the paper to his or her left. Each subsequent person adds a number (or idea) until the list is complete. Before adding something to the list, each person must check what was there before. If someone finds an error, he or she sends the paper back to the child who made the error. Afterward, each child does a complete list problem alone, then all four check each other's papers with another simultaneous round robin.

PUPIL'S EDITION pp. 283-284

Page 283 Have a volunteer read the problem at the top of the page.

■ **What do you need to do?** [Make a list of the possible numbers.]

Review the possible numbers shown. Guide children to see that making a list helps them to figure out the possible choices in an organized way.

■ **What did you learn?** [Possible response: Making a list can help you organize information to solve a problem.]

Check for Understanding

■ **What if the digits were 3, 7, and 8? What would the possible numbers be?** [37, 38, 73, 78, 83, 87]

GUIDED PRACTICE ex. 1: Work through problem 1 with the children. Make sure they understand how to solve the problem using the strategy of making a list.

Page 284 Have a volunteer read the problem at the top of the page. Help children read problems as necessary.

3 PRACTICE·APPLY PRACTICE ex. 1–4

CLOSE Guide children to summarize the lesson:

■ **How does making a list help you solve problems?** (Possible responses: It helps you organize information you need; it helps you see choices.)

Chapter 9 • Lesson 5   **284**

MAC Activity 175:
Basic-to-Average ▼

WRITING MATHEMATICS ▪ LIST BINGO

MAC Activity 175

On Your Own | Pair and Share | In a Group

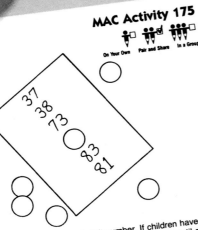

37
38
73
83
81

Materials counters or punchout counters, number cards for 1–9 (Teacher Aid 11)

Procedure Assign children to work in pairs. Give each pair six counters. Hold the number cards face down in front of each pair of children. Have them select three cards, record the numbers, and return the cards to the deck. Make sure each number is selected by at least one pair of children. Tell children to list all the possible 2-digit numbers using their three chosen numbers.

Explain to children that you will select two number cards at a time and read a 2-digit number. If children have that number on their list, they are to place a counter on it. You will continue selecting and reading numbers until one pair has covered all of their numbers. They should call out "done" or "Bingo" to show they have won the round. After the numbers have been checked, start another round.

To Win At the end of a few rounds, the pair who has won the most rounds wins the game.

MAC Activity 176: ▶
Average-to-Challenge

SPEAKING MATHEMATICALLY ▪ MYSTERY NUMBERS

MAC Activity 176

On Your Own | Pair and Share | In a Group

Materials worksheet

Setup Prepare a worksheet as shown and duplicate it.

Procedure Separate children into four groups. Give each group a worksheet. Tell each group to choose three digits and decide on a mystery number made up of two of those digits. Have one member of the group write the three digits at the top of the worksheet. Have the same child write a clue at the bottom of the worksheet. Then have the members of a group write their names around the outer edges of the worksheet. Have the groups exchange papers, make their lists, and figure out the mystery number. Then have the groups return the sheets to the groups that made them.

RETEACHING-88

Name

PROBLEM SOLVING STRATEGY: MAKING A LIST

Study

Sandy forgot her mailbox number.
She knows the number has two digits.
The digits are different.
The digits are 3, 7, or 8.

Sandy can make a list of possible numbers to help her.

Numbers to start with	Possible Numbers
3	37, 38
7	73, 78
8	83, 87

Check

Make a list to show all possible numbers.

1. Marian forgot her friend's address.
   She knows these things.
   The number has two digits.
   Each digit is different.
   The digits are 2, 5, or 1.

Start with	Possible Numbers
2	25, 21
5	52, 51
1	12, 15

2. Joshua forgot his classroom number.
   He remembers these things.
   The number has two digits.
   Each digit is different.
   The digits are 9, 3, or 6.

Start with	Possible Numbers
9	93, 96
3	39, 36
6	69, 63

Macmillan/McGraw-Hill, MATHEMATICS IN ACTION
Grade 2, Chapter 9, Lesson 5, pages 283–284

Reteaching-88

PRACTICE-88

Name

PROBLEM SOLVING STRATEGY: MAKING A LIST

These children forgot their ticket numbers.
Make a list to show all the possible numbers.

1. It has two different digits.
   The digits are 3, 1, or 8.

Start with	Possible Numbers
3	31, 38
1	13, 18
8	83, 81
→	83

Clue: The number is greater than 82.

2. It has two different digits.
   The digits are 9, 2, or 5.

Start with	Possible Numbers
9	92, 95
2	29, 25
5	59, 52
→	29

Clue: The number is between 25 and 35.

3. It has two different digits.
   The digits are 4, 8, or 7.

Start with	Possible Numbers
4	48, 47
8	84, 87
7	74, 78
→	87

Clue: The number is greater than 85.

4. It has two different digits.
   The digits are 6, 3, or 2.

Start with	Possible Numbers
6	63, 62
3	36, 32
2	26, 23
→	23

Clue: The number is less than 25.

Macmillan/McGraw-Hill, MATHEMATICS IN ACTION
Grade 2, Chapter 9, Lesson 5, pages 283–284

Practice-88

ENRICHMENT-88

Name

PROBLEM SOLVING

On Your Own   Pair and Share   In a Group

MATH SPEAKS OUT

List all possible numbers.
Use the digits in the order given. Find the letters that go with the numbers. Write a letter above each number below. Find out what the math book said to another math book.

The number has two different digits. The digits are 6, 1, or 4.

Start with	Possible Numbers	
6	O 61	D 64
1	V 16	L 14
4	P 41	H 46

The number has two different digits. The digits are 3, 9, 5.

Start with	Possible Numbers	
3	A 39	S 35
9	M 93	E 95
5	B 59	R 53

O   H,   D   O   I
61 46   64 61

H   A   V   E
46 39 16 95

P   R   O   B   L   E   M   S!
41 53 61 59 14 95 93 35

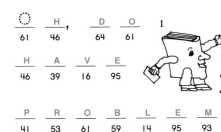

Macmillan/McGraw-Hill, MATHEMATICS IN ACTION
Grade 2, Chapter 9, Lesson 5, pages 283–284

Enrichment-88

Problem of the Day

Barney does not remember his mailbox number at the post office. He knows the number has two different digits. He remembers that the digits were either 8, 4, 3, or 1. How many different mailbox numbers are possible? [There are 12 possible numbers: 84, 83, 81, 48, 43, 41, 38, 34, 31, 18, 14, and 13.]

AT·A·GLANCE p. 285

LESSON OBJECTIVE
Use logical reasoning.

ASSIGNMENT GUIDE

COURSE	EXERCISES
Basic	p. 285: All
Average	p. 285: All
Challenge	p. 285: All

MATERIALS
Classroom Materials demonstration clock (optional)

Teacher Resources
Crit. Think. 17

PROBLEM SOLVING

THINKING MATHEMATICAL

Name _____

Pick A Path

Read the list.
Draw a line to show the path that Martha takes.
Answers will vary.

BANK
11:00-3:30

TIP TOP GROCERY

OPEN 24 HOURS

WOOD LIBRARY

HOURS
9:00-
4:30

BAKERY

CLOSING TODAY AT 5:00

HAPPY HOME PET STORE

OPEN UNTIL 5

START

It is already 3:00 and I have many places to go.

Places to Go
Grocery Store
Library- I owe a fine of $1.15.
Bakery
Pet Shop
Bank- I will not have any money until I go to the bank.

Talk about what you did.

Macmillan/McGraw-Hill

285

---

1 PLAN

AIMS AND ATTITUDES This lesson develops logical thinking skills in a problem-solving situation. Given certain time restrictions, children must plan a sequence of tasks. Before they can do that, they must read all the information available and organize the data.

Suggest to children that they not draw any path but organize the data first on their own. Some children may be able to read all of the data and organize it mentally. Others may make a list or draw a picture and revise the list or picture. Still others may write the names of the places on small pieces of paper with the time each place is open and arrange the papers in the order of the stops along the path. Encourage children to talk about how they went about solving the problem.

MANAGEMENT The activity is intended for all children and has been designed for independent work. It is also appropriate for pairs of chil-

dren. When pairing children, it may be particularly effective to pair a child having strong problem-solving and language skills with one having weaker skills.

Some children may have difficulty remembering the order of the hours and half hours. For these children, you may want to have a demonstration clock on hand.

2 GUIDE

Tell children that you will read some 2-step situations. Have them listen carefully and tell what they would do first and why. You may wish to read each situation twice before having children respond.

Drink milk. Pour milk into a glass.
Open a book. Read the book.

p. 283 *Make a list to show all the possible numbers.*

1. Carol is on the soccer team. She forgot her team number. She remembered that it had two digits. They were different. The digits were either 3, 7, or 8. She remembered the number was less than 50. The number is [37 or 38].

Start with	Possible numbers
3	[37], [38]
7	[73], [78]
8	[83], [87]

CHAPTER 9 • Lesson 7

AT·A·GLANCE pp. 287-288

LESSON OBJECTIVE

Order numbers to 1,000.

ASSIGNMENT GUIDE

COURSE	EXERCISES
Basic	p. 287: 1–5; p. 288: 1–10
Average	p. 287: 1–5; p. 288: 1–10
Challenge	p. 287: 1–5; p. 288: 1–10
Extra Practice, p. 295	Practice Plus, p. 296

MATERIALS

Classroom Materials index cards

Teacher Resources
Reteaching 89   Practice 89   Enrichment 89
MAC Act. 177, 178   Teacher Aid 11
Math Anthology, pp. 179–180

SKILLS TRACE	
NUMBERS TO 1,000	
Explore (Concrete) 276, 277–278	**Develop/Understand (Transitional/Abstract)** 279–280, 281–282, 287–288, 289–290
Practice 286, 295, 296, 297–298, 331, 361, 389	**Apply** 283, 284, 291–292, 293, 294, 300

See **MANIPULATIVES PLUS 55**, p. 274K.

Mathematics and Literature

1 PREPARE **WARM-UP** To prepare children for ordering numbers to 1,000, read *The Snow Parade.* Invite children to respond to the story. Ask them to say some numbers between 100 and 500 that you can write on separate index cards. Then have them suggest numbers that are more than 500. Again, write each number on an index card. Save the cards for use after **Close.**

2 TEACH **PATTERNING** Draw a number line on the chalkboard, starting with the number 81 and ending with 90. Point to each number and have children count aloud in unison. Then point to random numbers on the line and have children identify the number that comes just before and just after.

```
←—+——+——+——+——+——+——+——+——+——+—→
  81  82  83  84  85  86  87  88  89  90
```

Name _____

Ordering to 1,000

Lori wrote these numbers on the cartons.
Look for patterns.

What number comes just after 99? __100__

What number comes just after 999? __1,000__

Have you ever heard anyone use the number 1,000?   1,000
Tell about it. Answers will vary.

Count by ones. Write the missing numbers.

> one thousand

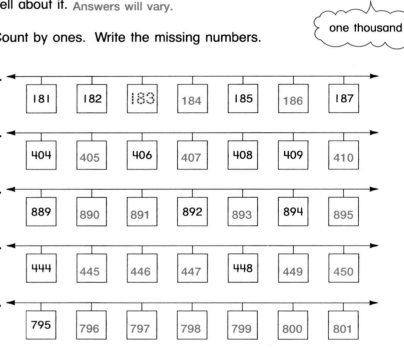

1.
| 181 | 182 | 183 | 184 | 185 | 186 | 187 |

2.
| 404 | 405 | 406 | 407 | 408 | 409 | 410 |

3.
| 889 | 890 | 891 | 892 | 893 | 894 | 895 |

4.
| 444 | 445 | 446 | 447 | 448 | 449 | 450 |

5.
| 795 | 796 | 797 | 798 | 799 | 800 | 801 |

Chapter 9   Understanding Numbers to 1,000   two hundred eighty-seven **287**

Directly below, draw another number line starting with the number 981 and ending with 990.

■ **Compare the numbers on the two lines. What pattern do you see?** [The tens and ones digits are the same.]

Extend the 2-digit number line to 100 as children count by ones. Repeat this procedure to extend the 3-digit number line to 1,000. As you write this number, introduce the word **thousand**. Then draw a place-value chart on the chalkboard and introduce the **thousands place.**

Point out the comma in 1,000 and explain that most people place a comma between the thousands place and the hundreds place to make the number easier to read.

1. What number comes just after?

222, __223__

704, __705__

645, __646__

2. What number comes just before?

__111__, 112

__238__, 239

__989__, 990

3. What number comes between?

206, __207__, 208

808, __809__, 810

237, __238__, 239

Working Together

Write a number between 100 and 999. Your partner writes the numbers that come just before and just after. Take turns.

	Number	Number that Comes Just Before	Number that Comes Just After
4.	600	599	601

For Exercises 5–9, answers will vary.

5. _____ _____ _____

6. _____ _____ _____

7. _____ _____ _____

8. _____ _____ _____

9. _____ _____ _____

Mixed Review

Subtract.

10.

56	72	61	48	37	25
− 29	− 60	− 29	− 19	− 29	− 13
27	12	32	29	8	12

Extra Practice, page 295 *Practice Plus,* page 296

Meeting Individual Needs

Alternative Teaching Strategy

AUDITORY Have children recite aloud the numbers 31 to 50. Then have them recite a related series of 3-digit numbers, such as 631 to 650. Separate the children into 9 groups. Assign each group a digit from 1 hundred to 9 hundreds. Tell children you will say a 2-digit counting series. As you point to a group, the group is to recite the same series, adding the value of their hundreds place to make it a 3-digit series.

For Students Acquiring English (SAE)

Work orally as a whole class up to Working Together. Ask a SAE volunteer to review the meaning of **pattern** for the class. Also review **before, after,** and **between** as they relate to numbers.

ACTIVITY Common Error and Remediation

MATERIALS number cards for 1–9 (Teacher Aid 11), number cards for 21–30

Some children may be unable to order 3-digit numbers. Work individually with each child. Place 2-digit number cards for 21 to 30 on a table. Have the child order them as he or she counts aloud. Give the child a set of 1-digit cards. Have the child put a 1-digit number card in front of each 2-digit number to form a 3-digit number, like 421, as he or she says it aloud. Repeat the activity.

PUPIL'S EDITION pp. 287-288

Page 287 Discuss the example at the top of the page with the children. Have children write the missing numbers and discuss times when they have heard the number 1,000 used.

Check for Understanding

■ **What are the next five numbers after 697?** [698, 699, 700, 701, 702]

GUIDED PRACTICE ex. 1–5: For reteaching, use Common Error and Remediation or Alternative Strategy.

Page 288 Do the first exercise in each column of ex. 1–3 with the children.

WORKING TOGETHER Have children work in pairs. Call on volunteers to read one set of numbers from ex. 4–6.

3 PRACTICE•APPLY PRACTICE ex. 1–10

CLOSE Guide children to summarize the lesson:

■ **What number comes just before and what number comes just after 899?** [898; 900]

Shuffle the number cards made earlier. Pass out several cards to small groups of children. Have the groups put their cards in number order. Have each group display its cards on the chalk tray. Then help the class combine all the cards into one long line in number order.

MAC Activity 177:
Basic-to-Average
▼

MANIPULATIVES ■ NUMBER FLIP BOOKS

MAC Activity 177

On Your Own   Pair and Share   In a Group

Materials   index cards, hole punch, 3 different-colored markers, yarn, scissors

Have children work with a partner to make number-flip books. Help them punch 2 holes in the tops of 10 index cards and fasten them together with yarn. Have them number the index cards in this set from 0 to 9 with one color marker. Repeat this procedure to have them make two more books using a different color marker for each set.

Have children place the 3 flip books side-by-side, and identify the books as the hundreds, tens, and ones books. Have one child turn the cards in each book to show a 3-digit number, such as 286, and read it aloud. The other child should then turn the cards in the ones book to show the 3-digit number that comes next. Children continue in this manner showing the numbers that follow 286 in sequential order, turning the cards in the tens and hundreds books as necessary.

MAC Activity 178:
Average-to-Challenge
▼

ESTIMATION ■ NUMBER GUESS

MAC Activity 178

On Your Own   Pair and Share   In a Group

Materials   clear plastic containers, dried beans, set of number cards for 0–9 (Teacher Aid 11)

Separate children into small groups. Give each group a plastic container and a sack of dried beans. Have the group count out between 100 and 999 beans and place them in the container. Tell one group member to record the number of beans. Then in front of the container, have children arrange the 3 number cards, in random order, that show each digit of the number of beans. For example, if there are 438 beans, the number cards 3, 4, and 8 would be placed randomly in front of the container.

When each group has contributed its container to a display, label each with a letter for easy identification. Distribute paper and have children list the letters on the containers down 1 side of their papers. Then have children use the number cards as clues in helping them estimate the number of beans in each container. Have them record this number.

Then have each group rearrange the number cards to show the actual number of beans in the container. Have children record the number of beans in each container and compare these numbers with their estimates.

Name _____

Ordering to 1,000

Study

| 68 | 69 | 70 | 71 | 72 | 73 | 74 | 75 | 76 | 77 |

| 268 | 269 | 270 | 271 | 272 | 273 | 274 | 275 | 276 | 277 |

Check

Count by ones. Write the missing numbers.

1. 35, 36, _37_, _38_, _39_, _40_, _41_, _42_

2. 435, 436, _437_, _438_, _439_, _440_, _441_, _442_

3. 97, 98, _99_, _100_, _101_, _102_, _103_, _104_

4. 597, 598, _599_, _600_, _601_, _602_, _603_, _604_

5. What number comes just after?	**6.** What number comes just before?	**7.** What number comes between?
609, _610_	_202_, 203	349, _350_, 351
826, _827_	_581_, 582	265, _266_, 267
914, _915_	_699_, 700	543, _544_, 545

Name _____

Ordering to 1,000

Count by ones. Write the missing numbers.

1. 235, 236, _237_, _238_, _239_, _240_, _241_, _242_

2. 777, 778, _779_, _780_, _781_, _782_, _783_, _784_

3. 596, 597, _598_, _599_, _600_, _601_, _602_, _603_

4. 803, 804, _805_, _806_, _807_, _808_, _809_, _810_

5. What number comes just after?	**6.** What number comes just before?	**7.** What numbers come between?
299, _300_	_845_, 846	319, _320_, _321_, 322
651, _652_	_477_, 478	704, _705_, _706_, 707
485, _486_	_999_, 1,000	598, _599_, _600_, 601
743, _744_	_515_, 516	211, _212_, _213_, 214

Use these digits: [4] [7] [3]

8. Write a number.   Number just before.   Number just after.

Answers will vary.

____   ____   ____

Name _____

Ordering to 1,000

On Your Own   Pair and Share   In a Group

LINE UP IN ORDER

Write each set of numbers in order from least to greatest.

1. [310] [130] [330] [103] [303]

| 103 | 130 | 303 | 310 | 330 |

2. [776] [847] [495] [983] [662]

| 495 | 662 | 776 | 847 | 983 |

3. [592] [952] [259] [295] [529]

| 259 | 295 | 529 | 592 | 952 |

4. [671] [776] [317] [267] [176]

| 176 | 267 | 317 | 671 | 776 |

5. [345] [378] [354] [387] [375]

| 345 | 354 | 375 | 378 | 387 |

6. [363] [763] [863] [663] [963]

| 363 | 663 | 763 | 863 | 963 |

Problem of the Day

The rooms in Hill Street School are numbered in order. The number on the science room door is 459. The math room is 4 doors down the hall. What is the number on the math room door? [463]

LESSON OBJECTIVE
Compare numbers to 1,000.

ASSIGNMENT GUIDE

COURSE	EXERCISES
Basic	p. 289: 1–2; p. 290: 1–7
Average	p. 289: 1–2; p. 290: 1–7
Challenge	p. 289: 1–2; p. 290: 1–7
Extra Practice, p. 295	

MATERIALS
Manipulatives 9 H, 9 T, 9 O models (or punchouts), Workmat 3 per child

Teacher Resources
Reteaching 90
MAC Act. 179, 180
Math Anthology, pp. 145–147
Practice 90
Teacher Aid 15
Enrichment 90
Prob. Solv. 43

SKILLS TRACE
NUMBERS TO 1,000

Explore (Concrete) 276, 277–278	Develop/Understand (Transitional/Abstract) 279–280, 281–282, 287–288, 289–290
Practice 286, 295, 296, 297–298, 331, 361, 389	Apply 283, 284, 291–292, 293, 294, 300

See *MANIPULATIVES PLUS 56*, p. 274L.

Mathematics and Literature CULTURAL CONNECTION

1 PREPARE **WARM-UP** To review the meaning of 1,000 and to prepare children for comparing numbers to 1,000, read *A Thousand Pails of Water*. Have the children figure out how many pails of water the class could carry to save the whale if each child carried 1 pail. Then help them figure out how many pails they could carry if each child carried 10 pails. Discuss whether this amount is more or less than 1,000 pails.

2 TEACH **MODELING** Write the number 326 on the chalkboard and have children model it on Workmat 3, using hundreds, tens, and ones models.

■ **What number is 1 less than 326?** [325]
■ **What number is 10 less than 326? Model that number.** [316]

Name _____

Comparing Numbers to 1,000

Working Together

Use Workmat 3. Use 9 ▫ , 9 ▭ , and 9 ▦ .
Use models to complete the chart.

I less than 214 is 213.

10 less than 21[ ] is 204.

1.

Number	I less	10 less	100 less
214	213	204	114
489	488	479	389
900	899	890	800

2.

Number	I more	10 more	100 more
423	424	433	523
572	573	582	672
199	200	209	299

Macmillan/McGraw-Hill

■ **What number is 100 less than 326? Model that number.** [226]
Use the same procedure to have them model 1 more, 10 more, and 100 more than 326. [327, 336, 426]

Next have children model the numbers 345 and 290 on copies of Workmat 3.

■ **Compare the two numbers. Which number is greater?** [345]
Help children to see that since 345 has more hundreds, 345 is greater than 290. Repeat with the numbers 431 and 413.

Repeat the activity to develop the concept of less than. Have children compare 289 and 405 and then 602 and 622.

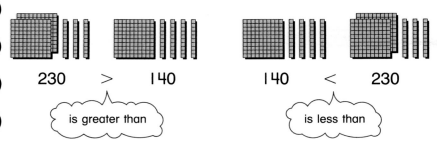

230 > 140   140 < 230

is greater than   is less than

Compare. Ring the greater number.

1. (312) 213   (988) 499   (459) 409

2. (502) 498   235 (274)   (906) 609

Compare. Write > or <.

3. 670 ⊙ 320   400 ⊙ 40   291 ⊙ 129
4. 560 ⊙ 390   681 ⊙ 701   352 ⊙ 411
5. 601 ⊙ 610   234 ⊙ 201   835 ⊙ 836

Which animal weighs more? Ring the picture.

6.

7.

Animals in Lynbrook Zoo

Gorilla	499 pounds
Lion	398 pounds
Tiger	420 pounds

Extra Practice, page 295

MEETING INDIVIDUAL NEEDS

ONGOING ASSESSMENT

OBSERVATION Determine whether children compare numbers correctly in the activity on pp. 289–290.

INTERVIEW Have the child explain each answer. **(1) What number is 10 less than 495? (2) Which is greater, 507 or 570? (3) What number is 100 more than 328?**

JOURNAL WRITING You may wish to have children record their responses in their math journals.

ᴀᴄᴛɪᴠɪᴛʏ *Common Error and Remediation*

MATERIALS 4 H, 16 T, 10 O models (or punchouts), Workmat 3

Some children may not be able to compare 3-digit numbers. Work individually with each child. Have the child model 23 and 13 on Workmat 3. Have the tens compared to determine which number is greater. Repeat numbers such as 54 and 45 and 88 and 82. Have the child model 223 and 213. Point out that since the hundreds are the same, the child should compare the tens.

ᴀᴄᴛɪᴠɪᴛʏ ALTERNATIVE TEACHING STRATEGY

MATERIALS Teacher Aids Transparency 11; punchouts for 5 H, 9 T, 10 O models (or Manipulatives Kit Transparencies 8, 9); overhead projector

VISUAL Use hundreds, tens, and ones models to model 489 on the workmat transparency. Discuss how 1 less could be shown. Remove 1 ones model and have the number identified as 488. Then model 10 less, 100 less, 1 more, 10 more, and 100 more. Have children look for patterns in the digits.

PUPIL'S EDITION pp. 289-290

Page 289 Working Together Have children work in pairs. Discuss the activity and do the first row of ex. 1 and 2 with them.

Check for Understanding

■ **How would you show a number that is 100 less than the number on your workmat?** [Remove 1 hundreds model.]

GUIDED PRACTICE ex. 1–2: For reteaching, use Common Error and Remediation or Alternative Strategy.

Page 290 Discuss the examples at the top of the page. Point out the greater than and less than signs used in comparing.

3 PRACTICE•APPLY   PRACTICE ex. 1–7

CLOSE Guide children to summarize the lesson:

■ **Which number is greater, 495 or 549?** [549] **How did you know?** [5 hundreds is more than 4 hundreds.]

MATH AND CONSUMERS ▪ COMPARISON SHOPPING

MAC Activity 179

On Your Own · Pair and Share · In a Group

Materials appliance store ads, scissors, paste, construction paper

Ask children to imagine that they are grown up and have their own home or apartment. Explain that they need to buy a new household appliance. Help each child name a major household appliance, such as a stove, washing machine, dryer, dishwasher, refrigerator, or microwave oven.

Using advertisements from appliance or department stores, have children locate ads for two different brands or models of the appliance they have decided to buy. Have them cut out the ads and paste them on a sheet of paper. Next to each appliance, have them draw a large price tag with the cost of the item. Then ask children to write a sentence in which they compare the prices of the items. Have children display their work.

▲ **MAC Activity 179:**
Basic-to-Average

MAC Activity 180:
Average-to-Challenge
▼

MATH AND SOCIAL STUDIES ▪ OBSERVATION DECK

MAC Activity 180

On Your Own · Pair and Share · In a Group

Materials *Guinness Book of World Records* or other reference books

Have children use reference books to find a list of tall buildings. Tell them to make a chart with the names of at least 10 tall buildings. Next to each building name, have them write the height of the building in meters. Then ask children to make up several problems in which they compare the height of 2 buildings. For example:

The World Trade Center is 411 meters tall. The Sears Tower is 443 meters tall. Which of the two buildings is taller? [Sears Tower]

Have children share their problems within their group. Then have groups exchange problems and solve them.

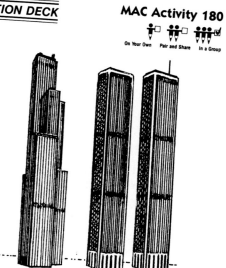

RETEACHING

Name _____

COMPARING NUMBERS TO 1,000

Study

325 is less than 412
325 < 412

234 is greater than 218
234 > 218

Check

Compare. Write < or >.

1.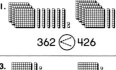

362 < 426

2.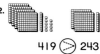

419 > 243

3.

116 > 106

4.

321 > 231

5. 281 < 300   782 < 827   524 > 425

6. 487 < 609   987 > 978   703 < 730

7. 911 > 901   442 < 448   659 > 658

8. 323 > 313   219 > 218   920 > 919

9. 651 < 671   107 < 771   312 > 291

Macmillan/McGraw-Hill, MATHEMATICS IN ACTION
Grade 2, Chapter 9, Lesson 8, pages 289–290   Reteaching-90

PRACTICE

Name _____

COMPARING NUMBERS TO 1,000

Write the missing numbers.

1. 10 less		10 more	2. 100 less		100 more
143	153	163	387	487	587
408	418	428	729	829	929
590	600	610	294	394	494
901	911	921	566	666	766
589	599	609	71	171	271
226	236	246	106	206	306

Compare. Write < or >.

3. 388 < 605   721 < 805   131 > 113

4. 123 > 120   581 > 518   661 > 616

5. 269 < 296   308 > 300   500 < 517

6. 472 > 427   887 > 878   473 < 477

7. 599 < 601   216 < 621   904 > 894

Macmillan/McGraw-Hill, MATHEMATICS IN ACTION
Grade 2, Chapter 9, Lesson 8, pages 289–290   Practice-90

ENRICHMENT

Name _____

COMPARING NUMBERS TO 1,000

On Your Own   Pair and Share   In a Group

SPINNING FOR NUMBERS

Play with two friends.
You need a spinner for 0 to 9.

1. Each child spins and writes the number in any place in the first chart.
2. Take two more turns.
3. Compare. The greatest number scores one point.
4. Play again.
5. The most points wins.

Children should develop a strategy for the placement of greater and lesser numbers.

GAME 1

hundreds	tens	ones

GAME 2

hundreds	tens	ones

GAME 3

hundreds	tens	ones

GAME 4

hundreds	tens	ones

GAME 5

hundreds	tens	ones

GAME 6

hundreds	tens	ones

My points: _____

Macmillan/McGraw-Hill, MATHEMATICS IN ACTION
Grade 2, Chapter 9, Lesson 8, pages 289–290   Enrichment-90

Problem of the Day

Mark sees some bedroom furniture on sale for $299. The regular price is $100 more. Is the regular price greater than or less than $400?
[Less than $400; possible solution: $100 more than $299 is $399; $399 < $400.]

AT·A·GLANCE pp. 291-292

LESSON OBJECTIVE
Use strategies to solve problems.

ASSIGNMENT GUIDE

COURSE	EXERCISES
Basic	p. 291: 1–2; p. 292: 1–5
Average	p. 291: 1–2; p. 292: 1–5
Challenge	p. 291: 1–2; p. 292: 1–5

Teacher Resources
Reteaching 91   Practice 91   Enrichment 91
Prob. Solv. 44   MAC Act. 181, 182

Problem Solving
Strategies Review

Mac sells 11 red balloons.
He sells 7 blue balloons.
How many more red balloons than
blue balloons did he sell?

Draw a picture to find how many more.

Subtract to find how many more.

$$\begin{array}{r} 11 \\ -7 \\ \hline 4 \end{array}$$

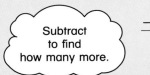

_4_ more red balloons

Solve.

1. There are 18 horses in the parade.
   9 horses are brown.
   How many are not brown?

   __9__ are not brown

2. 41 men march in the parade.
   37 women march.
   How many people march in all?

   __78__ people

Macmillan/McGraw-Hill

Chapter 9   Understanding Numbers to 1,000   two hundred ninety-one   **291**

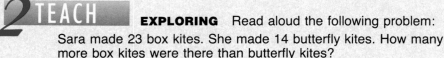

1 PREPARE   **WARM-UP**   To prepare children for choosing strategies to solve problems, have them give the following sums and differences:

15 − 9 [6]   12 + 4 [16]   21 − 13 [8]

2 TEACH   **EXPLORING**   Read aloud the following problem:
Sara made 23 box kites. She made 14 butterfly kites. How many more box kites were there than butterfly kites?

■ **What do you know?** [Sara made 23 box and 14 butterfly kites.]

■ **What do you need to find out?** [how many more box kites there are than butterfly kites]

Ask children to suggest different ways they might solve the problem. [Possible response: Think about whether to add or subtract; draw a picture to find how many more; try subtraction.]

Have children choose a plan and solve the problem. [Sara made 9 more box kites.] Ask children to explain how they solved the problem.

PUPIL'S EDITION pp. 291-292

Page 291   Have a volunteer read the problem at the top of the page.

■ **What do you know?** [Mac sells 11 red and 7 blue balloons.]

■ **What do you need to find out?** [how many more red balloons he sold than blue balloons]

■ **How can you find out how many more red balloons Mac sold than blue balloons?** [Possible response: Draw a picture or subtract.]

Solve.

balloons 9¢	
flags 18¢	
banners 8¢	
pinwheels 39¢	
badges 7¢	

1. Elsa spent 17¢.
   She bought two items.
   How much did each item cost?

   __9__ ¢ and __8__ ¢

2. Bart has 50¢.
   Does he have enough money to
   buy a pinwheel and a banner?

   __Yes.__

3. The parade ended at 4:00.
   It lasted for 3 hours.
   When did the parade begin?

   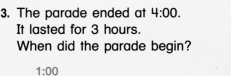

   __1:00__

4. Kari forgot her seat number.
   The number has two different digits.
   The digits are 2, 3, or 5.
   Make a list to show all the
   possible numbers.

Start with	Possible Numbers
2	23, 25
3	32, 35
5	52, 53

5. Frank is making 4 flags.
   Each flag has a different
   number of stars on it.
   Continue the pattern.
   How many stars will the
   last flag have?

   __17__ stars

292   two hundred ninety-two

Review the drawing and the subtraction with the children.

■ **What do you do when you have an answer?** [Check to see if the answer makes sense.]

■ **What have you learned?** [You can use different strategies to solve problems.]

Encourage children to explain other ways to solve this problem.

Check for Understanding

■ **What if you wanted to know how many balloons Mac sold in all? What would you do to solve the problem?** [Add: 11 + 7 = 18.]

GUIDED PRACTICE   ex. 1–2: Work through problem 1 with the children. Make sure they understand how to solve the problem using the strategies they have just learned.

TEACHER to TEACHER

COOPERATIVE LEARNING TIP 👥 I have children work in pairs to review problem-solving strategies. I encourage them to try alternative strategies for solving, using a different one for each exercise, and to check and coach one another. Explaining their strategies helps them clarify their thinking about the problem. They then join with another pair and compare answers. At this point, I switch partners *across* pairs for coaching and checking answers. Then all four compare the strategies used.

For Students Acquiring English (SAE)

Please refer to previous Problem Solving lessons for teaching suggestions about the strategies reviewed in this lesson.

Page 292   Discuss the problems with the children. Be sure they understand that they are to decide what strategy to use to solve the problem.

3 PRACTICE•APPLY   PRACTICE   ex. 1–5

C L O S E   Guide children to summarize the lesson:

■ **How do you know which strategy to choose to solve a problem?** [Possible response: Decide what you need to find out, then use what you know and choose the strategy that would find the answer.]

MAC Activity 181:
Basic-to-Average
▼

LOGICAL REASONING ■ POSTER PUZZLERS

MAC Activity 181

On Your Own   Pair and Share   In a Group

Materials   punchout clockfaces, punchout dimes and pennies, oaktag, magazines

Setup   Prepare a poster on a piece of oaktag by drawing or cutting pictures from magazines or catalogs of a teddy bear, a book, a race car, a robot, and a toy truck. Put price tags of 35¢ on the teddy bear, 28¢ on the book, 42¢ on the race car, 47¢ on the robot, and 18¢ on the truck.

Procedure   Assign children to work in small groups. Provide each group with a set of dimes and pennies and a clockface. Display the poster for all groups to see. Tell children that you will read them some problems. Explain that they are to decide which strategy to use to solve the problem. Have children find the answers to the problems and tell how they arrived at the solutions.

1. Virginia bought two items at the store. She paid the clerk 53¢. How much did each item cost? What were the items? [35¢ and 18¢; the teddy bear and the toy truck]
2. Mickey read her favorite book for 2 hours. She finished the book at 4:00. What time did she start reading? [2:00]

Continue the activity with similar problems that can be solved using different strategies.

MAC Activity 182:
Average-to-Challenge
▼

SPEAKING MATHEMATICALLY ■ PICK AND CHOOSE

MAC Activity 182

On Your Own   Pair and Share   In a Group

number sense

make a list

patterns

working backward

Materials   index cards

Setup   Prepare a set of strategy cards with the following strategies: estimation, use number sense, choose the operation, make a list, guess and test, find a pattern, identify extra information, work backward.

Procedure   Assign children to work in pairs. Have one member of each pair select a strategy card. Explain that they are to make up a problem that can be solved using the strategy on their card. Have pairs exchange problems and solve them.

Name _____

PROBLEM SOLVING STRATEGIES REVIEW

Study

How many beads will be on the next necklace?

Which strategy could you use?

8   10   12

The pattern is *2 more*.
There are 14 beads on the next necklace.

I could find a pattern.

Check

Ring how you will solve the problem. Solve.

Start with	Possible Numbers
6	61 69
1	16 19
9	96 91

1. Maureen lost her locker number.
   The number has 2 different digits.
   The digits are 6, 1, or 9.

   (make a list)   look for a pattern

2. Don had 23 boxes.
   He put things in 14 boxes.

   How many boxes are still empty? _____9_____ boxes

   use number sense   (add or subtract)

3. Phil cleaned his room for 2 hours.
   He finished at 1:00.

   When did he start? __11:00__

   (work backward)   use estimation

Reteaching-91

Macmillan/McGraw-Hill, MATHEMATICS IN ACTION
Grade 2, Chapter 9, Lesson 9, pages 291–292

Name _____

PROBLEM SOLVING STRATEGIES REVIEW

Solve.

1. Sam hangs up 17 yellow streamers.
   He hangs up 36 orange streamers.
   How many more orange streamers than
   yellow streamers did he hang?   __19__ more

2. There are 41 cups on the table.
   17 cups have juice in them.
   How many are empty?   __24__ are empty

3. Peggy spent 34¢.
   She bought two items.
   How much did each item cost?

   __22__¢ and __12__¢

   hats 19¢   stars 32¢   whistles 22¢   cups 7¢   plates 12¢

4. Tom has 55¢.
   Does he have enough money
   to buy a hat and a star?

   __yes__

5. Janice is making 4 hats
   Each hat has a different
   number of dots on it.
   Continue the pattern.
   How many dots will
   the last hat have?

   __12__ dots

Practice-91

Macmillan/McGraw-Hill, MATHEMATICS IN ACTION
Grade 2, Chapter 9, Lesson 9, pages 291–292

Name _____

PROBLEM SOLVING

On Your Own   Pair and Share   In a Group

CROSS NUMBERS

Solve.
Use your answers to complete the puzzle.

DOWN

1. The children voted for class president.
   How many children voted for Kim?

   Votes for President

   Bill   Kim   Pat

2. Sandra sold 53 fish.
   She still has 21 fish in a tank.
   How many more fish did she sell
   than are in the tank?

4. Bob is painting hearts on cards.
   Each card has a different
   number of hearts.
   How many hearts will be on the last card?

6. Jeff has 45 blue race cars.
   He gave away 18 cars.
   How many cars does he have left?

ACROSS

2. Nan read for 3 hours.
   She stopped at 6:00.
   When did she
   start reading?

3. Donna had 30 pencils.
   She lost 8.
   How many pencils were left?

5. Donna bought 20 more pencils.
   How many does she have now?

Enrichment-91

Macmillan/McGraw-Hill, MATHEMATICS IN ACTION
Grade 2, Chapter 9, Lesson 9, pages 291–292

Problem of the Day

Lori made 38 muffins.
Her brother and sister ate 11 of them.
Then she made 18 more, and her brother and
sister ate 6 of them. How many muffins are left?
[39; 38 − 11 = 27; 27 + 18 = 45; 45 − 6 = 39]

AT·A·GLANCE p. 293

LESSON OBJECTIVE
Make decisions using information.

ASSIGNMENT GUIDE

COURSE	EXERCISES
Basic	p. 293: All
Average	p. 293: All
Challenge	p. 293: All

Teacher Resources
Crit. Think. 18   Prob. Solv. 45

Name _____

Decision Making

COOPERATIVE LEARNING

Problem Solving: Planning a Recycling Drive

Papers - 20¢
Bring at least 20 newspapers

Aluminum Cans - 90¢
Bring at least 90 cans

Glass - 20¢
Bring at least 30 jars

Plan a recycling drive.
Complete this story for the school paper. Answers will vary.

> **Mrs. Gomez's Class Announces a Recycling Drive**
>
> We will collect newspapers, cans, and jars. We will use trash bags and cardboard boxes for containers. We will put 20 newspapers in each pile. We will put _____ cans in each container and _____ jars in each container.
>
> Each week we will try to collect _____ newspapers, _____ cans, and _____ jars. We hope to raise $_____ for newspapers, $_____ for cans, and $_____ for jars. We will donate the money to our school.

Macmillan/McGraw-Hill

---

1 PREPARE

WARM-UP To review numbers to 1,000, write these numbers on the chalkboard.

896, 897, 899, 900, 901, 902
986, 987, 988, 989, 990, 991
145, 146, 147, 148, 149, 150

Have volunteers read aloud each row of numbers. Then say a number to 1,000 and call on a child to write the number on the board. Continue with different numbers and other volunteers.

2 TEACH

DISCUSSING Define the word *recycling* for the children. Explain that it means "to collect used things and break them down to make new things." Have children name some things that could be recycled. [Possible responses: aluminum cans, newspapers, glass bottles] List children's responses on the chalkboard.

PUPIL'S EDITION p. 293

Discuss the pictures at the top of the page. Read the information in the pictures with the children.

Check for Understanding

■ **How much paper must you bring to the recycling drive?** [20 newspapers]

■ **How much money is paid for 90 aluminum cans?** [90 cents]

■ **How much money is paid for 30 glass jars?** [20 cents]

For Students Acquiring English (SAE)

Make a transparency of the story on page 293 and work through the page as a whole-class oral language lesson. If possible, have real things that can be recycled on display. Allow children to refer to the page while giving their answers orally.

3 PRACTICE•APPLY

Have children complete the page. Call on volunteers to tell how they decided to complete the blanks in the school newspaper story.

CLOSE Guide children to summarize the lesson:

■ **What should you do before you plan a recycling drive?** [Decide what items will be recycled, how much money will be paid for each item, and what will be done with the money that is collected.]

CLASS PROJECT

Materials oaktag, crayons, paints, collage materials

Provide children with oaktag, crayons, paints, and collage materials. Have them use any or all of the materials to make a poster that advertises a class recycling drive. Remind children to plan the drive before they make their poster. Explain that the poster should reflect their ideas for the drive.

When children have completed the project, call on volunteers to show and tell about their posters. Ask them to explain how they decided on their ideas for the recycling drive.

AT·A·GLANCE p. 294

OBJECTIVE
Use a calculator to explore place value.

MATERIALS
Calculator 1 calculator per pair

Teacher Resources
Calculator 9

Technology

Calculator: Find the Number

You can use a calculator to explore
place value.

Find each sum or difference.
Stop at the end of each row.
Turn the calculator upside down.
Do you see the word? Then press ⒞.

								Word
1. Press 308 ⊞ 10 ⊜ 318	⊞ 10 ⊜ 328	⊞ 10 ⊜ 338	bee
2. Press 693 ⊞ 100 ⊜ 793	⊞ 100 ⊜ 893	⊞ 100 ⊜ 993	egg
3. Press 410 ⊞ 100 ⊜ 510	⊞ 100 ⊜ 610	⊞ 100 ⊜ 710	oil
4. Press 604 ⊟ 100 ⊜ 504	⊟ 100 ⊜ 404	⊟ 100 ⊜ 304	hoe
5. Press 633 ⊞ 10 ⊜ 643	⊞ 100 ⊜ 743	⊟ 10 ⊜ 733	eel
6. Press 414 ⊞ 100 ⊜ 514	⊟ 10 ⊜ 504	⊞ 100 ⊜ 604	hog

7. Talk about how the display changed each time you pressed ⊜.
In their own words, children should note that the digits in tens or
hundreds place increased or decreased by 1.

1 PREPARE

WARM-UP To prepare children to use a calculator
to explore place value, have them give the number
of hundreds, tens, and ones in the following numbers.

875 [8 hundreds 7 tens 5 ones]
902 [9 hundreds 0 tens 2 ones]
681 [6 hundreds 8 tens 1 one]
790 [7 hundreds 9 tens 0 ones]
423 [4 hundreds 2 tens 3 ones]

2 TEACH

DISCUSSING Have children work in pairs. Give
each child a calculator. Review adding on the calculator as necessary. Then have children find the following sums and
differences. Work through each exercise with them.

400 + 10 = ___ [410]
300 − 10 = ___ [290]
500 + 100 = ___ [600]
600 − 100 = ___ [500]

■ **When you add 400 + 10, how many hundreds, tens, and ones
are in the sum?** [4 hundreds 1 ten 0 ones]

■ **When you subtract 300 − 10, how many hundreds, tens, and
ones are in the difference?** [2 hundreds 9 tens 0 ones]

Continue the activity with similar questions.

3 PRACTICE·APPLY

Read through the instructions with the
children. Remind them to clear their
calculators before beginning each new exercise. Do ex. 1 with the

For Students Acquiring English (SAE)

In ex. 1–6, provide oral language practice for SAE children. Direct one partner to read an exercise aloud while the other partner operates the calculator. Then have partners switch roles and complete the next exercise.

children. Help them read the word *bee* which is formed by calculator numbers 338 when viewed upside down.

Have children do ex. 2–7 and discuss their numerical answers in terms of hundreds, tens, and ones.

CLOSE Guide children to summarize the lesson:

■ **How does the number 574 change when you add 100 to it?**
[The hundreds place increases by 1.]

CHAPTER 9

EXTRA PRACTICE

Extra Practice items are provided so that children may have an opportunity for further practice.

The *Additional Practice* section also provides practice you may wish to assign.

Extra Practice

Ordering to 1,000, pages 287–288 . . . .

Write the missing numbers.

1. Which number comes just after?

337, __338__

580, __581__

909, __910__

2. Which number comes just before?

__514__, 515

__600__, 601

__846__, 847

3. Which numbers come between?

318, __319__, 320

652, __653__, 654

789, __790__, 791

Comparing Numbers to 1,000, pages 289–290 . . . .

Compare. Ring the greater number.

1. 198 ⟨210⟩   480 ⟨804⟩   352 ⟨632⟩

2. ⟨726⟩ 291   ⟨800⟩ 599   576 ⟨764⟩

3. ⟨910⟩ 615   ⟨244⟩ 229   ⟨499⟩ 479

Compare. Write > or <.

4. 499 ⟨<⟩ 501   372 ⟨>⟩ 297   650 ⟨>⟩ 638

5. 749 ⟨<⟩ 794   285 ⟨<⟩ 819   874 ⟨>⟩ 547

6. 121 ⟨<⟩ 211   430 ⟨>⟩ 150   954 ⟨<⟩ 958

7. 311 ⟨>⟩ 131   456 ⟨<⟩ 654   875 ⟨>⟩ 785

Macmillan/McGraw-Hill

ADDITIONAL PRACTICE

p. 287 *Write the missing numbers.*

1. Which number comes just after?

495, [496]   142, [143]

236, [237]   645, [646]

767, [768]   291, [292]

2. Which number comes just before?

[214], 215   [391], 392

[823], 824   [426], 427

[396], 397   [517], 518

3. Which numbers come between?

545, [546], [547], 548

357, [358], [359], 360

982, [983], [984], 985

618, [619], [620], 621

477, [478], [479], 480

p. 289 *Compare. Write > or <.*

1. 383 [<] 455   **2.** 757 [<] 810

3. 219 [>] 218   **4.** 912 [<] 915

5. 145 [>] 114   **6.** 675 [>] 665

7. 298 [>] 198   **8.** 313 [<] 315

9. 842 [>] 824   **10.** 163 [>] 151

Practice Plus

Key Skill: Place Value, page 282 . . . .

Write the number.

1. 3 hundreds   7 tens   4 ones   _374_

2. 7 hundreds   6 tens   0 ones   _760_

3. 4 hundreds   3 tens   1 ones   _431_

4. 8 hundreds   2 tens   8 ones   _828_

Write how many.

5. 333   _3_ hundreds   _3_ tens   _3_ ones

6. 517   _5_ hundreds   _1_ tens   _7_ ones

7. 781   _7_ hundreds   _8_ tens   _1_ ones

8. 909   _9_ hundreds   _0_ tens   _9_ ones

PRACTICE PLUS

Practice Plus is provided to supply additional practice for the two key skills in this chapter.

Key Skills
Page 282: Place Value
Page 288: Ordering to 1,000

The Additional Practice also provides practice you may wish to assign for key skills in this chapter.

Key Skill: Ordering to 1,000, page 288 . . . .

Count by ones. Write the missing numbers.

1.

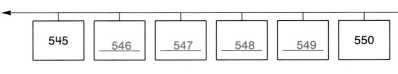

| 545 | _546_ | _547_ | _548_ | _549_ | 550 |

2.

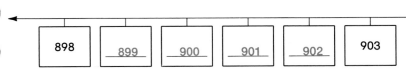

| 898 | _899_ | _900_ | _901_ | _902_ | 903 |

ADDITIONAL PRACTICE

p. 282   *Write the number.*

1. 2 hundreds 6 tens 3 ones   [263]

2. 4 hundreds 2 tens 8 ones   [428]

3. 5 hundreds 8 tens 4 ones   [584]

4. 1 hundred 7 tens 9 ones   [179]

5. 3 hundreds 5 tens 5 ones   [355]

Write how many.

6. 679 [6] hundreds [7] tens [9] ones

7. 248 [2] hundreds [4] tens [8] ones

8. 737 [7] hundreds [3] tens [7] ones

9. 332 [3] hundreds [3] tens [2] ones

p. 288   *Count by ones. Write the missing numbers.*

1. 649 [650] [651] 652

2. 317 [318] [319] 320

3. 432 [433] [434] 435

4. 810 [811] [812] 813

5. 540 [541] [542] 543

6. 919 [920] [921] 922

CHAPTER 9

Chapter Review/Test

Language and Mathematics

Choose the correct words.

1. In 358 the 3 means 3 ___hundreds___.

2. The sign < means ___is less than___.

3. 1 hundred 6 tens = 16 ___tens___.

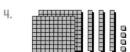

is less than
hundreds
tens

Concepts and Skills

Write the number.

4.

___2___ hundreds ___3___ tens ___4___ ones

___234___

5. 5 hundreds 7 tens 6 ones ___576___

6. 4 hundreds 9 tens 0 ones ___490___

Write how many.

7. 748 ___7___ hundreds ___4___ tens ___8___ ones

8. 650 ___6___ hundreds ___5___ tens ___0___ ones

Count by ones. Write the missing numbers.

9.
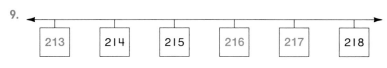

| 213 | 214 | 215 | 216 | 217 | 218 |

USING THE CHAPTER REVIEW/TEST

The Chapter Review/Test may be used as a review to survey children's knowledge and understanding of the chapter material. Or it may be used as a test to formally assess children's understanding of the concepts and skills taught in the chapter. If used as a test, you may wish to assign one or more of the resources listed in *Reinforcement and Remediation* on p. 298 after reviewing children's test results.

If the Chapter Review/Test is used as a review, you may wish to have children work in pairs to complete it. Have them talk about the value of the digit 3 in each of the numbers: 423, 631, 357. Then, you can use the Chapter Tests—Forms A, B, and C—provided in the *Testing Program Blackline Master and Teacher's Manual* for testing purposes. Any of these forms may be used for pretesting, posttesting, or retesting.

A performance assessment activity for the key concept in this chapter is provided on page 299.

10. Which number comes after?

125, _126_

11. Which number comes before?

_117_, 118

Compare. Write > or <.

12. 520 ⊗ 230   236 ⊗ 603   300 ⊗ 650
13. 442 ⊗ 501   714 ⊗ 696   900 ⊗ 899
14. 897 ⊗ 789   405 ⊗ 504   624 ⊗ 264

Problem Solving

Make a list to show all the possible numbers.
Then solve.

15. Gloria forgot her aunt's
    apartment number.
    She remembers these things.
    It had two digits.
    They were different.
    The digits were either 3, 7, or 9.
    The number was less than 73.

Start with	Possible Numbers
3	37, 39
7	73, 79
9	93, 97

The number is _37_ or _39_.

16. A number has two different digits.
    The digits are 2, 5, or 8.
    The number is greater than 82.

Start with	Possible Numbers
2	25, 28
5	52, 58
8	82, 85

The number is _85_.

MEETING INDIVIDUAL NEEDS

Reinforcement and Remediation

CHAP. OBJ.	TEST ITEMS	PUPIL'S EDITION pp.			TEACHER'S EDITION pp.	TEACHER RESOURCES	
		Lesson	Extra Practice	Practice Plus	Alt. Teaching Strategy	Reteaching	Practice
9A	1, 3–8	277–282	286		278, 280, 282	86, 87	86, 87
9B	9–11	287–288	295	296	288	89	89
9C	2, 12–14	289–290	295	296	290	90	90
9D	15–16	283–284, 291–292	286			88, 91	88, 91

For Students Acquiring English (SAE)

Before beginning the Chapter Review/Test with SAE children, scan the pages for any unfamiliar vocabulary that should be pretaught. You may wish to pair or group SAE children with non-SAE children. You may also wish to repeat some of the activities and techniques for SAE children that were suggested earlier in this chapter.

CHAPTER 9

AT·A·GLANCE p. 299

OBJECTIVE
Assess whether children understand place value and comparing and ordering numbers to 1,000.

MATERIALS
Manipulatives number cards for 0–9 (or punchouts) per pair

Teacher Resources
Performance Assessment booklet, pp. 36–38

For Students Acquiring English (SAE)

Before beginning the performance assessment with SAE children, scan the page for any unfamiliar vocabulary that should be pretaught. You may wish to pair or group SAE children with non-SAE children. You may also wish to repeat some of the activities and techniques for SAE children that were suggested earlier in this chapter.

Work with a partner.

Use number cards to make 3 different numbers.
Make a number between 100 and 999 each time.
Write each number you make.

	Numbers Made	Write how many.
1.		_____ hundreds _____ tens _____ ones
2.		_____ hundreds _____ tens _____ ones
3.		_____ hundreds _____ tens _____ ones

Rewrite the numbers in order, from least to greatest.
Then complete the table.
Use models and Workmat 3 if you want.

	Numbers in Order	1 Less	10 Less	100 Less
4.				
5.				
6.				

You may put this page in your Portfolio

Macmillan/McGraw-Hill

USING PERFORMANCE ASSESSMENT
The Performance Assessment activity may be used to informally assess children's understanding of the key concept(s) of the chapter. Additional assessment activities and Math Journal Options are provided in the *Performance Assessment* booklet.

Performing the Activity
Assign children to work in pairs. Have children work together to make three 3-digit numbers using number cards. Let children individually record the numbers in the top table. They should then rewrite the numbers in order from least to greatest, and complete the table at the bottom of the page.

Evaluation Guidelines
Use these criteria to help determine the holistic score for each child. The holistic scoring scale can be found in the Teacher's Reference Section.

- Can children form 3-digit numbers?
- Can children compare and order 3-digit numbers?
- Do children understand place value?

[Example Response: 725; 7 hundreds 2 tens 5 ones]

If children do not have a full understanding of the key concept(s), you may wish to use the Alternative Teaching Strategies or the MAC Activities within the chapter.

You may wish to have children put their final revised work in their portfolios.

A formal assessment of the concepts and skills taught in this chapter is provided on pages 297–298.

Enrichment For All

> I will round to the nearest hundred.

Rounding

Dory rode her bike 370 meters. About how far did she ride?

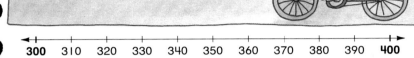

|—+—|—|—|—|—|—|—|—|—|—→
300 310 320 330 340 350 360 370 380 390 **400**

Dory rode about 400 meters.

> 370 is nearer to 400.

Solve. Round to the nearest hundred.

|—+—|—|—|—|—|—|—|—|—|—
200 210 220 230 240 250 260 270 280 290 **300**

1. Lisa walks from her house to school. It is 270 meters. About how far does she walk?

    about __300__ meters

2. Luis walks to the grocery store. It is 220 meters. About how far does he walk?

    about __200__ meters

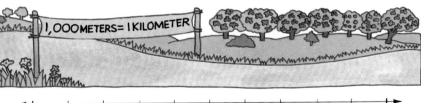

1,000 METERS = 1 KILOMETER

|—+—|—|—|—|—|—|—|—|—|—+
100 110 120 130 140 150 160 170 180 190 **200**

3. Alex drove 130 kilometers to visit his aunt. About how far did he drive?

    about __100__ kilometers

4. Tina drove 180 kilometers in one day. About how far did she drive?

    about __200__ kilometers

300 three hundred

A·T·A·GLANCE p. 300

OBJECTIVE
Round a number to the nearest hundred.

ASSIGNMENT GUIDE

COURSE	EXERCISES
Basic	p. 300: 1–4
Average	p. 300: 1–4
Challenge	p. 300: 1–4

For Students Acquiring English (SAE)

Read the page aloud to SAE children, explaining and demonstrating key vocabulary. Have children point to the number line in the textbook (or a similar one drawn on the chalkboard) as you explain concepts presented. For ex. 1–4, draw a number line on the chalkboard showing numbers from 100 to 300 by tens. To complete the exercises, read each one aloud. Ask one volunteer to stand under the number mentioned in the exercise and two more volunteers to stand under the hundreds on either side of the number. Then have children decide to which number they should round by asking which two children are standing closer together.

---

1 PREPARE

WARM-UP To prepare children for rounding to the nearest hundred, write these numbers in a row on the chalkboard: 10 20 30 40 50 60 70 80 90 100. Have children estimate each to the nearest ten.

1. 36 [40] 3. 41 [40] 5. 54 [50]
2. 17 [20] 4. 28 [30] 6. 82 [80]

2 TEACH

QUESTIONING Have a volunteer read the problem at the top of the page.

■ **What number is in the middle on the number line?** [350]

■ **How many meters did Dory ride?** [370]

■ **What hundreds would you round 370 to?** [400] **Why?** [because 370 is closer to 400 than 300]

Explain to children that they would round down to the nearest hundred for any number from 301 to 349, and that they would round up to the nearest hundred for any number from 350 to 399.

3 PRACTICE·APPLY

Have children complete ex. 1–4, using the number lines to help in rounding.

CLOSE Guide children to summarize the lesson:

■ **If Dory had ridden 340 meters, about how far would she have gone? Round to the nearest hundred.** [300 meters]

CHAPTER 9

Name _____

Cumulative Review

Fill in the ◯ to answer each question.

1.

$$\begin{array}{r} 3 \\ + 5 \\ \hline \end{array}$$

2	8	9	10
◯	⬤	◯	◯

2. Complete.

2, 4, 6, 8, _?_

9	10	11	12
◯	⬤	◯	◯

3. What is the temperature?

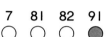
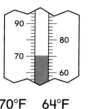

84°F	74°F	70°F	64°F
◯	◯	⬤	◯

4.

$$\begin{array}{r} 42 \\ + 49 \\ \hline \end{array}$$

7	81	82	91
◯	◯	◯	⬤

5.

$$\begin{array}{r} 78 \\ - 64 \\ \hline \end{array}$$

4	14	16	142
◯	⬤	◯	◯

6. What time is shown?

6:00	9:30	10:30	11:30
◯	◯	⬤	◯

7. Pedro has 24¢.
Larry gives him 17¢.
How much money does Pedro have now?

- ◯ 7¢
- ◯ 31¢
- ⬤ 41¢
- ◯ 51¢

Macmillan/McGraw-Hill

USING THE CUMULATIVE REVIEW

The Cumulative Review is presented in a multiple-choice format to provide practice in taking a standardized test. It gives children an opportunity to review previously learned skills. An answer sheet, similar to those used when taking standardized tests, can be found in the *Testing Program Blackline Masters and Teacher's Manual.*

The table that follows correlates the review items to the lesson pages on which the skills are taught.

Review Items	Text Pages		Review Items	Text Pages
1	29–30		5	221–225
2	61		6	251–252
3	172		7	203
4	191–195			

Testing Program Blackline Masters
In addition to the Cumulative Review in the Pupil's Edition, there are quarterly Cumulative Tests and an End-Year Test. These tests are multiple choice and provide additional opportunities for children to practice taking standardized tests.

Cumulative Tests measure children's performance on major skills and concepts taught during the previous quarters. The **End-Year Test** measures children's performance on major skills and concepts taught throughout the year.

Home Activity

Your child has been learning to read, write, and compare 3-digit numbers. Here is a game you can play to practice this skill.

Players:
2

Materials:
scissors
small box or paper bag
paper and pencil

Directions:

1. Help your child make number squares like the ones shown. Place the squares in the box or bag.

2. Each player draws boxes for 3 digits, as shown below.

3. Take turns picking one number at a time from the box or bag. Record the number in one of the digit places in the table. Place the numbers back in the box or bag. Repeat the activity until each player has recorded all 3 digits.

4. Players read and compare their numbers. The player with the larger 3-digit number scores 1 point. Repeat the activity 5 times. The first player to get 5 points wins that round. The loser goes first in the next game.

Variation:
Let the player with the smaller 3-digit number score 1 point.

8
5
0
6
1
4
9
3
2
7

AT·A·GLANCE p. 302

OBJECTIVE
Give family members an opportunity to share in their child's mathematics learning.

For Students Acquiring English (SAE)

Before assigning this Home Activity to SAE children, find out if someone at home will be able to work with them in English. If not, prepare them to complete the activity independently at home. Explain the directions of the activity and ask SAE children to restate them so you can check comprehension. Scan the page and preteach any difficult vocabulary or phrases that they may not know. If you feel that an SAE child will need extra help with the activity, you might assign that student a non-SAE partner and arrange a time for them to work on the activity in or out of school.

USING THE ACTIVITY

Have children look at the page. Explain that the page has a game that an adult in the family can help them complete. Read the page with the children, making sure that they understand what needs to be done. Tell children that they will do this page at home.

GEOMETRY

❝ *IN CHAPTER 10, you will be introducing your children to geometry. You will also have the opportunity to explore perimeter and area, symmetry, and congruent figures.* ❞

Notes
FROM THE AUTHOR

Here are some notes on the concepts presented in this chapter and how your children can apply them to solve problems.

DEVELOPING the CONCEPT of GEOMETRY

Encourage your children to examine and handle five common three-dimensional figures to get a feel for their shapes and notice their characteristics. Children are familiar with the shapes, but may not know their names.

sphere   cylinder   cone   cube   rectangular prism

Children should find ways to describe and classify the physical attributes of the shapes. For example, they might identify all shapes that have corners.

Your children then examine four common two-dimensional shapes.

    triangle

circle   triangle   rectangle   square

They again discuss these shapes in terms of their physical attributes. Children should identify shapes by the numbers of sides and corners.

Children can explore the relationship between three-dimensional and two-dimensional shapes by identifying the two-dimensional shape made by the face of a three-dimensional figure.

Gary Musser

PERIMETER and AREA

Children begin exploring perimeter by using arbitrary units to count the number of units around a figure. They then use standard units to find the perimeter.

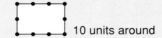 10 units around

Using square units to cover a shape allows children to explore area. They then count to find how many square units they used.

SYMMETRY

Folding paper shapes helps children determine which shapes have two sides that match, or a line of symmetry. They then can look at pictures and determine a line of symmetry.

CONGRUENT FIGURES

Help children use graph paper to draw figures that have the same size and same shape. They should understand that the figures they draw are congruent figures.

PROBLEM SOLVING

In **Problem Solving** your children (1) use a picture to solve a problem and (2) solve a problem by using a physical model.

In **Thinking Mathematically** children use logical reasoning to decide which pattern blocks they should use to cover the shapes in the Transform A Tron.

In **Decision Making** your children apply their knowledge about perimeter and area to plan how much yarn they need to decorate the perimeter of a bulletin board and how many pictures will fit on the board.

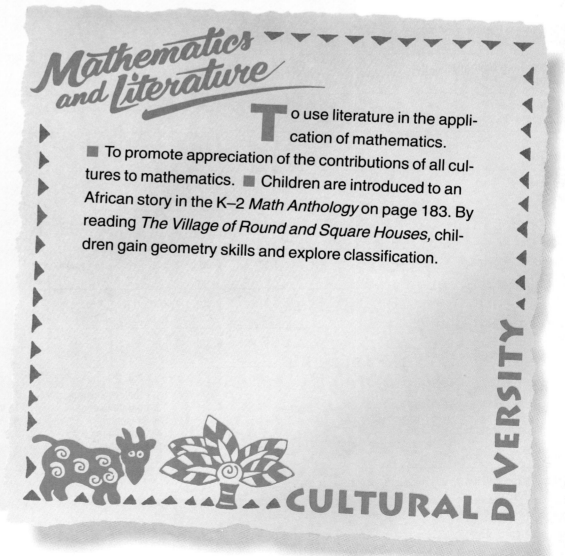

Mathematics and Literature

To use literature in the application of mathematics. ■ To promote appreciation of the contributions of all cultures to mathematics. ■ Children are introduced to an African story in the K–2 *Math Anthology* on page 183. By reading *The Village of Round and Square Houses*, children gain geometry skills and explore classification.

CULTURAL DIVERSITY

CHAPTER 10 • ORGANIZER

CHAPTER PLANNING GUIDE

A. Identify 3-dimensional figures — SAT, CTBS
B. Identify 2-dimensional figures and the number of sides and corners — MAT, CAT, SAT, ITBS
C. Find perimeter and area
D. Identify symmetrical and congruent figures — MAT, CAT, SAT, CTBS
E. Solve problems including those that invovle using a picture — MAT, CAT, SAT, ITBS, CTBS

SUGGESTED PACING-13 DAYS

LESSONS	NCTM STANDARDS	ASSIGNMENTS Basic/Average/Challenge	STUDENT EDITION Extra Practice/ Practice Plus	Manip. Plus	Reteach	Practice	Enrich	MAC Activities
Chapter Opener: "Surprises" page 303	1, 2, 3, 4, 9	p. 303: All						
1 Geometry page 304	1, 2, 3, 9	p. 304: All						
2 Three-Dimensional Figures pages 305–306	1, 2, 3, 9	p. 305: 5–7; p. 306: 1–6	p. 314	57, 58	92	92	92	183, 184
3 Two-Dimensional Figures pages 307–308	1, 2, 3, 9	p. 307: 1–4; p. 308: 1–8		59	93	93	93	185, 186
4 More Two-Dimensional Figures pages 309–310	1, 2, 3, 9	p. 309: 2–6; p. 310: 1–4, Reasoning	pp. 314, 326	60	94	94	94	187, 188
5 PS: Using a Picture pages 311–312	1, 2, 3, 9	p. 311: 1–5; p. 312: 1–8	p. 314		95	95	95	189, 190
6 PS: Thinking Mathematically page 313	1, 2, 3, 9	p. 313: All						
7 Perimeter pages 315–316	1, 2, 3, 9, 10	p. 315: 1–4, p. 316: 2–8	pp. 325, 326	61	96	96	96	191, 192
8 Area page 317	1, 2, 3, 9, 10	p. 317: 1–3	p. 325	62	97	97	97	193, 194
9 Volume page 318	1, 2, 3, 9, 10	p. 318: 1–6						
10 Symmetry page 319	1, 2, 3, 9	p. 319: 1–3	p. 325	63	98	98	98	195, 196
11 Congruent Figures page 320	1, 2, 3, 9	p. 320: 1–2	p. 325	64	99	99	99	197, 198
12 PS: Using a Physical Model pages 321–322	1, 2, 3, 8, 9	p. 321: 1–4; p. 322: 1–7			100	100	100	199, 200
13 PS: Decision Making page 323	1, 2, 3, 9, 10	p. 323: 1–5						

Technology: Computer page 324

Chapter Review/Test pages 327–328

Performance Assessment page 329

Cumulative Review page 331

Enrichment for All/Home Activity pages 330, 332

NATIONAL COUNCIL OF TEACHERS OF MATHEMATICS Grades K–4

1. Problem Solving
2. Communication
3. Reasoning
4. Connections
5. Estimation
6. Number Sense and Numeration
7. Concepts of Whole Number Operations
8. Whole Number Computation
9. Geometry and Spatial Sense
10. Measurement
11. Statistics and Probability
12. Fractions and Decimals
13. Patterns and Relationships

✓ Activity   Cooperative Learning

MEETING the NCTM STANDARDS

Problem Solving

Strategies and Skills	• using a picture pp. 311–312
	• using a physical model pp. 321–322
Applications	• **Decision Making** lesson p. 323
	• **Problem of the Day** TE pp. 304, 306B, 308B, 310B, 312B, 316B, 317C, 318A, 319C, 320C, 322B
Mathematical Investigations	• **Thinking Mathematically** lesson p. 313

Communication

Language	• using the language of mathematics TE pp. 305–306, 307–308, 309–310, 317, 318, 319, 324
Oral/Written	• using cooperative learning activities pp. 304, 305–306, 307–308, 313, 317, 318, 319, 320, 323; TE pp. 302I–302P
	• **Journal Writing** opportunities TE pp. 304, 306, 317A, 320A, 322

Reasoning

Critical Thinking	• answering questions that analyze and extend concepts pp. 303, 305, 309, 322, 323, 324

Connections

To other subject areas	• Literature p. 303; Literature TE pp. 303–304, 305
To all cultures	• African story, *The Village of Round and Square Houses*, *Math Anthology* p. 183

Concept Development

Geometry and Spatial Sense	• exploring the concept of geometry p. 304
	• using models to identify 3-dimensional figures pp. 305–306; TE pp. 302I–302J
	• using models to identify 2-dimensional figures and the number of sides and corners pp. 307–308, 309–310; TE p. 302L
	• using models to identify symmetrical and congruent figures pp. 319, 320; TE pp. 302O–302P
Measurement	• finding perimeter and area pp. 315–316, 317; TE pp. 302M–302N
	• exploring finding volume p. 318

ASSESSMENT OPTIONS

PERFORMANCE ASSESSMENT

Preassessment Activity

Before beginning Chapter 10, have children identify and describe geometric figures in the room. Assess children's descriptions of figures such as triangles, squares, circles, spheres, and rectangular prisms. Have children tell about the attributes of the figures, such as the corners and sides of objects, and whether they roll or are flat.

Ongoing Assessment

The Ongoing Assessment cards under MEETING INDIVIDUAL NEEDS on TE pp. 306, 317A, and 320A provide criteria and questions for assessing children's understanding of the key mathematical concepts developed in the chapter.

Journal Writing opportunities encourage children to write about mathematics. Their responses can be recorded either pictorially or in words. The journal writing opportunities on the Ongoing Assessment cards also allow you to assess children's understanding of the lessons.

In addition to the Ongoing Assessment cards, other assessment and journal writing opportunities in this chapter include:

• **CLOSE** TE pp. 304, 320A, 322

Performance Assessment Activity

The Performance Assessment activity on p. 329 provides an alternative to formal assessment. This activity assesses children's understanding of the key concepts of the chapter.

For performance assessment activities that are keyed to individual chapter objectives, see the *Performance Assessment* booklet.

BUILDING A PORTFOLIO

Children should be encouraged to keep a selection of their best work in portfolios. The portfolios provide a way of documenting children's growth in understanding mathematical concepts. Portfolio opportunities in this chapter include:

• **Performance Assessment** p. 329
• **Class Project** TE p. 323A

If you wish to provide additional opportunities for portfolio work, you may choose to use:

• **MAC Activities** 183, 185, 186, 189, 190, 191, 192, 193, 194, 195, 196, 197, 199

You may also wish to have children include their journal writing from the Ongoing Assessment on TE pp. 306, 317A, 320A in their portfolio.

Formal Assessment

The **Chapter Review/Test** assesses children's understanding of the concepts and skills developed in the chapter. The **Cumulative Review** assesses children's understanding of the concepts and skills developed from the beginning of the year.

You can use **Form A** or **Form B** of the **Chapter Test** found in the *Testing Program Blackline Masters and Teacher's Manual* if you wish to use a multiple-choice

format to assess children's understanding of the chapter concepts and skills. You can use **Form C** if you wish to use a free-response format. Any of the forms may be used as a pretest, posttest, or for retesting.

The **COMPUTER MANAGEMENT SYSTEM**, or **CMS**, enables you to score **Forms A** and **B** of the **Chapter Test** quickly and automatically. It also prescribes learning activities based on children's test results.

For more information about Assessment, see the *Professional Handbook*.

MEETING INDIVIDUAL NEEDS

Common Error and Remediation

The Teacher's Edition notes for each Develop/Understand (Transitional/Abstract) lesson provide a common error analysis and a remediation activity. Some errors defy quick analysis and can only be identified by interviewing the child.

ALTERNATIVE TEACHING STRATEGY

Alternative Teaching Strategies appear frequently in the chapter. These strategies provide other presentations of the lessons for children who might benefit from instruction in different learning modalities: kinesthetic, visual, and/or auditory.

For Students Acquiring English (SAE)

Preteach vocabulary for **sphere, cylinder, cone, cube,** and **rectangular prism,** using real objects. Have SAE children touch and move the objects to show comprehension.

SAE notes appear periodically in the chapter. These notes provide suggestions for how to work with children to improve comprehension and build vocabulary.

MANIPULATIVES WORKSHOP

Ones models and connecting cubes are used in this chapter to demonstrate the concepts of area and volume. They provide concrete representations of square units and cubic units.

USING MANIPULATIVES

Here a child finds the area of a figure. The child covers the figure with square units.

The child counts to find an area of 12 square units.

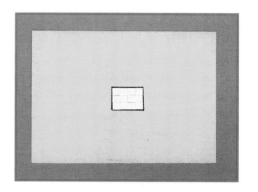

Here a child builds a box to explore volume.

The child makes a bottom layer with 4 cubes.

The child makes another layer.

The box has a volume of 8 cubic units.

MAKING MANIPULATIVES

See the Manipulatives section of the *Professional Handbook* for materials that can be used as a substitute for ones models and connecting cubes.

COOPERATIVE LEARNING WORKSHOP

GETTING STARTED

Accountability: Children can now be held responsible for **group products** and **projects** that call for high levels of **accountability.** In some of their small groups, they may also have begun to face the **problem of the "hitch-hiker,"** who wants to ride on the accomplishments of other members. Dividing the task into **jobs** and giving **roles** can help alleviate this problem. **Monitoring** small groups during the work followed by **feedback** from **teacher observation,** can also help emphasize to children that they are responsible for their contributions to group goals as well as for their individual learning.

Presenting their group product to other groups serves as both an authentic **performance assessment** and a good motivator for children. Finally, during the reflection period, children can use a number of **self-evaluation techniques** for both individuals and small groups.

IDEAS TO TRY

How Are We Doing? Children can now assess how well they played the roles, did the jobs, or completed the parts of the task assigned to them, and whether they remembered to use the cooperative skill. Each child should set goals for his or her own improvement and should be publicly acknowledged for them. Before each lesson, the group checks the learning log for everyone's improvement goals and pairs agree to coach one another on remembering them. Reflection at the end includes celebration of each member's improvement.

You can apply the assessment strategies in these lessons:
10-1 *Geometry* p. 304
10-2 *Three-Dimensional Figures* pp. 305–306
10-3 *Two-Dimensional Figures* pp. 307–308

Teaming Up: Children can work in groups of two pairs to make up and model geometry problems using a **pairs check** structure. Each pair first works separately to model a problem. For example in lesson 10-8, one

partner can be in charge of choosing the shape and the second partner decides how many units. Together they decide on the modeling. For the next problem, they switch roles. Then each pair chooses one problem to pose to the other pair, who must model it appropriately. Each pair checks the work of the other pair. Be sure to remind the partners to appreciate each other when they are correct, and to encourage one another when they need to try again.

You can apply the above team-building structures in these lessons:
10-8 *Area* p. 317
10-9 *Volume* p. 318
10-10 *Symmetry* p. 319

SEE ALSO

Cooperative Learning Tip for lessons 10-6 Thinking Mathematically p. 313A; 10-7 p. 316; 10-12 Problem Solving p. 322

The Cooperative Learning section of the *Professional Handbook* for additional information

---

ACTIVITY
INTERACTIVE BULLETIN BOARD

SETUP Cut rectangles, circles, squares, triangles, and so on from different-colored construction paper.

PROCEDURE 👥 Display many colorful paper shapes on the bulletin board. Have children cut out their own shapes to create make-believe animals, and ask them to write short stories about their animals.

Call on volunteers to describe their animals and read their stories aloud. Have children count the number of each different shape within their pictures.

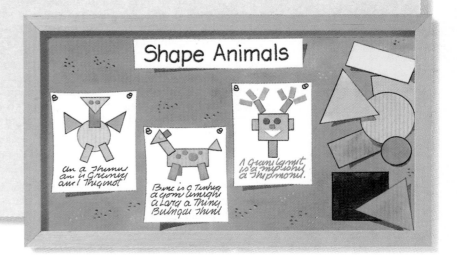

MANIPULATIVES plus ACTIVITY

For use before LESSON 10.2, pp. 305-306

57

THREE-DIMENSIONAL FIGURES

OBJECTIVES
Identify and classify three-dimensional figures.
Explore the attributes of three-dimensional figures.

MATERIALS
Classroom Materials
models of spheres, cones*, cubes*, cylinders*, and rectangular prisms*, small index cards
Teacher Resources
*Teacher Aids 13, 14

WHOLE GROUP ACTIVITY

Display on a table models of a sphere, a cone, a cube, a cylinder, and a rectangular prism, most of which can be made from copies of Teacher Aids 13 and 14. Gather children around the table and discuss the shapes.

Hold up a sphere and have it identified. Write *sphere* on a card and place it next to the model. Continue the activity to identify the cone, cube, cylinder, and rectangular prism.

Have the class decide on ways to sort the models into groups. Allow them to choose their own criteria. Have children explain their groupings. [Possible responses: figures with round parts and figures with flat parts; figures that roll and do not roll; figures that stack and do not stack]

Have children play "Inside Shapes" in an open area.

■ **Pretend you are inside a large cylinder. Use your hands to feel the sides. What do the sides feel like?** [round or curved]

■ **Are there any corners inside your cylinder?** [No.]
■ **Does it have a top?** [Yes.]
■ **What does the top feel like?** [round and flat]

Continue the activity by having children imagine they are inside a cube or a sphere.

EXTENDING THE ACTIVITY
Conduct an art lesson on how to draw a cube, a sphere, or a cylinder. Have children write a story entitled, "If I Were a _____ (Cube, Cylinder, Sphere)."

ONGOING ASSESSMENT
✓ Are children able to identify attributes of three-dimensional figures?

For use before LESSON 10.2, pp. 305–306

58

MORE THREE-DIMENSIONAL FIGURES

OBJECTIVE
Explore the attributes of three-dimensional figures.

MATERIALS
Classroom Materials
models of three-dimensional figures*, model of a sphere
Teacher Resources
*Teacher Aids 13, 14

WHOLE GROUP ACTIVITY ⬍

Display on a table models of spheres, cones, cubes, cylinders, and rectangular prisms, most of which can be made from copies of Teacher Aids 13 and 14. Have children gather around the table and identify each shape by name.

Hold up a cube. Point out the faces of the cube, the edges, and the corners. Pass around several cubes for children to examine.

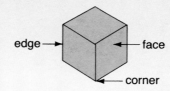

Have children describe the cube. During the discussion, elaborate on children's descriptions by introducing the terms *face, edge,* and *corner*. You may wish to have children find the number of each attribute—face, edge, and corner—on a cube.

Repeat the activity with a rectangular prism. Have children compare what they found for each shape.

Repeat the activity with a sphere, a cone, and a cylinder.

EXTENDING THE ACTIVITY

Have children write a letter to an imaginary friend who cannot see. Have them choose shapes to describe to the friend.

ONGOING ASSESSMENT

✓ Are children able to identify attributes of three-dimensional figures?

For use before LESSON 10.3, pp. 307-308

59

TWO-DIMENSIONAL FIGURES

OBJECTIVE
Identify and classify two-dimensional figures.

MATERIALS
Classroom Materials pipe cleaner models of two-dimensional figures, masking tape, index cards

WHOLE GROUP ACTIVITY ⬆️

Use masking tape to make large figures of a square, a rectangle, a triangle, and a circle on an open area of the classroom floor. Also make models of the figures with pipe cleaners (at least one per child).

Display the pipe cleaner models on a table and gather children around the table.

Hold up the square and have it identified. Write *square* on an index card and place it next to the model. Continue the activity for a rectangle, a triangle, and a circle.

Have the class decide on ways to sort the models into groups. Allow them to choose their own criteria. Have children explain their groupings. [Possible responses: figures with straight sides and figures that are round; figures that can roll and cannot roll; and so on]

Direct children's attention to the 4 shapes on the floor. Allow children time to move freely around the shapes. Then have them walk on the line around each shape as they say the name of the figure.

Give each child a model of one of the figures. Have children stand near the shapes on the floor that are the same as the shapes they are holding.

■ **Circles, spin around in a circle.**

■ **Squares, trace a square trampoline on the floor and pretend to jump up and down on it.**

■ **Triangles, use your arms to show a triangle shape for the roof of a house.**

■ **Rectangles, trace a rectangle picture frame in front of your face.**

EXTENDING THE ACTIVITY

Have groups hold hands and together form the shape they were assigned: circle, square, triangle, or rectangle. Assign groups different shapes. Repeat the activity.

ONGOING ASSESSMENT

✓ Are children able to identify two-dimensional figures?

For use before LESSON 10.4, pp. 309-310

60

MORE TWO-DIMENSIONAL FIGURES

OBJECTIVE
Explore the attributes of two-dimensional figures.

MATERIALS
Classroom Materials
square, circle, triangle, and rectangle models, masking tape, construction-paper shapes

WHOLE GROUP ACTIVITY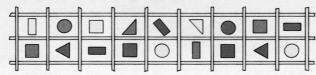

Display models of squares, circles, triangles, and rectangles on a table. Have children gather around the table.

Ask children to identify each shape by name. Have them identify the attributes of each shape, such as the number of sides and corners.

Use masking tape and construction-paper shapes to make a game board as shown.

Have children play "Shape Hop." Give each child an instruction to follow.

■ **Hop on all 3-sided figures.** [The child hops on the triangles.]

■ **Hop on all 4-sided figures.** [The child hops on the squares and rectangles.]

■ **Hop on all squares.** [The child hops on the squares.]

■ **Hop on all figures with corners.** [The child hops on the squares, rectangles, and triangles.]

■ **Hop on all circles.** [The child hops on the circles.]

EXTENDING THE ACTIVITY

Vary the game by having the child name the attribute of the shapes that he or she would like to hop on.

ONGOING ASSESSMENT

✓ Are children able to identify the attributes of two-dimensional figures?

For use before
**LESSON 10.7,
pp. 315-316**

61
PERIMETER

OBJECTIVE
Explore the concept of
perimeter.

MATERIALS
Classroom Materials
construction paper, glue,
crayons, 3 sizes of
macaroni

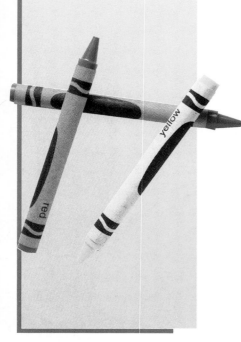

WHOLE GROUP ACTIVITY

Draw a 6-inch by 4-inch rectangle on a sheet of
construction paper for each child. Give each child
1 drawing and crayons.

Have children imagine that they are farmers and
that the rectangle drawing is a corral. Have children
choose animals for their farms and draw them inside the corral.

Discuss that the corral needs a fence. Give each
child 1 type of macaroni and glue. Tell children to
glue the macaroni around the corral to make a
fence.

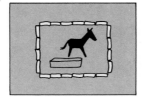 

Call on volunteers to tell how many pieces of macaroni they used to build their fences. [Answers will
vary based on the size of the macaroni used.]

■ **The distance around the corral is the same in
all pictures. Why do you think different farmers
used different numbers of macaroni? Discuss
this with your neighbor farmers.**

Have children share what they found. Guide them
to see that the different sizes of macaroni resulted
in the different number of pieces used.

■ **What other situations would you need to find
how long it is around a shape?** [Possible responses: when you are building a fence around a
house; when you are making a frame for a picture]

EXTENDING THE ACTIVITY

Have children make a frame around a piece of their
own artwork. Use macaroni or other uniform materials. Discuss the number of pieces that were needed
to make each frame.

ONGOING ASSESSMENT

✔ Are children able to use units to find
the length around a figure?

MANIPULATIVES *plus* ACTIVITY

For use before LESSON 10.8, p. 317

62
AREA

OBJECTIVE
Explore the concept of area.

MATERIALS
Classroom Materials
workmat per child
Manipulatives 10 , 10 ▢, 15 ▱, and 25 △ (or punchouts) per group

SMALL GROUP ACTIVITY

Make a workmat by drawing a 3-inch square on a sheet of paper. Duplicate and distribute 1 copy per child.

Assign children to work in groups of four. Give each group 10 yellow, 10 orange, 15 red, and 25 green pattern blocks. Assign each child a color and have the child work with that color of block.

Have children imagine that the square on the workmat is the floor of a room and that the blocks are floor tiles. Have children use blocks to cover the square. The floor should be completely covered.

Have children count how many blocks it took to cover the floor completely. Then have group members compare the number of blocks they used.

■ **Did it take more yellow blocks or more red blocks to cover the square?** [red]

■ **Did it take more blue blocks or more orange blocks to cover the square?** [orange]

■ **Which color needed the most blocks to cover the square?** [green]

■ **Which color block covered the square exactly?** [orange]

■ **What shape is the orange block?** [square]

EXTENDING THE ACTIVITY

Find a floor that is covered with square tiles. Have children work together to count how many square tiles were needed to cover the floor.

ONGOING ASSESSMENT
✓ Are children able to use units to determine the area of a figure?

WHOLE GROUP ACTIVITY 🕐

Draw lines through several sheets of construction paper as shown.

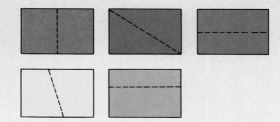

Hold up the first sheet of paper.

■ **If I fold this sheet of paper on the line, would the 2 sides fit together exactly?** [Yes.]

Fold the paper and have a volunteer verify that the 2 sides match. Continue with the other sheets.

■ **Why did some sheets of paper fold to make 2 parts that match and some did not?** [The folding line was in a different place on each sheet of paper.]

SMALL GROUP ACTIVITY 🕐 👥

Assign children to work in groups of three. Cut out 1 construction-paper square, circle, diamond, and heart shapes per group. Also cut out construction-paper shapes per group as shown.

Give each group a set of shapes. Have group members work together to fold each shape to see whether they can find 2 sides that match exactly. Encourage children to fold each shape to find all the possible ways to get 2 sides that match.

Have children share with the class what they found.

EXTENDING THE ACTIVITY

Provide small groups with pattern blocks. Have them work together to build designs that are symmetrical.

ONGOING ASSESSMENT

✓ Are children able to identify symmetry in shapes?

For use before LESSON 10.10, p. 319

63
SYMMETRY

OBJECTIVE
Explore the concept of symmetry.

MATERIALS
Classroom Materials
construction paper, scissors
Manipulatives 1 set of pattern blocks (or punchouts) per group (EXTENDING THE ACTIVITY only)

For use before LESSON 10.11, p. 320

64
CONGRUENCE

OBJECTIVE
Explore the concept of congruence.

MATERIALS
Classroom Materials
1 workmat per child
Manipulatives 5 ○,
5 ◢, 5 ▲, 5 ◣, 5 ◇,
5 ▢ (or punchouts) per child

WHOLE GROUP ACTIVITY 🕐

Prepare and duplicate a workmat per child by tracing each pattern block. Also draw the shapes in slightly smaller and slightly larger versions.

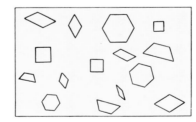

SMALL GROUP ACTIVITY ↕ 👥

Assign children to work in small groups of three. Give each child a set of pattern blocks (5 of each color). Tell children to sort the blocks by color.

■ **What is the same about the blocks in each group you made?** [same color, same size, same shape]

Have children stack the blocks to test.

Hold up two yellow pattern blocks.

■ **These two yellow blocks are the same size and the same shape. How can I check to be sure?** [Place 1 block on top of the other to see if they match exactly.]

Give each child a workmat. Tell children to use their pattern blocks to find the shapes on the worksheet that are the same size and same shape as the blocks.

EXTENDING THE ACTIVITY

Challenge children to find two objects that are congruent. Have children share the objects they found and describe why they are congruent.

ONGOING ASSESSMENT

✓ Are children able to identify objects that are congruent?

READ ALOUD

THE RANDOM HOUSE BOOK
OF POETRY FOR CHILDREN
Selected By Jack Prelutsky

Mathematics and Literature

Listening and Speaking

The Read-Aloud selection can be used
with the Chapter 10 Opener and Lesson 10-1
on pages 303-304.

**Tape 2, Side 2
Selection 1**

SURPRISES

by Jean Conder Soule
from *THE RANDOM HOUSE BOOK
OF POETRY FOR CHILDREN*

Surprises are round
Or long and tallish.
Surprises are square
Or flat and smallish.

Surprises are wrapped
With paper and bow,
And hidden in closets
Where secrets won't show.

Surprises are often
Good things to eat;
A get-well toy or
A birthday treat.

Surprises come
In such interesting sizes—
I LIKE
SURPRISES!

AT·A·GLANCE pp. 303-304

LESSON OBJECTIVES
Explore mathematical concepts through literature.
Explore the concept of geometry.

ASSIGNMENT GUIDE

COURSE	EXERCISES
Basic	p. 303: All; p. 304: All
Average	p. 303: All; p. 304: All
Challenge	p. 303: All; p. 304: All

MATERIALS
Classroom Materials balls, blocks, and other small classroom objects; large paper bags

Teacher Resources
Math Anthology, p. 182
Read-Aloud Cassette 2, Side 2, Selection 1

SKILLS TRACE
GEOMETRY

Explore (Concrete) 304, 318	Develop/Understand (Transitional/Abstract) 305–306, 307–308, 309–310, 315–316, 317, 319, 320
Practice 314, 325, 326, 327–328, 331, 389, 419	Apply 311–312, 313, 321–322, 323, 324

CHAPTER 10

Geometry

READ ALOUD

THE RANDOM HOUSE BOOK OF POETRY FOR CHILDREN Selected By Jack Prelutsky

👂 Listen to the poem <u>Surprises</u>.

🗣 Talk about some shapes that surprises might be.
Tell about the shape of a surprise you would like.
Answers will vary.

303

Mathematics and Literature

PUPIL'S EDITION pp. 303-304

Page 303 Read the poem "Surprises" found on page 302P or in *Math Anthology* to children, or play Read-Aloud Cassette 2, Side 2, Selection 1 for them.

■ **What are some of the shapes that surprises come in?** [round, long, tall, square, flat]

■ **What two ways are often used to keep surprises a secret?** [Surprises are wrapped in ribbons and paper; surprises can be hidden in closets.]

Discuss the directives on the page. Before children respond to the first directive, reread the first stanza of the poem.

Page 304 ■ Working Together Assign each child a partner. Supply each pair with small objects and a paper bag. Make sure the objects

① PREPARE
WARM-UP To review attributes, hold up pairs of classroom objects and have children tell which one is larger or smaller, which one is heavier or lighter, which one is red, and so on.

② TEACH
DISCUSSING Before reading the poem "Surprises," discuss with children times when they give or receive surprises. Birthdays and special holidays may be mentioned. Ask children if they have ever tried to guess a present by feeling the package. Invite them to tell another way the contents of a surprise package may often be guessed. [by looking at the shape of the package]

Name _____

Geometry

Working Together

Gather objects in the room. Then use a large grocery bag.

Have a partner close his or her eyes while you put one object in the bag.

Then have your partner feel the object and tell about its shape.

Give clues to help your partner guess the object.

do not have sharp edges. Have children identify the objects shown in the picture of the classroom. Read the directions aloud.

Check for Understanding

■ **What should you do when you feel the object?** [Tell about its shape.]

GUIDED PRACTICE Have one child place an object in the bag while the other child closes his or her eyes. Encourage children to guess the mystery object.

For reteaching, use Alternative Strategy.

PRACTICE Have children continue the activity.

MEETING INDIVIDUAL NEEDS

For Students Acquiring English (SAE)

The activity on page 304 may be difficult for SAE children with limited vocabularies. Be sure to pair SAE and non-SAE partners to collect the items from the room together. Before beginning the activity, have the non-SAE child state the name of each object and describe it aloud.

ALTERNATIVE TEACHING STRATEGY

ACTIVITY

MATERIALS classroom objects of various shapes, large bag

KINESTHETIC/AUDITORY Have children close their eyes as you place an object in the bag. Tie the bag closed and pass it around the group, having children feel the object through the bag. Then ask questions about the attributes of the object in the bag; for example: "Is it hard or soft? Is it round or square? Is it narrow or wide? Does it have sides and corners?" Write children's responses on the chalkboard. Then reread the description and have children guess the name of the object.

CLOSE Guide children to summarize the lesson:

■ **What object was the most difficult to guess? Why?** [Answers will vary, depending upon the objects used.]

Problem of the Day

Manny described a shape. It has 8 corners and 6 sides. Each side is the same. What shape did Manny describe? [a block or a cube]

AT·A·GLANCE pp. 305-306

LESSON OBJECTIVE
Identify three-dimensional figures.

ASSIGNMENT GUIDE

COURSE	EXERCISES
Basic	p. 305: 5–7; p. 306: 1–6
Average	p. 305: 5–7; p. 306: 1–6
Challenge	p. 305: 5–7; p. 306: 1–6
Extra Practice, p. 314	

MATERIALS
Classroom Materials objects such as balls, cans, and blocks in the shape of spheres, cylinders, cones, cubes, and rectangular prisms

Teacher Resources
Reteaching 92   Practice 92   Enrichment 92
MAC Act. 183, 184   Teacher Aids 13, 14
Math Anthology, pp. 183–188

SKILLS TRACE
GEOMETRY

Explore (Concrete) 304, 318	**Develop/Understand (Transitional/Abstract)** 305–306, 307–308, 309–310, 317, 320
Practice 314, 325, 326, 327–328, 419	**Apply** 311–312, 313, 321–322, 323

See *MANIPULATIVES PLUS 57–58,* pp. 302I–J.

PREPARE

WARM-UP To prepare children for identifying three-dimensional figures, hold up balls of various colors and sizes. Ask children to describe how they are alike and different. Repeat with blocks of various shapes and sizes.

Mathematics and Literature **CULTURAL CONNECTION**

TEACH

DISCUSSING Display a collection of solid objects. Read *The Village of Round and Square Houses.* Have the children pick shapes they think might look like the houses in the village. Encourage them to describe the characteristics of the shapes they chose.

Then have five children come to the front of the room and give each a **sphere, cylinder, cone, cube,** or **rectangular prism** to hold. As each

---

Three-Dimensional Figures

sphere   **cylinder**   **cone**   **cube**   **rectangular prism**

Working Together

Look in the room.
Find objects that are like the shapes above.
Possible answers given.

1. Which ones can roll? sphere, cylinder, cone

2. Which ones have flat sides? cube and rectangular prism, cylinder and cone have flat surfaces

3. Which ones have corners? cube, rectangular prism;

4. Which ones come to a point? Cone; some children may note that the surfaces of a cube and a rectangular prism have points.

Compare the objects.
How are they alike? How are they different? In their own words, children may note similarities and differences in surfaces and corners.

5. and

6. and

7. Tell what you think of the invention.
Is it useful? Answers will vary. Children may note that the box comes to a point at the bottom and cannot rest on a flat surface.

Macmillan/McGraw-Hill

---

shape is displayed, ask children to identify it by name. Supply the name if children are unable to do so.

Write the mathematical name for each shape on the chalkboard.

PUPIL'S EDITION pp. 305-306

Page 305 Discuss the shapes pictured at the top of the page.

WORKING TOGETHER Make sure objects with these shapes are available. Assign each child a partner and have them discuss ex. 1–4, while handling the objects.

Check for Understanding

■ **Which shapes could not roll off a table?** [cube, rectangular prism]

Ring the objects that have the same shape.

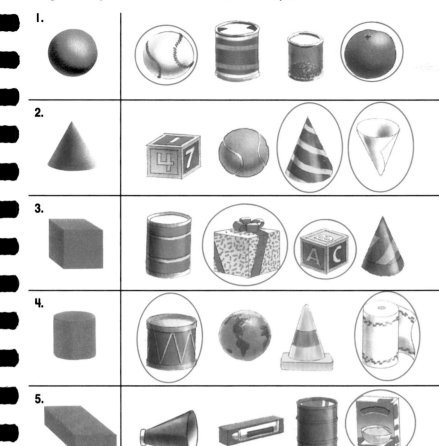

1.

2.

3.

4.

5.

Mixed Review ▪▪

Write > or <.

6. 457 ⊚> 299   721 ⊚< 754   899 ⊚< 988

Extra Practice, page 314

ACTIVITY *Common Error and Remediation*

MATERIALS 3-dimensional models (Teacher Aids 13, 14); picture and name cards

Some children may confuse the names of shapes. Work individually with each child. Display a sphere and identify it. Have the child repeat the name with you. Then display all the picture and name cards and have the child select the two cards that match the shape. Repeat for each shape.

ONGOING ASSESSMENT

OBSERVATION Determine if children identify three-dimensional figures and their characteristics correctly on p. 305.

INTERVIEW (1) What do you see in the classroom that is shaped like a sphere? like a cone? (2) Can you think of a common object that is shaped like a cylinder?

JOURNAL WRITING You may wish to have children record their responses in their math journals.

ACTIVITY

ALTERNATIVE TEACHING STRATEGY

MATERIALS oaktag, marker, bag; models of a cone, cylinder, cube, rectangular prism (Teacher Aids 13, 14); sphere

KINESTHETIC Display and identify a shape. Then pass it around the class and ask children to handle it. As they do so, have them describe what they feel. Write each shape name on a strip of oaktag and have children read the name with you. Repeat for all five shapes. Then have children cover their eyes as you select one shape and place it inside a bag. Pass the bag around the class and have children feel the shape without looking. Ask a volunteer to find the strip with the matching shape name. Repeat for all the shapes.

GUIDED PRACTICE   ex. 5–7: Have children identify the shape of the container in ex. 7. For reteaching, use Common Error and Remediation or Alternative Strategy.

Page 306   Review the names of the shapes shown in the left-hand column.

3 PRACTICE·APPLY   **PRACTICE**   ex. 1–6

C L O S E   Guide children to summarize the lesson:
■ **What is the shape of an orange?** [sphere]
■ **What is the shape of a book?** [rectangular prism]
■ **What is the shape of a metal pipe?** [cylinder]

■ **What is the shape of a wooden block?** [cube or rectangular prism]
■ **What is the shape of a party hat?** [cone or cylinder]

MAC Activity 183:
Basic-to-Average

MAC Activity 183

On Your Own   Pair and Share   In a Group

THINKING GEOMETRICALLY ■ CREATURE SHAPES

Materials modeling clay, craft sticks, toothpicks

Have children use modeling clay to create the five shapes presented in this lesson. You may wish to demonstrate how craft sticks can be used to mold the clay. Then have children use toothpicks to fasten the shapes together and create creatures which may either be realistic or imaginary. Each child should name his or her creature and write a description of the creature. Display children's creatures and descriptions around the classroom.

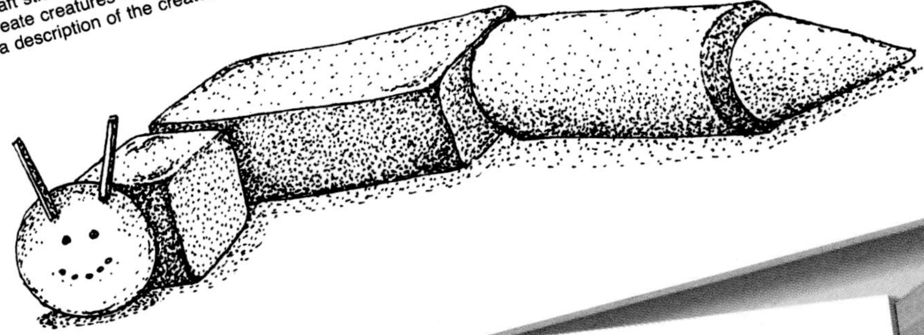

MAC Activity 184

On Your Own   Pair and Share   In a Group

MATH AND CONSUMERS ■ THE SHAPE STORE

Materials drawing paper, crayons

Have children tell about visits to the grocery store or supermarket. Discuss how most stores are organized by type of food or merchandise; for example, meat in one section, vegetables in another, soap products in another, and so on. Tell children to imagine that a new market has opened in which everything is organized by shape. Have children draw five shelves on their paper and label each shelf with these shape names: *sphere*, *cylinder*, *cone*, *cube*, *rectangular prism*. Have each child think of at least one item found in the grocery store that has each shape and draw it on the correct shelf.

SPHERES
CYLINDERS
CONES
CUBES
RECTANGULAR PRISM

▲ MAC Activity 184:
Average-to-Challenge

RETEACHING-92

Name

THREE-DIMENSIONAL FIGURES

Study

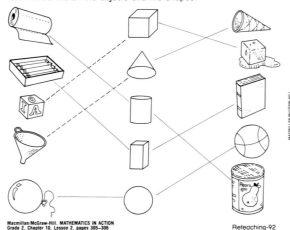

sphere   cylinder   cube   cone   rectangular prism

Check

Draw lines. Match the objects and the shapes.

MACMILLAN/McGRAW-HILL

Macmillan/McGraw-Hill, MATHEMATICS IN ACTION
Grade 2, Chapter 10, Lesson 2, pages 305–306

Reteaching-92

PRACTICE-92

Name

THREE-DIMENSIONAL FIGURES

sphere   cylinder   cube   cone   rectangular prism

Ring the objects with the same shape.

1.
2.
3.
4.
5.

MACMILLAN/McGRAW-HILL

Macmillan/McGraw-Hill, MATHEMATICS IN ACTION
Grade 2, Chapter 10, Lesson 2, pages 305–306

Practice-92

ENRICHMENT-92

Name

THREE-DIMENSIONAL FIGURES

On Your Own   Pair and Share   In a Group

SHAPE PATTERNS

Ring the shape that comes next in the pattern.

1.

2.

3.

4.

5. Draw a pattern.
   Have a friend draw the next shape.

Patterns will vary.

MACMILLAN/McGRAW-HILL

Macmillan/McGraw-Hill, MATHEMATICS IN ACTION
Grade 2, Chapter 10, Lesson 2, pages 305–306

Enrichment-92

Problem of the Day

Ann owns a toy store. She wants to group toys by shape. Which of the following would *not* belong with the spheres: baseball, basketball, football, tennis ball? [football]

AT·A·GLANCE pp. 307-308

LESSON OBJECTIVE
Identify two-dimensional figures.

ASSIGNMENT GUIDE

COURSE	EXERCISES
Basic	p. 307: 1–4; p. 308: 1–8
Average	p. 307: 1–4; p. 308: 1–8
Challenge	p. 307: 1–4; p. 308: 1–8

MATERIALS
Classroom Materials objects such as a clock, flag, pennant, and handkerchief in the shape of circles, rectangles, triangles, and squares; unlined paper, crayons per child

Teacher Resources
Reteaching 93
Prob. Solv. 46
Practice 93
MAC Act. 185, 186
Enrichment 93

SKILLS TRACE

GEOMETRY	
Explore (Concrete) 304	Develop/Understand (Transitional/Abstract) 305–306, 307–308, 309–310, 315–316, 317, 320
Practice 314, 325, 326, 327–328, 331, 389, 419	Apply 311–312, 313, 321–322, 323, 324

See **MANIPULATIVES PLUS 59**, p. 302K.

1 PREPARE **WARM-UP** To review three-dimensional shapes, ask children to visualize the following objects and identify the corresponding three-dimensional shape:
- ice cube   [cube]
- roll of paper towels   [cylinder]
- box of rice   [rectangular prism]
- cantaloupe   [sphere]
- paper cup   [cone or cylinder]

2 TEACH **DISCUSSING** Draw several **circles** of varying sizes on the chalkboard.
- **Do these figures have the same shape?** [Yes.]
- **What is the name of this shape?** [circle]

Name _____

Two-Dimensional Figures

circles

triangles

rectangles

squares

Working Together

Look around the room.
Find objects that look like the shapes above.
Describe each shape. Answers will vary.
How are they alike?
How are they different? In their own words, children should note similarities and differences in number and length of sides, and number of corners.

Find two punchouts with the same shape for each. Trace.
For Exercises 1–4, check students' drawings.

Use your own paper.

1.
2.
3.
4.

Chapter 10   Geometry

three hundred seven **307**

Repeat to have children identify and label **triangles, rectangles,** and **squares.**

Draw a rectangle and a square.
- **How are the sides of the figures alike?** [They both have four sides.]

Explain that a rectangle has four straight sides and four corners. Then tell children that a square is a special rectangle that has four sides of equal length.

PUPIL'S EDITION pp. 307-308
Page 307 Discuss the display at the top of the page.

Color inside the shapes that are the same.

1.

2.

3.

4.

5.

Mixed Review ░░░░░░░░░░░░░░░░░░░░░░░░

Write the time.

6.

7.

8.

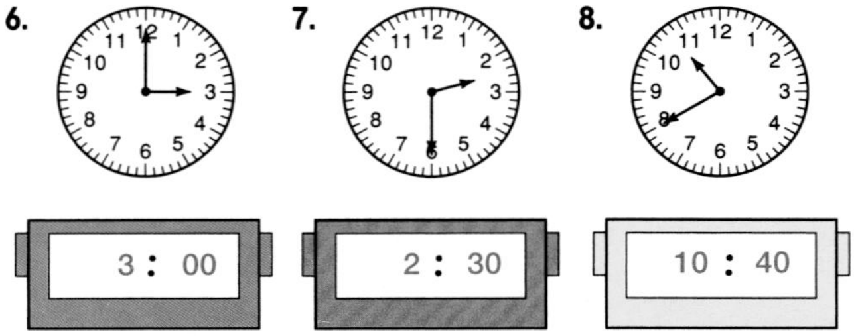

| 3 : 00 | 2 : 30 | 10 : 40 |

308 three hundred eight

MEETING INDIVIDUAL NEEDS

WORKING TOGETHER Make sure objects with these shapes are visible in the classroom. Assign each child a partner and have them do the activity.

Check for Understanding
■ **Which shape or shapes could a ruler help you draw? Why?**
[triangle, square, rectangle; because they all have straight sides]

GUIDED PRACTICE ex. 1–4: Distribute two-dimensional shapes of various sizes. Give children paper to do their tracings. For reteaching, use Common Error and Remediation or Alternative Strategy.

Page 308 Review the names of the shapes shown in the left-hand column.

3 PRACTICE•APPLY **PRACTICE** ex. 1–8

CLOSE Guide children to summarize the lesson:
■ **What shapes does each of these objects usually have?**
door [rectangle]
musical triangle [triangle]
clockface [circle]
window [square or rectangle]

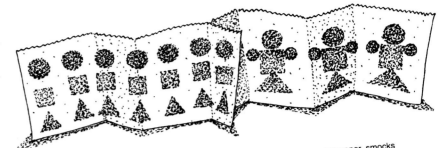

MAC Activity 186

MATH AND ART ▪ SHAPE PATTERN PAPER

On Your Own · Pair and Share · In a Group

Materials sponges, poster paint, saucers, large brown bags, scissors, water, newspaper, smocks

Show children how to cut up a sponge into the four shapes studied in this lesson (i.e., circle, triangle, rectangle, and square). Then have them cut down the sides of a large grocery bag and remove the bottom. Dilute the poster paint with water. Have children dip the sponge shapes into the paint and decorate the open bags. Some children may wish to create patterned rows based on shape and color. Others may decide to create shape pictures. After the paint is dry, the paper may be used as colorful book covers or as attractive gift wrap paper.

▲
MAC Activity 186:
Average-to-Challenge

THINKING GEOMETRICALLY ▪ MEET THE SHAPES

MAC Activity 185

On Your Own · Pair and Share · In a Group

MRS. CIRCLE
47 CIRCLES

Materials construction paper shapes: rectangles, squares, triangles, circles of different sizes; paste; drawing paper.

Give children cutouts of the four shapes introduced in this lesson. Have them use the shapes to make shape people; for example, Mrs. Circle, Mr. Square, Ms. Triangle, and Dr. Rectangle. Children can extend the project by using other shapes to create background buildings or landscapes. Have children write a brief caption for their picture, giving their character's name and telling how many of each shape they used to create the picture.

▲
MAC Activity 185:
Basic-to-Average

RETEACHING-93

Name

TWO-DIMENSIONAL FIGURES

Study

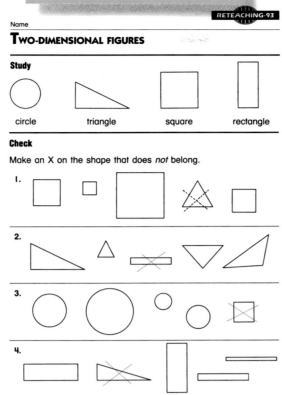

circle   triangle   square   rectangle

Check

Make an X on the shape that does *not* belong.

1.

2.

3.

4.

Reteaching-93

Macmillan/McGraw-Hill, MATHEMATICS IN ACTION
Grade 2, Chapter 10, Lesson 3, pages 307–308

PRACTICE-93

Name

TWO-DIMENSIONAL FIGURES

Color the shapes in the picture.

○))) blue →   □))) yellow →
circle   square

△))) green →   ▭))) red →
triangle   rectangle

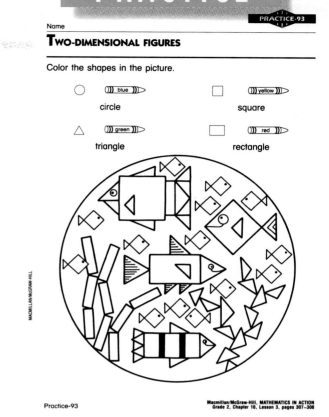

Practice-93

Macmillan/McGraw-Hill, MATHEMATICS IN ACTION
Grade 2, Chapter 10, Lesson 3, pages 307–308

ENRICHMENT-93

Name

TWO-DIMENSIONAL FIGURES

On Your Own   Pair and Share   In a Group

PUZZLE SHAPES

Find the number of shapes in each figure.
Work with a partner.

15 squares

63 rectangles

Answers may vary.

26 triangles   8 circles

Enrichment-93

Macmillan/McGraw-Hill, MATHEMATICS IN ACTION
Grade 2, Chapter 10, Lesson 3, pages 307–308

Problem of the Day

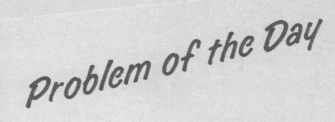

Mike has a square sandwich. How many triangles can he make by cutting it twice from one corner to the other?   [4 triangles]

AT·A·GLANCE pp. 309-310

LESSON OBJECTIVE
Identify the number of sides and corners of a two-dimensional figure.

ASSIGNMENT GUIDE

COURSE	EXERCISES
Basic	p. 309: 2–6; p. 310: 1–4, Reasoning
Average	p. 309: 2–6; p. 310: 1–4, Reasoning
Challenge	p. 309: 2–6; p. 310: 1–4, Reasoning
Extra Practice, p. 314	Practice Plus, p. 326

MATERIALS
Classroom Materials objects or blocks in the shape of a sphere, cylinder, cone, cube, rectangle, prism
Manipulatives two-dimensional shape punchouts per child

Teacher Resources
Reteaching 94   Practice 94   Enrichment 94
MAC Act. 187, 188   Teacher Aid 6

SKILLS TRACE	
GEOMETRY	
Explore (Concrete) 304	**Develop/Understand (Transitional/Abstract)** 305–306, 307–308, 309–310, 315–316, 317, 320
Practice 314, 325, 326, 327–328, 331, 389, 419	**Apply** 311–312, 313, 321–322, 323, 324

See **MANIPULATIVES PLUS 60**, p. 302L.

More Two-Dimensional Figures

Use △ , □ , ■ , ⬠ , and ● . two-dimensional shapes
Complete.

	How many sides?	How many corners?
1. △	3	3
2. ▭	4	4
3. ■	4	4
4. ⬠	5	5

5. Talk about the patterns you see. Children should note that the number of sides in each shape is the same as

6. Does a ● have sides or corners? __No.__   the number of corne[rs]

PREPARE **WARM-UP** To review the names of two-dimensional shapes, show the following on the chalkboard.

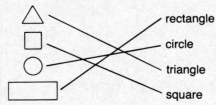

```
△ ────────┐  ┌──── rectangle
□ ──────┐ └──┼──── circle
○ ──────┼────┘ ┌── triangle
▭ ──────┘──────┴── square
```

Have children draw lines to match each shape with its name.

TEACH **DISCUSSING** Draw a square on the chalkboard. Point to each edge and identify it as a **side.** Then point to a corner and explain that the place where two sides meet is called a **corner.**

■ **How many sides does a square have?** [4]

■ **How many corners does a square have?** [4]

Draw a triangle, rectangle, circle, and pentagon on the chalkboard. Have pairs of children identify the number of sides and corners of each. Make sure children understand that a circle has no sides or corners.

Display a cone.

■ **What shape would you see if you traced around the bottom of the cone?** [circle]

Ring the shape you would make by tracing around the object.

1.
2.
3.
4.

····· **Reasoning** ·······························

open   closed

Color inside each closed figure.

●●

310   three hundred ten   *Extra* **Practice,** page 314 **Practice** *Plus,* page 326

MEETING INDIVIDUAL NEEDS

ACTIVITY *Common Error and Remediation*

MATERIALS 10 ◖ (or punchouts); two-dimensional shape punchouts

Some children may lose track when counting the number of sides and corners of a shape. Work individually with each child. Give the child counters and a shape. Have the child place a counter, red side up, on each side of the shape while counting. Have the child place a counter, yellow side up, on each corner while counting. Repeat the activity using the other shapes in the lesson.

TEACHER to TEACHER

MANIPULATIVES TIP The relationship between two- and three-dimensional figures became clearer to my children after they traced around the faces of solid figures.

ACTIVITY ALTERNATIVE TEACHING STRATEGY

MATERIALS three-dimensional shapes, unlined paper

KINESTHETIC Using a separate sheet of paper for each three-dimensional figure, have children trace the various faces of a cube, cone, rectangular prism, and cylinder. After identifying the shape, have them count and write the number of sides and corners under each.

Have a volunteer do this on the chalkboard. Repeat with faces of a square, rectangular prism, and cylinder.

PUPIL'S EDITION pp. 309-310

Page 309 Discuss the picture at the top of the page. Give children punchout 2-dimensional shapes and guide them through ex. 1.

Check for Understanding

■ **What is the corner of a figure?** [The corner is the place where two sides meet.]

GUIDED PRACTICE ex. 2–6: Have the question for ex. 5 read aloud. Guide children to use the data in the chart to answer the question. Discuss ex. 6.

For reteaching, use Common Error and Remediation or Alternative Strategy.

Page 310 Have children identify the shapes in the left-hand column.

3 PRACTICE•APPLY   PRACTICE   ex. 1–4

REASONING Using the examples, discuss the difference between open and closed figures.

C L O S E Guide children to summarize the lesson:

■ **What shape or shapes have 4 sides and 4 corners?** [square and rectangle]

Chapter 10 • Lesson 4   **310**

MAC ACTIVITY CENTER

MAC Activity 187:
Basic-to-Average ▼

MAC Activity 187

On Your Own   Pair and Share   In a Group

LOGICAL REASONING ▪ CAPTURE THE SQUARE

Materials dot paper (Teacher Aid 6), pencils

Procedure Assign children to work in groups. Give each group a sheet of dot paper duplicated from Teacher Aid 6. Have children take turns drawing a vertical or horizontal line to connect two dots on the paper to form a side of a square. The person drawing the last side to complete the square gets to "capture" it by writing his or her initial inside the square. The game continues until all squares have been completed.

To Win The player who has captured the most squares wins the game.

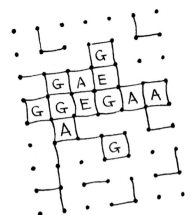

MAC Activity 188:
Average-to-Challenge ▶

LOGICAL REASONING ▪ HIDDEN SHAPE PUZZLES

MAC Activity 188

On Your Own   Pair and Share   In a Group

Materials oaktag, straightedge, scissors, envelopes, index cards

Draw the following puzzle on the chalkboard. Ask children to count the number of rectangles and triangles. Make sure they see that the larger shapes are made up of the smaller ones. Using oaktag, have children design and make their own Hidden Shape Puzzles. Then have them cut their puzzles apart by following the lines. They should note the number of each type of shape on an index card. Store the pieces and the answer card for each puzzle in an envelope. Then have children solve their puzzles.

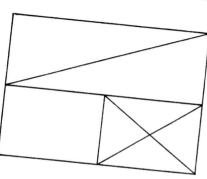

RETEACHING-94

Name _____

MORE TWO-DIMENSIONAL FIGURES

Study

__4__ sides   __4__ corners   __3__ sides   __3__ corners

Check

How many sides and corners?

1.
__4__ sides
__4__ corners

2.
__3__ sides
__3__ corners

3.
__4__ sides
__4__ corners

4.
__5__ sides
__5__ corners

5.
__4__ sides
__4__ corners

6.
__5__ sides
__5__ corners

Macmillan/McGraw-Hill, MATHEMATICS IN ACTION
Grade 2, Chapter 10, Lesson 4, pages 309–310

Reteaching-94

PRACTICE-94

Name _____

MORE TWO-DIMENSIONAL FIGURES

Ring the shape you would make
by tracing around the figure.

1.

2.

3.

4.

5.

Macmillan/McGraw-Hill, MATHEMATICS IN ACTION
Grade 2, Chapter 10, Lesson 4, pages 309–310

Practice-94

ENRICHMENT-94

Name _____

MORE TWO-DIMENSIONAL FIGURES

On Your Own   Pair and Share   In a Group

SHAPE UP

Choose one shape.
Draw a picture using *only* that shape.
Use different sizes of the shape.

Pictures will vary.

Titles will vary.
Title of Picture: _____

Macmillan/McGraw-Hill, MATHEMATICS IN ACTION
Grade 2, Chapter 10, Lesson 4, pages 309–310

Enrichment-94

Problem of the Day

Tina is making photo cubes for presents. She puts
1 photo on each face of the cube. How many
pictures does she need to make 3 photo cubes?
[18 photos. Possible solution: 6 + 6 + 6 = 18.]

AT·A·GLANCE pp. 311-312

LESSON OBJECTIVE
Use a picture to solve problems.

ASSIGNMENT GUIDE

COURSE	EXERCISES
Basic	p. 311: 1–5; p. 312: 1–8
Average	p. 311: 1–5; p. 312: 1–8
Challenge	p. 311: 1–5; p. 312: 1–8
Extra Practice, p. 314	

MATERIALS
Classroom Materials large hundred chart
Manipulatives stickers (buildings) per child

Teacher Resources
Reteaching 95
Prob. Solv. 47
Practice 95
MAC Act. 189, 190
Enrichment 95
Teacher Aid 4

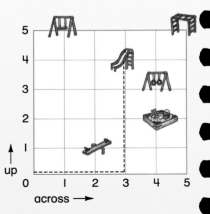

Problem Solving

Using a Picture

This grid shows where things
are in a playground.
Find the slide.

Always start at 0.
First count across →.
Then count up ↑.
To find the slide,
go across 3 and up 4.

Which thing would you find?
Ring the answer.

	Across →	Up ↑
1.	2	1
2.	1	5
3.	4	2
4.	5	5
5.	4	3

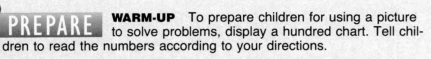

PREPARE **WARM-UP** To prepare children for using a picture
to solve problems, display a hundred chart. Tell children to read the numbers according to your directions.

Start at 41. Read across 5 more numbers to the right, and then read
the numbers going up to the top of the chart. [41, 42, 43, 44, 45, 46;
36, 26, 16, 6]

TEACH **DISCUSSING** Draw the grid shown on the right.

Explain that it shows where some tents are in a camping area. Tell
children they can find the location of the tents by starting at 0, counting across first, and then counting up.

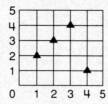

■ **To find the first tent, which is the first number you get to?** [1]
How many points do you count going up? [2]

Be sure children understand that both numbers are used to name the
location of the tent. Have children find the locations of the other tents
on the grid. [across 2, up 3; across 3, up 4; across 4, up 1]

Find each object.
Complete to show where it is.

		Across →	Up ↑
1.	●	_3_	_5_
2.	⬡	_4_	_2_
3.	■	_2_	_2_
4.	▲	_1_	_4_

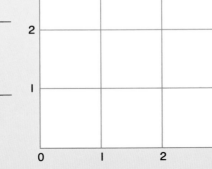

Make a grid of a neighborhood.
Put each building on a point.
Complete to show where it is.

Across → Up ↑
For exercises 5–8,
answers will vary.

5.   ___   ___

6.   ___   ___

7.   ___   ___

8.   ___   ___

Extra Practice, page 314

TEACHER to TEACHER

MANIPULATIVES TIP My children benefit from using counters to model where pictures are, or where they want them to be, on a grid. By moving counters across and up to points on a grid, children are able to see how pictures can help them understand a problem.

For Students Acquiring English (SAE)

Tape a grid on the floor and label the axes with numbers. Pair SAE children and non-SAE children to work together. Have pairs develop instructions for other students to follow on the grid.

PUPIL'S EDITION pp. 311-312

Page 311 Read the first two sentences.

■ **What do you know?** [The grid shows where things are.]

■ **What do you need to find out?** [where the slide is on the grid]

Have children place their fingers on 0. Then have them use their fingers to count across 3 and up 4 to the slide.

■ **What did you learn?** [Possible response: A grid can be used to find and describe where things are in a place.]

Check for Understanding

■ **What if the slide was on the point next to the sandbox? How would you find it?** [Count across 3, up 2.]

GUIDED PRACTICE ex. 1–5: Work through problem 1.

Page 312 Help children identify the shapes and the pictures. Make sure that on the bottom grid, children understand they are to decide on which points they want to put the buildings. Distribute and identify stickers of the buildings to the children.

3 PRACTICE•APPLY PRACTICE ex. 1–8

CLOSE Guide children to summarize the lesson:

■ **How can pictures on a grid help you solve problems?** [You can read a grid to find exactly where things are. You can draw pictures on a grid to show where you want them to be in an actual place.]

MAC Activity 189

On Your Own   Pair and Share   In a Group

CAREER—CITY PLANNER ■ PLANNING A NEIGHBORHOOD

Materials grid form (Teacher Aid 4), punchout pattern blocks

Setup Mark Teacher Aid 4 as shown and duplicate it for children.

Procedure Assign children to work in pairs. Give each pair a grid form and 6 pattern blocks (3 orange squares, 3 green triangles). Tell children that builders could use a grid to make a picture of where they plan to build things in a new neighborhood. Explain that you will read some directions. They are to locate these points and describe what is there, or place a block there.

1. In this neighborhood, a school is shown by a rectangle. Where is the school? [across 1, up 4]
2. The library is shown with a circle. Where is the library? [across 4, up 2]
3. The places where houses will be are shown with orange squares. Put houses on the points that are across 1, up 2; across 2, up 3; and across 4, up 4.
4. The places where stores will be are shown with green triangles. Put stores on the points that are across 5 and up 3; across 4, up 5; across 1, up 3.

**MAC Activity 189:
Basic-to-Average** ▶

WRITING MATHEMATICS ■ SCHOOL ON A GRID

MAC Activity 190

On Your Own   Pair and Share   In a Group

Materials grid form (Teacher Aid 4)

Setup Create a 5-by-5 square grid form. Duplicate a copy for each group. Make sure there are four to six distinct items in the classroom to identify (such as your desk, the door, a bookshelf, a plant, or a globe) positioned at various places in the classroom for children to picture on their grids. Create a simple diagram on the chalkboard to show approximate locations of these items so that children have a reference. The diagram might look like the one shown here.

Procedure Have children work in groups of three. Provide each group with a grid form. Have children work together to make a grid showing the items labeled in the diagram. Tell children to draw a picture of each item on the grid. Display the grids and have groups read and compare them.

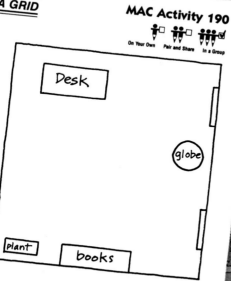

▲
**MAC Activity 190:
Average-to-Challenge**

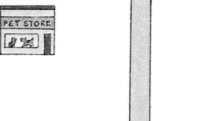

RETEACHING-95

Name

PROBLEM SOLVING: USING A PICTURE

Study

This grid shows where things are in a room.
You can find the table.

First start at 0.
Count across → to 4.
Count up ↑ to 3.

There is the table.

Check

Ring the answer.
Which thing would you find?

	Across→	Up↑
1.	2	2
2.	1	4
3.	3	4
4.	5	5

Where is it?

	Across→ Up↑	Across→ Up↑
5.	(1 1)	5 5
6.	1 3	(4 3)

Reteaching-95

Macmillan/McGraw-Hill, MATHEMATICS IN ACTION
Grade 2, Chapter 10, Lesson 5, pages 311–312

PRACTICE-95

Name

PROBLEM SOLVING: USING A PICTURE

Find each object.
Complete to show where it is.

		Across→	Up↑
1.	bicycle	__	__
2.	car	1	3
3.	skateboard	3	1
4.		2	2

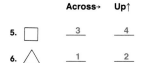

Draw each shape on a point.
Complete to show where it is.

**Answers will vary.
Possible answers given.**

		Across→	Up↑
5.	□	3	4
6.	△	1	2
7.	☆	4	1
8.	♡	2	3

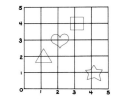

Practice-95

Macmillan/McGraw-Hill, MATHEMATICS IN ACTION
Grade 2, Chapter 10, Lesson 5, pages 311–312

ENRICHMENT-95

Name

PROBLEM SOLVING

On Your Own   Pair and Share   In a Group

TREASURE HUNT
Find the objects in the castle.
Complete to show where they are.

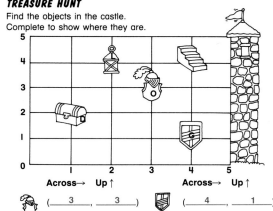

	Across→ Up↑		Across→ Up↑
head	(3 , 3)	shield	(4 , 1)
chest	(1 , 2)	lantern	(2 , 4)

Write the letters on each object. Find out what the treasure is.

G	O	L	D
(4, 1)	(3, 3)	(2, 4)	(1, 2)

What object was not found? Clue: Across 4
That is where the treasure is.

It is under the _____**stairs**_____

Enrichment-95

Macmillan/McGraw-Hill, MATHEMATICS IN ACTION
Grade 2, Chapter 10, Lesson 5, pages 311–312

Problem of the Day

Jeremy made a grid to show where he parks his car and the place where he works. The car was at a point across 2, up 3, and his workplace was at a point across 3, up 3. Are the car and workplace above each other, next to each other, or far apart on the grid? [They are right next to each other.]

AT·A·GLANCE p. 313

LESSON OBJECTIVE
Make shapes with pattern pieces.

ASSIGNMENT GUIDE

COURSE	EXERCISES
Basic	p. 313: All
Average	p. 313: All
Challenge	p. 313: All

MATERIALS
Classroom Materials crayons, drawing paper
Manipulatives set of pattern blocks (or punchouts) per pair

Teacher Resources
Crit. Think. 19

Name _____

Transform A Tron

Use △ , ▢ , ▱ , ◆ , ▱ , ⬡ to cover the shapes.

Answers will vary.

MacmillanMcGraw-Hill

Find different ways to cover the shapes.

313

---

1 PLAN

AIMS AND ATTITUDES This lesson develops visual reasoning skills by having children identify which geometric shapes are used to make up larger shapes. Emphasize the investigative nature of the activity, which you may compare to finding the missing pieces of a puzzle.

MANAGEMENT The activity is intended for all children and has been designed for independent work but is appropriate for pairs or groups of four children as well. If pairing children, it may be particularly effective to pair a child having strong mathematical skills with one having weaker skills.

2 GUIDE

Display the following pattern blocks:

⬡ △ ▢ ⬡ △ ▢   △ ▢

Have children identify the missing block in the pattern and tell the next three blocks of the pattern. Distribute pattern blocks to each pair of children and ask them to make patterns of shapes. Have partners extend the patterns.

Display the following pattern using pattern blocks:

Have children identify the pattern and tell the next set of blocks in the pattern. Assign children to make patterns by combining shapes. Have partners tell the next set of blocks in the pattern.

TEACHER to TEACHER

COOPERATIVE LEARNING TIP 👫 In deciding which shapes to use in this problem, I have groups of four do one problem by trial and error, then stop and discuss whether there is a different way to cover the shapes before trying again. They can practice the skills of **contributing ideas, listening to others' ideas,** and **summarizing** what ideas have been suggested. Then they must **come to an agreement** on which idea to try first and test it out. When they find a second idea that works, they give a team cheer or secret handshake to celebrate before going on to the next problem.

Read the directions on page 313 and identify the rebus pictures of the pattern blocks with the children.

■ **Suppose you found one block to fit part of the shape, how could you complete the shape?** [Possible response: Try the same block on other parts of the shape.]

Have individuals or pairs of children use the pattern blocks to cover each large shape on the page. Then have them color in the smaller shapes used to cover the larger shapes.

3 EXTEND Distribute drawing paper to each child. Ask them to work in pairs. Hidden from view, one partner makes up a shape from two or three pattern blocks and traces the outline of the overall shape. The other partner finds out which smaller pattern pieces were used to create the larger shape.

CHAPTER 10

EXTRA PRACTICE

Extra Practice items are provided so that children may have an opportunity for further practice.

The Additional Practice section also provides practice you may wish to assign.

EXTRA PRACTICE

Extra Practice

Three-Dimensional Figures, pages 305–306 ....

Ring the objects that have the same shape.

1.

More Two-Dimensional Figures, pages 309–310 ....

	How many sides?	How many corners?
1.	4	4
2.	3	3

Problem Solving: Using a Picture, pages 311–312 ....

Start at 0. Count across and up.
Find each shape.
Complete to show where it is.

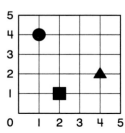

	Across →	Up ↑
1. ▲	4	2
2. ●	1	4
3. ■	2	1

314 three hundred fourteen

ADDITIONAL PRACTICE

p. 305 *Find objects in the room that have these shapes.*

1.   2.

3.   4.

p. 309 *Complete.*

1. How many sides? [3]
   How many corners? [3]

2. How many sides? [5]
   How many corners? [5]

p. 311 Distribute graph paper to the children. *Make a grid. Put each shape on a point. Complete to show where each is.* [Answers will vary.]

	Across	Up
1. ⬡	___	___
2. ▽	___	___
3. ◯	___	___

AT·A·GLANCE pp. 315-316

LESSON OBJECTIVE
Count to find the perimeter of a figure.

ASSIGNMENT GUIDE

COURSE	EXERCISES
Basic	p. 315: 1–4; p. 316: 2–8
Average	p. 315: 1–4; p. 316: 2–8
Challenge	p. 315: 1–4; p. 316: 2–8
Extra Practice, p. 325	Practice Plus, p. 326

MATERIALS
Classroom Materials paper clips
Manipulatives 10 macaroni punchouts per child

Teacher Resources
Reteaching 96
Prob. Solv. 48
Calculator 10
Practice 96
MAC Act. 191, 192
Enrichment 96
Teacher Aid 5

SKILLS TRACE
GEOMETRY

Explore (Concrete)	Develop/Understand (Transitional/Abstract)
304	305–306, 307–308, 309–310, 315–316, 317, 320
Practice 314, 325, 326, 327–328, 331, 389, 419	**Apply** 311–312, 313, 321–322, 323, 324

MANIPULATIVES plus ACTIVITY

See **MANIPULATIVES PLUS 61**, p. 302M.

Perimeter

How many ⬭ around the frame?

Use ⬭. punchout macaroni

Find the distance around the shape.

I.

___6___ units around

2.

___4___ units around

3.

___6___ units around

4.

___10___ units around

Macmillan/McGraw-Hill

 **PREPARE** **WARM-UP** To review two-dimensional shapes, give these descriptions and ask children to identify the shapes.

1. I have three corners and three sides. What shape am I? [triangle]
2. I have four corners and four sides. All my sides are the same length. What shape am I? [square]
3. I have no corners and I have no sides. What shape could I be? [circle]
4. I have four corners and four sides. Two of my sides are longer than the other two. What shape could I be? [rectangle]

TEACH **EXPLORING** Explore the concept of perimeter by asking children to identify some ways that they could figure out the distance around the classroom. Guide them to see

that one way is by using their feet as a unit. Have several children walk heel-to-toe around the classroom. Record the number of units each measures on the chalkboard. Discuss why these measurements vary. [The length of each person's feet differs.]

Have children measure the distance around their desk tops using their hands; the distance around their math books using paper clips. Have children compare measurements with a partner. Help them understand that when the same size unit, such as a paper clip, is used to measure the same object, the measurements will be about the same.

PUPIL'S EDITION pp. 315-316

Page 315 Discuss the example at the top of the page. Note that the child is framing a picture with pieces of macaroni. Make sure children understand that the macaroni are all the same length. Have them

Find the distance around the shape.

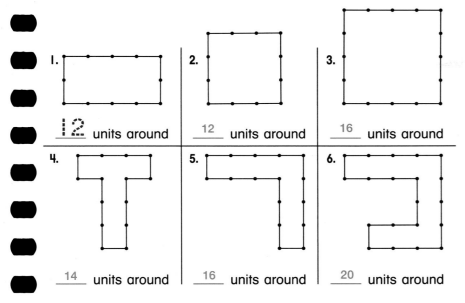

1. _12_ units around

2. _12_ units around

3. _16_ units around

4. _14_ units around

5. _16_ units around

6. _20_ units around

Find the distance around.

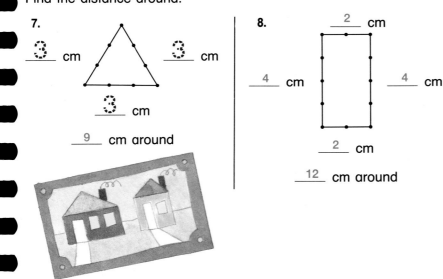

7. _3_ cm _3_ cm

_3_ cm

_9_ cm around

8. _2_ cm

_4_ cm _4_ cm

_2_ cm

_12_ cm around

Extra Practice, page 325 *Practice Plus,* page 326

count the macaroni to find the distance around (perimeter of) the frame.

Check for Understanding

■ **How could you use macaroni punchouts to find the distance around your math book?** [Line up macaroni punchouts around the outside edge of the book. Then count the units.]

GUIDED PRACTICE ex. 1–4: Remind children to line up the punch-out macaroni around the *outside* edge of each shape.

For reteaching, use Common Error and Remediation or Alternative Strategy.

Page 316 Work through ex. 1 with the children. Be sure children understand that the units are the lines between the dots and not the dots themselves.

MEETING INDIVIDUAL NEEDS

ALTERNATIVE TEACHING STRATEGY

MATERIALS 12-inch ruler, colored chalk

VISUAL Draw a 2-foot-by-4-foot rectangle on the chalkboard. Use a ruler and colored chalk to mark off each foot unit on the figure. Then lead children in counting the number of units around the figure, numbering each as it is counted. Repeat using other figures.

TEACHER to TEACHER

COOPERATIVE LEARNING TIP 👫 To understand perimeter, my children form groups of four to model the shapes in the lesson with a rope stretched around their bodies. If making a triangle, for example, three students stand inside the rope at each point, while a fourth helps the group model the figure on the page. They then take turns counting the steps it takes to walk around the figure's perimeter. Each group reports its findings to another group.

Common Error and Remediation

MATERIALS 1 T, 1 O models (or punchouts); worksheet with shapes, yarn, scissors

To help children understand the concept of distance around a figure, give each child a worksheet with large squares, rectangles, and triangles that can be measured evenly with tens models. Have the child place a piece of yarn around each shape and cut the yarn to size. The child then measures the yarn using a tens model and the shape using a ones model. Have the child compare the two measures.

3 PRACTICE•APPLY

PRACTICE ex. 2–8: Have children discuss their answers.

C L O S E Guide children to summarize the lesson:

■ **Each side of a triangle is 4 units long. What is the distance around the triangle?** [12 units around; Possible solution: 4 + 4 + 4 = 12]

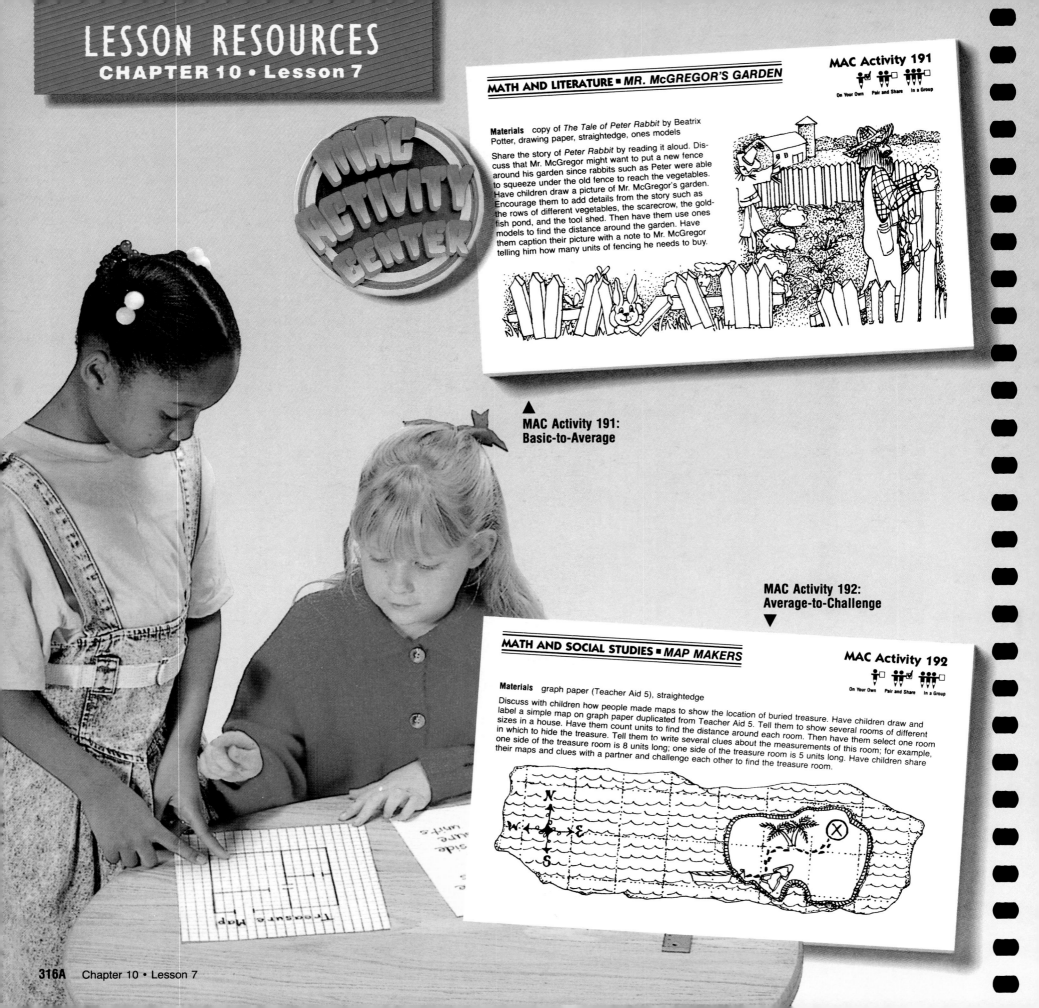

MAC ACTIVITY CENTER

MATH AND LITERATURE ▪ MR. McGREGOR'S GARDEN

MAC Activity 191

On Your Own Pair and Share In a Group

Materials copy of *The Tale of Peter Rabbit* by Beatrix Potter, drawing paper, straightedge, ones models

Share the story of *Peter Rabbit* by reading it aloud. Discuss that Mr. McGregor might want to put a new fence around his garden since rabbits such as Peter were able to squeeze under the old fence to reach the vegetables. Have children draw a picture of Mr. McGregor's garden. Encourage them to add details from the story such as the rows of different vegetables, the scarecrow, the goldfish pond, and the tool shed. Then have them use ones models to find the distance around the garden. Have them caption their picture with a note to Mr. McGregor telling him how many units of fencing he needs to buy.

▲
MAC Activity 191:
Basic-to-Average

MAC Activity 192:
Average-to-Challenge
▼

MATH AND SOCIAL STUDIES ▪ MAP MAKERS

MAC Activity 192

On Your Own Pair and Share In a Group

Materials graph paper (Teacher Aid 5), straightedge

Discuss with children how people made maps to show the location of buried treasure. Have children draw and label a simple map on graph paper duplicated from Teacher Aid 5. Tell them to show several rooms of different sizes in a house. Have them count units to find the distance around each room. Then have them select one room in which to hide the treasure. Tell them to write several clues about the measurements of this room; for example, one side of the treasure room is 8 units long; one side of the treasure room is 5 units long. Have children share their maps and clues with a partner and challenge each other to find the treasure room.

RETEACHING

Name _____

PERIMETER

Study

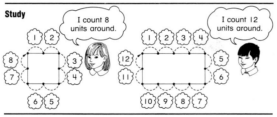

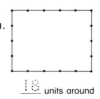

I count 8 units around.

I count 12 units around.

Check

Find the distance around the shape.

1.

16 units around

2.

16 units around

3.

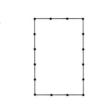

16 units around

4.

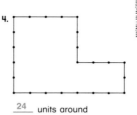

24 units around

Macmillan/McGraw-Hill, MATHEMATICS IN ACTION
Grade 2, Chapter 10, Lesson 7, pages 315–316

Reteaching-96

PRACTICE

Name _____

PERIMETER

Find the distance around the shape.

1.

18 units around

2.

20 units around

3.

18 units around

4.

20 units around

Find the distance around.

5.

4 cm

3 cm

3 cm

4 cm

14 cm around

6.

5 cm

2 cm

2 cm

5 cm

14 cm around

Macmillan/McGraw-Hill, MATHEMATICS IN ACTION
Grade 2, Chapter 10, Lesson 7, pages 315–316

Practice-96

ENRICHMENT

Name _____

PERIMETER

On Your Own   Pair and Share   In a Group

HOW MANY YARDS?

Work with a partner.
How many yards around the school yard?
Use a yardstick to measure.
Show what you found.

Check children's drawings of the school yard.
Have them label the length of each side.

Our school yard is _____ yards around.

Macmillan/McGraw-Hill, MATHEMATICS IN ACTION
Grade 2, Chapter 10, Lesson 7, pages 315–316

Enrichment-96

Problem of the Day

Noel has a figure that is 15 units around. One side is 5 units long. Is this figure a square or a triangle?   [A triangle; possible solution:
5 + 5 + 5 = 15]

AT·A·GLANCE p. 317

LESSON OBJECTIVE
Count units to find the area of a figure.

ASSIGNMENT GUIDE

COURSE	EXERCISES
Basic	p. 317: 1–3
Average	p. 317: 1–3
Challenge	p. 317: 1–3
Extra Practice, p. 325	

MATERIALS
Classroom Materials 12-inch ruler, square pieces of paper
Manipulatives 20 O models (or punchouts), Workmat 4 per pair

Teacher Resources
Reteaching 97
MAC Act. 193, 194
Practice 97
Teacher Aids 4, 5
Enrichment 97

SKILLS TRACE
GEOMETRY

Explore (Concrete)	Develop/Understand (Transitional/Abstract)
304	305–306, 307–308, 309–310, 315–316, 317, 320
Practice 314, 325, 326, 327–328, 331, 389, 419	**Apply** 311–312, 313, 321–322, 323, 324

See **MANIPULATIVES PLUS 62**, p. 302N.

1 PREPARE **WARM-UP** To review perimeter, draw several large squares, rectangles, and triangles on the chalkboard using a foot ruler. Mark off the units on each side. Have children determine the distance around each figure by counting the units.

2 TEACH **EXPLORING** Display a square piece of paper and introduce it as a **square unit.** Explain that you would like to cover a classroom table with pieces of this paper, each of which measures one square unit. Have several children help you as the rest of the class observes. After children count the units, explain that the **area** tells the number of square units that "cover" a shape.

Have children repeat this measuring activity to find the number of square units of paper it takes to cover a desk or a classroom bulletin board. Make sure children express their answers in square units.

Name _____

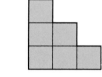

Area

I square unit 6 square units How many square units? 6

Working Together
Use Workmat 4 and 20 □ to make shapes.

I choose some square units and make a shape.

I tell how many square units.

Take turns.
Write how many square units.

1. ___9___ square units
2. ___12___ square units
3. ___10___ square units

Extra Practice, page 325

three hundred seventeen **317**

PUPIL'S EDITION p. 317
Discuss the display at the top of the page. Have children count to find the number of square units in each figure.

Check for Understanding
■ **How would you figure out the number of square units it takes to cover a rug?** [Cover the rug with square units. Then count the number of square units.]

GUIDED PRACTICE ■ **Working Together** Have children work in pairs to make shapes and then find the number of square units.

For reteaching, use Common Error and Remediation or Alternative Strategy.

Common Error and Remediation

ACTIVITY

MATERIALS ones models (or punchouts), worksheet

Some children may confuse area with perimeter. Work with each child individually. Give the child a worksheet with squares and rectangles that can be measured with ones models. Have the child place models around the outside of a shape and express the distance in *units*. Repeat having the child use models to cover the shape and expressing the area in *square units*. Repeat with other shapes.

ONGOING ASSESSMENT

MATH JOURNAL

OBSERVATION Determine whether children find the area of each figure correctly in the activity on p. 317.

INTERVIEW Give the child several sheets of paper. **(1) How can you use these sheets to find the area of a desktop? (2) Make a rectangle with the sheets. What is its area?**

JOURNAL WRITING You may wish to have children record their responses in their math journals.

ALTERNATIVE TEACHING STRATEGY

MATERIALS overhead projector, markers, Teacher Aid Transparency 3

VISUAL Draw a grid of squares on the chalkboard or display the graph paper transparency on the overhead projector. Color in one square and refer to it as one square unit. Have volunteers color in one additional square at a time and tell how many square units there are. Continue until the grid is covered. Guide children to see that the area of the shape tells the number of square units colored in.

3 PRACTICE•APPLY   PRACTICE   ex. 1–3

CLOSE Guide children to summarize the lesson:

■ **Which piece of paper is larger, a red one whose area is 27 square units or a blue one whose area is 32 square units?** [the blue paper]

MAC ACTIVITY CENTER

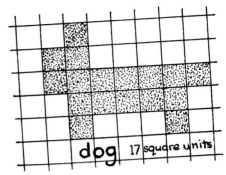

MAC Activity 193

THINKING GEOMETRICALLY ■ GRID ANIMALS

On Your Own   Pair and Share   In a Group

Materials graph paper (Teacher Aid 5), straightedge

Demonstrate how to create imaginary or real animals by shading in squares on graph paper as shown below.

Have children draw their own menagerie of grid animals. Have them count to determine the number of square units in each animal and record this under each figure. Remind them to use the label *square units*.

dog   17 square units

▲
MAC Activity 193:
Basic-to-Average

MAC Activity 194:
Average-to-Challenge
▼

MAC Activity 194

MATH AND LITERATURE ■ MISTRESS MARY'S GARDEN

On Your Own   Pair and Share   In a Group

Materials graph paper (Teacher Aid 4), straightedge

Write the familiar rhyme "Mistress Mary Quite Contrary" on the chalkboard. Read it and have children join in when they become familiar with the words.

Mistress Mary, quite contrary
How does your garden grow?
With silver bells and cockle shells,
And pretty maids all in a row.

Tell children they are going to help Mistress Mary plan her garden. Give each child a sheet of graph paper duplicated from Teacher Aid 4. Write instructions on the chalkboard. Have children draw and label a garden to meet these space requirements.

14 square units silver bells
10 square units cockle shells
8 square units roses
4 square units tulips
12 square units daffodils
6 square units lilies
9 square units pansies

RETEACHING

Name

AREA

Study

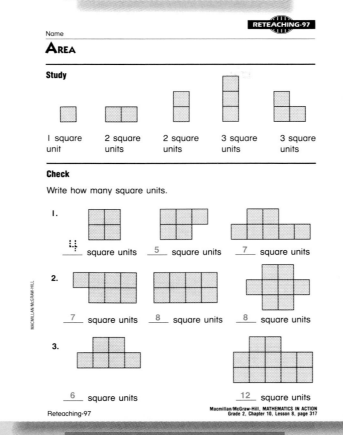

| 1 square unit | 2 square units | 2 square units | 3 square units | 3 square units |

Check

Write how many square units.

1.

___ square units   _5_ square units   _7_ square units

2.

_7_ square units   _8_ square units   _8_ square units

3.

_6_ square units   _12_ square units

MACMILLAN-MCGRAW-HILL

Reteaching-97

Macmillan/McGraw-Hill, MATHEMATICS IN ACTION
Grade 2, Chapter 10, Lesson 8, page 317

PRACTICE

Name

AREA

Write how many square units.

1.

_3_ square units   _6_ square units   _8_ square units

2.

_9_ square units   _13_ square units

3.

_11_ square units   _7_ square units   _6_ square units

Color to show the square units.
Coloring will vary.

6 square units   8 square units

MACMILLAN/McGRAW-HILL

Practice-97

Macmillan/McGraw-Hill, MATHEMATICS IN ACTION
Grade 2, Chapter 10, Lesson 8, page 317

ENRICHMENT

Name

AREA

On Your Own   Pair and Share   In a Group

COVER THE SHAPE

Work with a partner.

Use ☐ to cover each shape.
Write how many square units.

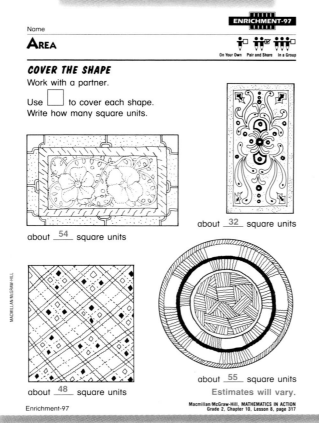

about _54_ square units

about _32_ square units

about _48_ square units

about _55_ square units

Estimates will vary.

MACMILLAN-MCGRAW-HILL

Enrichment-97

Macmillan/McGraw-Hill, MATHEMATICS IN ACTION
Grade 2, Chapter 10, Lesson 8, page 317

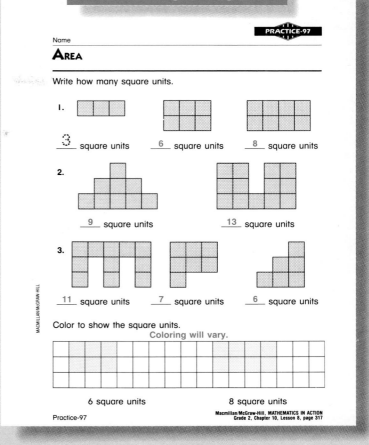

Problem of the Day

Marie wants to cover a bulletin board that is 3 units long on the top and on the bottom and 5 units long on each side. Will 16 pieces of paper that are 1 square unit each be enough? [Yes; possible solution: the surface of the bulletin board is 15 square units; 16 > 15.]

AT·A·GLANCE p. 318

LESSON OBJECTIVE
Explore the concept of volume.

ASSIGNMENT GUIDE

COURSE	EXERCISES
Basic	p. 318: 1–6
Average	p. 318: 1–6
Challenge	p. 318: 1–6

MATERIALS
Classroom Materials different-sized boxes
Manipulatives 27 ▢ per pair

SKILLS TRACE
VOLUME

Explore (Concrete) 318, Gr. 3: 436	Develop/Understand (Transitional/Abstract) Gr. 4: 326–327
Practice Gr. 4: 335	Apply 322

ACTIVITY

Volume

Working Together
Use two different size boxes
and some ▢ .

Tell how many cubes
fit in each box.
Answers will vary.

Build the shape with cubes.
Write how many unit cubes.

1.

__4__ unit cubes

2.

__4__ unit cubes

3.
__16__ unit cubes

4.
__12__ unit cubes

5.
__12__ unit cubes

6.
__27__ unit cubes

318   three hundred eighteen

PREPARE
WARM-UP To prepare children to explore volume, have children work with eight connecting cubes. Tell children to put the cubes together to make a shape other than a cube train. Display all the shapes to see how many different arrangements were made.

2 TEACH
DISCUSS Draw a line segment on the chalkboard and remind children that this is a unit that could be usd to find the distance *around* a figure. Next draw a small square and remind children that this is a square unit that can be used to find the measure *inside* a figure. Then show a connecting cube and tell children it is also a unit. Explain this unit can be used to measure in another way.

PUPIL'S EDITION p. 318

WORKING TOGETHER Assign each child a partner and give each pair two different-size boxes and connecting cubes. Discuss the picture at the top of the page and have children do the activity.

Check for Understanding

■ **What would you think if more cubes fit in your box than in your partner's box?** [My box is larger because more cubes fit inside.]

Point out that the box that holds more cubes has more space inside it, or **volume,** than the other box.

GUIDED PRACTICE ex. 1–2: For reteaching, use Alternative Strategy.

For Students Acquiring English (SAE)

SAE children may confuse **volume** with **area.** Discuss both concepts with the children and have them state each in their own words. Then pair SAE children with non-SAE children to complete the activities on the page.

ACTIVITY

ALTERNATIVE TEACHING STRATEGY

MATERIALS 27

VISUAL Display rectangular prisms made of connecting cubes as shown on page 318. Ask each child for an estimate of the number of cubes in the structure. Record these estimates on the chalkboard. Then ask a volunteer to take the structure apart and have children count the number of cubes. Have them compare the actual number with their estimate. Repeat with other structures made of cubes.

3 PRACTICE•APPLY   PRACTICE   ex. 3–6.

CLOSE Guide children to summarize the lesson.
■ **If 20 cubes fit in the red box and 10 cubes fit in the blue box, which box is bigger?** [red box]

Problem of the Day

Garrett wants to fill a box with cubes. He uses 9 cubes to cover the bottom of the box. If it takes 4 layers of cubes to fill the box, how many cubes will he need? [36 cubes. Possible solution: 9 + 9 + 9 + 9 = 36.]

CHAPTER 10 • Lesson 10

AT·A·GLANCE p. 319

LESSON OBJECTIVE
Identify figures with a line of symmetry.

ASSIGNMENT GUIDE

COURSE	EXERCISES
Basic	p. 319: 1–3
Average	p. 319: 1–3
Challenge	p. 319: 1–3
Extra Practice, p. 325	

MATERIALS
Classroom Materials drawing paper, marker
Manipulatives fraction models for halves (or punchouts)

Teacher Resources
Reteaching 98   Practice 98   Enrichment 98
MAC Act. 195, 196

SKILLS TRACE
GEOMETRY

Explore (Concrete) 304	Develop/Understand (Transitional/Abstract) 307–308, 309–310, 315–316, 317, 319, 320
Practice 314, 325, 326, 327–328	Apply 311–312, 313, 321–322, 323, 324

See **MANIPULATIVES PLUS 63**, p. 302O.

Symmetry

The yellow shape has a **line of symmetry**. The blue shape does not.

These two parts match.

These two parts do not match.

Working Together

Draw a line on a sheet of paper.
You start a shape on one side
of the line.
Your partner draws a part to match.

Ring the shape if it has a line of symmetry.

1.

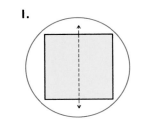

2.

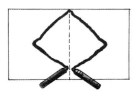

3.

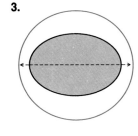

Macmillan/McGraw-Hill

Extra Practice, page 325

three hundred nineteen **319**

---

1 PREPARE **WARM-UP** To prepare children for work with symmetry, display fraction models for halves and have children identify the number of equal parts. [2]

2 TEACH **DISCUSSING** Display a sheet of paper with a clearly visible line drawn down the middle. Call attention to the line by tracing it with your finger.

■ **Is the shape of the paper exactly the same on both sides of the line?** [Yes.]

Discuss ways children could test to see if they are correct. Guide them to see that folding the paper on the line is one way to check if both sides match. Do this as children observe. Allow them to inspect the paper so they can see that both sides match. Then open the paper and identify the line as a **line of symmetry.** Repeat this procedure

with several other pieces of paper that do and do not have a line of symmetry.

PUPIL'S EDITION p. 319

Discuss the picture at the top of the page. Ask how children know that the blue shape on the paper at the right does not have a line of symmetry. [The parts on either side of the line do not match.]

WORKING TOGETHER Have children work with a partner to do the activity.

Check for Understanding

■ **How can you check to see if a figure has a line of symmetry?** [Fold the figure on the line to see if both sides match.]

GUIDED PRACTICE ex. 1: For reteaching, use Common Error and Remediation or Alternative Strategy.

ACTIVITY
Common Error and Remediation

MATERIALS pattern blocks (or punchouts), plain paper

Some children may be unable to identify a line of symmetry. Work individually with each child. Give the child a piece of paper with a vertical line on it. Then show the child how to place matching pattern blocks on either side of the line to form one figure. Help the child trace around the perimeter of the shape with a pencil. Have the child remove the blocks and identify the line of symmetry. Repeat the activity to create other symmetrical figures.

For Students Acquiring English (SAE)

Model the activity several times on the chalkboard. Ask children to tell you what to do to create a symmetrical design. Have them say **line of symmetry** as you draw a line through symmetrical forms.

ALTERNATIVE TEACHING STRATEGY

MATERIALS papers with a line drawn on each (some with a line of symmetry and some without)

KINESTHETIC Distribute the papers to children and have them fold each paper on the line. Point out that the line is a line of symmetry only if both parts match. Have children sort the papers into two groups, those having lines of symmetry and those not having lines of symmetry.

3 PRACTICE•APPLY **PRACTICE** ex. 2–3

CLOSE Guide children to summarize the lesson:

■ **Which of these figures could have more than one line of symmetry: a heart or a circle?** [a circle]

MAC ACTIVITY CENTER

MATH AND LANGUAGE ARTS ■ SYMMETRIC WORDS

MAC Activity 196

On Your Own   Pair and Share   In a Group

Write the word BOB on the chalkboard. Draw a horizontal line through the letters and guide children to see that this word has a line of symmetry. Give children lined paper. Have them work to discover other words that are symmetrical. Display these words on a bulletin board. Encourage children to add addition words as they are discovered.

▲
MAC Activity 196:
Average-to-Challenge

MATH AND SCIENCE ■ *BUTTERFLIES*

MAC Activity 195

On Your Own   Pair and Share   In a Group

Materials construction paper, thick poster paint, brushes, black markers

Show children pictures of butterflies and discuss the symmetry of their wings. Give children large sheets of construction paper. Have them fold the paper in half vertically. On one side of the fold, have them quickly apply a fairly thick coat of paint in the shape of a butterfly's wing. Then have them immediately fold the paper and gently use the heel of their hand to press the two sides together. Have them carefully peel the two sides apart and allow the painting to dry. Some children may wish to use black marker to add eyes, antennae, and other features to their butterflies. This technique can also be used to create abstract "ink blot" shapes that children can turn into animals or other objects suggested by the shape.

▲
MAC Activity 195:
Basic-to-Average

Name

SYMMETRY

Study

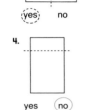

line of symmetry ——

These two parts match.   These two parts do not match.

Check

Do the two parts match?
Ring *yes* or *no*.

1. (yes) no

2. yes (no)

3. (yes) no

4. yes (no)

5. (yes) no

6. yes (no)

Macmillan/McGraw-Hill, MATHEMATICS IN ACTION
Grade 2, Chapter 10, Lesson 10, page 319

Reteaching-98

MACMILLAN/McGRAW-HILL

Name

SYMMETRY

Ring the shape if it has a line of symmetry.

1.

2.

3.

4.

5.

6.

7.

8.

9.

10.

11.

12.

Macmillan/McGraw-Hill, MATHEMATICS IN ACTION
Grade 2, Chapter 10, Lesson 10, page 319

Practice-98

MACMILLAN/McGRAW-HILL

Name

SYMMETRY

On Your Own   Pair and Share   In a Group

MORE DOTS

Make a shape with a line of symmetry.
Draw lines to complete the shape.

1.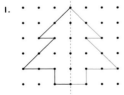

2.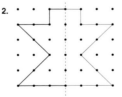

3.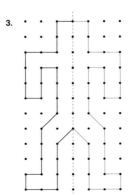

4.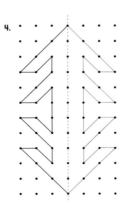

Macmillan/McGraw-Hill, MATHEMATICS IN ACTION
Grade 2, Chapter 10, Lesson 10, page 319

Enrichment-98

MACMILLAN/McGRAW-HILL

Problem of the Day

Which of these capital letters have a line of symmetry: R, M, F, C, and O? [M, C, and O]

AT·A·GLANCE p. 320

LESSON OBJECTIVE
Identify congruent figures.

ASSIGNMENT GUIDE

COURSE	EXERCISES
Basic	p. 320: 1–2
Average	p. 320: 1–2
Challenge	p. 320: 1–2
Extra Practice, p. 325	

MATERIALS
Manipulatives two-dimensional shapes punchouts

Teacher Resources
Reteaching 99   Practice 99   Enrichment 99
MAC Act. 197, 198   Teacher Aid 5

SKILLS TRACE
GEOMETRY

Explore (Concrete)	Develop/Understand (Transitional/Abstract)
304	307–308, 309–310, 315–316, 317, 320
Practice 314, 325, 326, 327–328, 419	**Apply** 311–312, 313, 321–322, 323, 324

See **MANIPULATIVES PLUS 64**, p. 302P.

Congruent Figures

These squares have the same shape.
They are not the same size.

These squares have the same shape.
They are the same size.

Working Together
Use shapes.

I pick a shape.

I find one that is the same shape and the same size.

Take three turns each.

Ring the one that is the same shape and same size.

1.

2.

Extra Practice, page 325

---

① PREPARE **WARM-UP** To review the concept of symmetry, draw these figures on the chalkboard and have volunteers draw one or more lines of symmetry on each.

② TEACH **EXPLORING** Display a set of squares, rectangles, circles, and triangles in various sizes. Separate children into groups and have them work together to sort the figures by shape.

■ **In what way are the objects in each group alike?** [They all have the same shape.]

■ **In what way are the objects in each group different?** [The shapes are different sizes.]

Collect the shapes again and have them re-sorted by size and shape. Discuss with children how the items in each group are alike. [They all have the same size and shape.]

PUPIL'S EDITION p. 320

Have children identify the shapes at the top of the page. Have a volunteer read the sentences. Compare the 2 sets of squares and have children discuss how the squares in the second set match each other, or are **congruent**.

ACTIVITY
Common Error and Remediation

MATERIALS various-sized paper circles, triangles, and squares

Some children may be unable to identify congruent figures. Work individually with each child. Give the child a set of paper shapes. (Make sure only two of each shape are the same size.) Guide the child to sort them by shape. Have the child work with each set to find two shapes that are also the same size by placing shapes one on top of another until a match is made.

ONGOING ASSESSMENT

OBSERVATION Determine whether children identify shapes that are the same shape and size in the activity on p. 320.

INTERVIEW (1) Point to 2 objects of the same shape but different sizes. **How are these shapes alike? different?**
(2) Find 2 things in the room that are the same shape and size.

JOURNAL WRITING You may wish to have children record their responses in their math journals.

ALTERNATIVE TEACHING STRATEGY

VISUAL Draw groups of circles, squares, and triangles on the chalkboard. Within each group, all figures should have the same shape but should be of different sizes. Have children describe the figures in each group as being the same shape. Then, draw figures that have the same size and shape. Have children describe these as having the same size and same shape.

Check for Understanding
■ **Are your math and reading books the same size and shape?**
[Answers will vary. They are probably the same shape but not the same size.]

WORKING TOGETHER Have children work in pairs to do the activity.

GUIDED PRACTICE ex. 1: For reteaching, use Common Error and Remediation or Alternative Strategy.

3 PRACTICE·APPLY PRACTICE ex. 2

CLOSE Guide children to summarize the lesson:
■ **What are two ways that figures can be the same?** [They can have the same shape; they can be the same size.]

MAC Activity 197:
Basic-to-Average
▼

MAC Activity 197

On Your Own   Pair and Share   In a Group

MATH AND ART ▪ PAPER DOLL CHAINS

Materials   4 inch-wide strips of drawing paper, scissors

Show children how to fold a strip of paper "accordion style." Have them draw a doll outline similar to the one shown below. Make sure the arms of the doll extend to the edges.

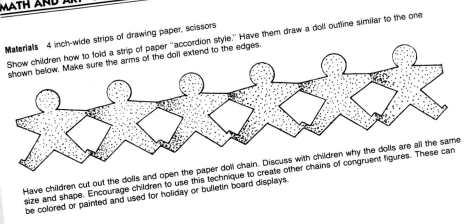

Have children cut out the dolls and open the paper doll chain. Discuss with children why the dolls are all the same size and shape. Encourage children to use this technique to create other chains of congruent figures. These can be colored or painted and used for holiday or bulletin board displays.

MAC Activity 198:
Average-to-Challenge ▶

CAREER—DRAFTERS ▪ COPYING A PICTURE

MAC Activity 198

On Your Own   Pair and Share   In a Group

Materials   centimeter graph paper (Teacher Aid 5), graph paper of various sizes, straightedge

Setup   Draw simple shapes on graph paper duplicated from Teacher Aid 5. Duplicate a copy for each child.

Procedure   Give each child a copy of the shapes. Discuss the work of a drafter and show samples of blueprints if possible. Explain that drafters draw pictures that are smaller or larger than the real object. Have children use other graph paper of various sizes to copy the shapes. Then have them use their work to answer these questions.

1. What happens to the size and shape of the figure when graph paper with a smaller grid is used? [The size of the figure is smaller; the shape remains the same.]
2. What happens to the size and shape of the figure when graph paper with a larger grid is used? [The size of the figure is larger; the shape remains the same.]
3. What kind of graph paper should be used to make a figure exactly the same shape and size? [the same size as that used for the original figure]

RETEACHING-99

Name

CONGRUENT FIGURES

Study

These figures are the same shape. They are the same size.

These figures are the same shape. They are not the same size.

Check

Look at each pair of figures.
Write same or different.

1.

shape? _same_

size? _same_

2.

shape? _same_

size? _different_

3.

shape? _same_

size? _different_

4.

shape? _same_

size? _same_

Reteaching-99

Macmillan/McGraw-Hill, MATHEMATICS IN ACTION
Grade 2, Chapter 10, Lesson 11, page 320

PRACTICE-99

Name

CONGRUENT FIGURES

Ring the figure that is the same shape and size.

1.

2.

3.

4.

5.

6.

Practice-99

Macmillan/McGraw-Hill, MATHEMATICS IN ACTION
Grade 2, Chapter 10, Lesson 11, page 320

ENRICHMENT-99

Name

CONGRUENT FIGURES

On Your Own   Pair and Share   In a Group

COLORING FIGURES

Color the two congruent figures.

1.

2.

3.

4.

Enrichment-99

Macmillan/McGraw-Hill, MATHEMATICS IN ACTION
Grade 2, Chapter 10, Lesson 11, page 320

Problem of the Day

How are all the pages in your math book alike?
[They are the same size and the same shape.]

AT·A·GLANCE pp. 321-322

LESSON OBJECTIVE
Use a physical model to solve problems.

ASSIGNMENT GUIDE

COURSE	EXERCISES
Basic	p. 321: 1–4; p. 322: 1–7
Average	p. 321: 1–4; p. 322: 1–7
Challenge	p. 321: 1–4; p. 322: 1–7

MATERIALS
Manipulatives set of pattern blocks (or punchouts); 16 🔲,
4 🔲, 4 🔲 (or square counter punchouts) per pair

Teacher Resources
Reteaching 100
Prob. Solv. 49
Practice 100
MAC Act. 199, 200
Enrichment 100

Name _____

Problem Solving

Strategy: Using a Physical Model

Norma made a necklace.
She used this pattern.
She showed it 4 times. 🔲 △ 🔲
How many orange squares did she use in all?

I can make a model

Use this pattern 🔲 △ 🔲 .
Show the pattern 4 times.
Then count to find the answer.

🔲 △ 🔲 🔲 △ 🔲 🔲 △ 🔲 🔲 △ 🔲

Norma used ___8___ orange squares.

Use models to solve.

1. Peg showed this pattern

3 times. ⬡ ⬡ 🔲 ⬟
How many shapes are not

yellow? ___6___

2. Ross showed this pattern

4 times. ▧ ⬦ △
How many shapes

are blue or green? ___8___

---

3. Lance showed this pattern

6 times. ⬡ ⬟ 🔲 ⬟
How many red shapes did he

use in all? ___12___

4. Alan showed this pattern

3 times. △ ⬦ ▧
How many shapes are not

green? ___6___

Macmillan/McGraw-Hill

---

1 PREPARE
WARM-UP To prepare children for using a physical model to solve problems, draw the following pattern on the chalkboard: square, triangle, circle, square, triangle, circle, circle, square, triangle, circle. Have children identify the rule for the pattern [square, triangle, circle]. Then have children cover their eyes while you erase the third square and replace it with a triangle. Have a volunteer identify the error in the pattern [triangle], while you correct it. Then place the letters A, B, C in the square, triangle, circle, respectively. Have volunteers continue the letter pattern [A,B,C,A,B,C].

2 TEACH
PATTERNING Give pairs of children a set of 24 connecting cubes: 16 red, 4 blue, and 4 yellow. Explain that you will create a pattern with your cubes and they should use their cubes to model your pattern. Create a pattern with 2 red, 1 blue, 1 yellow, and 2 red cubes. Read aloud the following problem.

Maryann showed this pattern 3 times. How many red cubes did she use? [12]

■ **How many red cubes do you have?** [12]

■ **How many cubes in the pattern are not red?** [6]

Repeat the activity by having children make a pattern of 3 red cubes and 1 yellow cube and show that pattern three times.

■ **How many red cubes are in the whole pattern?** [9]

PUPIL'S EDITION pp. 321-322

Page 321 Display a set of pattern blocks: 8 orange squares, 4 green triangles, 7 yellow hexagons, 12 red trapezoids, 4 blue rhombuses,

Tyrone built these castles.
How many cubes did he use to make each castle?

Use some , , and  to solve.

1.

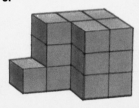

<u>6</u> cubes

2.

<u>9</u> cubes

3.

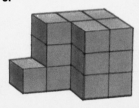

<u>16</u> cubes

4.

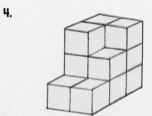

<u>13</u> cubes

5.

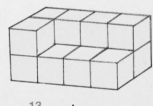

<u>13</u> cubes

6.

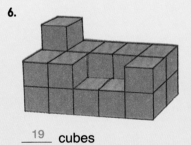

<u>19</u> cubes

7. What types of problems would
you use a model to solve?
Answers will vary.

and 4 white rhombuses. Also have a set of 20 connecting cubes available. Read the problem.

■ **What do you need to do to figure out this problem?** [Model the whole pattern and count the orange squares.]

Have two volunteers model the pattern.

■ **How many times will the pattern be repeated?** [4 times]

Have the entire group count the orange squares. [8]

Encourage children to explain other ways to solve this problem.

Check for Understanding

■ **What if Norma used 3 orange squares in her pattern? How many orange squares would she use in her necklace?** [12]

TEACHER to TEACHER

COOPERATIVE LEARNING TIP My groups like to bring their own connecting blocks from home, and then discuss how models are used by professional builders. Each small group of four breaks into pairs to work through the cube-model problem and to design and make a cube model. Then each pair has the other pair guess the number of cubes. They may send a **"roving representative"** to consult with other groups during design. Small groups then present their models in a **carousel** display format where one member stays to explain while the other three visit the other groups.

ACTIVITY ALTERNATIVE TEACHING STRATEGY

MATERIALS food coloring: blue, red, yellow; white paper towels

VISUAL Discuss that models can be used to conduct simple experiments. Provide groups of children with food coloring and paper towels. Have them determine what colors result from different combinations of blue, red, and yellow, such as: 4 drops of yellow with 1 drop of red, 1 drop of yellow with 5 drops of red, 2 drops of blue with 4 drops of red. Have each group make a display of the experiment and its results.

GUIDED PRACTICE ex. 1–4: Work through problem 1 with the children. Make sure they understand how to solve the problem using a physical model.

Page 322 Have a volunteer read the problem at the top of the page.

3 PRACTICE•APPLY

PRACTICE ex. 1–7: Children may use cubes of different colors for one

C L O S E Guide children to summarize the lesson:

■ **How can you use models to solve a problem?** [Possible response: Copy the data with models, repeat it to show all the information, and then count to find an answer. Build a model to find what is not visible in a picture.]

MAC Activity 199:
Basic-to-Average ▼

MAC Activity 199

On Your Own   Pair and Share   In a Group

MATH AND ART ■ PATTERN ART

2△ 3⬡
1▢ 2▱ 3△
2▱ 2⬡ 2◇

Materials punchout pattern blocks, worksheets, crayons

Setup Make a worksheet by drawing several pattern instructions on paper, using the shapes of the pattern blocks.

Procedure Have children work in groups. Provide each group with a set of pattern blocks and a copy of the pattern worksheet. Tell children to use their pattern blocks to create the patterns on the worksheets and repeat them 3 times. Then they should draw them on the worksheet. When children have completed their patterns, display the worksheets and discuss the different interpretations of the instructions that may occur.

MAC Activity 200:
Average-to-Challenge ▶

SPEAKING MATHEMATICALLY ■ CASTLE PATTERNS

MAC Activity 200

On Your Own   Pair and Share   In a Group

Materials index cards, pattern blocks or punchout pattern blocks, connecting cubes

Setup Prepare castle game cards by tracing or sketching cube structures on one set of cards. On the back of the cards, write the question, "How many cubes are used?" Prepare another set of pattern game cards by drawing patterns of shapes, using the shapes of the pattern blocks. Write a number showing how many times the pattern should be shown. On the back of each card, write a question about the pattern, such as "How many shapes are yellow?"

Procedure Have children play in small groups. Give each group of children a set of at least ten of each type of card, pattern blocks, and connecting cubes. Tell two children in each group to choose cards. Each child takes a card from a different deck. Have the children use the pattern blocks and connecting cubes to show physical models of the problems. Have each child then answer the question on his or her card. Each child who made an accurate physical model and correctly answered the question scores one point. Then two more members of the group draw cards.

To Win The child with the most points at the end of play is the winner.

How many cubes are used?

△⬠⬡◇
3

How many shapes are yellow?

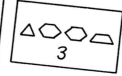

RETEACHING

Name _____

PROBLEM SOLVING STRATEGY: USING A PHYSICAL MODEL

Study

Lynn made a belt.
She used this pattern. □ □ △ △
She showed the pattern 3 times in the belt.
How many squares did she use in all?
Make a model to show Lynn's pattern 3 times.

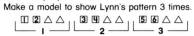

Count the squares. Lynn used 6 squares in her belt.

Check

Use pattern blocks to show the pattern.
Solve.

1. Jim showed this pattern
   4 times. ○ △ □
   How many triangles did
   he use? __4__

   ○ △ □ ○ △ □
   ○ △ □ ○ △ □

2. Millie showed this pattern
   5 times. □ □ ○ □
   How many shapes are
   not squares? __5__

3. Brian showed this pattern
   6 times. □ ◇ △ □
   How many shapes are
   squares? __12__

4. Frank showed this pattern
   3 times. △ △ △
   How many shapes are
   not triangles? __6__

5. Abe showed this pattern
   2 times. ○ ◇ △ △ △
   How many shapes are
   triangles? __4__

Macmillan/McGraw-Hill, MATHEMATICS IN ACTION
Grade 2, Chapter 10, Lesson 12, pages 321–322

Reteaching-100

PRACTICE

Name _____

PROBLEM SOLVING STRATEGY: USING A PHYSICAL MODEL

Use pattern blocks to solve.

△ □ ○ □ ○ △

1. Joyce showed this pattern
   4 times.
   How many shapes are
   squares or triangles? __16__

□ ◇ ○ □ □

2. Carl showed this pattern
   5 times.
   How many shapes are
   not squares? __15__

□ △ △ □ △

3. Dan showed this pattern
   3 times.
   How many shapes are
   not triangles? __6__

○ □ □ □ ⬡

4. Rick showed this pattern
   6 times.
   How many shapes are
   squares? __12__

Leroy built these forts.
How many cubes did he use to make each fort?
Use to solve.

5.
   __10__ cubes

6.
   __11__ cubes

7.
   __17__ cubes

8.
   __14__ cubes

Macmillan/McGraw-Hill, MATHEMATICS IN ACTION
Grade 2, Chapter 10, Lesson 12, pages 321–322

Practice-100

ENRICHMENT

Name _____

PROBLEM SOLVING

On Your Own   Pair and Share   In a Group

BUILDING PATTERNS
Use pattern blocks or to solve.

1. Betty knows her
   pattern key will
   open one door.
   She has to find the
   door that has her
   pattern 3 times.
   Key: □ △ □ ○
   Ring the door.

   □ □ △ ○   □ △ △ △
   □ △ □ ○   □ △ □ ○
   △ ○ □ △   △ ○ □ △
   □ △ □ ○   □ △ □ ○
   ○ △ ○ □   □ △ □ ○
   △ □ ○ △   ○ □ △ ○

2. A pattern is shown
   here 4 times.
   Find the pattern.
   Ring it in each row.

   △ □ ○ △ □ △ □
   □ △ ○ □ △ △ □
   ○ □ △ □ ○ △ □
   □ ○ △ □ △ ○ □

3. Walter wants to build
   a wall out of the stairs.
   How many more cubes
   does he need to add?

   __12__ cubes

4. LaToya wants to make a
   big cube out of small cubes.
   How many more cubes
   does she have to add?

   __8__ cubes

Macmillan/McGraw-Hill, MATHEMATICS IN ACTION
Grade 2, Chapter 10, Lesson 12, pages 321–322

Enrichment-100

Problem of the Day

Conrad saw a picture of a square house whose 4
walls were made up of cubes. In the front wall, he
counted 3 layers of cubes with 4 cubes in each
layer. How many cubes were there in all? [48; 4
+ 4 + 4 = 12, 12 + 12 + 12 + 12 = 48]

CHAPTER 10 • Lesson 13

LESSON OBJECTIVE
Make decisions using information.

ASSIGNMENT GUIDE

COURSE	EXERCISES
Basic	p. 323: 1–5
Average	p. 323: 1–5
Challenge	p. 323: 1–5

MATERIALS
Classroom Materials yarn, bulletin board
Manipulatives 1 measuring tape* per child

Teacher Resources
Crit. Think. 20   Prob. Solv. 50   *Teacher Aid 7

Name _____

Decision Making

Problem Solving: Planning a Bulletin Board

You are decorating your classroom bulletin board.
You need to put yarn around each side.

1. What will you use to measure each side? Answers will vary.

_____

2. How can you find out the distance
   around each side? Write your plan.

   Use your
   own paper.

3. Now try your plan.
   How much yarn will you need for each side?

   _____

   _____

4. How much yarn will you need in all?

   _____

 5. Talk about how many pictures can fit on the
   bulletin board. Think of a plan to find out.

 **PREPARE**   **WARM-UP** To review geometry, draw the following
shapes on the chalkboard.

Have each shape identified. Then have children tell the number of
sides of each shape.

TEACH   **DISCUSSING** Have children look at the bulletin
board in the classroom and identify its shape. Call
on volunteers to name the displays they see on the bulletin boards.
Then discuss with children the uses of bulletin boards.

PUPIL'S EDITION p. 323
Have children look at the picture at the top of the page and discuss
what is happening. [The child is measuring one side of the bulletin
board.]

Check for Understanding
■ **How can you find out how much yarn you will need to put
around the bulletin board?** [Measure the length of each side and
then add the numbers.]

PRACTICE·APPLY Have children complete ex. 1–5. Call
on volunteers to tell how they would
measure each side of a bulletin board, and how they could decide on
the number of pictures that could be displayed on a bulletin board.

For Students Acquiring English (SAE)

Have SAE children do this activity as an oral lesson. Let the children try out their ideas for measurement using the bulletin board in your classroom and then actually create a border for it.

CLOSE Guide children to summarize the lesson:

■ **What should you do before planning a bulletin board display?**
[Decide what to put on the bulletin board. Then measure the display items and the board to see how many items will fit.]

CLASS PROJECT

Materials crayons, construction paper, yarn, paste, and other collage materials

Have children work in groups. Assign each group to a bulletin board. Provide children with construction paper, crayons, paste, yarn, and other collage materials. Have them use the materials to decorate their assigned bulletin board. Remind children to measure the sides of the board to see how much of each material is needed.

When children have completed the project, have groups evaluate each other's boards.

AT·A·GLANCE p. 324

OBJECTIVE
Use a computer to model congruent and symmetrical figures.

MATERIALS
Classroom Materials Logo language disk
Computer per pair

Technology

Computer: Matching Shapes

The two parts in this figure match. The figure is **symmetrical**.

The two parts are the same size and same shape. They are **congruent**.

You can draw figures like this on a computer.

At the Computer

1. Type all of the first commands to draw part of the figure. Then your partner types all of the second commands to draw the other part.

First Commands	Second Commands
RT 90	LT 90
FD 30	FD 30
LT 90	RT 90
FD 70	FD 70
LT 90	RT 90
FD 30	FD 30
PU	
HOME	
PD	

2. Tell why the figure is symmetrical and its parts are congruent. *The parts of the figure match and are the same size and same shape.*

3. Talk about how the second commands helped to draw a matching part. *Possible answer: The second commands used directions opposite to the first commands for left and right.*

4. Draw your own symmetrical figures with congruent parts. You draw part of a figure on the computer. Your partner draws the matching part. Take turns.

1 PREPARE

WARM-UP To prepare children to model congruent and symmetrical shapes on a computer, have them point to real-life examples of these concepts.

2 TEACH

DISCUSSING Draw a square, a rectangle, a triangle, and an asymmetrical block letter L on the chalkboard. Have volunteers draw figures that are the same size and the same shape. Have volunteers draw lines of symmetry through the symmetrical figures.

Draw half of a triangle. Have a volunteer draw a part that matches to complete the triangle. Discuss that both parts match and have the same size and the same shape.

3 PRACTICE·APPLY

Discuss the display at the top of the page. Review the vocabulary terms: *congruent, symmetrical.*

AT THE COMPUTER Before children begin working in pairs at the computer, load the Logo language disk and identify the figure as a turtle. Review the commands in ex. 1 and introduce the terms PU (pen up) and PD (pen down). If the pen is down, a line will be drawn. If the pen is up, no line will be drawn. Tell them that the computer already has the pen down command to begin. Explain that when children type in HOME, the turtle will return home. Remind children to type in the letters and numbers exactly as shown on the page and to press RETURN after each number. Discuss how to correct mistakes before pressing RETURN (check your Logo documentation) and how to clear the screen and return home (Apple: CLEARSCREEN or CS; Krell or Terrapin: DRAW; Logo-Writer: CG).

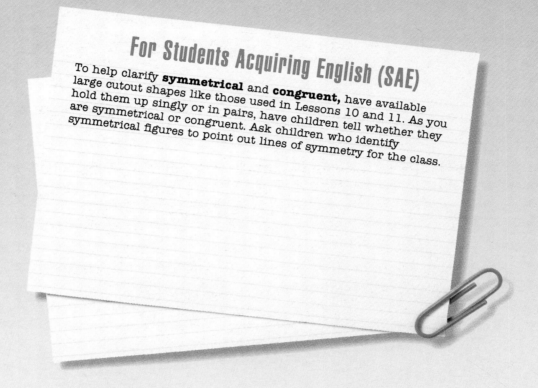

For Students Acquiring English (SAE)

To help clarify **symmetrical** and **congruent,** have available large cutout shapes like those used in Lessons 10 and 11. As you hold them up singly or in pairs, have children tell whether they are symmetrical or congruent. Ask children who identify symmetrical figures to point out lines of symmetry for the class.

Tell children that the line of symmetry does not appear on the computer screen and that they have to imagine it.

As children complete ex. 4, guide them as necessary to see that they must use opposite directions, left/right, to make a matching side. Children may find it helpful to record their commands and to draw the resulting figures. Children may find that when they input a large number for forward or backward, the turtle may move off the screen and reappear at the opposite side. Have them clear the screen and begin again using a smaller number.

CLOSE Guide children to summarize the lesson:

■ **What do you have to know to make symmetrical and congruent figures on a computer?** [Possible response: You have to know how to make part of a figure and another part that matches.]

CHAPTER 10

Name _____

Extra Practice

Perimeter, pages 315–316 ....

I. Find the distance around the shape.

___18___ units around

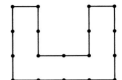

Area, page 317 ....

I. Write how many square units.

___9___ square units

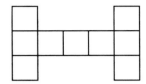

Symmetry, page 319 ....

I. Ring each shape that has a line of symmetry.

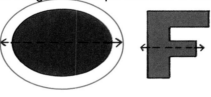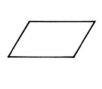

Congruent Figures, page 320 ....

I. Ring the one that is the same shape and same size.

ADDITIONAL PRACTICE

p. 317 *Make these shapes with ▢.*

Tell how many squares you used for each shape.

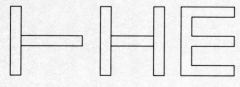

p. 319 *Ring each shape that has a line of symmetry.*

p. 320 *Ring the one that is the same shape and size.*

Practice Plus

Key Skill: Two Dimensional Figures, page 310

Ring the shape you would make by tracing around the object.

1.  △ ◯ ▭

2.  ◯ ▭ △

3.  ⬭ △ ◯

Key Skill: Perimeter, page 316

Find the distance around the shape.

1.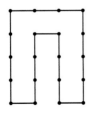

   ___20___ units around

2.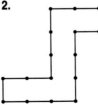

   ___18___ units around

PRACTICE PLUS

Practice Plus is provided to supply additional practice for the two key skills in this chapter.

Key Skills
Page 310: More Two-Dimensional Figures
Page 316: Perimeter

The *Additional Practice* also provides practice you may wish to assign for key skills in this chapter.

ADDITIONAL PRACTICE

p. 310 *Ring the shape you would make by tracing around the bottom.*

1. △ ◯ ▭ ▭

   [circle]

2.  △ ◯ ▭ ▭

   [square]

3.  △ ◯ ▭ ▭

   [rectangle]

4. 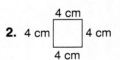 △ ◯ ▭ ▭

   [circle]

p. 316 Draw the figures as marked.

Find the distance around the shape. Use your ruler.

1. 2 cm △ 2 cm   __[6]__ cm around
   2 cm

2. 4 cm ▭ 4 cm   __[16]__ cm around
   4 cm (top) 4 cm (bottom)

Chapter 10 • Practice Plus   **326**

CHAPTER 10

AT·A·GLANCE pp. 327-328

OBJECTIVE
Review/test the concepts and skills presented in Chapter 10.

10A. Identify three-dimensional figures.
10B. Identify two-dimensional figures and the number of sides and corners.
10C. Find perimeter and area.
10D. Identify symmetrical and congruent figures.
10E. Solve problems including those that involve using a picture.

Teacher Resources
Testing Program, pp. 103–114

Name _____

Chapter Review/Test

Language and Mathematics

Choose the correct word.

1. This shape is a
   _____cube_____ .

2. This shape ☐ is a
   _____rectangle_____ .

rectangle
cube

Concepts and Skills

Write the correct letter.

3. Which is a cone? __c__   a.

4. Which is a sphere? __b__   b.

5. Which is a rectangular prism? __a__   c.

Write the number of sides and corners of each figure.

6.	7.	8.
__4__ sides	__3__ sides	__4__ sides
__4__ corners	__3__ corners	__4__ corners

Macmillan/McGraw-Hill

USING THE CHAPTER REVIEW/TEST

The Chapter Review/Test may be used as a review to survey children's knowledge and understanding of the chapter material. Or it may be used as a test to formally assess children's understanding of the concepts and skills taught in the chapter. If used as a test, you may wish to assign one or more of the resources listed in *Reinforcement and Remediation* on p. 328 after reviewing children's test results.

If the Chapter Review/Test is used as a review, you may wish to have children work in pairs to complete it. Challenge them to invent a new sport and have them talk about the shape of the objects they would use to play the sport. Then, you can use the Chapter Tests—Forms A, B, and C—provided in the *Testing Program Blackline Master and Teacher's Manual* for testing purposes. Any of these forms may be used for pretesting, posttesting, or retesting.

A performance assessment activity for the key concept in this chapter is provided on page 329.

9. Find the distance around.

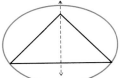

__18__ units in all

10. How many square units?

__12__ square units

11. Ring the shape if it has a line of symmetry.

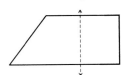

12. Draw the same shape. Make it the same size.

Drawing can be in any four squares on grid.

Problem Solving

Find each shape on the grid.
Complete to show where it is.

	Across →	Up ↑
13. ▲	5	2
14. ★	1	3
15. ■	5	3

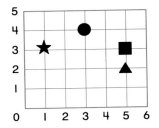

MEETING INDIVIDUAL NEEDS

Reinforcement and Remediation

CHAP. OBJ.	TEST ITEMS	PUPIL'S EDITION pp.			TEACHER'S EDITION pp.	TEACHER RESOURCES	
		Lesson	Extra Practice	Practice Plus	Alt. Teaching Strategy	Reteaching	Practice
10A	1, 3–5	305–306	314		306	92	92
10B	2, 6–8	307–310	314		308, 310	93, 94	93, 94
10C	9–10	315–317	325	326	316, 317A	96, 97	96, 97
10D	11–12	319–320	325	326	319A, 320A	98, 99	98, 99
10E	13–15	311–312, 321–322	314			95, 100	95, 100

For Students Acquiring English (SAE)

Before beginning the Chapter Review/Test with SAE children, scan the pages for any unfamiliar vocabulary that should be pretaught. You may wish to pair or group SAE children with non-SAE children. You may also wish to repeat some of the activities and techniques for SAE children that were suggested earlier in this chapter.

CHAPTER 10

AT·A·GLANCE p. 329

OBJECTIVE
Assess whether children can recognize 3-dimensional figures and their characteristics.

MATERIALS
Classroom Materials 3-dimensional figures*

Teacher Resources
Performance Assessment booklet, pp. 39–41
*Teacher Aids 13, 14

For Students Acquiring English (SAE)

Before beginning the performance assessment with SAE children, scan the page for any unfamiliar vocabulary that should be pretaught. You may wish to pair or group SAE children with non-SAE children. You may also wish to repeat some of the activities and techniques for SAE children that were suggested earlier in this chapter.

Performance Assessment

Work with a partner.

| sphere | cylinder | cone | cube | rectangular prism |

Talk about each shape.
How are they alike?
How are they different?

Pick two shapes.
Write what you know about them.
Then draw or name something around you that has the same shape.

Shape:_____	Real-life object
Shape:_____	Real-life object

Macmillan/McGraw-Hill

You may put this page in your .

USING PERFORMANCE ASSESSMENT
The Performance Assessment activity may be used to informally assess children's understanding of the key concept(s) of the chapter. Additional assessment activities and Math Journal Options are provided in the *Performance Assessment* booklet.

Performing the Activity
Assign children to work in pairs. Show them 3-dimensional figures: cube, rectangular prism, cone, cylinder. Have them describe the characteristics of each solid figure to each other. Then have children work individually to describe two of the figures and name a real-life object that has the same shape.

Evaluation Guidelines
Use these criteria to help determine the holistic score for each child. The holistic scoring scale can be found in the Teacher's Reference Section.

- Does the child recognize solid figures and their characteristics?
- Can children describe the solid figures?
- Can the child name a real-life shape with the same shape as each figure?

[Example Response: (cube) It has 6 sides and 8 corners. A real-life object might be a box or a number cube.]

If children do not have a full understanding of the key concept(s), you may wish to use the Alternative Teaching Strategies or the MAC Activities within the chapter.

You may wish to have children put their final revised work in their portfolios.

A formal assessment of the concepts and skills taught in this chapter is provided on pages 327–328.

PERFORMANCE ASSESSMENT

Enrichment For All

The map shows how many meters it is from one bug city to another.

Using a Map

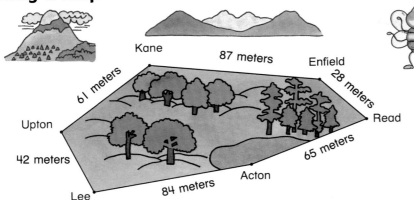

Use the map to answer the questions.

1. How far is it from Lee to Upton?

   _42_ meters

2. How far is it from Kane to Enfield?

   _87_ meters

3. You are in Read. Is it farther to Enfield or to Acton?

   _____Acton_____

4. Which city is 61 meters from Kane?

   _____Upton_____

5. Mr. Bug walked from Acton to Read. Then he walked to Enfield. How far did he walk?

   _93_ meters

6. Mrs. Bug walked from Lee to Acton in the morning. Then she walked to Read in the afternoon. How much farther did she walk in the morning?

   _19_ meters

AT·A·GLANCE p. 330

OBJECTIVE
Use a map to determine distance in meters.

ASSIGNMENT GUIDE

COURSE	EXERCISES
Basic	p. 330: 1–6
Average	p. 330: 1–6
Challenge	p. 330: 1–6

MATERIALS
Classroom Materials   road map

For Students Acquiring English (SAE)

Make sure that SAE children know the difference between the words **far** and **farther.** First develop the difference between **near** and **far** by having three volunteers stand in a line at different intervals. Extend the discussion to introduce **far** and **farther** by having two volunteers stand at a greater distance from the third. For ex. 1–6, model how to find the distance using ex. 1. State the response in a complete sentence. (*It is 42 meters from Lee to Upton*). Pair SAE children and non-SAE children for ex. 2–6; encourage pairs to answer in complete sentence, but accept brief answers from SAE children. If time permits, have pairs write an additional exercise to ask the other children.

1 PREPARE

WARM-UP   To prepare children for using a map, display a road map. Explain that people use road maps. Have volunteers identify the distances to and from specific places on the map.

2 TEACH

DISCUSSING   Have children study the map on the page. Explain that distances on this map are shown in meters. Have children point to and name the towns shown.

■ **What do the numbers between each town show?** [how many meters it is between two towns]

■ **How would you find the distance between Lee and Read?** [Add the meters shown between Lee and Acton and before Acton and Read.]

3 PRACTICE·APPLY

Have children complete ex. 1–6. Call on volunteers to explain answers for ex. 5–6.

CLOSE   Guide children to summarize the lesson:

■ **How would you figure out how much farther it is from Kane to Enfield than it is from Enfield to Read?** [Subtract 38 from 87; 87 − 38 = 49 meters.]

CHAPTER 10

OBJECTIVE
Review and maintain previously learned concepts and skills.

Name _____

Cumulative Review

Fill in the ○ to answer each question.

1.

$$\begin{array}{r} 18 \\ -\ 9 \\ \hline \end{array}$$

27	9	8	1
○	●	○	○

2. What amount is shown?

$1.31	$1.26	$1.25	$1.22
○	●	○	○

3.

$$\begin{array}{r} 14 \\ +\ 25 \\ \hline \end{array}$$

26	36	39	40
○	○	●	○

4.

$$\begin{array}{r} 54¢ \\ -\ 23¢ \\ \hline \end{array}$$

21¢	31¢	37¢	77¢
○	●	○	○

5. Which number is 6 hundreds 4 tens 2 ones?

12	246	624	642
○	○	○	●

6. How many square units?

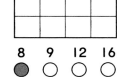

8	9	12	16
●	○	○	○

7. Ellie had 7 tapes.
She bought 5 more.
How many tapes did she have?

- ○ 2
- ○ 4
- ● 12
- ○ 13

Macmillan/McGraw-Hill

Chapter 10   Geometry

three hundred thirty-one   **331**

USING THE CUMULATIVE REVIEW

The Cumulative Review is presented in a multiple-choice format to provide practice in taking a standardized test. It gives children an opportunity to review previously learned skills. An answer sheet, similar to those used when taking standardized tests, can be found in the *Testing Program Blackline Masters and Teacher's Manual.*

The table that follows correlates the review items to the lesson pages on which the skills are taught.

Review Items	Text Pages	Review Items	Text Pages
1	107	5	279–282
2	135–136	6	317
3	191–195	7	93–94
4	233–234		

Testing Program Blackline Masters
In addition to the Cumulative Review in the Pupil's Edition, there are quarterly Cumulative Tests and an End-Year Test. These tests are multiple choice and provide additional opportunities for children to practice taking standardized tests.

Cumulative Tests measure children's performance on major skills and concepts taught during the previous quarters. The **End-Year Test** measures children's performance on major skills and concepts taught throughout the year.

Home Activity

Your child has been learning to identify 2- and 3-dimensional figures. Here is a way to strengthen your child's understanding of these figures.

1. Look together for things around your home that look like the 2-dimensional shapes below. List the objects that you find.

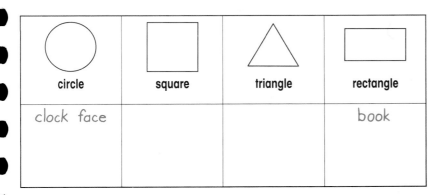

circle	square	triangle	rectangle
clock face			book

2. Repeat the activity, but this time look around the house for 3-dimensional figures.

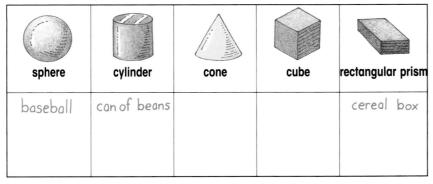

sphere	cylinder	cone	cube	rectangular prism
baseball	can of beans			cereal box

332 three hundred thirty-two

AT·A·GLANCE p. 332

OBJECTIVE
Give family members an opportunity to share in their child's mathematics learning.

For Students Acquiring English (SAE)

Before assigning this Home Activity to SAE children, find out if someone at home will be able to work with them in English. If not, prepare them to complete the activity independently at home. Explain the directions of the activity and ask SAE children to restate them so you can check comprehension. Scan the page and preteach any difficult vocabulary or phrases that they may not know. If you feel that an SAE child will need extra help with the activity, you might assign that child a non-SAE partner and arrange a time for them to work on the activity in or out of school.

USING THE ACTIVITY

Have children look at the page. Explain that the page has an activity that an adult in the family can help them complete. Read the page with the children, making sure that they understand what needs to be done. Tell children that they will do this page at home.

Previewing
CHAPTER 11

Audrey Jackson

FRACTIONS

> **IN CHAPTER 11, you will be introducing your children to fractions. You will also have the opportunity to explore fractions for parts of a set.**

Notes
FROM THE AUTHOR

Here are some notes on the concepts presented in this chapter and how your children can apply them to solve problems.

DEVELOPING FRACTION CONCEPTS

Encourage children to recognize their familiarity with fraction concepts by recalling that they have probably shared half an apple or half a sandwich. Then help them learn the concept of equal parts and fraction notation.

Children should begin by exploring equal parts of a region, or whole. Starting with equal parts of a whole, children learn to identify the number of equal parts and to name the parts as halves, fourths, thirds, sixths, and so on.

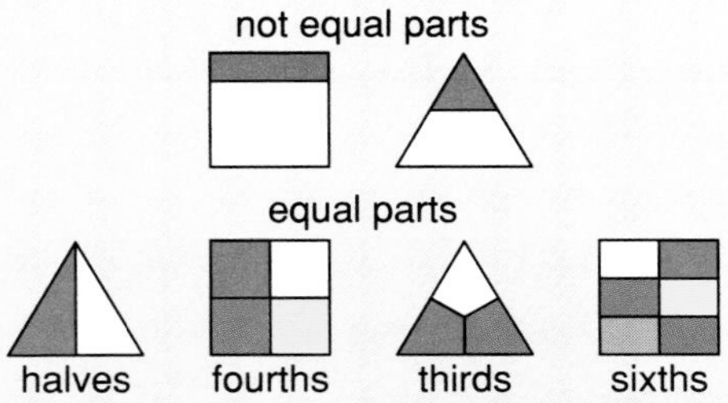

not equal parts

equal parts

halves   fourths   thirds   sixths

Then help children learn to identify the number of equal parts of a whole, as in the following examples.

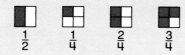

$\frac{1}{2}$ $\frac{1}{4}$ $\frac{2}{4}$ $\frac{3}{4}$

PARTS of a SET

Children extend their understanding of fractions by exploring the fractional parts of a set. Your children will find that modeling with connecting cubes or other manipulatives helps them understand the concept of parts of a set. Mastery of the concept is not expected at this level.

 $\frac{1}{4}$ red cube cubes

PROBLEM SOLVING

In **Problem Solving** your children (1) draw a picture to solve a problem and (2) review problem-solving strategies they have previously learned.

In **Thinking Mathematically** children demonstrate their knowledge of fractions by finding the halves and fourths pictured in a scene.

In **Decision Making** children use information about the sizes and costs of toppings to plan a pizza order using a certain amount of money.

Mathematics and Literature

To use literature in the application of mathematics.
■ To promote appreciation of the contributions of all cultures to mathematics. ■ Children are introduced to a poem in the K–2 *Math Anthology* on page 192. By reading "A Sum," children gain experience with fraction concepts.
■ In the Curriculum Connection on page 354, children apply their knowledge of fractions by describing the flags of Mali and Panama in fractional terms.

CULTURAL DIVERSITY

CHAPTER II • ORGANIZER

CHAPTER PLANNING GUIDE

CHAPTER OBJECTIVES
WITH STANDARDIZED TEST CORRELATIONS

A. Identify fractional parts of a region   CAT, SAT, ITBS, CTBS
B. Identify fractional parts of a set   CAT, SAT, ITBS, CTBS
C. Solve problems including those that involve drawing a picture

SUGGESTED PACING-11 DAYS

LESSONS	NCTM STANDARDS	ASSIGNMENTS Basic/Average/Challenge	STUDENT EDITION Extra Practice/ Practice Plus	ADDITIONAL RESOURCES Manip. Plus	Reteach	Practice	Enrich	MAC Activities
Chapter Opener: *How Many Ways Can You Cut a Pie?* page 333	1, 2, 3, 4, 12	p. 333: All						
✓ **1 Fractions** page 334	1, 2, 3, 12	p. 334: All						
✓ **2 Halves** pages 335–336	1, 2, 3, 12	p. 335: 1–3; p. 336: 1–4		65, 66	101	101	101	201, 202
✓ **3 Fourths** pages 337–338	1, 2, 3, 12	p. 337: 1–2; p. 338: 1–5	p. 344		102	102	102	203, 204
✓ **4 Thirds** pages 339–340	1, 2, 3, 12	p. 339: 1–3; p. 340: 1–10	p. 344		103	103	103	205, 206
✓ **5 Sixths** pages 341–342	1, 2, 3, 12	p. 341: 2–5; p. 342: 1–8, Reasoning	pp. 344, 356		104	104	104	207, 208
✓ **6 PS: Thinking Mathematically** page 343	1, 2, 3, 12	p. 343: All						
7 PS: Drawing a Picture pages 345–346	1, 2, 3, 12	p. 345: 1–2; p. 346: 1–4	p. 355		105	105	105	209, 210
✓ **8 Parts of a Set** pages 347–348	1, 2, 3, 12	p. 347: 1–3; p. 348: 1–9	pp. 355, 356	67, 68	106	106	106	211, 212
✓ **9 Probability** pages 349–350	1, 2, 3, 11	p. 349: 2–3; p. 350: 1–2						
10 PS: Strategies Review pages 351–352	1, 2, 3, 6, 8, 11	p. 351: 1–3; p. 352: 1–5			107	107	107	213, 214
11 PS: Decision Making page 353	1, 2, 3, 6, 8	p. 353: 1–5						

Curriculum Connection: Social Studies page 354 CC

Chapter Review/Test pages 357–358

Performance Assessment page 359

Cumulative Review page 361

Enrichment for All/Home Activity pages 360, 362

NATIONAL COUNCIL OF TEACHERS OF MATHEMATICS Grades K–4

1. Problem Solving
2. Communication
3. Reasoning
4. Connections
5. Estimation
6. Number Sense and Numeration

7. Concepts of Whole Number Operations
8. Whole Number Computation
9. Geometry and Spatial Sense

10. Measurement
11. Statistics and Probability
12. Fractions and Decimals
13. Patterns and Relationships

✓ Activity   👥 Cooperative Learning   CC Cultural Connection

MEETING the NCTM STANDARDS

Problem Solving

Strategies and Skills	• drawing a picture pp. 345–346 • strategies review pp. 351–352
Applications	• **Decision Making** lesson p. 353 • **Problem of the Day** TE pp. 334, 336B, 338B, 340B, 342B, 346B, 348B, 350, 352B
Mathematical Investigations	• **Thinking Mathematically** lesson p. 343

Communication

Language	• using the language of mathematics TE pp. 335–336, 337–338, 339–340, 341–342, 347–348
Oral/Written	• using cooperative learning activities pp. 334, 335–336, 337–338, 339–340, 343, 347–348, 349, 350, 353, 354; TE pp. 332I–332L • **Journal Writing** opportunities TE pp. 334, 336, 338, 340, 342, 348, 350

Reasoning

Critical Thinking	• answering questions that analyze and extend concepts pp. 334, 338, 346, 349, 353

Connections

To other subject areas	• Literature p. 333, Social Studies p. 354; Literature TE pp. 333–334, 339
To all cultures	• flags of Mali and Panama p. 354

Concept Development

Fractions and Decimals	• identifying fractional parts of a region pp. 334, 335–336, 337–338, 339–340, 341–342; TE pp. 332I–332J • identifying fractional parts of a set pp. 347–348; TE pp. 332K–332L
Statistics and Probability	• exploring finding probability pp. 349–350

ASSESSMENT OPTIONS

PERFORMANCE ASSESSMENT

Preassessment Activity

Before beginning Chapter 11, give each child a sheet of construction paper. Have children imagine that this is a cake to be shared equally by four people. Have children fold, cut, or draw lines on the paper to show how the cake should be shared. Have them explain the process they used. Assess children's knowledge of equal parts.

Ongoing Assessment

The Ongoing Assessment cards under MEETING INDI-VIDUAL NEEDS on TE pp. 340 and 348 provide criteria and questions for assessing children's understanding of the key mathematical concepts developed in the chapter.

Journal Writing opportunities encourage children to write about mathematics. Their responses can be re-corded either pictorially or in words. The journal writ-ing opportunities on the Ongoing Assessment cards also allow you to assess children's understanding of the lessons.

In addition to the Ongoing Assessment cards, other assessment and journal writing opportunities in this chapter include:

• **CLOSE** TE pp. 334, 336, 338, 340, 342, 350

Performance Assessment Activity

The Performance Assessment activity on p. 359 pro-vides an alternative to formal assessment. This activity assesses children's understanding of the key concepts of the chapter.

For performance assessment activities that are keyed to individual chapter objectives, see the *Performance Assessment* booklet.

BUILDING A PORTFOLIO

Children should be encouraged to keep a selection of their best work in portfolios. The portfolios provide a way of docu-menting children's growth in understanding mathematical concepts. Portfolio opportunities in this chapter include:

• **Performance Assessment** p. 359
• **Class Project** TE p. 353A

If you wish to provide additional opportunities for portfolio work, you may choose to use:

• **MAC Activities** 201, 206, 212, 214

You may also wish to have children include their journal writing from the Ongoing Assessment on TE pp. 340 and 348 in their portfolio.

Formal Assessment

The **Chapter Review/Test** assesses children's under-standing of the concepts and skills developed in the chapter. The **Cumulative Review** assesses children's understanding of the concepts and skills developed from the beginning of the year.

You can use **Form A** or **Form B** of the **Chapter Test** found in the *Testing Program Blackline Masters and Teacher's Manual* if you wish to use a multiple-choice

format to assess children's understanding of the chapter concepts and skills. You can use **Form C** if you wish to use a free-response format. Any of the forms may be used as a pretest, posttest, or for retesting.

The **COMPUTER MANAGEMENT SYSTEM**, or **CMS**, enables you to score **Forms A** and **B** of the **Chapter Test** quickly and automatically. It also prescribes learn-ing activities based on children's test results.

For more information about Assessment, see the *Professional Handbook*.

Common Error and Remediation

The Teacher's Edition notes for each Develop/Understand (Transitional/Abstract) lesson provide a common error analysis and a remediation activity. Some errors defy quick analysis and can only be identified by interviewing the child.

ALTERNATIVE TEACHING STRATEGY

Alternative Teaching Strategies appear frequently in the chapter. These strategies provide other presentations of the lessons for children who might benefit from instruction in different learning modalities: kinesthetic, visual, and/or auditory.

For Students Acquiring English (SAE)

For SAE children to follow more easily the concepts developed in this chapter, preteach fraction-related vocabulary. Use flashcards that show the fraction in number, word, and picture form. You can use the flashcards to play games such as "Around the World."

SAE notes appear periodically in the chapter. These notes provide suggestions for how to work with children to improve comprehension and build vocabulary.

MANIPULATIVES WORKSHOP

Pattern blocks are used in this chapter to investigate fraction concepts. They provide concrete representations of fractions of wholes and fractions of sets.

USING MANIPULATIVES

Here a child is exploring fractions of a whole.

The child builds a figure by putting together its two halves.

Here a child builds a figure by putting together 5 of the 6 parts needed to make the whole figure. The child shows $\frac{5}{6}$.

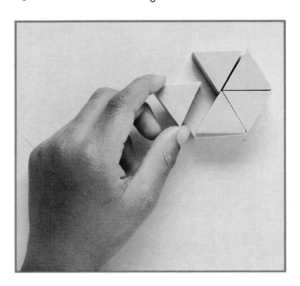

Here a child is exploring fractions of a set.

The child displays 3 pattern blocks, 2 of which are red, to demonstrate that $\frac{2}{3}$ of the pattern blocks are red.

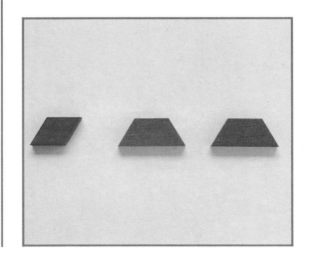

MAKING MANIPULATIVES See the Manipulatives section of the *Professional Handbook* for materials that can be used as a substitute for pattern blocks.

COOPERATIVE LEARNING WORKSHOP

GETTING STARTED

Decision Making: Small groups can now become acquainted with and learn the usefulness of **decision by compromise, by majority, by minority, by consent** (a person or persons disagreeing with the majority consents to their solution as equally valid), and **by consensus.** Decision-making tasks require both a **group-oriented leader** (encourager, facilitator), and a **task-oriented leader** (organizer, coordinator, timekeeper). Children can decide what the job description is for such **roles** by describing and writing in their group journal; for example, "What does a good recorder (cheerleader, materials person) do?"

IDEAS TO TRY

Group-Building Structures: Activities for the entire class that bring children together to form a whole—using numbers, words, or pictures—reinforce the concept of fractions. Team-building activities that require interdependence of parts make the concept concrete. For example, completing a puzzle in which each child in the small group must form a circle from the pieces received before anyone in the group can be considered finished, teaches this principle.

You can apply the above group-building structures in these lessons:
11-1 *Fractions* p. 334
11-2 *Halves* pp. 335–336
11-3 *Fourths* pp. 337–338

How Do We Come to Agreement? The lessons named below provide opportunities for the small group to consider a question and then decide how they will **come to agreement.** For example, in lesson 11-4, children can discuss and decide the relationship between colors and fractions. In lesson 11-5, they can **huddle** to identify the fractions in the shapes shown in the Warm-Up. In lesson 11-8, they can agree on the answers to the questions. Groups should check each member's understanding as anyone in the group can be called on to explain the group's answer to the class.

You can apply the above decision-making ideas in these lessons:
11-4 *Thirds* pp. 339–340

SEE ALSO

Cooperative Learning Tip for lessons 11-6 Thinking Mathematically p. 343A; 11-7 Problem Solving p. 346; 11-10 Problem Solving p. 352

The Cooperative Learning section of the *Professional Handbook* for additional information

INTERACTIVE BULLETIN BOARD

SETUP Cover a bulletin board with yellow construction paper. Cut out the shapes shown in the illustration. Divide each shape as shown and color part of each shape red. Prepare a set of fraction cards that correspond to the red parts.

PROCEDURE Call on volunteers to tack the cards below the correct shapes.

As a variation, you can change the title to "What Part Is White?" and prepare a set of fraction cards that corresponds to the white parts.

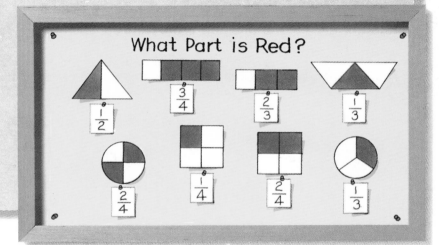

For use before LESSON 11.2, pp. 335-336

65

EQUAL PARTS

OBJECTIVE
Explore the concept of equal parts of a whole.

MATERIALS
Classroom Materials
construction-paper models (for equal parts and for unequal parts), scissors, construction-paper shapes; construction-paper shapes (EXTENDING THE ACTIVITY only)

WHOLE GROUP ACTIVITY

Prepare two sheets of construction paper for each child. Draw a line on one of the sheets to make 2 equal parts. Draw a line on the other to make 2 unequal parts.

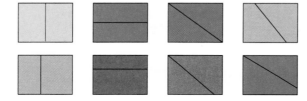

Distribute the 2 construction-paper models (1 with equal parts, 1 with unequal parts) to each child.

■ **Into how many parts are your papers divided?** [2]

■ **Are the parts equal?** [Guide children to see that some of the sheets of paper are divided into 2 equal parts and some are not.]

Give children scissors. Have them cut along the lines of their papers and place the 2 parts on top of each other to confirm which of the sheets of paper are divided into equal parts.

PAIRS ACTIVITY

Prepare construction-paper squares, rectangles, triangles, circles, and other shapes. Assign children to work in pairs. Give each pair 1 shape.

Challenge pairs to find whether the shape can be divided into 2 equal parts and 4 equal parts. Tell children to cut the shapes along the fold lines and stack the parts to check if they are equal.

Have pairs share what happened in their group.

EXTENDING THE ACTIVITY

Give each pair another shape and challenge them to find whether the shape can be divided into other numbers of equal parts.

ONGOING ASSESSMENT

✔ Are children able to determine equal parts and unequal parts of a whole?

For use before LESSON 11.2, pp. 335-336

66

MORE EQUAL PARTS

OBJECTIVES
Recognize equal parts. Identify how many equal parts.

MATERIALS
Classroom Materials
overhead projector
Manipulatives 5 ▲ (or punchouts), 21 ▲ per group

WHOLE GROUP ACTIVITY

Give each child 5 red pattern blocks. Hold up 1 red block and have children do the same. Tell them that the red block is a whole block. Place the block on the overhead projector and write *whole* under it.

■ **How many equal parts are in this whole?** [1]

Put 2 red blocks next to the first block and have children do the same. Write *whole* under this model.

■ **How many equal parts are in this whole?** [2]

Repeat the activity with 3 and then 4 blocks.

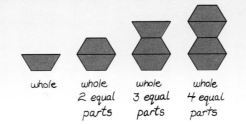

whole   whole 2 equal parts   whole 3 equal parts   whole 4 equal parts

SMALL GROUP ACTIVITY

Assign children to work in groups of three. Give each group 21 green pattern blocks and have them create *wholes* with 1–6 equal parts.

Repeat the activity with other pattern blocks.

EXTENDING THE ACTIVITY

Have children use orange blocks to model problems.

■ **Walt baked a cake. The size of the whole cake is 1 orange block. What does the whole cake look like?**

■ **Todd baked a cake. The size of each equal piece is 1 orange block. He has 2 equal pieces in the whole cake. What does the whole cake look like?**

■ **Janet baked a cake. The size of each equal piece is one orange block. She has 4 equal pieces in the whole cake. What does the whole cake look like?**

ONGOING ASSESSMENT

✓ Are children able to recognize that the same-size part can show different fractions depending on the whole?

For use before
LESSON 11.8,
pp. 347-348

67
PARTS OF
SETS

OBJECTIVE
Explore the concept of
parts of a set.

MATERIALS
Manipulatives 6 ▥, 6 ▥,
6 ▥ (or square counter
punchouts), and Workmat
5 per child

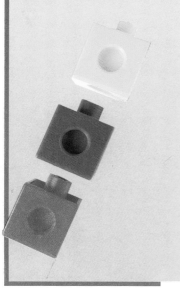

WHOLE GROUP ACTIVITY 🕐
Give each child 6 red, 6 blue, and 6 yellow connecting cubes and 1 Workmat 5. Tell children to put
1 red cube in the first space on the workmats and 1
blue cube in the second space on the workmats.

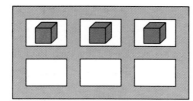

- **What part of the set of cubes is red?** [$\frac{1}{2}$]
- **What part of the set of cubes is blue?** [$\frac{1}{2}$]

Then have children put another blue cube in the
third space on the workmat.

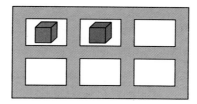

- **How many equal parts are in this set of
cubes?** [3]
- **What part of the set of cubes is red?** [$\frac{1}{3}$]
- **What part of the set of cubes is blue?** [$\frac{2}{3}$]

Repeat with 3 cubes of different colors. Also use
examples involving 4, 5, and 6 cubes.

EXTENDING THE ACTIVITY
Have children use cubes to model these problems.

■ **The sticker package has 6 stickers. 3 of the
stickers are blue dinosaurs. 3 of the stickers are
red dinosaurs. What part of the stickers is red?**
[$\frac{1}{2}$]

■ **The fruit basket had 3 fruits. 2 of the fruits
were yellow bananas. 1 of the fruits was a red
apple. What part of the fruits is red?** [$\frac{1}{3}$]

ONGOING ASSESSMENT
✓ Are children able to use fractions to
describe parts of a set?

MANIPULATIVES Plus ACTIVITY

For use before LESSON 11.8, pp. 347-348

68
MORE PARTS OF SETS

OBJECTIVE
Explore the concept of parts of a set.

MATERIALS
Manipulatives 6 ⬢, 6 ▢, 6 ▰, 6 ▲, 6 ⬠ (or punchouts) per pair

PAIRS ACTIVITY

Have children work in pairs. Give each pair 6 blue, 6 orange, 6 red, 6 green, 6 yellow pattern blocks. Have children show 3 blue blocks and 1 orange block.

- **How many blocks are in the set?** [4]
- **What part of the set is orange?** [$\frac{1}{4}$]
- **What part of the set is blue?** [$\frac{3}{4}$]
- **What part of the set is square-shaped?** [$\frac{1}{4}$]
- **What part of the set is diamond-shaped?** [$\frac{3}{4}$]

Then have children show 3 red blocks, 2 green blocks, and 1 yellow block.

- **How many blocks are in the set?** [6]
- **What part of the set is red?** [$\frac{3}{6}$]
- **What part of the set is green?** [$\frac{2}{6}$]

- **What part of the set is yellow?** [$\frac{1}{6}$]
- **What part of the set has 4-sided shapes?** [$\frac{3}{6}$]
- **What part of the set has 3-sided shapes?** [$\frac{2}{6}$]
- **What part of the set has 6-sided shapes?** [$\frac{1}{6}$]

EXTENDING THE ACTIVITY

Have children take turns showing a set of 2–6 shapes and identifying the fraction for each color and/or shape block in the set.

ONGOING ASSESSMENT

✓ Are children able to use fractions to describe parts of a set?

Mathematics and Literature

Listening and Speaking

The Read-Aloud selection can be used with the Chapter 11 Opener and Lesson 11-1 on pages 333-334.

Tape 2, Side 2
Selection 2

HOW MANY WAYS CAN YOU CUT A

P • I • E • ?

By Jane Belk Moncure

An understanding of parts of this story is dependent on the illustrations in the book. Descriptions of these illustrations are given in parentheses.

To help your children visualize the pie divisions given at the end of this story, draw pies on the chalkboard and divide them as shown.

The Library—
A Magic Castle

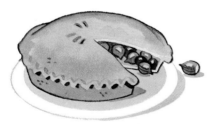

Come to the magic castle
When you are growing tall.
Rows upon rows of Word Windows
Line every single wall.
They reach up high,
As high as the sky,
And you want to open them all.
For every time you open one,
A new adventure has begun.

Dan opened a Word Window. He read . . . (Illustration shows Dan reading a book.)

One fall day Squirrel saw this sign. (Illustration shows a sign reading: Pie Contest Today. Signed, Pig)

"I will bake my best acorn pie for the pie contest," she said.

And she did.

The pie was still hot when Mouse came by

"My," said Mouse. "What a fine pie. Will you cut the pie in two pieces . . . one half for me, one half for you?"

"No," said Squirrel. "This pie is for the pie contest. If I win, I will share my pie with you."

Then Frog came by. "My," said Frog. "What a fine pie. I do like acorn pie," he said. "Will you cut the pie in three pieces . . . one piece for you . . . one for mouse . . . and one for me?"

"No," said Squirrel. "This pie is for the pie contest. If I win, I will share my pie with you."

The pie was still hot, so Squirrel put it in the window to cool. Then the three friends went for a walk in the woods.

While they were gone, Pig came by.

"My," said Pig. "What a fine pie. I will try just one little bite of pie. Very good," she said.

Then Pig ate another bite. "It is just right," she said.

Pig ate and ate and ate until she cleaned the plate.

Just then Squirrel and her friends came by.

"My pie!" cried Squirrel. "Why did you eat my pie?"

"Was your pie for my pie contest today?" asked Pig.

"It was," said Squirrel.

Pig took something out of her pocket.

"Surprise! You win my pie contest," she said. "Your pie was the very best."

"That is not fair," said Mouse.

"Not fair at all," said Frog. "You ate the whole pie that we were going to share."

"I did not mean to eat the whole pie," said Pig. "I will try to make things right."

Pig ran outside and found more acorns.

"Squirrel makes the best pies of all," said Pig. "Maybe she will make one more."

Squirrel did make one more pie. She cut it into four pieces, so everyone had a fair share.

Read some ways to cut
Squirrel's pie.

Here are more ways you
can cut a pie.

$\frac{1 \text{ pie in}}{2 \text{ pieces}}$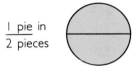

$\frac{1 \text{ pie in}}{5 \text{ pieces}}$

$\frac{1 \text{ pie in}}{3 \text{ pieces}}$

$\frac{1 \text{ pie in}}{6 \text{ pieces}}$

$\frac{1 \text{ pie in}}{4 \text{ pieces}}$

$\frac{1 \text{ pie in}}{7 \text{ pieces}}$

$\frac{1 \text{ pie in}}{8 \text{ pieces}}$

AT·A·GLANCE pp. 333-334

LESSON OBJECTIVES
Explore mathematical concepts through literature.
Explore the concept of fractions.

ASSIGNMENT GUIDE

COURSE	EXERCISES
Basic	p. 333: All; p. 334: All
Average	p. 333: All; p. 334: All
Challenge	p. 333: All; p. 334: All

MATERIALS
Classroom Materials string, scissors, rectangular piece of paper or adding machine tape
Manipulatives circle attribute shape punchouts

Teacher Resources
Math Anthology, pp. 189–191
Read-Aloud Cassette 2, Side 2, Selection 2

SKILLS TRACE
FRACTIONS

Explore (Concrete) 334	Develop/Understand (Transitional/Abstract) 335–336, 337–338, 339–340, 341–342, 347–348
Practice 344, 355, 356, 357–358, 361, 376, 389	**Apply** 343, 345–346, 352, 353, 354, 360

Fractions

CHAPTER 11

READ ALOUD

HOW MANY WAYS CAN YOU CUT A PIE?
By Jane Belk Moncure

Listen to the story How Many Ways Can You Cut a Pie?

Into how many pieces was the last pie cut? 4
Draw a picture to show how the pie could be cut.
Answers will vary.

333

Mathematics and Literature

PREPARE

WARM-UP To review the concept of equal parts, take a length of string and ask children what they would do to give two children an equal piece. [Possible response: Put the two ends together to find the center.] Demonstrate this and then cut the string and give each piece to a child. Then write the following on the chalkboard. Have children tell how many parts you would have to cut the string into in order to give each child an equal piece of string.

1. John, Carlos, Jan, Ann   [4]
2. Nancy, Bill, Rich, Sue, Tom   [5]
3. Toby, Chris, Zia   [3]
4. Tim, Anna, Lee, Jina, Betsy, Frank [6]

TEACH

DISCUSSING Before reading the story *How Many Ways Can You Cut a Pie?,* ask children to recall times when they have shared things with their friends or with their brothers or sisters. Discuss why it is important to try to give everyone an equal-sized piece. Mention that in many families, the person who cuts the pieces is the last one to take his or her share. Discuss how that might help to ensure that the pieces are equal.

PUPIL'S EDITION pp. 333-334

Page 333 Read *How Many Ways Can You Cut a Pie?* found on pages 332M–332N or in *Math Anthology* to children, or play Read-Aloud Cassette 2, Side 2, Selection 2 for them.

Discuss the question on the page. You may wish to have children use a punchout circle attribute when they draw the pie.

Name _____

Fractions

Working Together

Suppose 4 friends want to share a sandwich. How should the sandwich be shared? Answers will vary.

Make a plan to share the sandwich.
Use a sheet of paper to show the sandwich.
Fold the paper to show the parts that each friend gets.

Suppose the friends wanted to share the sandwich fairly.
What do you need to think about to plan how to share? Answers will vary. Children should note that the sandwich should be divided into 4 equal parts.

ACTIVITY ALTERNATIVE TEACHING STRATEGY

MATERIALS loaf of French bread, peanut butter, jelly, knife, paper plates or napkins.

KINESTHETIC/VISUAL Spread peanut butter and jelly on both halves of the bread. Ask four children to play the parts of the characters in the story. Discuss how many pieces the sandwich should be cut into for each story character to have a piece. [4 pieces] As children watch, cut the bread into four equal parts and place each in front of a character. Later, divide the sandwich into equal pieces for the entire class to enjoy as a snack.

Page 334 ■ Working Together Assign children to work in groups of four. Give each group a long rectangular piece of paper shaped like the sandwich shown. Discuss the picture with children. Read aloud the question at the top of the page.

Check for Understanding
■ **How many friends plan to share the sandwich?** [four friends]

GUIDED PRACTICE Discuss how the sandwich should be shared. For reteaching, use Alternative Strategy.

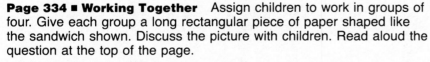

3 PRACTICE·APPLY **PRACTICE** Have children complete the activity.

C L O S E Guide children to summarize the lesson:

■ **How could you figure out how many pieces you would need to give everyone a fair share?** [Count the number of people and cut that number of pieces.]

Problem of the Day

Jenny invited 7 friends to help her eat a pie. How many pieces does she need to cut? [8 pieces]

AT·A·GLANCE pp. 335-336

LESSON OBJECTIVES
Recognize halves.
Recognize one-half of a whole.

ASSIGNMENT GUIDE

COURSE	EXERCISES
Basic	p. 335: 1–3; p. 336: 1–4
Average	p. 335: 1–3; p. 336: 1–4
Challenge	p. 335: 1–3; p. 336: 1–4

MATERIALS
Classroom Materials drawing paper
Manipulatives set of fraction models punchouts per pair

Teacher Resources
Reteaching 101   Practice 101   Enrichment 101
MAC Act. 201, 202   Teacher Aid 5

SKILLS TRACE
FRACTIONS

Explore (Concrete)	Develop/Understand (Transitional/Abstract)
334	335–336, 337–338, 339–340, 341–342, 347–348
Practice	**Apply**
344, 355, 356, 357–358, 361, 376, 389	343, 345–346, 352, 353, 354, 360

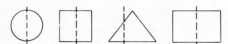

See **MANIPULATIVES PLUS 65–66**, pp. 332I–332J.

1 PREPARE **WARM-UP** To prepare children for identifying halves, draw the following figures on the chalkboard. Have children identify those shapes that have a line of symmetry.

2 TEACH **DISCUSSING** Refer back to the figures used in the Warm-Up. Remind children that figures that have lines of symmetry have two parts that match. Explain that when parts match, it means that the two parts are equal.

Fold a sheet of paper in half.

Halves

2 equal parts

$\frac{1}{2}$
one half

halves

These parts are not equal.

Ring the shapes that show halves.

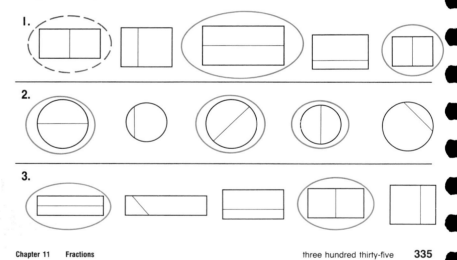

1.

2.

3.

Macmillan/McGraw-Hill

Chapter 11   Fractions   three hundred thirty-five **335**

■ **Does this shape show equal parts?** [Yes.]

Explain that two equal parts are called **halves.** Fold additional sheets in different ways to divide shapes into both equal parts and unequal parts. Have children identify those that show halves.

Cut a sheet of paper in half and identify each as **one half** of the whole shape. Write *one half* on the chalkboard and have children read the words. Tell children that one half is called a **fraction.** Display the circular fraction model for halves. Tell children that this is another model for halves and one half.

PUPIL'S EDITION pp. 335-336

Page 335 Discuss the display at the top of the page. Guide children to understand that the middle shape shows one half colored in.

Working Together

Use    and .
fraction models

> I hold up a shape.

> I tell if the shape shows halves. This shape does not show halves.

Talk about how many parts each shape shows. **Answers will vary.**

Ring the shapes that show $\frac{1}{2}$ shaded.

1.
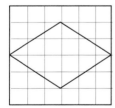

2.

Draw a line to show halves. Color $\frac{1}{2}$. **Answers will vary.**

3.

4.
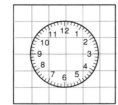

ACTIVITY — Common Error and Remediation

MATERIALS paper rectangles and squares, construction paper, crayons, paste

Some children may not be able to recognize the pictorial representation of halves or one half. Work individually with each child. Give the child rectangles and squares cut from paper. Have the child fold each shape and use a crayon to draw a line down the crease. Have the child mount the models on contrasting paper, sorting the pictures into those that do and do not show halves.

ACTIVITY — ALTERNATIVE TEACHING STRATEGY

MATERIALS clay, plastic knives, punchout fraction models

KINESTHETIC Ask children to pretend they are making crackers. Demonstrate how to flatten the clay. Using the punchout fractions as a model, show them how to use a plastic knife to cut out circular and rectangular "crackers." Have children create several clay crackers of each shape. Then have them fold each clay shape to create two equal parts. Have them cut along the fold and display the two halves.

Check for Understanding

■ **What do we call two equal parts of a shape?** [halves]

GUIDED PRACTICE ex. 1–3: For reteaching, use Common Error and Remediation or Alternative Strategy.

Page 336 ■ Working Together Have children do the activity using punch-out fraction models.

3 PRACTICE•APPLY **PRACTICE** ex. 1–4: Have children compare their responses to ex. 3 and 4 to see how many different ways halves can be shown with these shapes.

C L O S E Guide children to summarize the lesson:

■ **How can you tell if a shape shows halves?** [by checking to see if it has two equal parts]

**MAC Activity 201:
Basic-to-Average**
▼

THINKING SPATIALLY ▪ *GRID CUTOUTS*

MAC Activity 201

On Your Own   Pair and Share   In a Group

Materials graph paper (Teacher Aid 5), straightedge, markers, scissors

Assign each child a partner. Have each child draw several squares and rectangles of different sizes on graph paper duplicated from Teacher Aid 5. Then have children exchange papers with their partners and use markers to shade in one half of each figure. Tell children to check their work by cutting out each figure. Have them fold the shapes to see if the shaded part matches the unshaded part exactly.

**MAC Activity 202:
Average-to-Challenge**
▼

MATH AND HEALTH ▪ *SALAD HALVES*

MAC Activity 202

On Your Own   Pair and Share   In a Group

Materials pear or peach, shelled walnuts, cherries, shredded coconut, plastic knife, plate; or drawing paper and crayons

Explain that halves are used in many recipes. Share this recipe for a simple fruit salad with children and have them identify the halves.

Funny Face Fruit Salad
1. Cut a pear or a peach in half. Remove the pit or core.
2. Place one half facedown on a plate.
3. Break a walnut in half. Use one half to make a mouth.
4. Cut a cherry in half. Use each half to make an eye.
5. Use coconut for hair.

If possible, have children make the salad and eat it as a snack. If this is not possible, have children draw a picture showing what the salad would look like if the directions were followed.

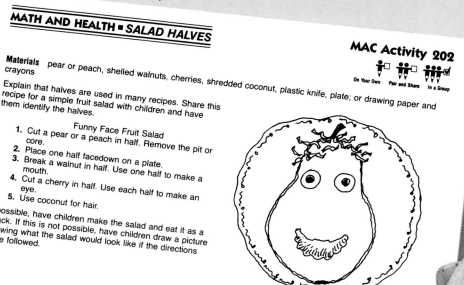

RETEACHING

Name

HALVES

Study

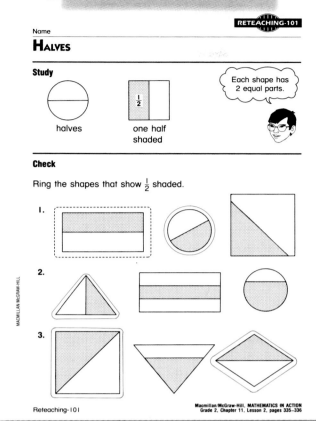

halves — one half shaded

Each shape has 2 equal parts.

Check

Ring the shapes that show $\frac{1}{2}$ shaded.

1.

2.

3.

Reteaching-101

Macmillan/McGraw-Hill, MATHEMATICS IN ACTION
Grade 2, Chapter 11, Lesson 2, pages 335–336

PRACTICE

Name

HALVES

Ring the shapes that show $\frac{1}{2}$ shaded.

1.

2.

3.

4.

Draw a line to show halves. Color $\frac{1}{2}$.   Answers will vary.

5.

6.

7.

Practice-101

Macmillan/McGraw-Hill, MATHEMATICS IN ACTION
Grade 2, Chapter 11, Lesson 2, pages 335–336

ENRICHMENT

Name

HALVES

On Your Own   Pair and Share   In a Group

LARRY'S SNACKS THIS WEEK

Draw a line to show the fraction.

Position of lines will vary.

1. Larry ate half a sandwich.

2. He drank half a glass of milk.

3. He ate half an apple.

4. Larry ate half a piece of pie.

5. He ate half a bag of popcorn.

6. Larry ate half an orange.

Enrichment-101

Macmillan/McGraw-Hill, MATHEMATICS IN ACTION
Grade 2, Chapter 11, Lesson 2, pages 335–336

Problem of the Day

Three children decide to share one pizza. Can each have half a pizza? Why? [No; halves means two equal parts and there are three children.]

CHAPTER 11 • Lesson 3

PREPARE **WARM-UP** To review halves, draw these figures on the chalkboard. Have children identify those that show halves. Then have them shade one half of the square, rectangle, and triangle with red chalk.

TEACH **DISCUSSING** Draw a large circle on the chalkboard and ask children to pretend it is a pizza. Divide it in half and have children identify each part as one half. Then draw another line dividing it into fourths.

■ **How many parts does the pizza have now?** [4 parts]
■ **Are these 4 parts equal?** [Yes.]

Name _____

ACTiViTY

Fourths

4 equal parts

fourths	$\frac{1}{4}$	$\frac{2}{4}$	$\frac{3}{4}$	$\frac{4}{4}$
	one fourth	two fourths	three fourths	four fourths

These are called **fractions**.

Working Together

Use four sheets of paper.

Fold each sheet of paper into 4 equal parts.

Color each sheet. Show $\frac{1}{4}$, $\frac{2}{4}$, $\frac{3}{4}$, and $\frac{4}{4}$.

Did you fold the same way each time?

Did you color the same way?
Answers will vary.

Color to show one fourth. Write the fraction.

1.

$\frac{\vdots}{\vdots}$ number of parts you colored / number of equal parts

---

2.

Coloring will vary.

$\frac{1}{4}$ number of parts you colored / number of equal parts

Explain that 4 equal parts are called **fourths.**

Draw red dots on one section of the pizza. Tell children these dots stand for their favorite pizza topping. Write *fourths* and the fraction $\frac{1}{4}$ on the chalkboard and read it for the children. Explain that the bottom number stands for the number of equal parts in the pizza and the top number stands for the part that has a special topping.

Repeat the activity to introduce $\frac{2}{4}$, $\frac{3}{4}$, and $\frac{4}{4}$. For each fraction, have children identify the number of equal parts, and the number of parts with a topping.

1. Color to show two fourths of each shape.
   Write the fraction. For Exercises 1–2 coloring will vary.

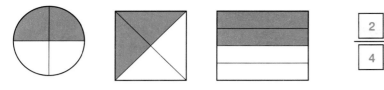

$\dfrac{2}{4}$

2. Color to show three fourths of each shape.
   Write the fraction.

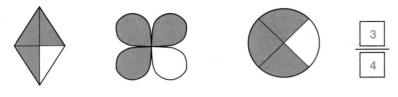

$\dfrac{3}{4}$

3. Color to show four fourths of each shape.
   Write the fraction.

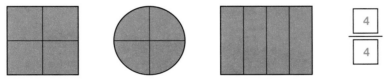

$\dfrac{4}{4}$

4. Talk about how many fourths are in a whole.
   Children should note that there are four fourths in a whole.

Mixed Review

Add or subtract.

| 5. | 58
+ 30
88 | 25
+ 16
41 | 81
− 28
53 | 64
− 36
28 | 44
+ 36
80 | 96
− 32
64 |

Extra Practice, page 344

MEETING INDIVIDUAL NEEDS

ACTIVITY

Common Error and Remediation

MATERIALS paper plates, markers

Some children may have difficulty with non-unit fractions. Work individually with each child. Give the child a paper plate and help him or her fold it into four equal parts. Have the child color one part to represent $\frac{1}{4}$. Have him or her identify the number of equal parts and the number of shaded parts and write the fraction $\frac{1}{4}$ on the shaded portion of the plate. Repeat with three more plates to develop the fractions $\frac{2}{4}$, $\frac{3}{4}$, and $\frac{4}{4}$.

ACTIVITY

ALTERNATIVE TEACHING STRATEGY

MATERIALS apple, plastic knife, peanut butter, napkins

KINESTHETIC Working in groups of four, have children follow as you cut and core an apple into four equal parts. Have children spread one part of the apple with peanut butter and identify this section as $\frac{1}{4}$ of the apple. Write the fraction on the chalkboard and explain that the bottom number is the number of equal parts and the top number is the part that has peanut butter. Repeat with the remaining apple sections to introduce the fractions $\frac{2}{4}$, $\frac{3}{4}$, and $\frac{4}{4}$.

PUPIL'S EDITION pp. 337-338

Page 337   Discuss the picture at the top of the page. Introduce the term **fraction** as part of a whole.

WORKING TOGETHER   Have children work with a partner to do the activity. Then have children share their fraction models with the rest of the class.

Check for Understanding

■ **What do we call the four equal parts of a shape?** [fourths]

GUIDED PRACTICE   ex. 1–2: For reteaching, use Common Error and Remediation or Alternative Strategy

Page 338   Read the direction lines with children.

3 PRACTICE•APPLY   **PRACTICE**   ex. 1–5: Tell children to refer to ex. 3 when discussing ex. 4.

CLOSE   Guide children to summarize the lesson:

■ **How would you show $\frac{2}{4}$ of a square?** [Draw a square and divide it into 4 equal parts. Then color 2 of the 4 parts.]

Chapter 11 • Lesson 3   **338**

MATH AND HEALTH ▪ SPARKLING RAINBOW PUNCH

MAC Activity 203

On Your Own Pair and Share In a Group

Materials pitchers, measuring cups, spoons, plastic glasses, apple juice, grape juice, cranberry juice, seltzer

Have children work with a partner to make this recipe for two servings of a healthful fruit punch. If you have a limited number of supplies, have children take turns using the pitcher and measuring cup.

Rainbow Punch

Mix together in a pitcher:

$\frac{1}{4}$ cup apple juice

$\frac{1}{4}$ cup grape juice

$\frac{1}{4}$ cup cranberry juice

$\frac{1}{4}$ cup seltzer

Pour into two glasses and enjoy.

After children have made the punch, discuss how many cups of punch each recipe makes. [1 cup]

**MAC Activity 203:
Basic-to-Average** ▶

MANIPULATIVES ▪ COINS AND FRACTIONS

MAC Activity 204

On Your Own Pair and Share In a Group

Materials punchout dimes, quarters, dollars

Show children one dollar and one quarter. Ask children if they know a fraction that describes a quarter. Explain that a quarter is one-fourth of one dollar. [$\frac{1}{4}$] Then show one dime and ask how many dimes equal one dollar. [10] Explain that one dime is one-tenth of one dollar. Continue the activity with the following questions. Have children use sets of four quarters and ten dimes to find the answers.

1. What part of one dollar is two quarters? [$\frac{2}{4}$]
2. What part of one dollar is three dimes? [$\frac{3}{10}$]
3. What part of one dollar is six dimes? [$\frac{6}{10}$]
4. What part of one dollar is three quarters? [$\frac{3}{4}$]
5. What part of one dollar is eight dimes? [$\frac{8}{10}$]

▲ **MAC Activity 204:
Average-to-Challenge**

Name

FOURTHS

Study

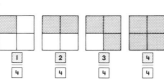

← parts shaded

← number of equal parts

Check

Match the shapes to each fraction.

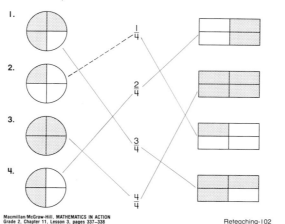

1.

2.

3.

4.

$\frac{1}{4}$

$\frac{2}{4}$

$\frac{3}{4}$

$\frac{4}{4}$

Macmillan/McGraw-Hill, MATHEMATICS IN ACTION
Grade 2, Chapter 11, Lesson 3, pages 337–338

Reteaching-102

Name

FOURTHS

Color to show three fourths of each shape.
Write the fraction.

1.

 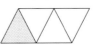

Color to show one fourth of each shape.   **Coloring will vary.**
Write the fraction.

2.

$\frac{1}{4}$

Color to show four fourths of each shape.
Write the fraction.

3.

$\frac{4}{4}$

Color to show two fourths of each shape.
Write the fraction.

4.

$\frac{2}{4}$

Macmillan/McGraw-Hill, MATHEMATICS IN ACTION
Grade 2, Chapter 11, Lesson 3, pages 337–338

Practice-102

Name

FOURTHS

On Your Own   Pair and Share   In a Group

SHARING

Show how you would share.

1. How many friends can you invite to share the pizza with you?

   3 friends

2. How many friends can you invite to share the sandwich?

   1 friend

3. How many friends can you invite to share the muffins?

   7 friends

4. How many friends can you invite to share the milk?

   3 friends

Macmillan/McGraw-Hill, MATHEMATICS IN ACTION
Grade 2, Chapter 11, Lesson 3, pages 337–338

Enrichment-102

Problem of the Day

Four friends plan to split a pizza. Three want extra cheese. What fraction of the pizza should be made with extra cheese?   [$\frac{3}{4}$ of the pizza]

CHAPTER 11 • Lesson 4

AT·A·GLANCE pp. 339-340

LESSON OBJECTIVES
Recognize thirds.
Recognize one-third of a whole.

ASSIGNMENT GUIDE

COURSE	EXERCISES
Basic	p. 339: 1–3; p. 340: 1–10
Average	p. 339: 1–3; p. 340: 1–10
Challenge	p. 339: 1–3; p. 340: 1–10
Extra Practice, p. 344	

MATERIALS
Classroom Materials clay, plastic knives
Manipulatives 1 set fraction models per child

Teacher Resources
Reteaching 103
MAC Act. 205, 206
Practice 103
Math Anthology, p. 192
Enrichment 103

SKILLS TRACE
FRACTIONS

Explore (Concrete) 334	Develop/Understand (Transitional/Abstract) 335–336, 337–338, 339–340, 341–342, 347–348
Practice 344, 355, 356, 357–358, 361, 376, 389	Apply 343, 345–346, 352, 353, 354, 360

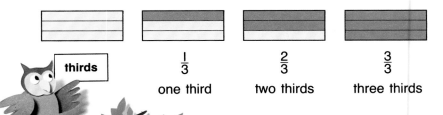

Thirds

3 equal parts

thirds

$\frac{1}{3}$ one third

$\frac{2}{3}$ two thirds

$\frac{3}{3}$ three thirds

Working Together

Use a sheet of paper.
Fold it into 3 equal parts.
Color each third in a
different color.

What fraction will I color make? $\frac{1}{3}$
What fraction will 2 colors make? $\frac{2}{3}$
What fraction will 3 colors make? $\frac{3}{3}$

Color. Write the fraction.

1. one third

 number of parts you colored

number of equal parts

2. two thirds
Coloring will vary.

3. three thirds

Macmillan/McGraw-Hill

Chapter 11   Fractions

three hundred thirty-nine **339**

---

1 PREPARE
WARM-UP To review halves and fourths, draw these figures on the chalkboard. Have children tell what fraction of each figure has been shaded by identifying the number of shaded parts and the number of equal parts for each figure.

2 TEACH
MODELING Give children pieces of clay and plastic knives. Have them roll the clay to make a rope. Tell them to cut the clay into three equal parts. Explain that three equal parts are called **thirds.** Write the word on the chalkboard and have children read it.

Have children use their pencils to make little holes in one of the three parts. Write the fraction $\frac{1}{3}$ on the chalkboard and read it for the children.

■ **Which number tells you how many equal parts there are?** [the bottom number]

■ **Which number tells you how many parts have been marked in a special way?** [the top number]

Repeat to develop $\frac{2}{3}$ and $\frac{3}{3}$. For each fraction, have children identify the number of equal parts and the number of parts that have been marked.

Ring the fraction for the shaded part.

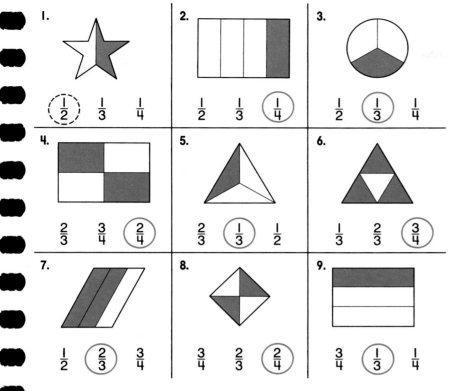

1.
$\left(\frac{1}{2}\right)$ $\frac{1}{3}$ $\frac{1}{4}$

2.
$\frac{1}{2}$ $\frac{1}{3}$ $\left(\frac{1}{4}\right)$

3.
$\frac{1}{2}$ $\left(\frac{1}{3}\right)$ $\frac{1}{4}$

4.
$\frac{2}{3}$ $\frac{3}{4}$ $\left(\frac{2}{4}\right)$

5.
$\frac{2}{3}$ $\left(\frac{1}{3}\right)$ $\frac{1}{2}$

6.
$\frac{1}{3}$ $\frac{2}{3}$ $\left(\frac{3}{4}\right)$

7.
$\frac{1}{2}$ $\left(\frac{2}{3}\right)$ $\frac{3}{4}$

8.
$\frac{3}{4}$ $\frac{2}{3}$ $\left(\frac{2}{4}\right)$

9.
$\frac{3}{4}$ $\left(\frac{1}{3}\right)$ $\frac{1}{4}$

Solve.

10.

TRAIL MIX
Mix together:
$\frac{1}{3}$ cup $\frac{1}{3}$ cup $\frac{1}{3}$ cup

How many cups of trail mix does

the recipe make? ___1___

Extra Practice, page 344

ACTIVITY Common Error and Remediation

MATERIALS circular fractions for halves, thirds, and fourths (or punchouts); 3 small boxes labeled *halves, thirds,* and *fourths*

Some children may confuse halves, thirds, and fourths. Work individually with each child. Display the boxes. Help the child read each label. Discuss that halves means 2 equal parts, thirds means 3 equal parts, and fourths means 4 equal parts. Have the child look at each fraction and count the number of equal parts.

ONGOING ASSESSMENT

OBSERVATION Determine whether children identify thirds and one-third correctly in the activity on p. 339.

INTERVIEW (1) How would you divide a piece of paper into 3 equal parts? Draw lines to show me. (2) Point to one part. **What is it called? (3) How many parts make a whole?**

JOURNAL WRITING You may wish to have children record their responses in their math journals.

ACTIVITY ALTERNATIVE TEACHING STRATEGY

MATERIALS red and blue construction paper, scissors, clips

VISUAL Fold 1 sheet each of red and blue construction paper into thirds. Display the blue sheet and have children count the number of equal parts. [3] Cut the red sheet along the folds into three sections. Clip one red section over the blue sheet and ask how many of the equal parts are red. [1] Write the fraction $\frac{1}{3}$ on the chalkboard and read it for the children. Continue this procedure to develop the fractions $\frac{2}{3}$ and $\frac{3}{3}$. For each fraction, emphasize that the bottom number refers to the number of equal parts and the top number refers to the part that is red.

PUPIL'S EDITION pp. 339–340

Page 339 Discuss the display at the top of the page.

WORKING TOGETHER Have children work with a partner to ao the activity and answer the questions.

Check for Understanding

■ **What do we call each of three equal parts of a shape?** [one third]

GUIDED PRACTICE ex. 1–3: For reteaching, use Common Error and Remediation or Alternative Strategy.

Page 340 Point out the recipe in ex. 10. Make sure children understand that "Trail Mix" is a snack food. This trail mix has $\frac{1}{3}$ cup raisins, $\frac{1}{3}$ cup walnuts, and $\frac{1}{3}$ cup peanuts.

Mathematics and Literature

3 PRACTICE•APPLY   PRACTICE   ex. 1–10

Distribute fraction models of halves, thirds, and fourths to each child. Read the poem "A Sum." Be sure the children understand the meaning of the phrase "quarters four." Have them use the fraction models to show each fraction mentioned in the third line of the poem. Discuss how the models are alike and different. [All show 1 whole, but with different-sized parts.]

CLOSE Guide children to summarize the lesson:

■ **How would you show $\frac{2}{3}$ of a circle?** [Draw a circle and divide it into 3 equal parts. Then color 2 of the 3 parts.]

MAC ACTIVITY CENTER

MAC Activity 205

SPEAKING MATHEMATICALLY ■ FRACTION STORIES

On Your Own   Pair and Share   In a Group

Materials drawing paper, crayons or markers

Assign each child a partner. Explain that one child is to tell a fraction story about sharing a fruit snack with friends. The other child is to listen to the story and then draw a picture showing the answer. To get children started, tell this story and illustrate it as shown below.

Sam and two friends bought a big peach. Sam cut the peach so everyone would get an equal part. How many parts did Sam cut? [3]

Have children reverse roles and repeat the activity.

▲
**MAC Activity 205:
Basic-to-Average**

**MAC Activity 206:
Average-to-Challenge**
▼

MATH AND SOCIAL STUDIES ■ FRACTION FLAGS

MAC Activity 206

On Your Own   Pair and Share   In a Group

NIGERIA
$\frac{2}{3}$ green $\frac{1}{3}$ white

PARAGUAY
$\frac{1}{3}$ red $\frac{1}{3}$ white $\frac{1}{3}$ blue

Materials reference books such as encyclopedia or almanac with pictures of flags, drawing paper, crayons, yarn, world map

Have children find flags with three equal stripes. [Possibilities include Belgium, Germany, Hungary, France, Ireland, Luxembourg, Paraguay, Italy, Chad, Ethiopia, Gabon, Guinea, Mali, Nigeria, and Sierra Leone.] Have each child use drawing paper and crayons to make one of these flags. Have children label their flags with the name of the country and fractions telling what part of the whole flag is made up of each color. The labeled flags can be displayed around a map of the world. Have children use yarn to connect each flag with its country.

Name _____

THIRDS

RETEACHING-103

Study

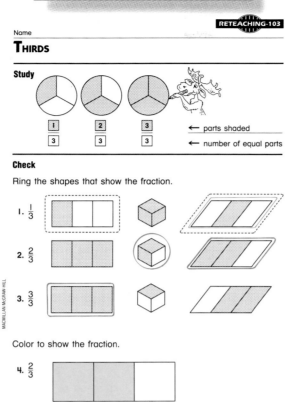

← parts shaded

← number of equal parts

Check

Ring the shapes that show the fraction.

1. $\frac{1}{3}$

2. $\frac{2}{3}$

3. $\frac{3}{3}$

Color to show the fraction.

4. $\frac{2}{3}$

Reteaching-103

Macmillan/McGraw-Hill, MATHEMATICS IN ACTION
Grade 2, Chapter 11, Lesson 4, pages 339–340

Name _____

THIRDS

PRACTICE-103

Ring the fraction for the shaded part.

1. $\frac{1}{2}$ $\frac{1}{3}$ ($\frac{1}{4}$)

2. ($\frac{1}{2}$) $\frac{1}{3}$ $\frac{2}{3}$

3. $\frac{3}{4}$ ($\frac{2}{3}$) $\frac{1}{3}$

4. $\frac{2}{3}$ ($\frac{3}{4}$) $\frac{1}{2}$

5. $\frac{1}{3}$ $\frac{1}{2}$ ($\frac{1}{4}$)

6. $\frac{2}{3}$ ($\frac{2}{4}$) $\frac{3}{4}$

7. ($\frac{1}{3}$) $\frac{1}{2}$ $\frac{1}{4}$

8. $\frac{2}{3}$ $\frac{3}{4}$ ($\frac{2}{4}$)

9. ($\frac{3}{4}$) $\frac{1}{4}$ $\frac{2}{4}$

10. $\frac{1}{2}$ ($\frac{2}{3}$) $\frac{1}{3}$

11. ($\frac{3}{4}$) $\frac{2}{3}$ $\frac{2}{4}$

12. $\frac{1}{2}$ $\frac{1}{4}$ ($\frac{1}{3}$)

Practice-103

Macmillan/McGraw-Hill, MATHEMATICS IN ACTION
Grade 2, Chapter 11, Lesson 4, pages 339–340

Name _____

THIRDS

ENRICHMENT-103

On Your Own   Pair and Share   In a Group

COMPARING FRACTIONS

1. Write the fraction for the shaded part.

$\frac{1}{2}$ $\frac{1}{4}$ $\frac{3}{4}$ $\frac{1}{3}$

2. Compare. Write < or >.

$\frac{1}{2}$ (>) $\frac{1}{4}$ $\frac{1}{3}$ (>) $\frac{1}{4}$ $\frac{1}{2}$ (<) $\frac{3}{4}$ $\frac{3}{4}$ (>) $\frac{1}{3}$

3. Write the fraction for the shaded part.

$\frac{2}{4}$ $\frac{3}{4}$ $\frac{1}{2}$ $\frac{1}{4}$ $\frac{2}{3}$

4. Compare. Write <, >, or =.

$\frac{2}{4}$ (<) $\frac{3}{4}$ $\frac{2}{4}$ (=) $\frac{1}{2}$ $\frac{2}{3}$ (>) $\frac{1}{2}$ $\frac{3}{4}$ (>) $\frac{2}{3}$

Enrichment-103

Macmillan/McGraw-Hill, MATHEMATICS IN ACTION
Grade 2, Chapter 11, Lesson 4, pages 339–340

Problem of the Day

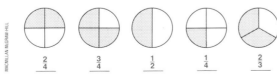

Pam makes a skirt with 3 equal stripes. 2 stripes are blue. What fraction of the skirt is blue? [$\frac{2}{3}$]

AT·A·GLANCE pp. 341-342

LESSON OBJECTIVES
Recognize sixths.
Recognize one-sixth of a whole.

ASSIGNMENT GUIDE

COURSE	EXERCISES
Basic	p. 341: 2–5; p. 342: 1–8, Reasoning
Average	p. 341: 2–5; p. 342: 1–8, Reasoning
Challenge	p. 341: 2–5; p. 342: 1–8, Reasoning
Extra Practice, p. 344	Practice Plus, p. 356

MATERIALS
Classroom Materials fabric rectangle or drawing paper, marker
Manipulatives 1 set of pattern blocks (or punchouts) per child

Teacher Resources
Reteaching 104
MAC Act. 207, 208
Practice 104
Teacher Aids 4, 17
Enrichment 104

SKILLS TRACE
FRACTIONS

Explore (Concrete) 334	Develop/Understand (Transitional/Abstract) 335–336, 337–338, 339–340, 341–342, 347–348
Practice 344, 355, 356, 357–358, 361, 376, 389	Apply 343, 345–346, 352, 353, 354, 360

WARM-UP Draw these figures on the chalkboard and have children identify which show halves, thirds, and fourths.

Then have volunteers shade $\frac{1}{2}$ of the heart, $\frac{2}{4}$ of the diamond, $\frac{2}{3}$ of the triangle, and $\frac{1}{4}$ of the square.

DISCUSSING Display a large fabric rectangle cut from an old sheet and ask children to pretend it is a quilt. (If fabric is not available, use a large sheet of paper.) Draw lines

---

Right page (Activity)

Name _____

ACTiViTY

Sixths

6 equal parts

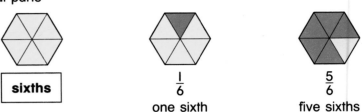

sixths	$\frac{1}{6}$	$\frac{5}{6}$
	one sixth	five sixths

Color. Write the fraction. For Exercises 2–4 coloring will vary.

1. one sixth

$\boxed{1}$ number of parts you colored
$\boxed{6}$ number of equal parts

2. two sixths

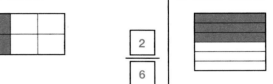 $\frac{\boxed{2}}{\boxed{6}}$

3. three sixths

$\frac{\boxed{3}}{\boxed{6}}$

4. four sixths

 $\frac{\boxed{4}}{\boxed{6}}$

5. six sixths

$\frac{\boxed{6}}{\boxed{6}}$

Macmillan/McGraw-Hill

---

to divide the rectangle into six equal parts. Introduce the word **sixths** and tell children it means six equal parts.

As children watch, use a marker to decorate one of the quilt parts with a simple design. Write the fraction $\frac{1}{6}$ on the chalkboard and have a volunteer read it.

■ **What does the bottom number tell you?** [that there are 6 equal parts]

■ **What does the top number tell you?** [that 1 of the parts has been decorated]

Continue decorating successive quilt sections to develop $\frac{2}{6}$ through $\frac{6}{6}$. Call on volunteers to explain the meaning of each fraction.

What part is blue? Write the fraction.

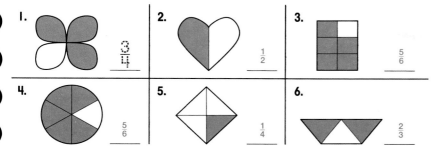

1. $\frac{3}{4}$

2. $\frac{1}{2}$

3. $\frac{5}{6}$

4. $\frac{5}{6}$

5. $\frac{1}{4}$

6. $\frac{2}{3}$

Look at the rectangles. Write the fraction.

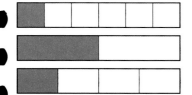

7. What fraction names the smallest blue part? $\frac{1}{6}$

8. What fraction names the largest blue part? $\frac{1}{2}$

Reasoning

Use ⬡, ▲, ▰, ◢.

Find how many of each shape covers the whole ⬡ exactly.

> Use only I kind of shape each time.

How many ▲ parts cover the whole? 6

How many ▰ parts cover the whole? 2

How many ◢ parts cover the whole? 3

Extra Practice, page 344 *Practice Plus,* page 356

MEETING INDIVIDUAL NEEDS

ACTIVITY ALTERNATIVE TEACHING STRATEGY

MATERIALS graph paper (Teacher Aid 4), scissors, paste, drawing paper, crayons

KINESTHETIC Have children cut out a section of graph paper that contains exactly six squares, paste it on a sheet of paper, and color in one square. Explain that they have colored $\frac{1}{6}$ of the shape. Write this fraction on the chalkboard. Repeat to develop $\frac{2}{6}$ to $\frac{6}{6}$.

For Students Acquiring English (SAE)

Use flashcards for sixths and review the fractions before beginning the lesson. Pair SAE children with non-SAE children for Reasoning.

ACTIVITY Common Error and Remediation

MATERIALS drawing paper, crayons

Some children may have difficulty with the concept of sixths. Work with each child. Help the child fold paper into thirds. Have the child shade $\frac{1}{3}$ and write the fraction on that part of the paper. Then help the child fold another sheet of paper into thirds, and then sixths. Have the child shade $\frac{1}{6}$ and write the fraction on that part of the paper. Guide the child in comparing the papers to discover the relationship between $\frac{1}{3}$ and $\frac{1}{6}$.

PUPIL'S EDITION pp. 341-342

Page 341 Discuss the display at the top of the page. Point out that the green part equals $\frac{1}{6}$ in the middle figure and $\frac{5}{6}$ in the figure at the right. Guide children through ex. 1.

Check for Understanding

■ If a shape is divided into sixths, how many equal parts does it have? [6]

GUIDED PRACTICE ex. 2–5: For reteaching, use Common Error and Remediation or Alternative Strategy.

Page 342 Read the direction lines for each activity.

③ PRACTICE•APPLY PRACTICE ex. 1–8

REASONING Make sure children understand that they are to choose one kind of pattern block. Then they find out how many blocks are needed to completely cover the shape.

CLOSE Guide children to summarize the lesson:

■ How would you show a quilt that is $\frac{3}{6}$ red and $\frac{3}{6}$ blue? [Divide it into 6 equal parts and color 3 parts red and 3 parts blue.]

MANIPULATIVES ▪ ROLL A FRACTION

MAC Activity 208

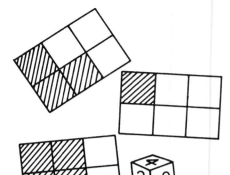

Materials number cube (Teacher Aid 17), graph paper (Teacher Aid 4), crayons

Make a worksheet by outlining six blocks of six squares on graph paper. Assign each child a partner. Give each child a worksheet and crayons. Have partners take turns rolling a number cube. After each roll, the child should color the squares for the number that appears on the cube and then write the fraction. For example, if a 4 is rolled, 4 squares are shaded and the fraction $\frac{4}{6}$ is written. Have children continue the activity until the fractions from $\frac{1}{6}$ to $\frac{6}{6}$ have been shaded and written.

▲ **MAC Activity 208:**
Average-to-Challenge

MATH AND PHYSICAL EDUCATION ▪ *SIX-PIN BOWLING*

MAC Activity 207

Materials masking tape, 6 empty cans, tennis ball

Procedure Assign children to small groups. Tell children that they are going to play a game of bowling. Ask them to describe any previous bowling experiences. Explain that they are going to play a bowling game with six pins made from empty cans. Demonstrate how the pins should be set up using the following arrangement:

```
   X   X   X
     X   X
       X
```

Put small pieces of masking tape under each can and tape it to the floor. Have children stand about 12 feet from the pins and gently roll the ball. They should record their scores using fractions. For example, if four cans are knocked down, the score would be written as $\frac{4}{6}$ of the cans. Play several rounds. Remind children to set up the pins after their turns.

To Win The child with the greatest fraction scores one point for the round. The child with the most points at the end of play wins the game.

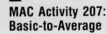

▲ **MAC Activity 207:**
Basic-to-Average

RETEACHING-104

Name _____

SIXTHS

Study

$\frac{1}{6}$ $\frac{2}{6}$ $\frac{3}{6}$ $\frac{4}{6}$ $\frac{5}{6}$ $\frac{6}{6}$

Check

Ring the fraction for the shaded part.

1. $\frac{1}{6}$ $\left(\frac{2}{6}\right)$ $\frac{4}{6}$

2. $\left(\frac{1}{6}\right)$ $\frac{3}{6}$ $\frac{5}{6}$

3. $\frac{2}{6}$ $\frac{3}{6}$ $\left(\frac{4}{6}\right)$

4. $\frac{2}{6}$ $\left(\frac{3}{6}\right)$ $\frac{5}{6}$

5. $\frac{4}{6}$ $\frac{5}{6}$ $\left(\frac{6}{6}\right)$

6. $\left(\frac{5}{6}\right)$ $\frac{4}{6}$ $\frac{2}{6}$

7. Color to show the fraction. $\frac{4}{6}$

Macmillan/McGraw-Hill, MATHEMATICS IN ACTION
Grade 2, Chapter 11, Lesson 5, pages 341–342

Reteaching-104

PRACTICE-104

Name _____

SIXTHS

What part is shaded? Write the fraction.

1. $\frac{6}{8}$
2. $\frac{1}{3}$
3. $\frac{1}{2}$

4. $\frac{4}{6}$
5. $\frac{2}{4}$
6. $\frac{3}{6}$

7. $\frac{2}{6}$
8. $\frac{1}{4}$
9. $\frac{5}{6}$

Look at the shapes. Write the fraction.

10. Which fraction names the smallest part? $\frac{1}{6}$

11. Which fraction names the largest part? $\frac{1}{2}$

Macmillan/McGraw-Hill, MATHEMATICS IN ACTION
Grade 2, Chapter 11, Lesson 5, pages 341–342

Practice-104

ENRICHMENT

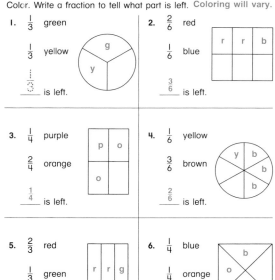

ENRICHMENT-104

Name _____

SIXTHS

On Your Own   Pair and Share   In a Group

LEFT OVER

Color. Write a fraction to tell what part is left. *Coloring will vary.*

1. $\frac{1}{3}$ green
   $\frac{1}{3}$ yellow
   $\frac{1}{3}$ is left.

2. $\frac{2}{6}$ red
   $\frac{1}{6}$ blue
   $\frac{3}{6}$ is left.

3. $\frac{1}{4}$ purple
   $\frac{2}{4}$ orange
   $\frac{1}{4}$ is left.

4. $\frac{1}{6}$ yellow
   $\frac{3}{6}$ brown
   $\frac{2}{6}$ is left.

5. $\frac{2}{3}$ red
   $\frac{1}{3}$ green
   $\frac{0}{}$ is left.

6. $\frac{1}{4}$ blue
   $\frac{1}{4}$ orange
   $\frac{2}{4}$ is left.

Macmillan/McGraw-Hill, MATHEMATICS IN ACTION
Grade 2, Chapter 11, Lesson 5, pages 341–342

Enrichment-104

Problem of the Day

A juice-pack holds 6 cans of juice. If 4 people each drink 1 can, what fraction of the juice-pack is left? $\left[\frac{2}{6}\right]$

AT·A·GLANCE p. 343

AT·A·GLANCE p. 343

LESSON OBJECTIVE
Identify fractional parts.

ASSIGNMENT GUIDE

COURSE	EXERCISES
Basic	p. 343: All
Average	p. 343: All
Challenge	p. 343: All

MATERIALS
Classroom Materials flannel board and felt circle, square, and rectangle shapes; felt line; magazine pictures of objects
Manipulatives fraction model halves and fourths (or punch-outs) per child

Teacher Resources
Crit. Think. 21

Name _____

Finding Fractions

Ring each picture that shows halves.
Draw an x on each picture that
shows fourths.

MacmillanMcGraw-Hill

343

---

1 PLAN

AIMS AND ATTITUDES This lesson develops number sense by having children identify fractional parts depicted in a picture. The concept of fractions is often confusing to young children, as it is an abstract one.

Let children who may have difficulty identifying fractional parts be allowed to use their punchout fraction models for reference. They may trace the fraction parts and label them as "halves" or "fourths."

MANAGEMENT The activity is intended for all children and has been designed for independent work or for groups of four. It is also appropriate for pairs of children. When pairing children, it may be particularly effective to pair a child having strong mathematical skills with one having weaker skills.

The activity in the **EXTEND** section of this lesson requires additional planning. Cut out pictures of objects from magazines that are suitable

for illustrating wholes, halves, and fourths. You will need a sufficient amount for each group. Fold the pictures to show halves and fourths. Be sure to leave some pictures unfolded to represent wholes.

2 GUIDE

Display a flannel board and felt shapes. Place a felt circle on the board. Then place a felt line to divide the circle in two equal halves.

■ **Into how many parts is the circle divided?** [2]

■ **What is each part called?** [half]

■ **How can you tell that each part of the circle is one-half?** [Both parts are the same size, and both parts together make one whole.]

Repeat the activity by displaying a rectangle and square felt shape and dividing each into fourths.

TEACHER to TEACHER

COOPERATIVE LEARNING TIP 👥 Groups of four can **brainstorm** everyday foods that can be broken down into fractions (such as pizzas, cakes, and so on) and then discuss which foods can be distributed in equal fractions for a class party. Have a recorder keep a record during the discussion of how many times each person speaks by putting a tally next to their name on an observation sheet. Afterward, each small group finds what fraction of the discussion was contributed by each member. Some groups may want to work on the skills of **equal participation** and **encouraging contributions.**

Along with the children, read the directions on page 343. Point out the variety of shapes in the picture. Have children ring the pictures that show halves and draw an X on pictures that show fourths.

Allow children who may have difficulty identifying fractional parts to use punchout fraction models as a reference.

After children complete the page, have volunteers tell in their own words why they think each of the pictures shows either halves or fourths.

3 EXTEND Distribute magazine pictures of whole objects, objects folded into halves, and objects folded into fourths. Have groups sort the pictures by their fractional parts and explain their reasoning. If time allows, each group may exchange their pictures with another group and repeat the activity.

Extra Practice

EXTRA PRACTICE

Fourths, pages 337–338 . . . .

1. Color to show three fourths of each shape. Write the fraction. Coloring will vary.

Thirds, pages 339–340 . . . .

1. Color to show two thirds. Write the fraction.
   Coloring will vary.

Sixths, pages 341–342 . . . .

1. Color to show two sixths. Write the fraction. Coloring will vary.

 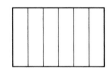

2. Color to show five sixths. Write the fraction.

ADDITIONAL PRACTICE

p. 337

1. *Color to show two-fourths of each shape. Write the fraction.*

 [2/4]

2. *Color to show one-fourth of each shape. Write the fraction.*

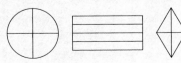 [1/4]

[Coloring will vary.]

p. 339

1. *Color to show one-third of each shape. Write the fraction.*

  [1/3]

[Coloring will vary.]

p. 341

Color to show three-sixths. Write the fraction.

Color to show one-sixth. Write the fraction.

Color to show four-sixths. Write the fraction.

1. $\left[\frac{3}{6}\right]$

[Coloring will vary.]

2. $\left[\frac{1}{6}\right]$

[Coloring will vary.]

3. $\left[\frac{4}{6}\right]$

[Coloring will vary.]

AT·A·GLANCE pp. 345-346

LESSON OBJECTIVE
Draw a picture to solve problems.

ASSIGNMENT GUIDE

COURSE	EXERCISES
Basic	p. 345: 1–2; p. 346: 1–4
Average	p. 345: 1–2; p. 346: 1–4
Challenge	p. 345: 1–2; p. 346: 1–4
Extra Practice, p. 355	

MATERIALS
Classroom Materials scissors, crayons, paper circles and squares per child

Teacher Resources
Reteaching 105   Practice 105   Enrichment 105
Prob. Solv. 52   MAC Act. 209, 210

Name _____

Problem Solving

UNDERSTAND
✓ PLAN
✓ TRY
CHECK
✓ EXTEND

Strategy: Drawing a Picture

A pizza is cut into sixths.
3 friends share the pizza fairly.
How many parts does each friend get?

| What can I do? |

I can draw a picture.

Draw a circle.
Make 6 equal parts.
Color to show 3 equal parts

Each friend gets __2__ parts.

Draw a picture. Solve.

1. A round pizza is cut
   into fourths.
   Carl and Diana share the
   pizza fairly.

   How many parts does each friend get? __2__ parts

---

2. A square sandwich is cut
   into halves.
   Ryan and Lyle share the
   sandwich fairly.

   How many parts does each friend get? __1__ parts

Chapter 11   Fractions   three hundred forty-five   **345**

---

1 PREPARE   **WARM-UP**   To prepare children for drawing a picture to solve problems, have them model different ways to fold paper circles into halves and fourths and paper squares into halves, thirds, and fourths.

2 TEACH   **MODELING**   Give each child a paper circle, a sheet of paper, a crayon, and scissors. Explain that you will read them a problem and that they should use the circle to solve the problem.

   Debbie shares a pie with 3 friends. How many parts does each person get?

■ **How many people share the pie?** [4]

■ **How did you fold your circle to show fourths?** [in half one way and then in half the other way]

Have children draw lines on the fold lines, and then cut the circle into fourths.

■ **How many parts does each person get?** [1]

PUPIL'S EDITION pp. 345-346

Page 345   Have a volunteer read the problem at the top of the page.

■ **What do you know?** [A pizza is cut into sixths; 3 friends share the pizza.]

■ **What do you need to find out?** [how many parts of the pizza each person gets]

Discuss the plan on the page. Guide children to see that they can draw a circle to show the pizza.

Draw a picture. Solve.

1. Joel and Nola are sharing
   a square cake fairly.
   It was cut into fourths.

   How many parts does each friend get? __2__ parts

2. A round pizza is cut
   into thirds.
   Jeremy shares the pizza fairly
   with Cory and Trish.

   How many parts does each friend get? __1__ parts

3. A square sandwich is cut into fourths.
   4 friends want to share the
   sandwich fairly.

   How many parts does each friend get? __1__ parts

4. You want to share a round apple
   pie fairly with 2 friends.
   You can cut it into 3 parts,
   4 parts, or 6 parts.
   Which way would you choose? Answers will vary. 3 parts or 6 parts
   Which would not be a good choice? 4 parts   are correct choices.
   Talk about your answer.

Extra Practice, page 355

TEACHER to TEACHER

COOPERATIVE LEARNING TIP 👥 Before drawing pictures to show equal parts, my children benefit by using fraction models and giving one another a quiz on equal parts for each type of model. Then using a **round robin,** each member of the group tells of a time he or she remembers when food was shared fairly, or when it was not. After working the problems, the group discusses how they will share the food fairly at the class party.

For Students Acquiring English (SAE)

Have children work in heterogeneous groups of four. Provide a paper shape for each of the exercises in the lesson. Have groups work together to divide the shapes according to the directions. Children should also paste the divided shapes on a separate piece of paper and write a description of how they decide to divide each one.

■ **How do you know the pizza has been shared fairly?** [Each person gets 2 equal parts.]

■ **What did you learn?** [Possible response: You can draw a picture to show equal parts and solve a problem.]

Encourage children to explain other ways to solve this problem.

Check for Understanding

■ **What if there were 6 friends? How many parts of the pizza would each person get?** [1]

GUIDED PRACTICE   ex. 1–2: Work through problem 1 with the children. Make sure they understand how to solve the problem by drawing a picture.

Page 346   Have a volunteer read the directions at the top of the page.

 **PRACTICE•APPLY**   **PRACTICE**   ex. 1–4: Have children discuss their answers to ex. 4.

C L O S E   Guide children to summarize the lesson:

■ **How can a picture help you solve a problem?** [Possible response: It can show how things are divided.]

MAC Activity 209:
Basic-to-Average
▼

MAC Activity 209

On Your Own   Pair and Share   In a Group

LOGICAL REASONING ▪ THE LUNCH BUNCH

Materials   paper circles and squares, crayons

Setup   Prepare several large paper circles and squares.

Procedure   Assign children to work in pairs. Give each pair of children a set of paper circles and squares. Tell children you will read to them some problems about a group of children who are having lunch. Explain that they are to work together to solve the problems by using a paper square or circle. Ask children to draw lines on the paper to make equal parts, then color with a different crayon color the part or parts each person gets. Have children explain their solutions.

1. An apple is cut into 4 parts. 2 of the children share the apple. How many parts does each get?   [2]
2. A cake is cut into sixths. 6 of the children share the cake. How many parts does each get?   [1]
3. A square slice of cheese is cut into halves. 2 of the children share the cheese. How many parts does each person get?   [1]

Continue the activity with similar problems.

MAC Activity 210:
Average-to-Challenge
▼

SPEAKING MATHEMATICALLY ▪ PIZZA PARTY

MAC Activity 210

On Your Own   Pair and Share   In a Group

Materials   paper circles, scissors, crayons

Procedure   Have children play in groups of six. Give each group of children several paper circles, crayons, and a pair of scissors. Explain to children that two members of a group will play at a time. One child says whether a pizza will be cut into halves, thirds, fourths, or sixths, and how many members of the group will be sharing the pizza. The second child draws a picture of the pizza on one of the circles, then cuts the pieces. He or she decides whether the pieces can be shared equally with the number of people the first child named. If the pieces can be shared equally, the child distributes them to the appropriate number of people in the group. The players are each given a point if they correctly complete their part of the game. Two more members of the group then play. When all members of the groups have played both roles, the game is over.

To Win   The child in each group with the most points is a winner.

RETEACHING-105

Name

PROBLEM SOLVING STRATEGY: DRAWING A PICTURE

Study

A sandwich is cut into fourths.
4 friends share the sandwich fairly
How many parts does each friend get?

Draw a square to show the sandwich.

Draw lines to show fourths or 4 equal parts.

Each friend gets 1 part.

Check

Draw a picture. Solve.

1. A round pie is cut into sixths.
   3 people share the pie fairly.
   How many parts does each one get?
   __2__ parts

2. Diane cuts a square dog cracker into halves.
   She shares the cracker fairly between her 2 dogs.
   How many parts does each dog get?
   __1__ parts

3. A round pizza is cut into fourths.
   4 friends share it fairly.
   How many parts does each one get?
   __1__ parts

Reteaching-105

Macmillan/McGraw-Hill, MATHEMATICS IN ACTION
Grade 2, Chapter 11, Lesson 7, pages 345–346

PRACTICE-105

Name

PROBLEM SOLVING STRATEGY: DRAWING A PICTURE

Draw a picture. Solve.

1. Abe, Lily, and Carol share a round pie fairly.
   They cut it into thirds.
   How many parts does each one get?
   __1__ parts

2. Lou cuts a square piece of cheese into fourths.
   He shares the cheese fairly between his 2 pet mice.
   How many parts does each mouse get?
   __2__ parts

3. Bob cuts a square sandwich into halves.
   He shares it fairly with Ann.
   How many parts does each one get?
   __1__ parts

4. A pizza is cut into sixths.
   6 friends share the pizza fairly.
   How many parts does each friend get?
   __1__ parts

Practice-105

Macmillan/McGraw-Hill, MATHEMATICS IN ACTION
Grade 2, Chapter 11, Lesson 7, pages 345–346

ENRICHMENT-105

Name

PROBLEM SOLVING

On Your Own   Pair and Share   In a Group

EQUAL CUTS

See how many people want to share each item.
Draw lines to cut each item into equal parts.
Solve.   **Number of parts may vary.**

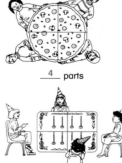

__4__ parts

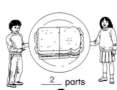

__2__ parts

__4__ parts

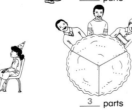

__3__ parts

__6__ parts

Enrichment-105

Macmillan/McGraw-Hill, MATHEMATICS IN ACTION
Grade 2, Chapter 11, Lesson 7, pages 345–346

Problem of the Day

Four children shared 2 square sandwiches. The first pair of children cut a sandwich in half and shared it equally. The second pair of children cut a sandwich in fourths and shared it equally. Did any child get more sandwich than any other child? [No; the first pair each got 1 half, the second pair each got 2 fourths. One half equals 2 fourths.]

AT·A·GLANCE pp. 347-348

LESSON OBJECTIVE
Recognize the fractional part of a set.

ASSIGNMENT GUIDE

COURSE	EXERCISES
Basic	p. 347: 1–3; p. 348: 1–9
Average	p. 347: 1–3; p. 348: 1–9
Challenge	p. 347: 1–3; p. 348: 1–9
Extra Practice, p. 355	Practice Plus, p. 356

MATERIALS
Classroom Materials crayons
Manipulatives circular fractions; 8 ▰, 8 ▱, 8 ▰ per pair; 5 ◯ (or punchouts) per child

Teacher Resources
Reteaching 106   Practice 106   Enrichment 106
Prob. Solv. 53   MAC Act. 211, 212

SKILLS TRACE
FRACTIONS

Explore (Concrete)	Develop/Understand (Transitional/Abstract)
334	335–336, 337–338, 339–340, 341–342, 347–348
Practice 344, 355, 356, 357–358, 361, 376, 389	**Apply** 343, 345–346, 352, 353, 354, 360

See **MANIPULATIVES PLUS 67–68**, pp. 332K–332L.

PREPARE **WARM-UP** To review halves, thirds, fourths, and sixths, display the circular fractions for each. Have children identify the number of equal parts and what fraction the model shows. Remove one or more pieces from a model and ask what fraction of the circle remains. Repeat to review different fractions.

TEACH **MODELING** Give each child 5 counters. Have children turn the counters red side up and identify the total number in the set. [5] Tell children to turn 1 counter so the yellow side is faceup.
■ **How many counters do you have in all?** [5]
■ **How many counters are yellow?** [1]

Name _____

Parts of a Set

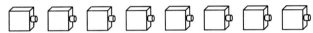

1 blue cube	3 red cubes
4 cubes in the set	4 cubes in the set
$\frac{1}{4}$ of the set is blue	$\frac{3}{4}$ of the set is red

Working Together
Use ▰, ▱, and ▰.

Choose a set of 8 cubes.
Choose some of each color.
Color. Answers will vary.

Write the fraction. For Exercises 1–3 answers will vary.

1. What part of the set is blue?

☐ number of blue cubes
8 number of cubes in the set

2. What part of the set is yellow?

☐ number of yellow cubes
8 number of cubes in the set

3. What part of the set is red?

☐ number of red cubes
8 number of cubes in the set

Write the fraction $\frac{1}{5}$ on the chalkboard and explain that $\frac{1}{5}$ of the set is yellow. Follow a similar procedure to develop that $\frac{4}{5}$ of the set is red.

Have children turn additional counters over and identify what **part of each set** is yellow and red.

PUPIL'S EDITION pp. 347-348
Page 347 Discuss the display at the top of the page.
Check for Understanding
■ **How would you show a set of cubes that is $\frac{4}{6}$ red?** [Show 4 red cubes in a set of 6 cubes.]

WORKING TOGETHER Have children work with a partner to choose the set of 8 cubes and complete the exercises.

Color. *Coloring will vary.*

1. $\frac{1}{2}$ of the set

2. $\frac{1}{3}$ of the set

3. $\frac{1}{4}$ of the set

4. $\frac{2}{3}$ of the set

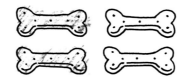

5. $\frac{3}{4}$ of the set

6. $\frac{2}{4}$ of the set

Mixed Review

7. What number comes just after 353? _____354_____

8. What number comes just before 800? _____799_____

9. What numbers come between 238 and 242?

238, _____239_____, _____240_____, _____241_____, 242

Extra Practice, page 355 *Practice Plus*, page 356

MEETING INDIVIDUAL NEEDS

ACTIVITY *Common Error and Remediation*

MATERIALS 6 , 6 ▪ (or punchout square counters)

Some children may not be able to recognize the fractional part of a set. Have a child make a yellow and blue train using six connecting cubes. Have the child identify the fractions for both parts of the train. Have the child break the train into separate cubes. Ask what part of the set is blue and what part is yellow. Repeat with other combinations of cubes.

ONGOING ASSESSMENT

OBSERVATION Determine whether children identify fractional parts correctly in the activity on p. 347.

INTERVIEW Using 8 connecting cubes and a ruler to separate parts of the set, make a model of $\frac{3}{8}$. **(1) What fraction is this?** **(2) Use 4 cubes. Show me a model of $\frac{3}{4}$.**

JOURNAL WRITING You may wish to have children record their responses in their math journals.

ACTIVITY ## ALTERNATIVE TEACHING STRATEGY

MATERIALS snack crackers, peanut butter, plastic knife, napkins

VISUAL Display six crackers on a napkin. As children watch, spread 2 with peanut butter. Have children identify the number of crackers in the set and the number spread with peanut butter.

[6; 2] Write the fraction $\frac{2}{6}$ on the chalkboard and explain that this fraction tells what part of the set has peanut butter. Repeat with other fractions and sets of crackers.

GUIDED PRACTICE ex. 1–3: For reteaching, use Common Error and Remediation or Alternative Strategy.

Page 348 Help children identify the animals in each set.

3 PRACTICE•APPLY **PRACTICE** ex. 1–9

CLOSE Guide children to summarize the lesson:
■ **If you have a set of 6 pencils and 2 are red, what part of the set is red?** [$\frac{2}{6}$]

MAC Activity 211

On Your Own   Pair and Share   In a Group

ESTIMATING ▪ FRACTIONS AT A GLANCE

Materials tray; sets of small objects such as crayons, pencils, markers, or balls; sheet of paper

Arrange a tray with four to ten small objects. The objects should be identical except for color or size; for example, a set of eight crayons could contain one red crayon, three black crayons, and four green crayons. Tell children you are going to display the set for a few seconds. Then you will cover it with paper and ask them to make estimates about each part of the set. Use questions such as the following:

1. What part of the set is red? $[\frac{1}{8}]$
2. What part of the set is black? $[\frac{3}{8}]$
3. What part of the set is green? $[\frac{4}{8}]$

After making their estimates, have children look at the tray again and check their estimates against the actual fractional parts of the set.

WRITING MATHEMATICS ▪ PARTS OF A PICTURE

MAC Activity 212

On Your Own   Pair and Share   In a Group

Materials books containing pictures of animal groups

Have children find pictures containing up to eight animals in a group. The group may either consist of one type of animal or several different types of animals. Tell children that they are to write at least three questions about their picture that can be answered with a fraction. Explain that the questions may deal with the size, movement, color, or type of animals in the group. To get children started, share the following questions that could be asked about a flock of ducks on a pond.

What part of this set is flying?
What part of this set is swimming?
What part of this set is sitting on a nest?

Have children share their pictures and accompanying questions with a partner. Remind them that answers should be given as fractions.

▲
MAC Activity 212:
Average-to-Challenge

▲
MAC Activity 211:
Basic-to-Average

RETEACHING-106

Name

PARTS OF A SET

Study

1 shaded ball.
2 balls in the set.
$\frac{1}{2}$ of the balls are
shaded.

3 shaded balls.
4 balls in the set.
$\frac{3}{4}$ of the balls are
shaded.

Check

Ring the fraction for the shaded part.

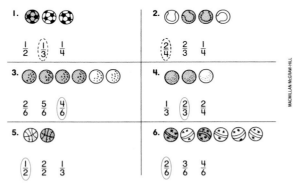

1.
$\frac{1}{2}$ $\left(\frac{1}{3}\right)$ $\frac{1}{4}$

2.
$\left(\frac{2}{4}\right)$ $\frac{2}{3}$ $\frac{1}{4}$

3.
$\frac{2}{6}$ $\frac{5}{6}$ $\left(\frac{4}{6}\right)$

4.
$\frac{1}{3}$ $\left(\frac{2}{3}\right)$ $\frac{2}{4}$

5.
$\left(\frac{1}{2}\right)$ $\frac{2}{2}$ $\frac{1}{3}$

6.
$\left(\frac{2}{6}\right)$ $\frac{3}{6}$ $\frac{4}{6}$

Macmillan/McGraw-Hill, MATHEMATICS IN ACTION
Grade 2, Chapter 11, Lesson 8, pages 347–348

Reteaching-106

PRACTICE-106

Name

PARTS OF A SET

Color. Coloring will vary.

1. $\frac{2}{3}$ of the set

2. $\frac{3}{4}$ of the set

3. $\frac{1}{2}$ of the set

4. $\frac{2}{6}$ of the set

5. $\frac{1}{4}$ of the set

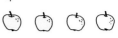

6. $\frac{4}{6}$ of the set

7. $\frac{3}{6}$ of the set

8. $\frac{2}{4}$ of the set

9. $\frac{5}{6}$ of the set

10. $\frac{1}{3}$ of the set

Macmillan/McGraw-Hill, MATHEMATICS IN ACTION
Grade 2, Chapter 11, Lesson 8, pages 347–348

Practice-106

ENRICHMENT-106

Name

PARTS OF A SET

On Your Own   Pair and Share   In a Group

MONEY FRACTIONS

 = 1 whole   = $\frac{1}{10}$ = $\frac{1}{20}$

Write the fraction for the part of a dollar the coins show.

1.

$\frac{4}{10}$

2.
$\frac{5}{20}$

3.
$\frac{7}{20}$

4.
$\frac{6}{10}$

5.
$\frac{9}{20}$

6. Try this.
$\frac{1}{4}$

Macmillan/McGraw-Hill, MATHEMATICS IN ACTION
Grade 2, Chapter 11, Lesson 8, pages 347–348

Enrichment-106

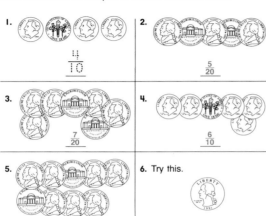

Problem of the Day

There are 6 cars in the parking lot. Jim sees that
2 are red, 1 is blue, and the others are black.
What part of the set is not black? $\left[\frac{3}{6}\right]$

AT·A·GLANCE pp. 349-350

LESSON OBJECTIVE
Explore probability.

ASSIGNMENT GUIDE

COURSE	EXERCISES
Basic	p. 349: 2–3; p. 350: 1–2
Average	p. 349: 2–3; p. 350: 1–2
Challenge	p. 349: 2–3; p. 350: 1–2

MATERIALS
Classroom Materials chalk, coin
Manipulatives 1 🟨, 3 🟥, 3 🟥 (or square counter punch-outs) per pair
Computer Software *Graphs, Stat., and Prob.:* Exploration 9 Act. 1

SKILLS TRACE

PROBABILITY	
Explore (Concrete) Gr. 2: 349–350 Gr. 3: 392–393	Develop/Understand (Transitional/Abstract) Gr. 3: 394–395, 396–397

ACTIVITY

Probability

Working Together

Use a paper bag, a 🟨, and a 🟥.

Put the cubes in the bag.
Are you more likely to pick yellow than red?
No.

Pick 1 cube. Color the box
the same color as the cube.
Put the cube back and shake the bag.
Do this 20 times.
Coloring will vary.

Pick:	1	2	3	4	5	6	7	8	9	10

Pick:	11	12	13	14	15	16	17	18	19	20

1. How many times did you pick yellow?

   Answers will vary.

Now try using 1 🟨 and 3 🟥.

Pick:	1	2	3	4	5	6	7	8	9	10

Pick:	11	12	13	14	15	16	17	18	19	20

2. How many times did you pick yellow? Answers will vary.

3. In which activity are you more likely to
   pick yellow more times? Tell why. Possible answer: the first
   activity because it has fewer red cubes than in the second activity.

---

1 PREPARE **WARM-UP** To prepare children for exploring probability, conceal a piece of chalk in one hand and then hold both hands out in front of you. Ask a volunteer to guess in which hand you are holding the chalk. Repeat the activity ten times, having children keep track of the number of correct and incorrect guesses.

2 TEACH **DISCUSSING** Display a coin and identify the two sides as heads and tails. Write the numbers 1 to 20 on the chalkboard. Then flip the coin 20 times and have a volunteer record *H* for heads or *T* for tails for each toss. Have children count to find the total for each.

■ **How many heads turned up in 20 tosses?** [Answers will vary.]
■ **How many tails turned up in 20 tosses?** [Answers will vary.]

Discuss with children that in each toss, one of two things can happen. Have them identify these two events. [Either heads or tails will turn up.]

■ **What do you think would happen if we flipped the coin 100 times? 1,000 times?** [Answers will vary. Some may conclude that if the coin is flipped many times, about half the time it will be heads and about half the time it will be tails.]

PUPIL'S EDITION pp. 349-350

Page 349 ■ **Working Together** Assign partners and give each pair one yellow and one red connecting cube and a paper bag. Discuss the instructions at the top of the page and have children do ex. 1.

Working Together

Use a paper bag, 3 ⬛, and 3 ⬛.

1. Suppose you pick 20 times. Guess how many times you would pick blue.

Answers will vary.

Put the cubes in the bag.
Pick I cube. Color the box
the same color as the cube.
Put the cube back and shake the bag.
Do this 20 times.

Coloring will vary.

Pick:	I	2	3	4	5	6	7	8	9	10

Pick:	11	12	13	14	15	16	17	18	19	20

2. How many times did you pick blue? _Answers will vary._
Compare your answer with your guess.

350   three hundred fifty

For Students Acquiring English (SAE)

Explain **more likely** and have children practice it in examples involving their own experiences; for example "Are you more likely to wear shorts in summer or in winter? Show SAE children what they are to do in the Working Together sections by reading the directions while modeling the steps. For a comprehension check and language development, have them give you the directions.

ALTERNATIVE TEACHING STRATEGY

Activity

MATERIALS index cards with two different color sides

VISUAL Have each child flip a card 20 times and record what color turned up on each flip. After finding the total of each color, have children compare these results with a partner or in a small group and discuss them.

Check for Understanding

■ **Suppose you have two red cubes and one yellow cube. Which would you pick more often, red or yellow?** [red]

GUIDED PRACTICE   ex. 2–3: Have children explain in which activity—the example at the top of the page or ex. 1—they are more likely to pick yellow. For reteaching, use Alternative Strategy.

Page 350 ■ Working Together   Make sure children have red and blue cubes.

PRACTICE•APPLY   **PRACTICE**   ex. 1–2

C L O S E   Guide children to summarize the lesson:
■ **Suppose you wanted to improve your chances of picking a certain color cube. How could you do this?** [Add more of this color cube to the bag.]

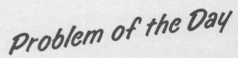

Problem of the Day

A bag has 10 rolls. There are 3 plain ones and 7 with seeds. If you take a roll without looking, are you more likely to get one that is plain or one with seeds? Why? [One with seeds; there are more of those in the bag so your chances are greater.]

CHAPTER 11 · Lesson 10

AT·A·GLANCE pp. 351-352

LESSON OBJECTIVE
Use strategies to solve problems.

ASSIGNMENT GUIDE

COURSE	EXERCISES
Basic	p. 351: 1–3; p. 352: 1–5
Average	p. 351: 1–3; p. 352: 1–5
Challenge	p. 351: 1–3; p. 352: 1–5

MATERIALS
Classroom Materials paper
Manipulatives 6 ▢, 3 ▢, 6 ▢ (or square counter punch-outs) per pair

Teacher Resources
Reteaching 107   Practice 107   Enrichment 107
Prob. Solv. 54   MAC Act. 213, 214

Name _____

Problem Solving
UNDERSTAND / PLAN / TRY / CHECK / EXTEND

Strategies Review

Make a plan to solve each problem.
Then solve.

1. Marv used 28 tickets for rides.
   He used 19 tickets for food.
   How many fewer tickets did
   he use for food than for rides?

   __9__ fewer tickets

2. Vera scores 38 points at the
   bag toss and 21 more points at
   the ring toss. A prize costs
   50 points. Does she have
   enough points for a prize?

   __Yes.__

3. Sandra has 11 tickets. She
   wants to go on 2 different
   rides. What rides can
   she go on?

   __Boat__ and __Whip__
              or
   __Bumper__ and __Whip__

Ride	Number of Tickets
Boat	6
Whip	4
Coaster	8
Bumper	7

Macmillan/McGraw-Hill

PREPARE **WARM-UP** To prepare children for using strategies to solve problems, have them give the following sums and differences:

36 − 17 [19]   43 + 28 [71]   53 − 25 [28]   64 + 17 [81]

TEACH **DISCUSSING** Assign children to work in pairs. Explain that you will read two problems aloud and they will decide which strategy to use to solve each problem.

A square cake is cut into fourths. Jerry, Leo, Marcia, and Brenda share the cake fairly. How many parts does each person get?

■ **What do you know and what do you need to find out?** [Four people shared a square cake cut into fourths. You need to find out how many parts each person gets.]

■ **What strategy can you use to solve this problem?** [Draw a picture.]

Have children draw a square, then lines to make 4 equal parts.

■ **How many parts does each person get?** [1]

Jamal shows a pattern 3 times. The pattern shows 2 blue squares, 1 red square, and 2 yellow squares. How many squares are not blue?

■ **What do you know and what do you need to find out?** [The pattern shows 2 blue, 1 red, and 2 yellow squares. It is shown 3 times. You need to find out how many squares are not blue.]

■ **What strategy can you use to solve this problem?** [Make a model.]

Give each pair of children a set of connecting cubes: 6 blue, 3 red, and 6 yellow. Have them show the pattern 3 times.

Make a plan to solve each problem.
Then solve.

1. A round apple pie is cut into sixths.
   Jimmy and Milly share the pie fairly.
   How many parts does each one get?

   __3__ parts

2. Flags are placed around the game park
   in this pattern.

   The pattern is shown 4 times.

   Use models to show all the flags.
   How many flags are not blue?

   __8__ flags

Find each ride or booth.
Complete to show where it is.

Across → Up ↑

3. __2__ __2__

4. __4__ __1__

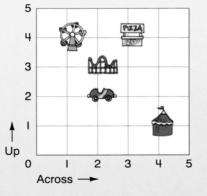

PIZZA

5. __3__ __4__

TEACHER to TEACHER

COOPERATIVE LEARNING TIP My children enjoy using the Strategies Review as a challenge. Each group makes up a problem and discusses which strategies might be best for solving it. After trading problems with another group, they decide which strategies to try. Each group member tries one strategy. The group then decides which worked best. Next, the two groups that have swapped problems present their solutions and strategies to one another, receiving feedback on their strategies. The class community resolves disagreements about the best strategy for solving the problem.

For Students Acquiring English (SAE)

Please refer to previous Problem Solving lessons for teaching suggestions about the strategies reviewed in this lesson.

■ **How many squares are not blue?** [9]

PUPIL'S EDITION pp. 351-352

Page 351 Have a volunteer read the directions at the top of the page.

■ **What do you do before you make a plan to solve a problem?** [Think about what you understand and what you need to find out.]

■ **What do you do after you understand the problem?** [Plan a way to solve the problem.]

List the problem-solving strategies on the chalkboard.

■ **After you have a plan, what do you do?** [Try the plan and check whether or not the answer makes sense.]

■ **What have you learned?** [There are many different ways to solve problems.]

Check for Understanding

■ **If a problem asks you to find how many fewer, what plan could you use?** [subtraction]

GUIDED PRACTICE ex. 1–3: Work through problem 1 with children.

Page 352 Remind children that they can use any strategy.

PRACTICE•APPLY PRACTICE ex. 1–5

CLOSE Guide children to summarize the lesson:

■ **How do you know what strategy to use to solve a problem?** [Possible response: Find out what is needed, and then choose a strategy that will most easily and quickly find the answer to the problem.]

MAC Activity 213

LOGICAL REASONING ■ CHOICES

Materials   connecting cubes

Setup   List the following problem-solving strategies and skills on the chalkboard: **choose the operation, use data from a chart, draw a picture, find a pattern, use a picture, guess and test.** Also draw a 5-by-5 grid on the chalkboard as shown.

Give each child a set of connecting cubes. Tell children that you will read them some problems. Explain that they are to choose a problem-solving strategy or skill and use the connecting cubes or the grid on the chalkboard to solve the problems. Then have children explain their solutions.

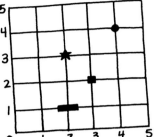

1. Hanna made a bracelet with beads. She used a pattern of 1 red bead, 2 yellow beads, and 1 blue bead. She repeated this pattern 5 times. How many beads are yellow?   [10]
2. Find the star on the grid. Write the numbers across and up to show where it is.   [2 across, 3 up]
3. Cathy cut a round melon into fourths. She shared the melon fairly with a friend. How many parts did each person get?   [2]

Continue the activity with similar problems.

▲ **MAC Activity 213:
Basic-to-Average**

**MAC Activity 214:
Average-to-Challenge**
▼

WRITING MATHEMATICS ■ WHAT'S THE PROBLEM?

MAC Activity 214

Review problem-solving strategies with the children. Ask children to think of different problems that could be solved by each strategy. Children might suggest that a grid could be used to show the location of objects in a playroom, a picture could be drawn to show how a pizza is cut into equal parts, or a clock could be used to work backward to find when someone started an activity.

Then have children work in small groups and write their own problems based on one or more of the problem-solving strategies they have learned. Tell each group to write two problems. Then have groups exchange their problems and solve them.

UNDERSTAND
PLAN
TRY
CHECK
EXTEND

Name

PROBLEM SOLVING STRATEGIES REVIEW

Study

Choose a plan to solve a problem.

Draw a picture?

Find a pattern?

Sally bought 42 pears.
She used 19 in a pie.
How many pears are left?

Add or subtract?

You can subtract.

42 − 19 = 23 pears

Check

Make a plan to solve each problem.
Then solve.

1. This pattern is shown 3 times.
   How many shapes are squares?
   Use pattern blocks to show
   the pattern 3 times. Count.

   △ □ □ ⬡ □ △

   __9__ squares

2. Marla bought 36 sun stickers.
   She bought 48 moon stickers.
   Add or subtract to find how many she bought.   __84__ stickers

Find each sky sticker.
Write the numbers to show where each
one is.

	Across→	Up↑
3. ☀	1	4
4. 🌙	3	3
5. ⭐	2	2

Reteaching-107

Macmillan/McGraw-Hill, MATHEMATICS IN ACTION
Grade 2, Chapter 11, Lesson 10, pages 351–352

Name

PROBLEM SOLVING STRATEGIES REVIEW

Make a plan to solve each problem.
Then solve.
Find each item in the yard.
Complete to show where it is.

	Across→	Up↑
1. 🏆	1	2
2. 🎄	4	1
3. ⛏	1	4

4. Ring the two things that are
   on the same line across.

5. A square cake is cut in halves.
   Joel and Wanda share the cake fairly.
   How many parts does each one get?

   __1__ parts

6. Karen picked 32 tomatoes in her garden.
   She dug up 17 carrots.
   How many more tomatoes than
   carrots did she find? __15__ more tomatoes

7. Roy has 11¢. He wants to
   buy 2 different flowers.
   Which flowers can he buy?

   __daisy__ and __tulip__
   or
   __carnation__ and __mum__

Flowers	
daisy 5¢	mum 7¢
carnation 4¢	tulip 6¢

Answers may vary.

Practice-107

Macmillan/McGraw-Hill, MATHEMATICS IN ACTION
Grade 2, Chapter 11, Lesson 10, pages 351–352

Name

PROBLEM SOLVING

On Your Own   Pair and Share   In a Group

A DAY AT THE ZOO

Plan a strategy to solve each problem at the zoo.
Then solve.

Show us how to cut this pizza.
We want to share it fairly.
How many parts will each one get?

__1 or 2__ parts

The lions get 34 pounds of meat.
The leopards get 27 pounds.
How many pounds do I need?

__61__ pounds of meat

I want to show this pattern 5 times.
How many squares do I need?

__15__ squares

I saw 45 parrots.
I saw 36 flamingoes.
How many more
parrots than flamingoes
did I see?

__9__ parrots

How do we
find the elephant?

Zoo Map

Go across __1__

Go up __4__

Enrichment-107

Macmillan/McGraw-Hill, MATHEMATICS IN ACTION
Grade 2, Chapter 11, Lesson 10, pages 351–352

Problem of the Day

Owen is making a flag. It will have four equal
parts. Each part will have a pattern of a red
square, a blue square, and a green square. What
will the flag look like?   [Check children's drawings
or models. Flags will vary.]

CHAPTER 11 • Lesson 11

AT·A·GLANCE p. 353

LESSON OBJECTIVE
Make decisions using information.

ASSIGNMENT GUIDE

COURSE	EXERCISES
Basic	p. 353: 1–5
Average	p. 353: 1–5
Challenge	p. 353: 1–5

Teacher Resources
Crit. Think. 22   Prob. Solv. 55

Decision Making

Problem Solving: Planning a Pizza Order

Mel's Pizza Palace

Small Cheese Pie $4.00	Large Cheese Pie $7.00
Extra Toppings $1.00 each	Extra Toppings $1.00 each
Extra cheese Peppers Mushrooms	Extra cheese Peppers Mushrooms

You and 2 friends want to share pizza.
You have $10.00 to spend.
Each of you wants two slices.
One of you wants an extra topping.
Two of you want cheese pizza.

Think of two ways you could order pizza.
Write each order. Answers will vary.

1. _____   2. _____

_____   _____

_____   _____

3. Which way would you like to order? Why?

_____

4. Do you have enough money for your order? _____

 5. Talk about your order with 2 friends.
How did you make your decisions?

Chapter 11   Fractions   three hundred fifty-three   **353**

PREPARE

WARM-UP Draw a square on the chalkboard. Then draw a line to divide the shape into two equal parts. Have each part identified. [one half] Continue the activity by dividing rectangles into thirds, fourths, and sixths.

TEACH

DISCUSSING Call on volunteers to share their experiences of ordering pizza in a restaurant. Explain to children that there are many different kinds of toppings that can be put on pizza. Have children think of foods that they would like as toppings for pizza. [Possible responses: cheese, mushrooms, eggplant, sausage, meatballs, green peppers]

PUPIL'S EDITION p. 353
Help children read the menu and prices at the top of the page.

Check for Understanding
■ **How much is a small cheese pie?** [$4.00]
■ **How much does each extra topping cost?** [$1.00]

PRACTICE·APPLY
Have children complete ex. 1–5. Call on volunteers to tell how they would order the pizza.

CLOSE Guide children to summarize the lesson:

■ **What should you do before you order a pizza?** [Decide what you want on the pizza and how many people will be sharing it.]

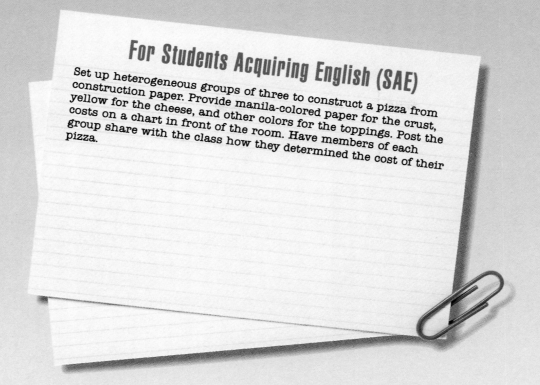

For Students Acquiring English (SAE)

Set up heterogeneous groups of three to construct a pizza from construction paper. Provide manila-colored paper for the crust, yellow for the cheese, and other colors for the toppings. Post the costs on a chart in front of the room. Have members of each group share with the class how they determined the cost of their pizza.

CLASS PROJECT

Materials oaktag

Have children work in small groups. Have each group pretend that they work in a pizza restaurant. Tell children to plan a menu together for their restaurant. Have them write their menu on oaktag.

When children have completed the project, have them display their menus on the chalkboard. Have children pretend to be in a pizza restaurant. Assign some children to be waiters/waitresses and others, customers. Have the customers refer to the menus and give their food orders to the waiters/waitresses.

CHAPTER 11

OBJECTIVE
Use fractions to describe patterns in flags.

MULTICULTURAL OUTCOME
Increase children's awareness and knowledge of the various patterns that appear in the flags of many nations.

MATERIALS
Classroom Materials reference books (encyclopedias or almanacs) with pictures of world flags, drawing paper, crayons, yarn, world map

---

Curriculum Connection

Math and Social Studies

Every country of the world has a special flag.

This is the flag of Mali. Mali is in Africa.

You can use fractions to describe the flag of Mali.

It is $\frac{1}{3}$ green, $\frac{1}{3}$ yellow, and $\frac{1}{3}$ red.

This is the flag of Panama. Panama is in Central America.

Different fractions fit this flag.

1. What fraction of the flag is red? _____ $\frac{1}{4}$

2. What fraction of the flag is blue? _____ $\frac{1}{4}$

3. What fraction of the flag has stars?
$\frac{1}{2}$ stars on white; $\frac{1}{4}$ white with red star, $\frac{1}{4}$ white with blue star

Working Together

Work with a partner. Look at a book on flags.
Find a flag you can describe with fractions.
Draw the flag. Write the name of its country.
Use fractions to describe the flag.

354   three hundred fifty-four

---

1 PREPARE   **WARM-UP**   Have volunteers describe the flag of the United States by shape, color, and pattern. [rectangle with red and white horizontal stripes and a blue area with white stars] Tell them that every country of the world has its own special flag that is different from every other country's flag. Ask:

■ **Why do you think a country has its own flag?** [Answers will vary.]

Talk about the places where flags are customarily seen, such as on public buildings, in parades, or at sporting events.

2 TEACH   **DISCUSSING**   Read the opening statement together. Examine the flags shown on the page and ask children if they have ever seen flags like these. [Some children

may have seen flags of many nations at the Olympic Games, at museums, or in other countries where they have traveled or lived.]

Read the page together. Locate each country and continent on the world map. Discuss ways to verify that the fractions accurately describe the flags shown.

■ **Why do we say that the flag of Mali is in thirds?** [It has three equal parts.]

Discuss the flag of Panama. Encourage children to describe it in several ways, using the fractions $\frac{1}{4}$ and $\frac{1}{2}$.

CULTURAL DIVERSITY

FLAGS

Every country of the world has a unique flag. Flags of countries that share a relationship may share common elements. For instance, most flags of African nations include the colors green, yellow, or red. The flags of the Scandinavian nations—Denmark, Finland, Iceland, Norway, and Sweden—have a similar pattern to each other.

3 **PRACTICE•APPLY** Before children work on their own, display several other flags that can be described in fractional terms. For example, the flag of Indonesia is $\frac{1}{2}$ red and $\frac{1}{2}$ white, and the flag of Yemen is $\frac{1}{3}$ red, $\frac{1}{3}$ white, and $\frac{1}{3}$ black.

WORKING TOGETHER Divide the class into pairs. Give each pair some drawing paper, crayons, and a book with pictures of world flags. Each pair picks a flag that clearly shows fractional parts, draws the flag with the appropriate colors, labels the name of the country, and writes a description of the flag using fractions. As pairs finish, help them locate the countries on a world map. Display the flags around the map, attaching them to the countries with a piece of yarn.

CLOSE Guide children to summarize the lesson:

■ **How can you describe the flag of Panama with fractions?**

[$\frac{1}{2}$ stars on white, $\frac{1}{2}$ solid color; $\frac{1}{4}$ red, $\frac{1}{4}$ blue, $\frac{1}{4}$ white with red star, $\frac{1}{4}$ white with blue star]

CHAPTER 11

Problem Solving: Drawing a Picture, pages 345–346 ....

Draw a picture. Solve.

1. A square pan of corn bread is cut into sixths. Nadine and Leo each eat 2 parts. How many parts are left?

___2___ parts

Parts of a Set, pages 347–348 ....

Coloring will vary.

1. Color $\frac{3}{4}$ of the set.

2. Color $\frac{1}{3}$ of the set.

3. Color $\frac{5}{6}$ of the set.

4. Color $\frac{3}{6}$ of the set.

ADDITIONAL PRACTICE

p. 345 *Solve.*

1. A round pizza is cut into thirds. Steve eats one part. Does he have enough left to share fairly with Rick and Rose? [Yes.] How many parts are left? [2]

p. 347

Color $\frac{1}{2}$ of the set.

1.

Color $\frac{4}{4}$ of the set.

2.

Color $\frac{2}{6}$ of the set.

3.

[Coloring will vary.]

Practice Plus

Key Skill: Fractions, page 342 ....

What part is shaded? Write the fraction.

1.

$\frac{1}{6}$

2.

$\frac{2}{3}$

3.

$\frac{1}{2}$

4.

$\frac{3}{4}$

5.

$\frac{1}{4}$

6.

$\frac{5}{6}$

Key Skill: Parts of a Set, page 348 ....

Answers will vary.

1. Color $\frac{2}{4}$ of the set.

2. Color $\frac{2}{3}$ of the set.

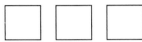

3. Color $\frac{1}{6}$ of the set.

4. Color $\frac{2}{6}$ of the set.

PRACTICE PLUS

Practice Plus is provided to supply additional practice for the two key skills in this chapter.

Key Skills
Page 342: Sixths
Page 348: Parts of a Set

The *Additional Practice* also provides practice you may wish to assign for key skills in this chapter.

---

p. 342 *What part is shaded? Write the fraction.*

1.

$\left[\frac{2}{6}\right]$

2.

$\left[\frac{3}{6}\right]$

3.

$\left[\frac{1}{4}\right]$

4.

$\left[\frac{1}{3}\right]$

5.

$\left[\frac{2}{6}\right]$

6.

$\left[\frac{1}{2}\right]$

p. 348

1. Color $\frac{1}{6}$ of the set.

2. Color $\frac{2}{3}$ of the set.

CHAPTER 11

AT·A·GLANCE pp. 357-358

OBJECTIVE
Review/test the concepts and skills presented in Chapter 11.

11A. Identify fractional parts of a region.
11B. Identify fractional parts of a set.
11C. Solve problems including those that involve drawing a picture.

Teacher Resources
Testing Program, pp. 115–126

Name _____

Chapter Review/Test

Language and Mathematics
Choose the correct words.

1. $\frac{1}{2}$ means ___one___ ___half___ .

2. has 4 ___equal___ ___parts___ .

Concepts and Skills

3. Ring the shapes that show $\frac{1}{4}$.

4. Color $\frac{1}{3}$ of each shape.   Answers will vary.

Ring the fraction for the shaded part.

5.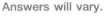

$\left(\frac{1}{2}\right)$ $\frac{1}{3}$ $\frac{1}{4}$

6.
$\frac{1}{2}$ $\left(\frac{2}{3}\right)$ $\frac{3}{4}$

7.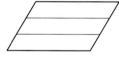
$\left(\frac{2}{4}\right)$ $\frac{2}{3}$ $\frac{3}{4}$

USING THE CHAPTER REVIEW/TEST

The Chapter Review/Test may be used as a review to survey children's knowledge and understanding of the chapter material. Or it may be used as a test to formally assess children's understanding of the concepts and skills taught in the chapter. If used as a test, you may wish to assign one or more of the resources listed in *Reinforcement and Remediation* on p. 358 after reviewing children's test results.

If the Chapter Review/Test is used as a review, you may wish to have children work in pairs to complete it. Have them talk about objects that come in sets of four. Then, you can use the Chapter Tests—Forms A, B, and C—provided in the *Testing Program Blackline Master and Teacher's Manual* for testing purposes. Any of these forms may be used for pretesting, posttesting, or retesting.

A performance assessment activity for the key concept in this chapter is provided on page 359.

What part is shaded? Write the fraction.

8.

$\frac{3}{4}$

9.

$\frac{1}{2}$

10.

$\frac{5}{6}$

11. Color $\frac{2}{3}$ of the set.

Answers will vary.

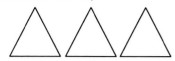

12. Color $\frac{3}{4}$ of the set.

Answers will vary.

13. Color $\frac{2}{6}$ of the set. Answers will vary.

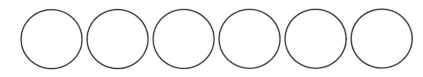

Problem Solving

Draw a picture. Solve.

14. Jessica made a spinach pie.
She cut it into 6 pieces.

She ate $\frac{2}{6}$ of the pie.

Timothy ate $\frac{3}{6}$ of the pie.

How much of the pie was left?

$\frac{1}{6}$ of the pie

15. How much more pie did Timothy eat than Jessica? $\frac{1}{6}$

MEETING INDIVIDUAL NEEDS

Reinforcement and Remediation

CHAP. OBJ.	TEST ITEMS	PUPIL'S EDITION pp.			TEACHER'S EDITION pp.	TEACHER RESOURCES	
		Lesson	Extra Practice	Practice Plus	Alt. Teaching Strategy	Reteaching	Practice
11A	1–10	335–342	344	356	336, 338, 340, 342	101, 102, 103, 104	101, 102, 103, 104
11B 11C	11–13 14–15	347–348 345–346, 351–352	355 355	356	348	106 105, 107	106 105, 107

For Students Acquiring English (SAE)

Before beginning the Chapter Review/Test with SAE children, scan the pages for any unfamiliar vocabulary that should be pretaught. You may wish to pair or group SAE children with non-SAE children. You may also wish to repeat some of the activities and techniques for SAE children that were suggested earlier in this chapter.

AT·A·GLANCE p. 359

OBJECTIVE
Assess whether children can identify fractional parts.

Teacher Resources
Performance Assessment booklet, pp. 42–44

For Students Acquiring English (SAE)

Before beginning the performance assessment with SAE children, scan the page for any unfamiliar vocabulary that should be pretaught. You may wish to pair or group SAE children with non-SAE children. You may also wish to repeat some of the activities and techniques for SAE children that were suggested earlier in this chapter.

Work with a partner.

Make a design on each flag showing halves, fourths, or thirds. Show a different fraction for each flag. Color in the flag. Then write what each flag shows.

Macmillan/McGraw-Hill

You may put this page in your *Portfolio*.

USING PERFORMANCE ASSESSMENT
The Performance Assessment activity may be used to informally assess children's understanding of the key concept(s) of the chapter. Additional assessment activities and Math Journal Options are provided in the *Performance Assessment* booklet.

Performing the Activity
Assign children to work in pairs. Have them create a design for each flag showing halves, thirds, or fourths. Then have children record individually their flags and their description of what each flag shows: halves, thirds, or fourths.

Evaluation Guidelines
Use these criteria to help determine the holistic score for each child. The holistic scoring scale can be found in the Teacher's Reference Section.

● Can the child identify fractional parts of a region?
● Can children identify halves, thirds, and fourths?

[Example Response: This flag shows fourths because it is in four equal parts.]

If children do not have a full understanding of the key concept(s), you may wish to use the Alternative Teaching Strategies or the MAC Activities within the chapter.

You may wish to have children put their final revised work in their portfolios.

A formal assessment of the concepts and skills taught in this chapter is provided on pages 357–358.

Enrichment For All

Using Half Inches

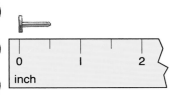

The nail is $\frac{1}{2}$ inch long.

The bandage is $2\frac{1}{2}$ inches long.

Use a 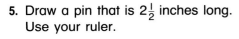.
Measure each picture.
Ring the correct measurement.

1.  $\left(2\frac{1}{2}\text{ inches}\right)$ $3\frac{1}{2}$ inches

2.    3 inches $\left(3\frac{1}{2}\text{ inches}\right)$

3.  $\left(4\text{ inches}\right)$ $4\frac{1}{2}$ inches

4. $\left(3\frac{1}{2}\text{ inches}\right)$ $4\frac{1}{2}$ inches

5. Draw a pin that is $2\frac{1}{2}$ inches long.
   Use your ruler.

360   three hundred sixty

CHAPTER 11

AT·A·GLANCE p. 360

OBJECTIVE
Measure using half inches.

ASSIGNMENT GUIDE

COURSE	EXERCISES
Basic	p. 360: 1–5
Average	p. 360: 1–5
Challenge	p. 360: 1–5

MATERIALS
Manipulatives   1 inch ruler punchout per child

For Students Acquiring English (SAE)

Read the page aloud to SAE children, explaining and demonstrating key vocabulary. Elicit the names of the items shown in ex. 1–4 and have children point to them as you explain them. Use visuals, gestures, and body movements to convey meaning. To check comprehension of the directions, ask SAE children to restate them. Pair SAE children and non-SAE children to complete the exercises together. In reviewing the exercises, encourage SAE children to answer in complete sentences.

---

1 PREPARE   **WARM-UP**   To review using inch rulers, give each child an inch ruler. Have children measure the lengths and widths of different objects to the nearest inch. Then have them draw lines of inch lengths.

2 TEACH   **DISCUSSING**   Have children study the pictures and the rulers at the top of the page. Explain that the marks between the numbers on the rulers are half-inch marks.

■ **To what mark does the nail come to on the first ruler?** [the half-inch mark between 0 and 1]

■ **To what mark does the bandage come to on the second ruler?** [the half-inch mark between 2 and 3]

Have children read the sentences below the rulers. Help them read the lengths correctly. Explain that $2\frac{1}{2}$ inches long is read as "two and a half inches long."

3 PRACTICE·APPLY   Have children complete ex. 1–5, using their inch rulers to measure and draw.

CLOSE   Guide children to summarize the lesson:

■ **How long would the nail at the top be if it measured to the half-inch mark between 1 and 2?** [$1\frac{1}{2}$ inches long]

CHAPTER 11

Cumulative Review

AT·A·GLANCE p. 361

OBJECTIVE
Review and maintain previously learned concepts and skills.

Fill in the ◯ to answer each question.

1. Compare.

245 ◯ 259

<	>	+	=
●	◯	◯	◯

2.

22 + 14 + 6 = __?__

46	36	42	32
◯	◯	●	◯

3.

4:05	3:05	2:15	1:15
◯	◯	◯	●

4.

$$64 - 28$$

46	44	36	34
◯	◯	●	◯

5. Which number is 3 hundreds 4 tens 6 ones?

643	463	346	300
◯	◯	●	◯

6. What part is shaded?

$\frac{1}{2}$	$\frac{1}{3}$	$\frac{2}{4}$	$\frac{5}{6}$
◯	◯	◯	●

7. Becky had 38¢ in her pocket. Melissa had 54¢ in her pocket. How much more money did Melissa have than Becky?

- ◯ 82¢
- ◯ 54¢
- ◯ 92¢
- ● 16¢

Macmillan/McGraw-Hill

USING THE CUMULATIVE REVIEW

The Cumulative Review is presented in a multiple-choice format to provide practice in taking a standardized test. It gives children an opportunity to review previously learned skills. An answer sheet, similar to those used when taking standardized tests, can be found in the *Testing Program Blackline Masters and Teacher's Manual.*

The table that follows correlates the review items to the lesson pages on which the skills are taught.

Review Items	Text Pages	Review Items	Text Pages
1	290	5	279–282
2	204	6	340–342
3	257–260	7	233
4	221–225, 234		

Testing Program Blackline Masters
In addition to the Cumulative Review in the Pupil's Edition, there are quarterly Cumulative Tests and an End-Year Test. These tests are multiple choice and provide additional opportunities for children to practice taking standardized tests.

Cumulative Tests measure children's performance on major skills and concepts taught during the previous quarters. The **End-Year Test** measures children's performance on major skills and concepts taught throughout the year.

Home Activity

Your child has been learning about fractions that show the parts of a whole object and fractions that show the parts of a set of objects. This activity will help strengthen these skills.

Players:
2

Materials:
6 red buttons and 6 blue buttons
small paper bag
pencils

Directions:

1. Show your child the buttons and then place them in the bag.

2. Take turns reaching into the bag and pulling out 6 buttons without looking.

3. The player lays out the buttons, decides what part of the set of 6 is red, and marks an X on the correct fraction on his or her fraction chart. If the correct fraction has already been marked, the player skips a turn. After each turn all buttons are returned to the bag.

4. Play continues until one player has marked all the fractions on his or her playing board.

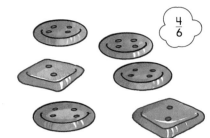

Player 1

$\frac{1}{6}$	$\frac{2}{6}$	$\frac{3}{6}$
$\frac{4}{6}$	$\frac{5}{6}$	$\frac{6}{6}$

Player 2

$\frac{1}{6}$	$\frac{2}{6}$	$\frac{3}{6}$
$\frac{4}{6}$	$\frac{5}{6}$	$\frac{6}{6}$

Variation:
Pull out different numbers of buttons from the bag and each time write the appropriate fraction for the red part.

362   three hundred sixty-two

A·T·A·G·L·A·N·C·E p. 362

OBJECTIVE
Give family members an opportunity to share in their child's mathematics learning.

For Students Acquiring English (SAE)

Before assigning this Home Activity to SAE children, find out if someone at home will be able to work with them in English. If not, prepare them to complete the activity independently at home. Explain the directions of the activity and ask SAE children to restate them so you can check comprehension. Scan the page and preteach any difficult vocabulary or phrases that they may not know. If you feel that an SAE child will need extra help with the activity, you might assign that student a non-SAE partner and arrange a time for them to work on the activity in or out of school.

USING THE ACTIVITY

Have children look at the page. Explain that the page has an activity that an adult in the family can help them complete. Read the page with the children, making sure that they understand what needs to be done. Tell children that they will do this page at home.

EXPLORE MULTIPLICATION and DIVISION FACTS

66 *IN CHAPTER 12, you will be introducing your children to exploring multiplication and division facts. You will also have the opportunity to explore interpreting multiplication sentences.* 99

Notes
FROM THE AUTHOR

Here are some notes on the concepts presented in this chapter and how your children can apply them to solve problems.

THE MEANING of MULTIPLICATION

Introduce your children to the concept of multiplication as repeated addition of same-sized groups. Help children build on their understanding of addition to understand the concept. To emphasize the idea of same-size groups, children should work with manipulatives to show equal groups. They then write addition sentences for the groups and finally write the multiplication sentence.

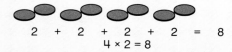

$$2 + 2 + 2 + 2 = 8$$
$$4 \times 2 = 8$$

Richard Lodholz

INTERPRETING MULTIPLICATION SENTENCES

Most of your children can read 5 x 2 as "5 times 2," but they probably do not understand that it means 5 groups of 2. Modeling, and writing the intermediate number sentence, helps children gain needed practice in understanding the meaning of multiplication sentences.

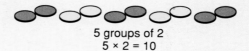

5 groups of 2
5 × 2 = 10

Introduce children to examples of the order property of multiplication. Modeling sentences like the following helps children understand the meaning of the sentences.

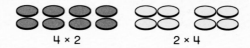

4 × 2   2 × 4

EXPLORING DIVISION

Children at this level can explore division as an extension of multiplication. To introduce the concept of division, your children can separate groups of objects into smaller groups. Children also gain understanding of the concept of division by relating division to sharing and recalling times they have tried to share food or objects equally with their friends. Encourage your children to participate in "sharing" exercises. For example, a child shows 10 counters to represent 10 cookies. Then the child separates the counters into groups of 2 and tells how many groups were made. Children can model another meaning of division by using the 10 counters to show 5 groups and telling how many are in each group.

PROBLEM SOLVING

In **Problem Solving** your children (1) guess and test to solve a problem and (2) solve a problem by choosing the operation.

In **Thinking Mathematically** children complete a table showing how many patches or buttons they use. In "Sew It Up," children use counters to demonstrate their multiplication skills.

In **Decision Making** children read and use information and then apply multiplication and division and their knowledge about money to plan a catalog order.

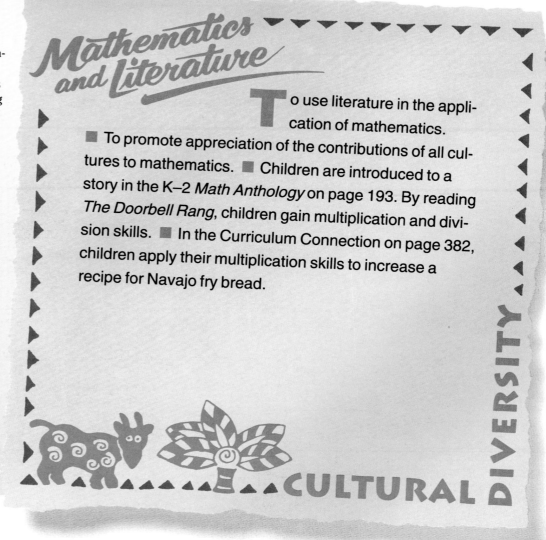

Mathematics and Literature

To use literature in the application of mathematics. ■ To promote appreciation of the contributions of all cultures to mathematics. ■ Children are introduced to a story in the K–2 *Math Anthology* on page 193. By reading *The Doorbell Rang*, children gain multiplication and division skills. ■ In the Curriculum Connection on page 382, children apply their multiplication skills to increase a recipe for Navajo fry bread.

CULTURAL DIVERSITY

CHAPTER PLANNING GUIDE

CHAPTER OBJECTIVES WITH STANDARDIZED TEST CORRELATIONS

A. Find products for multiplication sentences and related pictures

B. Find how many groups; how many in each group

C. Solve problems including those that involve choosing the operation

CTBS

MAT, CAT, SAT, ITBS, CTBS

LESSONS	NCTM STANDARDS	ASSIGNMENTS Basic/Average/Challenge	STUDENT EDITION Extra Practice/ Practice Plus	Manip. Plus	Reteach	Practice	Enrich	MAC Activities
Chapter Opener: *The Doorbell Rang* page 363	1, 2, 3, 4, 7, 8	p. 363: All						
✓ **1 Multiplication and Division Facts** page 364	1, 2, 3, 8	p. 364: All						
✓ **2 Multiplying 2 and 3** pages 365–366	1, 2, 3, 8	p. 365: 2–6; p. 366: 1–7		69	108	108	108	215, 216
✓ **3 Multiplying 3 and 4** pages 367–368	1, 2, 3, 8	p. 367: 2–6; p. 368: 1–5, Calculator	p. 372		109	109	109	217, 218
✓ **4 Informal Algebra: Multiplication Patterns** pages 369–370	1, 2, 3, 8, 13	p. 369: 3–9; p. 370: 2–5	pp. 372, 384	70, 71	110	110	110	219, 220
✓ **5 PS: Thinking Mathematically** page 371	1, 2, 3, 13	p. 371: All						
6 PS: Guess and Test pages 373–374	1, 2, 3, 8	p. 373: 1; p. 374: 1–4			111	111	111	221, 222
✓ **7 Division: How Many Groups?** pages 375–376	1, 2, 3, 7, 8	p. 375: 1–6; p. 376: 2–9	p. 383	72	112	112	112	223, 224
✓ **8 Division: How Many in Each Group?** pages 377–378	1, 2, 3, 7, 8	p. 377: 1–6; p. 378: 1–8	pp. 383, 384		113	113	113	225, 226
9 PS: Choosing the Operation pages 379–380	1, 2, 3, 7, 8	p. 379: 1; p. 380: 1–5	p. 383		114	114	114	227, 228
10 PS: Decision Making page 381	1, 2, 3, 6, 8	p. 381: 1–3						

Curriculum Connection: Reading page 382 ㏄

Chapter Review/Test pages 385–386

Performance Assessment page 387

Cumulative Review page 389

Enrichment for All/Home Activity pages 388, 390

NATIONAL COUNCIL OF TEACHERS OF MATHEMATICS
Grades K–4

1. Problem Solving
2. Communication
3. Reasoning
4. Connections
5. Estimation
6. Number Sense and Numeration
7. Concepts of Whole Number Operations
8. Whole Number Computation
9. Geometry and Spatial Sense
10. Measurement
11. Statistics and Probability
12. Fractions and Decimals
13. Patterns and Relationships

✓ Activity   Cooperative Learning   ㏄ Cultural Connection

MEETING the NCTM STANDARDS

Problem Solving

Strategies and Skills	• guess and test pp. 373–374
	• choosing the operation pp. 379–380
Applications	• **Decision Making** lesson p. 381
	• **Problem of the Day** TE pp. 364, 366B, 368B, 370B, 374B, 376B, 378B, 380B
Mathematical Investigations	• **Thinking Mathematically** lesson p. 371

Communication

Language	• using the language of mathematics TE pp. 365–366, 367–368, 375–376
Oral/Written	• using cooperative learning activities pp. 364, 365, 366, 367, 368, 369–370, 371, 375–376, 377–378, 381; TE pp. 362I–362L
	• **Journal Writing** opportunities TE pp. 364, 370, 378, 380

Reasoning

Critical Thinking	• answering questions that analyze and extend concepts pp. 363, 366, 369, 370, 377, 381

Connections

To other subject areas	• Literature p. 363, Reading p. 382; Literature TE pp. 363–364, 365, 369
To all cultures	• Navajo fry bread p. 382

Concept Development

Concepts of Whole Number Operations	• using models to explore the meaning of multiplication and division p. 364
Whole Number Computation	• finding products for multiplication sentences and related pictures pp. 365–366, 367–368; TE p. 362I
	• finding how many groups; how many in each group (division) pp. 375–376, 377–378; TE p. 362L
Patterns and Relationships	• identifying patterns in multiplication pp. 369–370; TE pp. 362J–362K

ASSESSMENT OPTIONS

PERFORMANCE ASSESSMENT

Preassessment Activity

Before beginning Chapter 12, have children work in groups. Give each group a bag with 10 to 20 buttons. Have one student reach in the bag and grab a handful of buttons and lay them out on the table. Each student should count the buttons and estimate how many groups of two, three, four, and five could be made by distributing the buttons evenly. Have children check their estimates.

Ongoing Assessment

The Ongoing Assessment cards under MEETING INDI-VIDUAL NEEDS on TE pp. 370 and 378 provide criteria and questions for assessing children's understanding of the key mathematical concepts developed in the chapter.

Journal Writing opportunities encourage children to write about mathematics. Their responses can be re-corded either pictorially or in words. The journal writ-ing opportunities on the Ongoing Assessment cards also allow you to assess children's understanding of the lessons.

In addition to the Ongoing Assessment cards, other assessment and journal writing opportunities in this chapter include:

• **CLOSE** TE pp. 364, 378, 380

Performance Assessment Activity

The Performance Assessment activity on p. 387 pro-vides an alternative to formal assessment. This activity assesses children's understanding of the key concepts of the chapter.

For performance assessment activities that are keyed to individual chapter objectives, see the *Performance Assessment* booklet.

BUILDING A PORTFOLIO

Children should be encouraged to keep a selection of their best work in portfolios. The portfolios provide a way of docu-menting children's growth in understanding mathematical concepts. Portfolio opportunities in this chapter include:

• **Performance Assessment** p. 387
• **Class Project** TE p. 381A

If you wish to provide additional opportunities for portfolio work, you may choose to use:

• **MAC Activities** 221, 223, 224, 225

You may also wish to have children include their journal writing from the Ongoing Assessment on TE pp. 370 and 378 in their portfolio.

Formal Assessment

The **Chapter Review/Test** assesses children's under-standing of the concepts and skills developed in the chapter. The **Cumulative Review** assesses children's understanding of the concepts and skills developed from the beginning of the year.

You can use **Form A** or **Form B** of the **Chapter Test** found in the *Testing Program Blackline Masters and Teacher's Manual* if you wish to use a multiple-choice

format to assess children's understanding of the chapter concepts and skills. You can use **Form C** if you wish to use a free-response format. Any of the forms may be used as a pretest, posttest, or for retesting.

The **COMPUTER MANAGEMENT SYSTEM**, or **CMS**, enables you to score **Forms A** and **B** of the **Chapter Test** quickly and automatically. It also prescribes learn-ing activities based on children's test results.

For more information about Assessment, see the *Professional Handbook*.

Common Error and Remediation

The Teacher's Edition notes for each Develop/Understand (Transitional/Abstract) lesson provide a common error analysis and a remediation activity. Some errors defy quick analysis and can only be identified by interviewing the child.

ALTERNATIVE TEACHING STRATEGY

Alternative Teaching Strategies appear frequently in the chapter. These strategies provide other presentations of the lessons for children who might benefit from instruction in different learning modalities: kinesthetic, visual, and/or auditory.

For Students Acquiring English (SAE)

In order for SAE children to follow the lessons more easily, preteach the terminology used in the chapter and describe the multiplication process as repeated addition. Have SAE children act out stories using terminology such as **how many in each group, how many in all, multiplication sentence.**

SAE notes appear periodically in the chapter. These notes provide suggestions for how to work with children to improve comprehension and build vocabulary.

MANIPULATIVES WORKSHOP

Counters are used in this chapter to explore multiplication and division. They provide a concrete representation of the concepts of adding same-sized groups and separating a set into same-sized groups.

USING MANIPULATIVES

Here a child begins to make groups of 5 counters to find out how many are in 3 groups of 5.

The child completes making 3 groups of 5. Then the child counts by fives to find that 3 x 5 = 15.

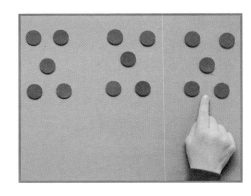

Here a child models 14 ÷ 2.

The child begins with 14 counters.

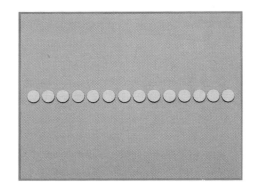

The child separates the counters into 2 groups.

There are 7 counters in each group.

The model shows that 14 ÷ 2 = 7.

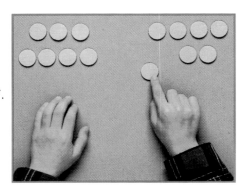

MAKING MANIPULATIVES

See the Manipulatives section of the *Professional Handbook* for materials that can be used as a substitute for counters.

COOPERATIVE LEARNING WORKSHOP

GETTING STARTED

Rotating Groups: Children can benefit now from a **rotating review** that covers the material learned during the year. Each small group has a large sheet of chart paper, posted in their bulletin board area, that covers a different topic. They stand by their sheet and their recorder writes for one minute, in a marker with the group's color, all the information they can think of on the topic. At a signal from the teacher, all groups rotate to the next topic sheet clockwise, and review for one minute what has been written by the previous group. Each group then chooses a new recorder and spends another minute adding any additional information they can to the new chart. Groups keep rotating until all have visited each topic. A final round gives each group one minute at each sheet to read all statements.

IDEAS TO TRY

Comparing Results: Groups can expand their knowledge base by comparing results with other groups in the class. During work, groups can send a **roving reporter** to gain ideas from other groups. Since some groups work faster than others, it is a good plan to have extension activities or cooperative games available. When all groups are finished, try a **group concentric circles** structure: Groups form an inside and an outside circle and present their work to each other, giving suggestions and receiving feedback. After several rounds of presenting, team members make any necessary revisions to their work. Another set of rounds will show significant improvement in group reports.

You can apply the above group-comparison strategies in these lessons:
12-2 *Multiplying 2 and 3* pp. 365–366
12-3 *Multiplying 4 and 5* pp. 367–368
12-4 *Informal Algebra: Multiplication Patterns* pp. 369–370

Interviews: Children may enjoy holding a **team interview review** after working together on the lessons named below. Each member of the group of four is interviewed by other members in turn for a specified time. Interviewers use questions from the text or ones they develop themselves. If the interviewed child cannot answer the question asked, he or she has the right to pass or to answer another question he or she would like to have been asked. The unanswered question can then be asked of the next interviewee.

You can apply the above interview structure in these lessons:
12-7 *Division: How Many Groups?* pp. 375–376
12-8 *Division: How Many in Each Group?* pp. 377–378

SEE ALSO

Cooperative Learning Tip for lessons 12-6 Problem Solving p. 374; 12-9 Problem Solving p. 380

The Cooperative Learning section of the *Professional Handbook* for additional information

ACTIVITY

INTERACTIVE BULLETIN BOARD

SETUP Use oaktag to make an umbrella pattern. Trace the umbrella pattern onto 12 sheets of construction paper, each a different color. Cut out the umbrellas and write each of the following labels on a different umbrella: *5 groups of 4, 3 groups of 5, 4 groups of 3, 4 groups of 4, 5 groups of 5, 4 groups of 5, 5 groups of 3, 3 groups of 4, 5 groups of 2, 4 groups of 2, 3 groups of 3, 3 groups of 2*. Then draw the corresponding groups of raindrops as shown in the illustration.

PROCEDURE 👥 Display the umbrellas on a table. Have volunteers match the umbrellas to the groups of raindrops by tacking the umbrellas under the appropriate group.

CHAPTER 12 • ORGANIZER

MANIPULATIVES
plus
• ACTIVITY •

For use before LESSON 12.2, pp. 365-366

69

CONCEPT OF MULTIPLICATION

OBJECTIVE
Explore the concept of multiplication.

MATERIALS
Classroom Materials
index cards, dried beans in small containers, overhead projector
Manipulatives 12 ○ (or punchouts); Workmat 5 per child

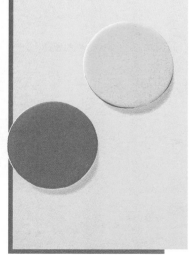

WHOLE GROUP ACTIVITY 🕐

Place 3 groups of 2 counters each on an overhead projector. Write *2* below each group and *3 groups of 2* below the display.

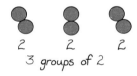

2   2   2
3 groups of 2

■ **How can we find how many counters in all?**
[Possible answers: count; skip count; add]

Have a volunteer count each counter to find a total of 6. Then have another volunteer skip count to find a total of 6. Next, write plus signs between the 2s, and have another volunteer add to find the sum of 6. Repeat the activity with 4 groups of 2.

SMALL GROUP ACTIVITY ↕ 👥

Prepare 3 task cards per group by writing *count, skip count,* and *add* on index cards. Assign children to work in groups of three. Give each group the 3 task cards and a container of 50 dried beans. Give each child Workmat 5.

Display one of the following groups of counters on the overhead projector. Have each child copy the group, using beans on the workmat.

Have each child in a group choose a task card and then find the total number of counters using the method described on her or his task card.

Then children are to compare totals. If the totals do not agree, they should exchange tasks and check their work. After each round, children should pass their task cards to the group member on their right and repeat the activity.

EXTENDING THE ACTIVITY

Have children write about what they think multiplication is. Challenge them to write a story problem about the groups of counters.

ONGOING ASSESSMENT

✓ Are children able to model equal groups and find the total?

For use before LESSON 12.4, pp. 369-370

70

MULTIPLICATION PATTERNS

OBJECTIVE
Explore patterns in multiplication.

MATERIALS
Classroom Materials
dried beans in small containers, overhead projector
Manipulatives 50 ◯ (or punchouts) per child

WHOLE GROUP ACTIVITY

Give each child a container of 50 beans or counters. Show the following groups of counters on an overhead projector and have children copy the groups.

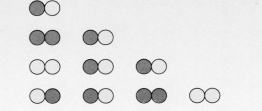

■ **How many groups of 2 are in each row?** [1, 2, 3, 4, 5]
■ **What is the total for each row?** [2, 4, 6, 8, 10]
■ **What patterns do you see?** [There is one more group in each row and the total increases by 2.]

Then show these groups and have children copy them.

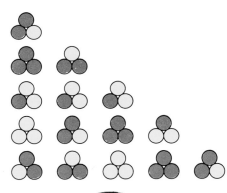

■ **How many groups of 3 are in each row?** [1, 2, 3, 4, 5]
■ **What is the total for each row?** [3, 6, 9, 12, 15]
■ **What patterns do you see?** [There is one more group in each row and the total increases by 3.]

EXTENDING THE ACTIVITY

Have children work in pairs to create other patterns. Then have other pairs of children identify the patterns in each display.

ONGOING ASSESSMENT

✓ Are children able to model arrays of equal groups and find patterns?

71

MULTIPLICATION PROPERTIES

OBJECTIVE
Explore properties of multiplication.

MATERIALS
Classroom Materials
index cards, overhead projector
Manipulatives 12 ○ (or punchouts)

WHOLE GROUP ACTIVITY 🕐

Display 2 groups of 3 and 3 groups of 2 counters on an overhead projector. Label each as shown.

$2 \times 3 = 6$ $3 \times 2 = 6$

■ **How are these groups the same?** [In their own words, children may note that they have the same product.]

■ **How are these groups different?** [In their own words, children may note that the number of groups is different, the number in each group is different, and the order of the factors is different.]

Repeat the questioning with 4 groups of 3 and 3 groups of 4.

SMALL GROUP ACTIVITY 🕐 👬

Prepare 12 index cards for each group of three. Vary the numbers for each group.

3×2	2×3	○○○ ○○○
○○ ○○ ○○	3 groups of 2	2 groups of 3

Assign children to play "Concentration" in groups of three. Give each group 12 index cards. Children should take turns matching cards that show related

forms of the same product. Show children the following examples as matches:

3×2	○○ ○○ ○○	3 groups of 2
2×3	○○○ ○○○	2 groups of 3

The child with the most matches at the end wins. Have groups of children trade cards and play again.

EXTENDING THE ACTIVITY

Have children write a story that involves two groups of objects that have the same product.

ONGOING ASSESSMENT

✓ Are children able to identify related forms of the same product?

For use before LESSON 12.7, pp. 375-376

72

CONCEPT OF DIVISION

OBJECTIVE
Explore the concept of division.

MATERIALS
Manipulatives 25 ○ (or punchouts) per pair

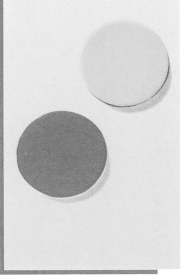

WHOLE GROUP ACTIVITY 🕐

Have 10 children stand at the front of the room. Explain that you want to divide the children into 2 teams. Have volunteers help divide the children.

■ **How many children are on each of the 2 teams?** [5]

■ **How many teams of 5 children do we have?** [2]

Repeat the activity with 15 children. Divide them into teams of 5 children and then 3 children.

PAIRS ACTIVITY 🕐 👥

Assign children to work in pairs. Give each pair 25 counters. Have children work together to model and solve the following problems.

1. Show 20 basketball players. Make teams of 5 players on each team. How many teams are there? [4]

2. Show 20 basketball players. Make 4 teams with the same number of players on each team. How many players are on each team? [5]

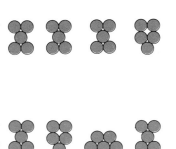

3. Show 12 runners. Make relay teams of 4 runners on each team. How many relay teams are there? [3]

4. Show 12 runners. Make 3 relay teams with the same number of runners on each team. How many runners are on each team? [4]

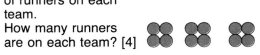

EXTENDING THE ACTIVITY

Continue the activity with similar problems. Include some problems that do not come out even. Identify the leftover counters as *remainders*.

ONGOING ASSESSMENT

✓ Are children able to model separating sets into equivalent sets?

READ ALOUD

The Doorbell Rang
by Pat Hutchins

THE DOORBELL RANG
By Pat Hutchins

Mathematics and Literature

Listening and Speaking

The Read-Aloud selection can be used
with the Chapter 12 Opener and Lesson 12-1
on pages 363-364.

Tape 2, Side 2
Selection 3

The DOORBELL Rang

BY PAT HUTCHINS

"I've made some cookies for tea," said Ma.

"Good," said Victoria and Sam. "We're starving."

"Share them between yourselves," said Ma. "I made plenty."

"That's six each," said Sam and Victoria.

"They look as good as Grandma's," said Victoria.

"They smell as good as Grandma's," said Sam.

"No one makes cookies like Grandma," said Ma as the doorbell rang.

It was Tom and Hannah from next door.

"Come in," said Ma. "You can share the cookies."

"That's three each," said Sam and Victoria.

"They smell good as your Grandma's," said Tom.

"And look as good," said Hannah.

"No one makes cookies like Grandma," said Ma as the doorbell rang.

It was Peter and his little brother.

"Come in," said Ma. "You can share the cookies."

"That's two each," said Victoria and Sam.

"They look as good as your Grandma's," said Peter. "And smell as good."

"Nobody makes cookies like Grandma," said Ma as the doorbell rang.

It was Joy and Simon with their four cousins.

"Come in," said Ma. "You can share the cookies."

"That's one each," said Sam and Victoria.

"They smell as good as your Grandma's," said Joy.

"And look as good," said Simon.

"No one makes cookies like Grandma," said Ma as the doorbell rang and rang.

"Oh dear," said Ma as the children stared at the cookies on their plates. "Perhaps you'd better eat them before we open the door."

"We'll wait," said Sam.

It was Grandma with an enormous tray of cookies.

"How nice to have so many friends to share them with," said Grandma. "It's a good thing I made a lot!"

"And no one makes cookies like Grandma," said Ma as the doorbell rang.

362N

Explore Multiplication and Division Facts

CHAPTER 12

READ ALOUD

The Doorbell Rang
by Pat Hutchins

THE DOORBELL RANG
By Pat Hutchins

Listen to the story The Doorbell Rang.

Talk about how many cookies Ma made.
Draw a picture to help find how many.

AT·A·GLANCE pp. 363-364

LESSON OBJECTIVES
Explore mathematical concepts through literature.
Explore the concept of multiplication.

ASSIGNMENT GUIDE

COURSE	EXERCISES
Basic	p. 363: All; p. 364: All
Average	p. 363: All; p. 364: All
Challenge	p. 363: All; p. 364: All

MATERIALS
Manipulatives 25 ○ (or punchouts), spinner for 1–5 (or punchout) per pair

Teacher Resources
Math Anthology, pp. 193–194
Read-Aloud Cassette 2, Side 2, Selection 3

SKILLS TRACE
MULTIPLICATION AND DIVISION FACTS

Explore (Concrete) 364	Develop/Understand (Transitional/Abstract) 365–366, 367–368, 369–370, 375–376, 377–378
Practice 372, 383, 384, 385–386, 389, 408	Apply 371, 373–374, 379–380, 381, 382, 388, 411

---

1 PREPARE

WARM-UP To review addition, have children give the following sums:

$2 + 2 =$ ___ [4]
$2 + 2 + 2 + 2 =$ ___ [8]
$3 + 3 + 3 =$ ___ [9]
$4 + 4 =$ ___ [8]
$4 + 4 + 4 + 4 =$ ___ [16]

2 TEACH

DISCUSSING Before reading the story *The Doorbell Rang,* ask children to recall what happened in the story *How Many Ways Can You Cut a Pie?* [Squirrel shared a pie with some of her forest friends.] Discuss what happened to the number and size of the pieces as more friends asked for a piece. [When the piece was divided into more pieces, each piece got smaller.] Ex-

plain that the story they are about to hear is also about sharing among friends.

Mathematics and Literature

PUPIL'S EDITION pp. 363-364

Page 363 Read *The Doorbell Rang* found on page 362N or in *Math Anthology* to children, or play Read-Aloud Cassette 2, Side 2, Selection 3 for them.

■ **How many cookies did Sam and Victoria get when they shared among themselves?** [6 cookies each]

■ **What happens when Tom and Hannah arrive?** [Each child gets 3 cookies.]

■ **How many children are there after Joy and Simon and their four cousins arrive?** [12 children]

ACTIVITY

Multiplication and Division Facts

Working Together

Use a ⊞ and 25 ○ to stand for apples.

Put the same number of apples on each plate. Answers
Spin to find how many apples to show on a plate. will vary.

Talk about how many plates there are.

5

How many apples are on each plate?

Answers will vary.

How many apples are there in all?

Answers will vary.

ACTIVITY

ALTERNATIVE TEACHING STRATEGY

MATERIALS paper plates; 25 ○ (or punchouts)

VISUAL Gather children around you at a table. Place 2 paper plates on the table. Discuss how many plates there are, how many counters there are on each plate, and how many counters there are in all. Repeat, increasing the number of counters on each plate. Guide children to see that as the number of counters on each plate increases, the total number of counters increases.

■ **How many cookies does each child get then?** [1 cookie]
Discuss the directive on the page.

Page 364 ■ Working Together   Assign children to work in small groups. Give each group 25 counters and a spinner.

Check for Understanding

■ **How do you know how many apples to put on a plate?** [Spin spinner; the same number of counters goes on the plate.]

GUIDED PRACTICE   Have the group discuss the number of plates, the number of apples on each plate, and the number of apples in all. For reteaching, use Alternative Strategy.

PRACTICE•APPLY   **PRACTICE**   Have children complete the activity.

C L O S E   Guide children to summarize the lesson:

■ **What do you need to know to find out the total number of apples?** [You have to know how many plates there are and how many apples are on each plate.]

Problem of the Day

There were 4 plates with 3 apples on each plate. How many apples were there in all? [12 apples]

AT·A·GLANCE pp. 365-366

LESSON OBJECTIVE
Multiply 2 and 3.

ASSIGNMENT GUIDE

COURSE	EXERCISES
Basic	p. 365: 2–6; p. 366: 1–7
Average	p. 365: 2–6; p. 366: 1–7
Challenge	p. 365: 2–6; p. 366: 1–7

MATERIALS
Manipulatives 15 ○ (or punchouts), Workmat 5 per pair

Teacher Resources
Reteaching 108   Practice 108   Enrichment 108
MAC Act. 215, 216
Math Anthology, p. 195

SKILLS TRACE
MULTIPLICATION & DIVISION FACTS

Explore (Concrete) 364	Develop/Understand (Transitional/Abstract) 365–366, 367–368, 369–370
Practice 372, 383, 384, 385–386, 389, 408	Apply 371, 373–374, 379–380, 381, 382, 388, 411

See **MANIPULATIVES PLUS 69**, p. 362I.

Mathematics and Literature

1 PREPARE **WARM-UP** To review skip counting by 2s, read the poem "Ten Little Squirrels" to the class. Give the children 10 counters to stand for the 10 squirrels. Reread the poem as children use the counters to model each two squirrels mentioned. Then have them skip count by 2s to find how many squirrels in all.

2 TEACH **MODELING** Draw 4 groups of 2 circles on the chalkboard. Have children use counters to copy the chalkboard drawing.

■ **How could you find how many counters there are in all?** [by skip counting or repeated addition]

Write 2, 4, 6, 8 and 2 + 2 + 2 + 2 = 8 on the chalkboard, and review skip counting and **repeated addition** with children. Explain that another way to find how many there are in all is by **multiplying.**

Name _____

Multiplying 2 and 3

How many cherries in all?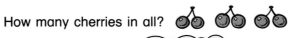

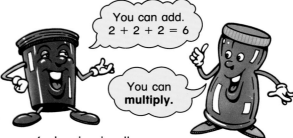

You can add.
2 + 2 + 2 = 6

You can **multiply.**

► 3 groups of 2

► 3 times 2 equals 6

► 3 × 2 = 6

There are 6 cherries in all.

Working Together
Use Workmat 5 and 10 ●.
Show groups of 2.

Show	Complete.	Multiplication Sentence
1. 1 group of 2	2	1 × 2 = 2
2. 2 groups of 2	2 + 2	2 × 2 = 4
3. 3 groups of 2	2 + 2 + 2	3 × 2 = 6
4. 4 groups of 2	2 + 2 + 2 + 2	4 × 2 = 8
5. 5 groups of 2	2 + 2 + 2 + 2 + 2	5 × 2 = 10

6. Do you see any patterns?
Write what you know about groups of 2.
Answers will vary.

Use your own paper.

■ **How many groups of 2 are there?** [4 groups of 2]

■ **How many counters in all?** [8]

Then write 4 × 2 = 8 on the chalkboard. Explain that this **multiplication sentence** is another way to describe 4 groups of 2. Point to the × and tell children that this is a **multiplication sign** and is read as **times.** Then point to each part of the sentence as children read it as 4 times 2 equals 8.

Repeat the activity with 3 groups of 3.

PUPIL'S EDITION pp. 365-366

Page 365 Work through the example at the top of the page with the children. Have volunteers read the addition and multiplication sentences.

How many groups of oranges? 4
How many oranges in each group? 3
How many oranges in all?

$3 + 3 + 3 + 3 = 12$ $4 \times 3 = 12$

12 oranges in all.

Working Together

Use Workmat 5 and 15 ◯.
Show groups of 3.

Show	Complete.	Multiplication Sentence
1. 1 group of 3	3	$\underline{1} \times 3 = \underline{3}$
2. 2 groups of 3	$\underline{3} + \underline{3}$	$\underline{2} \times 3 = \underline{6}$
3. 3 groups of 3	$\underline{3} + \underline{3} + \underline{3}$	$\underline{3} \times 3 = \underline{9}$
4. 4 groups of 3	$\underline{3} + \underline{3} + \underline{3} + \underline{3}$	$\underline{4} \times 3 = \underline{12}$
5. 5 groups of 3	$\underline{3} + \underline{3} + \underline{3} + \underline{3} + \underline{3}$	$\underline{5} \times 3 = \underline{15}$

6. Each bag must have 3 limes.
How many limes will

5 bags have? __15__ limes

7. Talk about different ways to solve the problem. Answers will vary.
In their own words children may note skip counting, repeated addition,
and multiplication as methods to solve the problem.

366   three hundred sixty-six

ACTIVITY Common Error and Remediation

MATERIALS 12 ▢

Some children may not grasp the concept of multiple groups.
Work individually with each child, using a set of connecting
cubes. Snap together 2 groups of 3 cubes and ask the child how
many groups there are, how many cubes in each group, and how
many cubes in all. Then have the child snap together 3 groups of
2 cubes and tell how many groups there are, and so on. Continue
the activity with 4 groups of 2 and 4 groups of 3.

ACTIVITY ALTERNATIVE TEACHING STRATEGY

MATERIALS 10 ▢, overhead projector, marker, blank
transparency

VISUAL Show two cubes on an overhead projector. Have a
volunteer tell how many groups of 2 you have shown. [1] Write
$1 \times 2 = 2$ on the transparency and have children read it as 1
times 2 equals 2. Show two more cubes and have another
volunteer tell how many groups of 2 you have shown. [2] Write
$2 \times 2 = 4$ on the transparency and have children read it.
Continue the activity with 2×3, 2×4, and 2×5.

WORKING TOGETHER   Have children work in pairs and give each
pair ten counters and Workmat 5. Guide children through ex. 1.

Check for Understanding

■ **How would you model 2 groups of 2?** [show 2 counters and 2
counters]

GUIDED PRACTICE   ex. 2–6: For reteaching, use Common Error
and Remediation or Alternative Strategy.

Page 366   Work through the problem at the top of the page with the
children.

WORKING TOGETHER   Have children continue to work in pairs. Be
sure each pair has 15 counters.

3 PRACTICE•APPLY
PRACTICE   ex. 1–7: Discuss children's answers to ex. 7.

CLOSE   Guide children to summarize the lesson:

■ **What are the addition sentence and the multiplication sentence
for 5 groups of 3?** [$3 + 3 + 3 + 3 + 3 = 15$; $5 \times 3 = 15$]

**MAC Activity 215:
Basic-to-Average** ▼

MAC Activity 215

On Your Own   Pair and Share   In a Group

CAREER—PET SHOP OWNER ■ THE PET SHOP

Materials   counters or punchout counters

Discuss how a pet shop owner buys, sells, and cares for different kinds of pets. Encourage children to share experiences that they may have had at a pet shop.

Assign children to work in pairs and give each pair of children a set of counters. Tell children that you will read aloud problems about a pet shop. Explain that they are to work together using counters to solve the problems.

> Mr. Smith's pet shop has 5 large cages for cats.
> There are 2 cats in each cage.
> How many cats are in the cages?   [10]

> Parakeets share cages.
> There are 4 cages with 2 parakeets in each.
> How many parakeets are there?   [8]

Continue the activity with similar problems.

**MAC Activity 216:
Average-to-Challenge** ▶

NUMBER SENSE ■ TRIPLE PLAY

MAC Activity 216

On Your Own   Pair and Share   In a Group

Materials   index cards

Procedure   Make game cards using index cards. Draw two to four groups of two to three dots on each card as shown.

Assign children to play in pairs. Give each pair of children a deck of game cards. Tell children to mix the cards and place them facedown in a pile. Have Player A take the top card from the pile and turn it faceup. The child describes the dots in terms of group and number; for example, "I see 3 groups of 2 dots." Player B says the multiplication sentence for the dots: "3 x 2 = 6." If the sentence is correct, Player B gets one point and takes the next turn. If the sentence is incorrect, Player A gets one point and takes another turn.

To Win   The first player to score three points gets a "triple play" and wins the round.

RETEACHING

Name

MULTIPLYING 2 AND 3

RETEACHING-108

Study

3 groups, 2 in each group, 6 in all $3 \times 2 = 6$

4 groups, 3 in each group, 12 in all $4 \times 3 = 12$

Check

Complete.

1.
   2 groups, 2 in each group, __4__ in all   __2__ $\times 2 =$ __4__

2.
   2 groups, 3 in each group, __6__ in all   __2__ $\times 3 =$ __6__

3.
   4 groups, 2 in each group, __8__ in all   __4__ $\times 2 =$ __8__

4.
   3 groups, 3 in each group, __9__ in all   __3__ $\times 3 =$ __9__

Macmillan/McGraw-Hill, MATHEMATICS IN ACTION
Grade 2, Chapter 12, Lesson 2, pages 365–366   Reteaching-108

PRACTICE

Name

MULTIPLYING 2 AND 3

PRACTICE-108

Draw circles to show the groups.
Complete the multiplication sentence.

OO OO OO

1. 3 groups of 2   __3__ $\times 2 =$ __6__

ooo ooo ooo

2. 3 groups of 3   __3__ $\times 3 =$ __9__

oo oo oo oo

3. 4 groups of 2   __4__ $\times 2 =$ __8__

ooo ooo ooo ooo

4. 4 groups of 3   __4__ $\times 3 =$ __12__

oo oo oo oo oo

5. 5 groups of 2   __5__ $\times 2 =$ __10__

ooo ooo ooo ooo ooo

6. 5 groups of 3   __5__ $\times 3 =$ __15__

Macmillan/McGraw-Hill, MATHEMATICS IN ACTION
Grade 2, Chapter 12, Lesson 2, pages 365–366   Practice-108

ENRICHMENT

Name

MULTIPLYING 2 AND 3

ENRICHMENT-108

On Your Own   Pair and Share   In a Group

MULTIPLICATION JUMPS

You can multiply on a numberline.

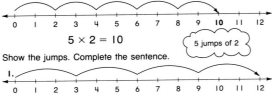

$5 \times 2 = 10$ 5 jumps of 2

Show the jumps. Complete the sentence.

1.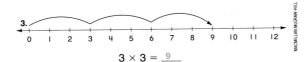

$4 \times 3 =$ __12__

2.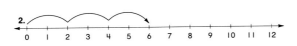

$3 \times 2 =$ __6__

3.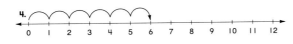

$3 \times 3 =$ __9__

4.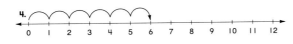

$6 \times 1 =$ __6__

Macmillan/McGraw-Hill, MATHEMATICS IN ACTION
Grade 2, Chapter 12, Lesson 2, pages 365–366   Enrichment-108

Problem of the Day

Jenny had a party. 4 children came. Jenny gave each child 3 prizes. How many prizes did Jenny give all together?   [12]

Name _____

Multiplying 4 and 5

How many groups of juice boxes? 2
How many juice boxes in each group? 4
How many juice boxes in all?

2 fours $2 \times 4 = 8$ product

There are 8 juice boxes in all.

Working Together
Use Workmat 5. Use 20 ▯ and a ⊗.
Spin to find how many groups of 4 to show.

Show	How many fours?	Multiplication Sentence
1. __2__ groups of 4	__2__ fours	__2__ × 4 = __8__
2. __1__ groups of 4 *(Possible answers:)*	__1__ fours	__1__ × 4 = __4__
3. __3__ groups of 4	__3__ fours	__3__ × 4 = __12__
4. __4__ groups of 4	__4__ fours	__4__ × 4 = __16__
5. __5__ groups of 4	__5__ fours	__5__ × 4 = __20__

6. Len bought 3 packs of juice.
   There are 4 juice boxes in
   each pack.
   How many juice boxes did he buy in all? __12__ juice boxes

Macmillan/McGraw-Hill

---

1 PREPARE
WARM-UP To review multiplying 2 and 3, write the following exercises on the chalkboard. Call on volunteers to read each multiplication sentence, describe it in terms of groups, and complete it.

$3 \times 2 =$ _____ [3 groups of 2; 6]
$2 \times 3 =$ _____ [2 groups of 3; 6]
$4 \times 3 =$ _____ [4 groups of 3; 12]
$2 \times 2 =$ _____ [2 groups of 2; 4]
$5 \times 2 =$ _____ [5 groups of 2; 10]

2 TEACH
MODELING Give 20 cubes to pairs of children. Tell them to arrange the cubes to show 5 groups of 4 connected cubes. Have children add to find out how many cubes there are in all. [20]

■ **Could you use multiplication to find out how many cubes there are in all? Why?** [Yes, because each group has the same number of cubes.]

Call on a volunteer to say the multiplication sentence for the cubes. [5 × 4 = 20] Write the sentence on the chalkboard. Point to the 20 and identify it as the **product.**

Repeat the activity having children use their cubes to make 4 groups of 5. Have them say the multiplication fact for these cubes.

PUPIL'S EDITION pp. 367-368

Page 367 Work through the problem at the top of the page with the children.

How many groups of 5? 3
How many fingers in all? 15
Say the multiplication sentence.
"Three times five equals fifteen."

Working Together

Use a .

Work with two partners.
Use 5 fingers to stand for a group of 5.

Spin. Then show	How many fives?	Multiplication Sentence
Possible answers: 1. __1__ groups of 5	__1__ fives	__1__ × 5 = __5__
2. __2__ groups of 5	__2__ fives	__2__ × 5 = __10__
3. __3__ groups of 5	__3__ fives	__3__ × 5 = __15__
4. __4__ groups of 5	__4__ fives	__4__ × 5 = __20__
5. __5__ groups of 5	__5__ fives	__5__ × 5 = __25__

···· *Calculator* ····

You can use your calculator to count by fives.

Press 0 ⊕ 5 ⊜ .
Write what the display shows.

Press ⊜ four more times.
Each time write what the display shows.
Try this activity with other numbers.

__5__ , __10__ , __15__ , __20__ , __25__

Extra Practice, page 372

ACTIVITY

ALTERNATIVE TEACHING STRATEGY

VISUAL/KINESTHETIC Call on eight children to stand in front of the classroom. Have them arrange themselves in 2 groups of 4. Write 2 × 4 = 8 on the chalkboard. Then have another child join each group of 4. Have a volunteer describe the groups. [2 groups of 5] Write 2 × 5 = 10 on the chalkboard. Repeat the activity with 3 groups of 4 and 3 groups of 5.

TEACHER to TEACHER

CALCULATOR TIP My children benefited from exploring skip counting patterns on a calculator. Many of them used skip counting as a strategy for finding the products of facts they did not know.

ACTIVITY

Common Error and Remediation

MATERIALS multiplication fact cards, number line (Teacher Aid 12)

Some children may not be able to find the product without counting all of the cubes. Work individually with each child, using multiplication fact cards and a number line. Have the child begin with the fact card 3 × 2. Discuss with the child that the second number shows how many there are in a group, or 3 groups of 2. Then have the child skip count by twos on the number line to find 3 twos or the number 6. Repeat with other facts.

WORKING TOGETHER Assign children to work in pairs. Give each pair 20 cubes and a five-part punchout spinner. Guide children through ex. 1.

Check for Understanding

■ **How many are in 3 groups of 4?** [12]

GUIDED PRACTICE ex. 2–6: For reteaching, use Common Error and Remediation or Alternative Strategy.

Page 368 Work through the example at the top of the page with the children.

WORKING TOGETHER Have children work in groups of three. Be sure each group has a spinner.

3 PRACTICE·APPLY **PRACTICE** ex. 1–5

CALCULATOR Check that the sequence of key strokes works with the children's calculators. Encourage children to explore other counting sequences, using the same procedure.

C L O S E Guide children to summarize the lesson:

■ **What is the multiplication sentence for 4 fives?** [4 × 5 = 20]

SPEAKING MATHEMATICALLY ▪ QUIZ WHIZ

MAC Activity 218

On Your Own   Pair and Share   In a Group

Materials   2 spinners for 1-5 (Teacher Aid 16)

Procedure   Assign children to play in groups. Give each group two spinners. Explain to children that they will take turns. Have the first child in each group spin each spinner. Tell the child to say a multiplication sentence for the two numbers. For example, if the numbers are 3 and 4, the multiplication sentence would be 3 x 4 = 12. Then the next player takes a turn. Players score one point for each correct sentence.

To Win   The player with the most points at the end of play wins the game.

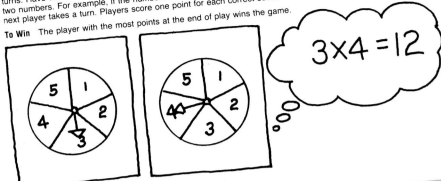

▲
MAC Activity 218:
Average-to-Challenge

NUMBER SENSE ▪ MATCH AND MULTIPLY

MAC Activity 217

On Your Own   Pair and Share   In a Group

Materials   index cards

Procedure   Prepare game cards for multiplication facts to 5 x 5 as shown.

Assign children to play in groups of three or four. Give each group a set of game cards. Tell children that they will play a version of the game "Concentration." Have each group place their cards facedown on the table in rows.

4×4	4 FOURS
3×5	3 FIVES
1×3	1 THREE

Have children take turns turning over two cards to find a match. If the cards match, the child must name the product. If the product is correct, the child keeps the cards and the next child takes a turn. The cards are returned to the rows if the product is incorrect or if the player does not make a match.

To Win   The player with the most cards at the end of play is the winner.

▲
MAC Activity 217:
Basic-to-Average

RETEACHING

Name

MULTIPLYING 4 AND 5

Study

2 × 4 = 8   3 × 5 = 15

(groups) (in each)   (groups) (in each)

Check

Complete.

1. 3 groups of 4   12   5. 2 groups of 5   10

2. 4 groups of 4   16   6. 4 groups of 5   20

3. 2 groups of 4   7. 3 groups of 5

    2 × 4 = 8   3 × 5 = 15

4. 5 groups of 4   8. 5 groups of 5

    5 × 4 = 20   5 × 5 = 25

Reteaching-109

MACMILLAN/McGRAW-HILL, MATHEMATICS IN ACTION
Grade 2, Chapter 12, Lesson 3, pages 367–368

PRACTICE

Name

MULTIPLYING 4 AND 5

Complete.

1. 3 groups of 4
    3 fours
    3 × 4 = 12

2. 4 groups of 5
    4 fives
    4 × 5 = 20

3. 2 groups of 4
    2 fours
    2 × 4 = 8

4. 3 groups of 5
    3 fives
    3 × 5 = 15

5. 5 groups of 4
    5 fours
    5 × 4 = 20

6. 5 groups of 5
    5 fives
    5 × 5 = 25

7. 4 groups of 4
    4 fours
    4 × 4 = 16

8. 2 groups of 5
    2 fives
    2 × 5 = 10

Practice-109

Macmillan/McGraw-Hill, MATHEMATICS IN ACTION
Grade 2, Chapter 12, Lesson 3, pages 367–368

ENRICHMENT

Name

MULTIPLYING 4 AND 5

On Your Own   Pair and Share   In a Group

HOW MANY?

Think about what you know.
Write a multiplication sentence to solve.

1. How many legs?
    3 × 4 = 12

2. How many eyes?
    5 × 2 = 10

3. How many tails?
    4 × 1 = 4

4. How many legs?
    5 × 4 = 20

5. How many wheels?
    3 × 3 = 9

6. How many fingers?
    4 × 5 = 20

Enrichment-109

Macmillan/McGraw-Hill, MATHEMATICS IN ACTION
Grade, 2, Chapter 12, Lesson 3, pages 367–368

Problem of the Day

Emily played a card game with Sam and Mark. She was the dealer. Emily gave each player 5 cards. How many cards were the players holding all together?   [15]

AT·A·GLANCE pp. 369-370

LESSON OBJECTIVES
Understand the order property of multiplication.
Use 0 and 1 as factors.

ASSIGNMENT GUIDE

COURSE	EXERCISES
Basic	p. 369: 3–9; p. 370: 2–5
Average	p. 369: 3–9; p. 370: 2–5
Challenge	p. 369: 3–9; p. 370: 2–5
Extra Practice, p. 372	Practice Plus, p. 384

MATERIALS
Classroom Materials paper cups
Manipulatives 5 ○ per child; 12 ■, 12 ■ (or red and blue
square counter punchouts) per pair; Workmat 6 per child

Teacher Resources
Reteaching 110   Practice 110   Enrichment 110
MAC Act. 219, 220   Teacher Aid 17
Math Anthology, pp. 196–197
Math Songs Cassette, Side 2, Selection 12

SKILLS TRACE
MULTIPLICATION & DIVISION FACTS

Explore (Concrete)	Develop/Understand (Transitional/Abstract)
364	365–366, 367–368, 369–370
Practice	**Apply**
372, 383, 384, 385–386, 389, 408	371, 373–374, 379–380, 381, 382, 388, 411

See **MANIPULATIVES PLUS 70–71,**
pp. 362J–362K.

Mathematics and Literature

1 PREPARE **WARM-UP** To review multiplication, play the song "Hop Up, My Ladies." Give each child some counters. Have them put "three in a row" every time they hear that phrase in the refrain, and say a multiplication sentence to fit the counters. [3 × 3 = 9] Repeat the activity for Verse 2. Explain that a horse carrying double means that 2 people can ride. Have children group 2 counters every time they hear the phrase, and say a multiplication sentence to fit the counters. [3 × 2 = 6]

2 TEACH **MODELING** Display 4 stacks of 2 cubes. Write 4 × 2 = 8 on the chalkboard. Display 2 stacks of 4 cubes. Call on a volunteer to write the multiplication fact, 2 × 4 = 8. Have children compare the two sentences.

■ **What is the same about these two multiplication sentences?** [They have the same numbers and product.]

Name _____

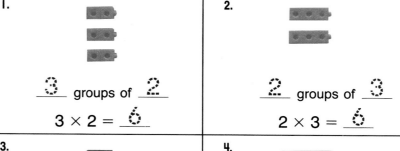

ACTIVITY

Informal Algebra: Multiplication Patterns

Use Workmat 6. Use 12 ▦ and 12 ▣.

Show the groups. Complete.

1.

_3_ groups of _2_

3 × 2 = _6_

2.

_2_ groups of _3_

2 × 3 = _6_

3.

_4_ groups of _2_

4 × 2 = _8_

4.

_2_ groups of _4_

2 × 4 = _8_

5. Did you see any patterns? Talk about them with a partner.
In their own words children should note the order property and that different arrays can show the same product.

Use cubes. Show	Complete.
6. 5 groups of 2	5 × 2 = _10_
7. 2 groups of 5	2 × 5 = _10_
8. 3 groups of 4	3 × 4 = _12_
9. 4 groups of 3	4 × 3 = _12_

Chapter 12   Explore Multiplication and Division Facts   three hundred sixty-nine   **369**

■ **What is different about the models?** [One shows 4 groups of 2 and the other shows 2 groups of 4.]

Guide children in understanding that changing the order of the numbers does not change the product, but the order of the numbers stands for two different groupings.

Have children show 3 counters in a row. Tell them that the multiplication fact for the display is 3 × 1 = 3 for 3 groups of 1. Repeat to show 4 groups of 1 and 5 groups of 1. Help children realize that when they multiply 1, the product is always the same as the other number.

Then draw 5 rings on the chalkboard. Tell children there are five groups but no counters.

■ **What number could you use to tell how many counters are in each group?** [0]

Working Together

Use 5 cups and 5 .
Each cup will hold a group of cubes.
Start with empty cups each time.

Number of Cups	Number of Cubes in Each Cup	How many groups?	How many cubes are in the cups?	Multiplication Sentence
1. 5	1	_5_ groups of 1	_5_	$5 \times 1 = $ _5_
5	0	_5_ groups of 0	_0_	$5 \times 0 = $ _0_
2. 4	1	_4_ groups of 1	_4_	$4 \times 1 = $ _4_
4	0	_4_ groups of 0	_0_	$4 \times 0 = $ _0_
3. 2	1	_2_ groups of 1	_2_	$2 \times 1 = $ _2_
2	0	_2_ groups of 0	_0_	$2 \times 0 = $ _0_
4. 3	1	_3_ groups of 1	_3_	$3 \times 1 = $ _3_
3	0	_3_ groups of 0	_0_	$3 \times 0 = $ _0_

5. Talk with a partner. What happens when you

The answer is always the number you are multiplying. | multiply by 1? | | multiply by 0? | The answer is always 0.

Extra Practice, page 372 *Practice Plus*, page 384

ALTERNATIVE TEACHING STRATEGY

VISUAL/KINESTHETIC Call on eight children to stand in front of the classroom. Have a volunteer arrange them into 2 groups of 4. Write $2 \times 4 = 8$ on the chalkboard. Then have the groups reassemble into a row of eight. Have a volunteer arrange them into 4 groups of 2. Write $4 \times 2 = 8$ on the chalkboard. Repeat the activity with 2 groups of 3 and 3 groups of 2; 5 groups of 1 and 1 group of 5.

ONGOING ASSESSMENT

OBSERVATION Determine whether children correctly complete the multiplication table on p. 370.

INTERVIEW Have the child explain each answer. **(1) What is 4×1? (2) Is 1×4 the same as 4×1? (3) What is 25×0?**

JOURNAL WRITING You may wish to have children record their responses in their math journals.

Common Error and Remediation

MATERIALS 12 ○ (or punchouts), Workmat 5

Some children may not understand order property. Work individually with each child. Have the child use counters and Workmat 5 to model pairs of multiplication exercises, such as 2×3 and 3×2. Have the child describe the models for each fact and compare the two products. The child should observe that reversing the order of the numbers in multiplication does not change the product, but the groupings in the facts are different.

Write $5 \times 0 = 0$ on the chalkboard. Explain that this shows 5 groups of 0.

PUPIL'S EDITION pp. 369-370

Page 369 Give each child Workmat 6 and 12 connecting cubes of each color. Guide children through ex. 1 and 2 and compare the two exercises.

Check for Understanding

■ Do 2 groups of 4 and 4 groups of 2 each equal 8? [Yes.]

GUIDED PRACTICE ex. 3–9: For reteaching, use Common Error and Remediation or Alternative Strategy.

Page 370 ■ **Working Together** Have children work in pairs and give each pair 5 paper cups and 5 cubes. Discuss the procedure for the activity and guide children through ex. 1.

PRACTICE·APPLY

PRACTICE ex. 2–5: Discuss children's answers to ex. 5.

CLOSE Guide children to summarize the lesson:

■ **What is the multiplication sentence for 4 groups of 1?** $[4 \times 1 = 4]$

■ **What is the multiplication sentence for 5 groups of 0?** $[5 \times 0 = 0]$

MAC Activity 219:
Basic-to-Average
▼

MAC Activity 219

On Your Own Pair and Share In a Group

MANIPULATIVES ▪ NUMBERS UP

Materials number cubes labeled 0-5 (Teacher Aid 17), connecting cubes

Provide pairs of children with two number cubes labeled 0-5 and a set of connecting cubes. Have one child roll the number cubes and identify the two numbers that come up. Tell the second child to model a multiplication fact based on the numbers and say the fact; for example, 3 x 4 = 12. Next have the first child model the related multiplication and say the fact, 4 x 3 = 12. Then have children reverse roles.

MAC Activity 220:
Average-to-Challenge ▶

CALCULATOR ▪ KEY IT!

MAC Activity 220

On Your Own Pair and Share In a Group

Materials multiplication fact cards for 2-5, calculators

Demonstrate how children can use a calculator to multiply. Then have them work in pairs with multiplication fact cards for 2, 3, 4, and 5 and a calculator. Have one child choose three cards and read the facts one at a time. Have the other child perform the multiplication on the calculator and give the products aloud. Tell the first child to check the card to see if the product is correct. Then have children reverse roles.

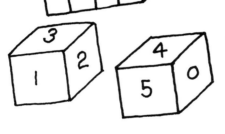

7224

4×5=20

4×4=16

3×4=12

RETEACHING-110

Name

MULTIPLICATION PATTERNS

Study

2 groups of 4
$2 \times 4 = 8$

4 groups of 2
$4 \times 2 = 8$

Check

Complete.

1.

4 groups of 3
$4 \times 3 = \underline{12}$

2. 3 groups of 4
$3 \times 4 = \underline{12}$

3. 3 groups of 2
$3 \times 2 = \underline{6}$

4. 2 groups of 3
$2 \times 3 = \underline{6}$

Match. Complete.

5. 2 groups of 1 $3 \times 1 = \underline{3}$

6. 4 groups of 0 $2 \times 1 = \underline{2}$

7. 3 groups of 1 $4 \times 0 = \underline{0}$

Macmillan/McGraw-Hill, MATHEMATICS IN ACTION
Grade 2, Chapter 12, Lesson 4, pages 369–370

Reteaching-110

PRACTICE-110

Name

MULTIPLICATION PATTERNS

Complete. Match products.

1. 4 groups of 3
$4 \times 3 = \underline{12}$

2. 2 groups of 3
$2 \times 3 = \underline{6}$

3. 2 groups of 5
$2 \times 5 = \underline{10}$

4. 3 groups of 4
$3 \times 4 = \underline{12}$

5. 3 groups of 2
$3 \times 2 = \underline{6}$

6. 4 groups of 5
$4 \times 5 = \underline{20}$

7. 5 groups of 4
$5 \times 4 = \underline{20}$

8. 5 groups of 2
$5 \times 2 = \underline{10}$

Match. Complete.

9. 4 groups of 1 $5 \times 0 = \underline{0}$

10. 3 groups of 0 $2 \times 1 = \underline{2}$

11. 5 groups of 0 $3 \times 0 = \underline{0}$

12. 2 groups of 1 $4 \times 1 = \underline{4}$

Macmillan/McGraw-Hill, MATHEMATICS IN ACTION
Grade 2, Chapter 12, Lesson 4, pages 369–370

Practice-110

ENRICHMENT-110

Name

MULTIPLICATION PATTERNS

On Your Own   Pair and Share   In a Group

MULTIPLICATION TABLE
Multiply to complete the table.

×	0	1	2	3	4	5
0	0	0	0	0	0	0
1	0	1	2^A	3	4	5°
2	0	2	4	6	8	10
3	0	3	6	9	12^W	15
4	0	4	8	12	16	20
5	0	5	10	15	20	25

$2 \times 5 = 10$

$3 \times 0 = 0$

Find the letters to match the numbers.

What kind of bow do you see in the sky?

A	R	A	I	N	B	O	W
2	4	20	0	15	6	5	12

Macmillan/McGraw-Hill, MATHEMATICS IN ACTION
Grade 2, Chapter 12, Lesson 4, pages 369–370

Enrichment-110

Problem of the Day

Felix bought 4 lizards and 1 tank in the pet shop. Then Felix decided that it would be better if he put the lizards in separate tanks. How many more tanks did Felix need? [3; possible solution: $4 \times 1 = 4$; $4 - 1 = 3$]

AT·A·GLANCE p. 371

LESSON OBJECTIVE
Make a table.

ASSIGNMENT GUIDE

COURSE	EXERCISES
Basic	p. 371: All
Average	p. 371: All
Challenge	p. 371: All

MATERIALS
Classroom Materials sheets of paper
Manipulatives 25 ◯ (or punchouts) per child

Teacher Resources
Crit. Think. 23

PROBLEM SOLVING
THINKING MATHEMATICA

Name _____

SEW IT UP

Each pair of pants has 3 patches. How many patches would 7 pairs of pants have? Use a sheet of paper to show each pair of pants. Use a ◯ to show each patch.

Complete the table.

Number of Pants	1	2	3	4	5	6	7
Number of Patches	3	6	9	12	15	18	21

Design a shirt. Use ◯ to show buttons. How many buttons will you need to make 2 shirts? To make 10 shirts? Make a table to show the answer.
Answers will vary.

Macmillan/McGraw-Hill

371

---

1 PLAN

AIMS AND ATTITUDES This lesson develops number sense by having children complete a table involving patterns in multiplication.

Encourage children to talk about the strategies they used to complete the table. Some children will need to use their counters to complete the table, but others will be able to identify a pattern in the numbers quickly and complete the table without using counters. Some children may even suggest the use of a calculator. By discussing the strategies they used, children will gain confidence in problem solving and learn that there are often several methods to solve a problem.

MANAGEMENT The activity is intended for all children and has been designed for independent work. It is appropriate for pairs of children as well. When pairing children, it may be particularly effective to pair a child having strong problem-solving skills with one having weaker skills.

2 GUIDE

Distribute 25 counters to each child. Have children arrange their counters in 5 rows of 5 counters each.
- **How many counters are in each row?** [5 counters]
- **How many rows of counters are there?** [5 rows]
- **What multiplication fact tells about this?** [5 × 5 = 25]

Repeat the activity by having children arrange their counters in other groups to review multiplication facts to 25.

For Students Acquiring English (SAE)

Pair SAE and non-SAE children to design a shirt together. Provide real buttons, scissors, and a large piece of construction paper. Direct children to draw a shirt, cut it out, and tape buttons on it. Help pairs decide the number of buttons to put on the shirt. Then direct each pair to make a table about its shirt. Circulate to help pairs set up the tables. Have pairs display the completed tables and shirts together and present them to the class.

Read along with children the directions on page 371. Point out that there are 3 patches on each pair of pants. Make certain that children understand the directions by asking the following questions:

■ **How can you show the patches on 1 pair of pants?** [Show 3 counters on 1 sheet of paper. Children may find it helpful to draw a pair of pants on the paper.]

■ **What can you do to find out how many patches are on 2 pairs of pants?** [Show 3 counters on each of 2 sheets of paper.]

Distribute paper to each child and have children complete the table to record the work that they do with counters.

When children have completed their tables, ask volunteers to describe the method they used to complete the table. Then turn to a discussion about the patterns in the table.

■ **What pattern did you see for the pants and patches?** [As the number of pants increased by 1, the number of patches increased by 3.]

■ **What multiplication facts tell about this?** [1×3, 2×3, 3×3, . . .]

Finally, have children design their own shirts using sheets of paper for the shirt and counters to show the buttons. Remind children to make a table to show their answers. Then ask volunteers to talk about their shirts and how they got the numbers they did.

3 EXTEND Have children repeat the activity of designing a shirt. This time, ask them to use a different method to find the number of buttons on 2 shirts and 10 shirts. Have them discuss the results.

CHAPTER 12

EXTRA PRACTICE

Extra Practice items are provided so that children may have an opportunity for further practice.

The *Additional Practice* section also provides practice you may wish to assign.

EXTRA PRACTICE

Extra Practice

Multiplying Facts to 5, pages 367–368 . . . .

Multiply.

1.

$4 \times 2 = \underline{8}$

2.

$2 \times 3 = \underline{6}$

3.

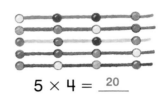

$5 \times 4 = \underline{20}$

4.

$1 \times 5 = \underline{5}$

Multiplication Patterns, pages 369–370 . . . .

Complete.

1. $\underline{2}$ groups

of $\underline{3}$

$2 \times 3 = \underline{6}$

 $\underline{3}$ groups

of $\underline{2}$

$3 \times 2 = \underline{6}$

2.

3 groups of 1

$3 \times 1 = \underline{3}$

3 groups of 0

$3 \times 0 = \underline{0}$

372   three hundred seventy-two

ADDITIONAL PRACTICE

p. 367   *Complete.*

1. $5 \times 3 = \underline{[15]}$ 2. $4 \times 4 = \underline{[16]}$ 7. $1 \times 5 = \underline{[5]}$ 8. $4 \times 3 = \underline{[12]}$

3. $3 \times 3 = \underline{[9]}$ 4. $5 \times 2 = \underline{[10]}$ 9. $3 \times 5 = \underline{[15]}$ 10. $3 \times 2 = \underline{[6]}$

5. $2 \times 4 = \underline{[8]}$ 6. $1 \times 4 = \underline{[4]}$ 11. $4 \times 5 = \underline{[20]}$ 12. $3 \times 1 = \underline{[3]}$

p. 369 *Use cubes. Show and complete.*

1. 5 groups of 2 $5 \times 2 = \underline{[10]}$

2. 2 groups of 5 $2 \times 5 = \underline{[10]}$

3. 4 groups of 3 $4 \times 3 = \underline{[12]}$

4. 3 groups of 4 $3 \times 4 = \underline{[12]}$

5. 1 group of 5 $1 \times 5 = \underline{[5]}$

6. 5 groups of 0 $5 \times 0 = \underline{[5]}$

7. 2 groups of 3 $2 \times 3 = \underline{[6]}$

8. 3 groups of 2 $3 \times 2 = \underline{[6]}$

9. 4 groups of 1 $4 \times 1 = \underline{[4]}$

10. 0 groups of 3 $0 \times 3 = \underline{[0]}$

AT·A·GLANCE pp. 373-374

LESSON OBJECTIVE
Use a guess-and-test strategy to solve problems.

ASSIGNMENT GUIDE

COURSE	EXERCISES
Basic	p. 373: 1; p. 374: 1–4
Average	p. 373: 1; p. 374: 1–4
Challenge	p. 373: 1; p. 374: 1–4

MATERIALS
Calculator per pair
Classroom Materials classroom objects with price tags

Teacher Resources
Reteaching 111   Practice 111   Enrichment 111
Prob. Solv. 57   MAC Act. 221, 222
Computer Software *Mathematics Skills:* Disk 13 Act. 1

Name _____

Problem Solving

UNDERSTAND
✓ PLAN
✓ TRY
✓ CHECK
✓ EXTEND

Strategy: Guess and Test

Linda is going to the farmers' market.
She has 53¢.
She wants to buy one fruit and one vegetable.
Which two can she buy?

Fruits	Vegetables
Melon 28¢	Artichoke 34¢
Peach 26¢	Squash 27¢

Make a guess. Then test it.

Use your  to help.

Press 28 ⊞ 34 ⊟ __62__   (62¢ – Too large)

Press 28 ⊞ 27 ⊟ __55__   (55¢ – Too large)

Press 26 ⊞ 27 ⊟ __53__   (53¢ – Correct)

Suppose your first guess was too large.
How should you choose your next guess?
Possible answer: I can choose smaller numbers to add.

| Onion 18¢ | Melon 29¢ | Cabbage 38¢ |

Make a guess. Then test it. You may use a ▢ to help.

1. Nell spent 47¢.
   She bought two items.
   How much did each one cost?

   __18__ ¢ and __29__ ¢

---

1 PREPARE

WARM-UP To prepare children for using a guess-and-test strategy to solve problems, have them give the following sums.

34¢ + 17¢ [51¢]   28¢ + 29¢ [57¢]   39¢ + 52¢ [91¢]
46¢ + 36¢ [82¢]   15¢ + 14¢ [29¢]

2 TEACH

DISCUSSING Prepare classroom objects with price tags and display the objects on a table. Put a 37¢ tag on a book, a 34¢ tag on a box of crayons, a 23¢ tag on a pencil, and a 29¢ tag on a ruler.

Assign children to work in pairs. Explain to them that you will read a problem aloud and they should use the prices to solve the problem.

Lori spent 63¢. She bought two items. How much was each item?

- **What do you know?** [Lori spent 63¢ on two items.]
- **What do you need to find out?** [the cost of each item]
- **What do you need to do?** [Find two prices that add up to 63¢.]

Tell children that if they add two prices and the answer is larger or smaller than 63¢, they should select two more prices and test them.

- **How much did each item cost?** [34¢ and 29¢]
- **Which two items did Lori buy?** [a box of crayons and a ruler]

PUPIL'S EDITION pp. 373-374

Page 373 Have a volunteer read the problem at the top of the page.

- **What do you know?** [Linda has 53¢. She wants to buy 1 fruit and 1 vegetable.]
- **What do you need to find out?** [which two items Linda can buy]

Make a guess. Then test it. You may use a  to help.

1. Dale spent 55¢.
   Which two items did he buy?

   _____cabbage_____ and _____tomato_____

2. Taki bought two vegetables.
   He spent 65¢.
   How much did each vegetable cost?

   __36__ ¢ and __29__ ¢

3. Jon spent 80¢.
   Which two items did he buy?

   _____corn_____ and _____squash_____

4. Marilyn bought three
   different vegetables.
   She spent 71¢.
   How much did each one cost?

   __14__ ¢, __19__ ¢, and __38__ ¢

For Students Acquiring English (SAE)

Use picture cards of fruits and vegetables to make a store in your classroom. Give each heterogeneous group of four a different amount of money to spend. Have groups decide on which vegetable and fruit they would like to buy with their money.

TEACHER to TEACHER

 **CALCULATOR TIP** My children enjoy working in pairs to use the calculator. One child selects the numbers to solve the problem and the other child tests them on a calculator.

TEACHER to TEACHER

COOPERATIVE LEARNING TIP I find problem solving is enhanced by having pairs of children answer questions posed to the class. Each partner thinks silently about his or her response for a moment, then each takes turns telling the other his or her thoughts on the question. After both partners have done this, I quiet the class and have one partner tell in his or her own words the ideas of the other partner. In this way, alternative perspectives are respected. Occasionally partners **come to a consensus** on the answer to the question.

Distribute a calculator to each pair. Discuss that using a calculator is another method to help solve this problem. Work through the steps of the calculator example with the children.

■ **Does your answer make sense?** [Yes; 1 fruit is 26¢ and 1 vegetable is 27¢; 26¢ + 27¢ = 53¢.]

Check for Understanding

■ **What if Linda spent 60¢? Which two items did she buy?** [peach, artichoke]

GUIDED PRACTICE ex. 1: Work through problem 1 with the children. Make sure they understand how to solve the problem using a guess-and-test strategy. Encourage them to choose a method, such as paper and pencil or a calculator, to help solve it.

Page 374 Have a volunteer read the directions at the top of the page. Discuss the pictures and help children identify the names of the vegetables.

PRACTICE·APPLY   PRACTICE   ex. 1–4

CLOSE Guide children to summarize the lesson:

■ **How do you know when you should guess and test to solve a problem?** [Possible response: With more than two number choices for solving a problem, you guess which ones are correct. You test them to see if you have the correct answer.]

MAC Activity 222

SPEAKING MATHEMATICALLY ■ COSTLY WORDS

On Your Own   Pair and Share   In a Group

Materials index cards, calculators

Setup Write the alphabet on the board. Write a price from 10¢ to 35¢ under each letter. Then write several two- and three-letter words on index cards. Select words that use as many letters in the alphabet as possible, such as wow, box, red, pin, add, fin, to, two, so, at, yes, and zip. Write the value of each word on the back of the card.

Procedure Separate the class into two teams. Give each team a calculator. Hold up two words at a time and ask such questions as "Which word is worth more?", "Which word is worth less?", or "Nan spent 78¢. Which word did she buy?" Explain to children that each team will look at the value of the letters in each word, then make a guess. The teams will check their guess on their calculators. If neither team is right, both teams get another guess. If one team is right, they earn one point.

To Win After several rounds of play, the team with the most points wins.

A B C D E F G H I J K L M N O P Q R S T
14¢ 23¢ 18¢ 27¢ 10¢ 28¢ 16¢ 21¢ 33¢ 24¢ 11¢ 30¢ 17¢ 35¢ 31¢ 26¢ 13¢ 20¢ 15¢ 22¢

U V W X Y Z
34¢ 12¢ 29¢ 19¢ 32¢ 25¢

▲
MAC Activity 222:
Average-to-Challenge

MATH AND CONSUMERS ■ MONEY STRETCHERS

MAC Activity 221

On Your Own   Pair and Share   In a Group

Materials newspapers or catalogs, punchout coins, scissors, black marker

Have children work in pairs. Give each pair a newspaper or catalog, a pair of scissors, and a marker. Have them cut out three pictures of objects that they would like. Then have them write a price for each item from 11¢ to 75¢.

Collect the pictures and then redistribute 3 pictures to each pair of children. Also give each pair a set of coins for a different amount from 55¢ to 75¢. Tell children to choose the pictures of items that they could buy for the amount of money they have. Tell children to spend as much of their money as they can.

When children have made their selections, call on each pair to show and tell what they have bought.

▲
MAC Activity 221:
Basic-to-Average

RETEACHING

Name _____

RETEACHING-111

PROBLEM SOLVING STRATEGY: GUESS AND TEST

Study

Sam spent 66¢.
He bought 1 juice and 1 muffin.
Which two did he buy?
Guess 1 juice and 1 muffin.

Juice	Muffins
apple—24¢	bran—27¢
orange—37¢	corn—29¢

Test the prices.
Try again if your answer
is more or less than 66¢.

Guess	**Guess**
24¢ apple	37¢ orange
+ 27¢ bran	+ 29¢ corn
51¢	66¢
(too small)	(correct)

Check

Solve. Make a guess. Then test it.
Ring your answer.

1. Mike bought two fruits.
   He spent 53¢.
   How much did each fruit cost?
   (34¢ and 19¢)   26¢ and 19¢

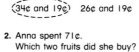

apple—34¢   Pear—26¢

banana—45¢   Plum—19¢

2. Anna spent 71¢.
   Which two fruits did she buy?
   apple, plum   (banana, pear)

4. Corey bought three
   different fruits.
   He spent 79¢.
   How much did each
   fruit cost?
   (26¢, 19¢, 34¢)
   45¢, 19¢, 26¢

3. Morgan has 59¢.
   Which fruits can he buy?
   (plum, pear) or (apple, plum)

Reteaching-111

Macmillan/McGraw-Hill, MATHEMATICS IN ACTION
Grade 2, Chapter 12, Lesson 6, pages 373–374

PRACTICE

Name _____

PRACTICE-111

PROBLEM SOLVING STRATEGY: GUESS AND TEST

Solve. Make a guess. Then test it.

 Socks—24¢   mittens—38¢   hat—27¢

1. Arthur bought two items.
   He spent 65¢.
   How much did each item cost?
   38 ¢ and 27 ¢

2. Paula spent 51¢.
   Which two items did she buy?
   socks and hat

 cap 26¢   belt 42¢   name pin 17¢   wristband 14¢

3. Ivan spent 43¢.
   Which two items did he buy?
   cap and pin

4. Ruth bought three
   different items.
   She spent 82¢.
   How much did each one cost?
   42 ¢, 26 ¢, and 14 ¢

Practice-111

Macmillan/McGraw-Hill, MATHEMATICS IN ACTION
Grade 2, Chapter 12, Lesson 6, pages 373–374

ENRICHMENT

Name _____

ENRICHMENT-111

PROBLEM SOLVING

On Your Own   Pair and Share   In a Group

WHAT'S IN THE BAG?
Each person has two or three items in a shopping bag.
Guess and test.
Then solve.

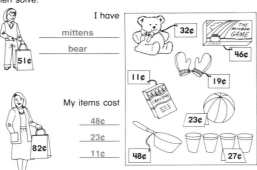

I have
mittens
bear
51¢

32¢   46¢   11¢   19¢

My items cost
48¢
23¢
11¢
82¢

23¢   48¢   27¢

I have
games
cups
crayons
84¢

My items cost
23¢
48¢
71¢

Enrichment-111

Macmillan/McGraw-Hill, MATHEMATICS IN ACTION
Grade 2, Chapter 12, Lesson 6, pages 373–374

Problem of the Day

Taki bought two vegetables for 20¢. One
vegetable cost 2¢ more than the other vegetable.
How much did each vegetable cost?   [9¢ and
11¢]

AT·A·GLANCE pp. 375-376

LESSON OBJECTIVE
Understand the concept of division.

ASSIGNMENT GUIDE

COURSE	EXERCISES
Basic	p. 375: 1–6; p. 376: 2–9
Average	p. 375: 1–6; p. 376: 2–9
Challenge	p. 375: 1–6; p. 376: 2–9
Extra Practice, p. 383	

MATERIALS

Classroom Materials books
Manipulatives 16 ○ (or punchouts), Workmat 5 per pair

Teacher Resources
Reteaching 112   Practice 112   Enrichment 112
Prob. Solv. 58   MAC Act. 223, 224

SKILLS TRACE
MULTIPLICATION & DIVISION FACTS

Explore (Concrete) 364	Develop/Understand (Transitional/Abstract) 375–376, 377–378
Practice 372, 383, 384, 385–386, 389, 408	Apply 371, 373–374, 379–380, 381, 382, 388, 411

See **MANIPULATIVES PLUS 72**, p. 362L.

Division: How Many Groups?

There are 6 nuts in all.
There are 2 nuts in each shell.
How many groups of 2?

Working Together
Use Workmat 5 and 10 ○.

There are 3 groups of 2.

Take	Put them in	How many groups?
1. 10 counters	groups of 2	5 groups of 2
2. 8 counters	groups of 2	4 groups of 2
3. 6 counters	groups of 2	3 groups of 2
4. 4 counters	groups of 2	2 groups of 2

5. Karen had 8 nuts.
   She put 2 nuts on each muffin.
   How many nut muffins
   did she make?

   __4__ nut muffins

6. What if Karen had 9 nuts?
   How many nut muffins
   could she make?

   __4__ nut muffins

   How many nuts would be left?

   __1__ nut

PREPARE
WARM-UP To review multiplication, write the following number descriptions on the chalkboard. Have children say a multiplication fact for each.

1 group of 4	[1 × 4 = 4]
3 groups of 2	[3 × 2 = 6]
5 groups of 0	[5 × 0 = 0]
5 groups of 5	[5 × 5 = 25]

2 TEACH
MODELING Display 4 groups of 2 books each. Have children use counters to show 4 groups of 2.

■ **How many groups of books are there?** [4]

■ **How many books in each group?** [2]

■ **How many books in all?** [8]

■ **What operation did you use to find how many in all?** [multiplication]

Remind children that when they have equal-sized groups and they want to find out how many in all, they should multiply.

Next combine the 8 books and place them in a stack. Have children do the same with their counters. Then have children **divide** the counters into groups of 2.

■ **How many groups of 2 are in 8?** [4]

Have children work in pairs to discover how many equal groups of 2 there are in 10 and 12. [5, 6]

Use Workmat 5 and 16 .

	Take	Put them in	How many groups?
1.	12 counters	groups of 3	__4__ groups of 3
2.	8 counters	groups of 4	__2__ groups of 4
3.	15 counters	groups of 3	__5__ groups of 3
4.	16 counters	groups of 4	__4__ groups of 4

5. There are 6 bread slices.
It takes a group of 3 bread slices
to make a sandwich.
How many sandwiches can be made?

__2__ sandwiches

6. There are 12 tomatoes.
It takes a group of 4 tomatoes
to make a pack.
How many packs can be made?

__3__ packs

Mixed Review

Ring the fraction for the shaded part.

7.

$\left(\dfrac{1}{2}\right)$ $\dfrac{1}{3}$

8.

$\dfrac{1}{4}$ $\left(\dfrac{2}{4}\right)$

9.

$\left(\dfrac{2}{3}\right)$ $\dfrac{2}{4}$

Extra Practice, page 383

MEETING INDIVIDUAL NEEDS

Activity
Common Error and Remediation

MATERIALS 12

Some children may not understand the concept of equal groups.
Work individually with each child, using connecting cubes. Have
the child build a train of 8 cubes. Then ask him or her to divide
the cube train into groups of 2. After the child has done this, ask
him or her to tell how many groups of 2 there are in 8. [4]
Repeat the activity by having the child find the number of groups
of 2 and then 3 in a train made of 12 cubes.

For Students Acquiring English (SAE)

Read the story problems aloud to assist SAE students. Allow
children to use counters or other manipulatives as they complete
all the exercises on pages 375 and 376.

Activity
ALTERNATIVE TEACHING STRATEGY

MATERIALS blank overhead transparency, marker; 12 ○ or
Manipulatives Kit Transparency 7

VISUAL Display 9 counters on an overhead transparency. Tell
children that you want to divide the counters into groups of 3.
Draw a ring around each group of 3. Have a volunteer tell how
many groups of 3 there are in 9. [3] Repeat the activity with 10
counters and groups of 2 and of 5; 12 counters and groups of 2,
6, 3, and 4.

PUPIL'S EDITION pp. 375-376

Page 375   Guide children through the example at the top of the page.

Check for Understanding

■ **How many groups of 2 can you make with 8 counters?** [4
groups of 2]

WORKING TOGETHER   Assign children to work in pairs. Give each
pair ten counters and Workmat 5.

GUIDED PRACTICE   ex. 1–6: For reteaching, use Common Error
and Remediation or Alternative Strategy.

Page 376   Have children continue to work in pairs. Be sure each pair
has 16 counters and Workmat 5. Work through ex. 1 with the children.

PRACTICE•APPLY
PRACTICE   ex. 2–9: Have ex. 5 and
6 read aloud.

CLOSE   Guide children to summarize the lesson:

■ **How many groups of 2 can you make with 10 counters?** [5
groups of 2]

MAC ACTIVITY CENTER

MAC Activity 223:
Basic-to-Average
▼

MATH AND CONSUMER ■ *AT THE TOY STORE*

MAC Activity 223

On Your Own   Pair and Share   In a Group

Materials   punchout pennies

Have children work in pairs. Give each pair 15 punchout pennies. Write the following problems on the chalkboard.

1. A toy car costs 5¢. How many toy cars can you buy with 15¢?   [3]
2. A sticker costs 3¢. How many stickers can you buy with 9¢?   [3]
3. A pencil costs 4¢. How many pencils can you buy with 16¢?   [4]

Read the problems with the children. Then have them solve the problems, using the pennies as models. Continue the activity by having children take turns making up word problems for their partners to solve.

MAC Activity 224:
Average-to-Challenge
▼

NUMBER SENSE ■ *TRUE OR FALSE?*

MAC Activity 224

On Your Own   Pair and Share   In a Group

TRUE?   FALSE?

Write the following exercises on the chalkboard. Have children copy the statements. Then explain that they are to decide whether each statement is true or false and ring the answer. After children have completed the exercises, have them discuss their answers.

There are more than 3 threes in 6.   True False   [F]
There are more than 5 twos in 15.   True False   [T]
There are less than 4 threes in 12.   True False   [F]
There are less than 2 sixes in 10.   True False   [T]
There are more than 3 fives in 20.   True False   [T]

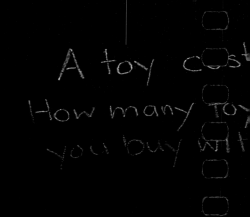

Name _____

DIVISION: HOW MANY GROUPS?

RETEACHING-112

Study

 I have 6 blocks.

 I put the 6 blocks in 2 groups of 3.

Check

Complete.   How many groups?

1. 4 blocks. Make groups of 2.   __2__ groups of 2

2. 6 blocks. Make groups of 2.   __3__ groups of 2

3. 9 blocks. Make groups of 3.   __3__ groups of 3

4. 8 blocks. Make groups of 4.   __2__ groups of 4

Macmillan/McGraw-Hill, MATHEMATICS IN ACTION
Grade 2, Chapter 12, Lesson 7, pages 375–376   Reteaching-112

MACMILLAN/McGRAW-HILL

Name _____

DIVISION: HOW MANY GROUPS?

PRACTICE-112

Make groups.

1.

   How many groups of 3 in 12?   _____ groups

2.

   How many groups of 5 in 10?   __2__ groups

3.

   How many groups of 4 in 20?   __5__ groups

4. How many groups of 2 in 8?   __4__ groups

5. How many groups of 3 in 9?   __3__ groups

6. How many groups of 4 in 16?   __4__ groups

Macmillan/McGraw-Hill, MATHEMATICS IN ACTION
Grade 2, Chapter 12, Lesson 7, pages 375–376   Practice-112

MACMILLAN/McGRAW-HILL

Name _____

DIVISION: HOW MANY GROUPS?

ENRICHMENT-112

On Your Own   Pair and Share   In a Group

PRODUCE FOR SALE

The children grew fruits and vegetables to sell at the school fair. They are putting them into boxes and bags.

Work with a partner to solve.

1. John has 12 carrots. He puts the carrots in bags of 4. How many bags of carrots does he have?   __3__ bags

2. Lucy has 15 tomatoes. She puts the tomatoes in boxes of 5. How many boxes of tomatoes does she have?   __3__ boxes

3. Carol grew 25 big potatoes. She can fit 3 potatoes in a bag. How many bags can she fill?   __8__ bags

   How many potatoes would be left?   __1__ potatoes

4. Ted grew 30 onions. He puts the onions in bags of 4. How many bags does he need?   __8__ bags

   Will all the bags have 4 onions?   __no__

5. Lee picked 30 strawberries. She puts them in boxes of 10. How many boxes does she need?   __3__ boxes

Macmillan/McGraw-Hill, MATHEMATICS IN ACTION
Grade 2, Chapter 12, Lesson 7, pages 375–376   Enrichment-112

MACMILLAN/McGRAW-HILL

Problem of the Day

Mavis has 8 straws and 5 glasses of juice. If she puts 2 straws in each glass, how many glasses will have straws?   [4]

AT·A·GLANCE pp. 377-378

LESSON OBJECTIVE
Understand the concept of division.

ASSIGNMENT GUIDE

COURSE	EXERCISES
Basic	p. 377: 1–6; p. 378: 1–8
Average	p. 377: 1–6; p. 378: 1–8
Challenge	p. 377: 1–6; p. 378: 1–8
Extra Practice, p. 383	Practice Plus, p. 384

MATERIALS
Manipulatives 25 ○ per child; 20 ▢ (or punchout squares), Workmat 5 per pair

Teacher Resources
Reteaching 113   Practice 113   Enrichment 113
MAC Act. 225, 226

SKILLS TRACE
MULTIPLICATION & DIVISION FACTS

Explore (Concrete) 364	Develop/Understand (Transitional/Abstract) 375–376, 377–378
Practice 372, 383, 384, 385–386, 389, 408	Apply 371, 373–374, 379–380, 381, 382, 388, 411

Name _____

Division: How Many in Each Group?

Each team must have the same number of children.

There are 20 children in all. Mrs. Lee wants to form them into 5 teams. How many children should she put on each team?

➤ Talk about different ways to find the answer. Answers will vary.

There are 5 groups of __4__ in 20.

Complete. Use counters to help.

Remember that each team must have the same number of players.

	Number of Players	Number of Teams	How many on each team?
1.	15	5	3
2.	20	4	5
3.	25	5	5
4.	16	4	4
5.	9	3	3

6. There are 10 players in the gym. They form 2 equal teams. How many players are on each team? __5__ players

Macmillan/McGraw-Hill

---

1 PREPARE

WARM-UP To review the concept of dividing to find how many groups, have children answer these questions.

How many groups of 3 in 6?   [2]
How many groups of 2 in 12?   [6]
How many groups of 4 in 8?   [2]
How many groups of 5 in 10?   [2]

2 TEACH

DISCUSSING Call on 15 children to come to the front of the room and have them form 3 equal groups.

■ **How many children are there in each group?** [5]

Point out that there are 3 groups of 5. Next have the same children form groups of 3. Point out that now there are 5 groups of 3 in the 15.

Repeat the activity by having 12 other children come to the front of the room. Have them form 4 equal groups. Call on a volunteer to tell how many children there are in each group. [3] Then have the same volunteer form 3 equal groups.

■ **How many children are there in each group?** [4]

PUPIL'S EDITION pp. 377-378

Page 377 Guide children through the example. Discuss the strategies children used to find the answer.

Working Together

We have 12 cubes in all.

We need to show 3 groups.

Remember that each group must have the same number of cubes.

We need to put them into 4 groups.

Use Workmat 5 and 20 🗔 to help complete the table.

	How many in all?	Number of Groups	Number of Cubes in Each Group
1.	12	4	3
2.	12	3	4
3.	8	2	4
4.	8	4	2
5.	10	2	5
6.	10	5	2
7.	20	4	5
8.	20	5	4

Extra Practice, page 383 *Practice Plus,* page 384

MEETING INDIVIDUAL NEEDS

ACTIVITY

Common Error and Remediation

MATERIALS 20 🗔; paper cups

Some children may confuse the number of groups with the number in each group. Give a child 12 cubes and 4 cups. Have the child put one cube at a time into each cup. Then have the child identify the cups as groups and tell how many there are. Have him or her count the cubes in a cup and tell how many in each group. Repeat with other combinations.

ACTIVITY

ALTERNATIVE TEACHING STRATEGY

MATERIALS chart paper, red and green crayons

Draw 10 squares in a row on chart paper. Have a child color 5 squares with a red crayon. Have another child color the remaining 5 squares with a green crayon. Draw a ring around each of the 2 groups. Ask how many groups there are and how many squares in each group. [2; 5] Repeat the activity to develop 5 groups of 2, 4 groups of 3, and 3 groups of 4.

ONGOING ASSESSMENT

OBSERVATION Determine whether children correctly complete the division table on p. 378.

INTERVIEW (1) If you have 8 toys and put them into 4 equal groups, how many toys will be in each group? (2) You want to put 15 chairs in 3 rows so that each row has the same number of chairs. How would you do it?

JOURNAL WRITING You may wish to have children record their responses in their math journals.

Check for Understanding

■ How many players should be on each team if there are 20 children and 4 teams? [5]

GUIDED PRACTICE ex. 1–6: For reteaching, use Common Error and Remediation or Alternative Strategy.

Page 378 Discuss the example at the top of the page with the children.

WORKING TOGETHER Assign children to work in pairs. Give each pair 20 cubes and Workmat 5.

3 PRACTICE·APPLY

PRACTICE ex. 1–8

C L O S E Guide children to summarize the lesson:

■ **What are two ways you can group 20 cubes into equal groups?**
[Possible responses: 5 groups of 4, 4 groups of 5, 2 groups of 10, 10 groups of 2]

MAC Activity 226

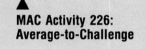

MENTAL MATH ■ TEAMS!

Materials number cards for 4-25 (numbers divisible by 2, 3, 4, 5)

Procedure Assign children to two teams and have them stand in lines facing each other. Hold up a number card from 4 to 25; for example, the number 6. Have the first player from Team A tell how many equal teams of children can be formed if there are 6 children in all. [2 groups of 3 or 3 groups of 2] If the answer is correct, Team A scores one point and the player moves to the end of the line. Then give the first player from Team B the opportunity to give another answer for the number 6. If the answer is correct, Team B scores one point and the player moves to the end of the line. If a team gives an incorrect answer, no point is scored.

Continue to provide numbers one at a time. The team that scores the most points at the end of play wins the game.

▲
MAC Activity 226:
Average-to-Challenge

MATH AND SOCIAL STUDIES ■ CLEAN-UP TIME

MAC Activity 225

Discuss with children some of the ways that they could make their community cleaner or more attractive. Possible areas of discussion include clean-up projects in neglected areas, planting flowers around trees, in public spaces, or empty lots, and raising money to buy more public litter baskets for areas where they are needed. Have children work in pairs and decide on four or five jobs that 20 children, working in equal groups, could do to carry out a community improvement project. Tell children to explain each job, how the children would be grouped, and how many children would be in each group.

▲
MAC Activity 225:
Basic-to-Average

RETEACHING-113

Name

DIVISION: HOW MANY IN EACH GROUP?

Study

I have 10 beads.

I made 2 groups. There are 5 beads in each group.

Check

Trace. Complete

Number in each group.

1. 12 in all. Make 2 groups.   6

2. 16 in all. Make 4 groups.   4

3. 15 in all. Make 3 groups.   5

4. 10 in all. Make 5 groups.   2

Reteaching-113

Macmillan/McGraw-Hill, MATHEMATICS IN ACTION
Grade 2, Chapter 12, Lesson 8, pages 377–378

PRACTICE-113

Name

DIVISION: HOW MANY IN EACH GROUP?

Draw dots. Complete.

Number in each group.

1. 15 in all.   3 groups.   5

2. 15 in all.   5 groups.   3

3. 20 in all.   4 groups.   5

4. 20 in all.   5 groups.   4

5. 12 in all.   2 groups.   6

6. 12 in all.   6 groups.   2

Practice-113

Macmillan/McGraw-Hill, MATHEMATICS IN ACTION
Grade 2, Chapter 12, Lesson 8, pages 377–378

ENRICHMENT-113

Name

DIVISION: HOW MANY IN EACH GROUP?

On Your Own   Pair and Share   In a Group

FRUIT GROUPS

JoAnn wants to share 9 pieces of fruit with 2 friends. She can make 3 groups of fruit in different ways.

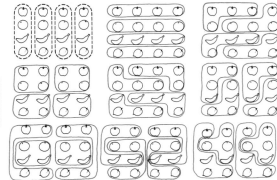

Draw rings to show how many ways Michael can share 16 pieces of fruit with 3 friends.

Answers will vary. Possible answers given.

Compare your groups with your partner's groups.

Enrichment-113

Macmillan/McGraw-Hill, MATHEMATICS IN ACTION
Grade 2, Chapter 12, Lesson 8, pages 377–378

Problem of the Day

Mr. Miller works in a toy factory. He packs giant teddy bears into cartons. Mr. Miller can get 3 bears into each carton. He has 15 bears to pack. How many cartons will he need? [5]

AT·A·GLANCE pp. 379-380

LESSON OBJECTIVE
Choose the operation to solve problems.

ASSIGNMENT GUIDE

COURSE	EXERCISES
Basic	p. 379: 1; p. 380: 1–5
Average	p. 379: 1; p. 380: 1–5
Challenge	p. 379: 1; p. 380: 1–5
Extra Practice, p. 383	

MATERIALS
Manipulatives 25 ◐ (or punchouts) per child

Teacher Resources
Reteaching 114
Prob. Solv. 59
Practice 114
MAC Act. 227, 228
Enrichment 114
Teacher Aid 16
Computer Software *Mathematics Skills:* Disk 13 Act. 1–3

Name _____

Problem Solving

✓ UNDERSTAND
✓ PLAN
✓ TRY
✓ CHECK
✓ EXTEND

Strategy: Choosing the Operation

Lily bought 4 packs of applesauce.
There are 3 cups in each pack.
How many cups did Lily buy in all?

What do I know?

There are 4 packs.
There are 3 cups in each pack.

What do I need to find out?

How many cups in all?

What can I do?

There are the same number of cups in each group.
I can multiply.

$4 \times 3 = 12$

Lily bought __12__ cups in all.

Solve. Use ◐, mental math, or paper and pencil.

1. Randy bought 5 bags of lemons. Each bag had 5 lemons. How many lemons did he buy in all?

__25__ lemons

---

1 PREPARE

WARM-UP To prepare children for choosing the operation to solve problems, have them give the following sums, differences, and products:

2 + 2 + 2 [6]	3 × 2 [6]	5 − 3 [2]
4 + 4 [8]	4 × 2 [8]	4 − 1 [3]
5 + 5 + 5 [15]	5 × 3 [15]	3 − 2 [1]

2 TEACH

MODELING Assign children to work in pairs. Give each pair a set of 15 counters. Explain that you will read a problem aloud and they should use the counters to model the numbers in the problem.

Matt bought 3 packages of pencils. There are 5 pencils in each package. How many pencils did Matt buy in all?

■ **How many groups of counters did you make?** [3]

■ **How many counters are in each group?** [5]

■ **What do you need to find out?** [how many pencils there are in all]

■ **How can you find how many in all?** [Combine and count the counters, add 5 + 5 + 5 = 15, or multiply 3 × 5 = 15.]

■ **If I told you that Matt gave away 7 of his pencils, what would you do to find how many pencils he had left?** [Subtract; 15 − 7 = 8.]

PUPIL'S EDITION pp. 379-380

Page 379 Have a volunteer read the problem at the top of the page. Discuss joining groups by adding and by multiplying. Guide children to see that they can multiply to find how many in all when each group has an equal number.

Solve. Use ◐, mental math, or paper and pencil.

1. There are 3 green grapes.
   Each grape has 4 seeds.

   How many seeds in all? __12__ seeds

2. There are 5 melons.
   Marty sells 3 melons.

   How many melons are left? __2__ melons

3. 2 people are in the market.
   Each person buys 3 tomatos.

   How many tomatos do they buy? __6__ tomatos

4. Lois makes 4 fruit cups.
   She uses 4 grapes in each cup.

   How many grapes does she use in all? __16__ grapes

5. Mary Jane buys 2 bags of oranges.
   Each bag has 4 oranges.

   How many oranges in all? __8__ oranges

Extra Practice, page 383

TEACHER to TEACHER

COOPERATIVE LEARNING TIP  By the end of the year, my children are usually comfortable using different strategies in their groups and comparing strategies across groups. This is a good time to share the *reasons* behind the use of one strategy versus another or the use of more than one strategy. After each group discusses these issues, it presents its point of view to the class. I stimulate controversy by having two teams switch positions to argue the other's point of view. Then the two teams join to consider a new position that reflects both points of view.

For Students Acquiring English (SAE)

Pair SAE children and non-SAE children to work together. The non-SAE child should read a problem while the SAE child draws a picture. They should then work together to find the solution. Have partners switch roles after they complete each problem.

■ **Does the answer 12 make sense?** [Yes; when you multiply 4 × 3 you get 12.]

■ **What did you learn?** [Possible response: You can multiply to find how many in all when you have two or more equal groups.]

Encourage children to explain other ways to solve this problem.

Check for Understanding

■ **What if Lily bought 3 packs of applesauce that had 5 cups in each pack. How many cups would she have?** [15]

GUIDED PRACTICE ex. 1: Distribute counters to children. Before working through the problem with them, make sure children understand how to solve the problem by choosing the operation.

Page 380 Have a volunteer read the problem at the top of the page. Explain to children that they must first decide whether to add, subtract, or multiply to solve the problem.

3 PRACTICE·APPLY PRACTICE ex. 1–5

CLOSE Guide children to summarize the lesson:

■ **How do you know if you should add, subtract, or multiply to solve a problem?** [Possible response: If two or more groups have the same number of items, you can join the groups by adding or multiplying. You subtract when you separate a group and take some away or compare two groups.]

MAC Activity 227:
Basic-to-Average

MAC Activity 227

MATH AND LANGUAGE ARTS ■ SQUIRREL STORY

Materials counters or punchout counters, spinner for 1-5 (Teacher Aid 16)

Assign children to work in pairs. Give each pair of children a set of 25 counters and a spinner for 1 to 5. Tell children that you will read them a story. Explain that they are to work together to model the numbers in the story. Begin by having volunteers spin the spinner twice. These numbers will be used to start. Read the following story. Sample numbers 3 and 4 are used.

Sammy Squirrel hurried to gather his acorns for the winter. He had 4 favorite places to put acorns. He put 3 acorns in each place. Now he had —— [4 x 3 = 12]. Another squirrel found one of Sammy's places and ate the 3 acorns. Sammy now had —— [12 − 3 = 9] acorns left. Sammy found another place to hide acorns. He put 11 more acorns inside an old, hollow log. Now he had —— [9 + 11 = 20] acorns.

Continue the activity with similar stories.

MAC Activity 228

SPEAKING MATHEMATICALLY ■ FROGS

Materials index cards, spinner for 1–5 (Teacher Aid 16), counters or punchout counters

Setup Prepare game cards by writing *add*, *subtract*, and *multiply* on several index cards.

Procedure Discuss with children what frogs in a pond might do. Write idea words on the chalkboard, such as *lily pad*, *log*, *flies*, *jumps*, and *croaks*. Then have children play in small groups. Give each group a set of cards, a spinner, and a set of 25 counters. Explain to children that they will use the spinner and the cards to make up problems about frogs in a pond and use the counters to solve the problems.

Have one child in each group choose a card from the deck and spin the spinner twice. Then the child makes up a problem using the card and the two numbers. The child may also use the words on the chalkboard for ideas. For example, if a child chooses *multiply* and spins to the numbers 2 and 4, a problem could be: "2 lilypads floated on the pond while 4 frogs sat on each pad. How many frogs were there in all?" If the child uses the card and the numbers correctly, he or she scores two points. The first child in the group to give the correct answer to the problem is the next player.

To Win The child in the group with the most points at the end of play is the winner.

▲ MAC Activity 228:
Average-to-Challenge

RETEACHING-114

Name

PROBLEM SOLVING STRATEGY:
CHOOSING THE CORRECT OPERATION

Study

Neal bought 3 packs of baseball cards.
There were 4 cards in each pack.
How many cards did Neal buy in all?

4 cards

1	2	3	4
5	6	7	8
9	10	11	12

3 packs

You can count the cards.

You can add the cards. $4 + 4 + 4 = 12$

Each pack has the same number of cards.

This means you can multiply. 3 packs × 4 cards = 12 cards

Check

Ring the fact that solves the problem.
Solve.

1. 5 people are in the hobby shop.
   Each person buys 2 cans of clay.
   How many cans do they buy?

   $5 + 2$ (5×2)

   __10__ cans

2. The store has 4 paint kits.
   Ginger buys 1 kit.
   How many kits are left?

   $(4 - 1)$ $4 + 1$

   __3__ kits

3. Paul buys 5 sets of paint brushes.
   Each set has 3 brushes.
   How many brushes in all?

   (5×3) $5 - 2$

   __15__ brushes

Macmillan/McGraw-Hill, MATHEMATICS IN ACTION
Grade 2, Chapter 12, Lesson 9, pages 379–380

Reteaching-114

MACMILLAN McGRAW-HILL

PRACTICE-114

Name

PROBLEM SOLVING STRATEGY:
CHOOSING THE CORRECT OPERATION

Solve.

1. Frank put 3 pictures on a wall.
   He put 5 pictures on another wall.
   How many pictures did he

   put up in all? __8__ pictures

2. Jackie brought 2 chairs for the table.
   She brought 2 more chairs.

   How many chairs in all? __4__ chairs

3. Leroy got 4 nails.
   He used 3 nails to fix a shelf.

   How many nails are left? __1__ nails

4. Rosa opened 4 cupboards.
   Each cupboard had 4 cups in it.

   How many cups in all? __16__ cups

5. Lee pours 2 glasses of juice.
   He puts 3 ice cubes in each glass.

   How many ice cubes in all? __6__ cubes

6. Grace puts 2 pillows on a chair.
   She puts 5 pillows on a couch.

   How many pillows in all? __7__ pillows

Macmillan/McGraw-Hill, MATHEMATICS IN ACTION
Grade 2, Chapter 12, Lesson 9, pages 379–380

Practice-114

MACMILLAN McGRAW-HILL

ENRICHMENT-114

Name

PROBLEM SOLVING

On Your Own   Pair and Share   In a Group

TABLE TALK
Solve.
Then draw a line to match a number sentence to the correct
picture.

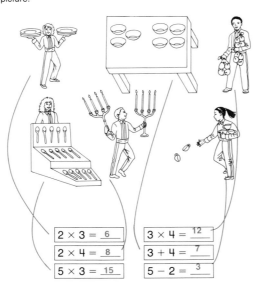

$2 \times 3 =$ __6__	$3 \times 4 =$ __12__
$2 \times 4 =$ __8__	$3 + 4 =$ __7__
$5 \times 3 =$ __15__	$5 - 2 =$ __3__

Macmillan/McGraw-Hill, MATHEMATICS IN ACTION
Grade 2, Chapter 12, Lesson 9, pages 379–380

Enrichment-114

MACMILLAN McGRAW-HILL

Problem of the Day

Fran bought 5 packages of buttons. There were 4
buttons in each package. Did she buy more than
15 buttons? [Yes; $5 \times 4 = 20$ and $20 > 15$.]

CHAPTER 12 • Lesson 10

AT·A·GLANCE p. 381

LESSON OBJECTIVE
Make decisions using information.

ASSIGNMENT GUIDE

COURSE	EXERCISES
Basic	p. 381: 1–3
Average	p. 381: 1–3
Challenge	p. 381: 1–3

Teacher Resources
Crit. Think. 24   Prob. Solv. 60

Name _____

Decision Making

Problem Solving: Planning a Catalog Order

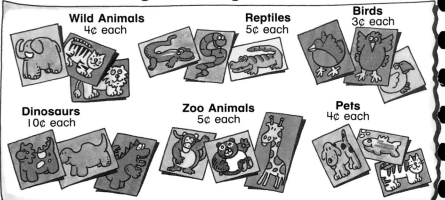

Wild Animals 4¢ each   **Reptiles** 5¢ each   **Birds** 3¢ each

Dinosaurs 10¢ each   **Zoo Animals** 5¢ each   **Pets** 4¢ each

You have 75¢ to spend on stickers.

1. Fill out the order form to show the stickers you want to buy.
Answers will vary.

Item	How Many	Cost for One	Total Cost

2. What is the total cost of your order? _____

 3. Talk about your order.
Did you order some of the same stickers?

Macmillan/McGraw-Hill

PREPARE **WARM-UP** To review multiplication and division facts, draw 4 rows of 5 circles on the chalkboard. Have children say a multiplication sentence that tells about the drawing. [4 × 5 = 20] Then have them say a division sentence that tells the number of rows of circles. [20 ÷ 5 = 4] Continue with other numbers as needed.

TEACH **DISCUSSING** Define the word *catalog* for the children. Explain that it is a book that shows many different kinds of objects that can be purchased through the mail. Have children name some things that could be ordered from a catalog. List their responses on the chalkboard. [Possible responses: clothing, toys, garden supplies, jewelry, books]

PUPIL'S EDITION p. 381
Identify the pictures and prices at the top of the page with the children.

Check for Understanding
- **How many zoo animal stickers could you buy with 5¢?** [1]
- **What could you buy with 3¢?** [one bird sticker]
- **How many kinds of stickers are 4¢ each?** [2]

PRACTICE·APPLY Have children complete ex. 1–3. Call on volunteers to tell how they would fill out the catalog order form.

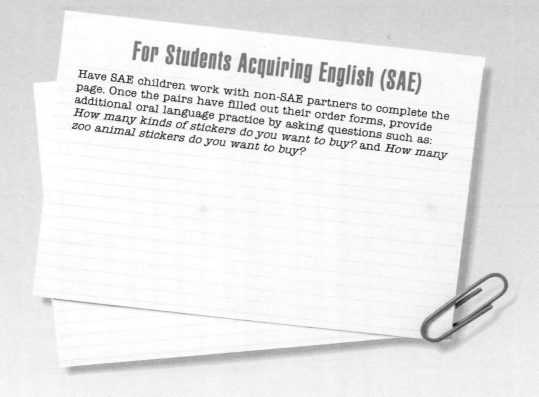

For Students Acquiring English (SAE)

Have SAE children work with non-SAE partners to complete the page. Once the pairs have filled out their order forms, provide additional oral language practice by asking questions such as: *How many kinds of stickers do you want to buy?* and *How many zoo animal stickers do you want to buy?*

C L O S E Guide children to summarize the lesson:

■ **What should you do before you plan a catalog order?** [Decide what you want to order and then how much each item costs.]

CLASS PROJECT

Materials drawing paper, crayons

Give children drawing paper and crayons to make their own page from a catalog. Tell them to decide on one kind of object to show on their page, such as clothing, toys, books, shoes, and so on. Remind them to include a price for each object. Then have children make an order form similar to the one on page 381.

When children have finished the project, have them exchange their catalog pages and fill out the order form.

CHAPTER 12

AT·A·GLANCE p. 382

OBJECTIVE
Apply multiplication to increase a recipe.

MULTICULTURAL OUTCOME
Introduce children to a recipe for Navajo fry bread.

Curriculum Connection

Math and Reading

People in every culture eat some kind of bread.
The Navajo make a kind known as *fry bread*.
Here is a recipe for Navajo fry bread.

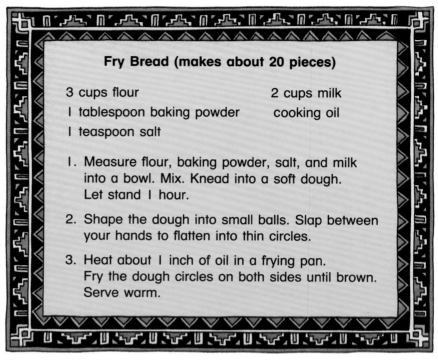

Fry Bread (makes about 20 pieces)

3 cups flour	2 cups milk
1 tablespoon baking powder	cooking oil
1 teaspoon salt	

1. Measure flour, baking powder, salt, and milk into a bowl. Mix. Knead into a soft dough. Let stand 1 hour.

2. Shape the dough into small balls. Slap between your hands to flatten into thin circles.

3. Heat about 1 inch of oil in a frying pan. Fry the dough circles on both sides until brown. Serve warm.

Working Together

Imagine you and your partner want to make *twice* as much fry bread.
How many pieces will that make? ____40____
How much of each ingredient will you need?
6 c flour, 2 T baking powder, 2 t salt, 4 c milk

---

1 PREPARE **WARM-UP** Ask children to name all the different kinds of breads they have eaten, such as bagels, pita, or tortillas and list them on the board. If possible, bring in several kinds of bread children can taste and compare. Ask:

■ **Why do you think there are so many different kinds of breads?** [Accept all reasonable answers.]

Explain that bread is made from flour that comes from grains, such as wheat, corn, rye, oats, or rice.

2 TEACH **DISCUSSING** Read the opening paragraph together. Introduce the Navajo, using the background information. Before reading the recipe, ask:

■ **Why does the recipe tell how much it makes?** [so you know how many batches you need to make]

Have the children read the recipe and the steps. Ask:

■ **What is the first thing to do?** [Measure the ingredients into a bowl.]

3 PRACTICE·APPLY If possible, prepare some Navajo fry bread according to the recipe so that children can experience its preparation and taste. Increase or decrease the recipe as needed. Powdered milk and water may be substituted for fresh milk. Caution children to exercise care near the stove because the oil will get very hot.

CULTURAL DIVERSITY

NAVAJO FRY BREAD

The Navajo form the largest Native American tribe in the United States. Today, many Navajo reside in Arizona, New Mexico, and Utah where they live in homes similar to others in the Southwest. Some maintain *hogans* for ceremonial purposes and for retaining traditional customs. When early Spanish explorers introduced livestock, especially sheep, to the Navajo, it had a profound influence on their way of life. The Navajo became sheep farmers, and have grown famous for their fine woolen rugs and weavings.

BIBLIOGRAPHY

Blood, Charles L. and Martin Link. *The Goat in the Rug.* New York: Four Winds, 1984. ISBN 0-02-710920-8

WORKING TOGETHER Divide the class into pairs. Have each pair work through the questions, which lead to a rewriting of the recipe to double a batch of fry bread. Ask:

■ **How would you find twice as much of each ingredient?** [Double it; multiply by 2.]

■ **Do the steps change when you make twice as much fry bread?** [No.]

C L O S E Guide children to summarize the lesson:

■ **What if you made three times as much fry bread? How many pieces would you have?** [20 x 3 = 60 pieces]

CHAPTER 12

EXTRA PRACTICE

Extra Practice items are provided so that children may have an opportunity for further practice.

The Additional Practice section also provides practice you may wish to assign.

Extra Practice

Division: How Many Groups, pages 375–376 . . . .

Write how many.

1.

___12___ apples   ___3___ groups of 4

Division: How Many in Each Group, pages 377–378 . . . .

Write how many.

1.

5 groups

___10___ cherries   ___2___ in each group

Problem Solving: Choosing the Operation, pages 379–380 . . . .

Solve.

1. Maureen bought 3 packs of pens.
   There are 4 pens in each pack.
   How many pens did she buy altogether? ___12___ pens

2. Al bought 9 pencils.
   He bought 13 colored pencils.
   How many pencils did he buy in all? ___22___ pencils

Macmillan/McGraw-Hill

ADDITIONAL PRACTICE

p. 375 *Use counters. Complete.*

1. Put 10 counters in groups of 2.
   [5] groups of 2

2. Put 6 counters in groups of 3.
   [2] groups of 3

3. Put 15 counters in groups of 5.
   [3] groups of 5

p. 377 *Write how many.*

1. Put 20 counters in 5 groups.
   [4] in each group

2. Put 12 counters in 4 groups.
   [3] in each group

3. Put 18 counters in 3 groups.
   [6] in each group

p. 379 *Solve.*

1. Nancy buys 3 packs of stickers. Each pack has 3 stickers. How many stickers did she buy in all? [9] stickers

2. José has 26 stamps. Luis gave him 15 more. How many stamps does José have in all? [41] stamps

Practice Plus

Key Skill: Multiplication Patterns, page 370 . . . .

Complete.

1.

___5___ groups of ___4___

$5 \times 4 =$ ___20___

___4___ groups of ___5___

$4 \times 5 =$ ___20___

Key Skill: Division: How Many in Each Group, page 378 . . . .

Write how many.

1.

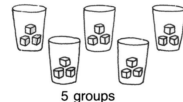

5 groups

___15___ ice cubes

___3___ in each group

2.

2 groups

___8___ tomatoes

___4___ in each group

PRACTICE PLUS

Practice Plus is provided to supply additional practice for the two key skills in this chapter.

Key Skills
Page 370: Multiplication Patterns
Page 378: Division: How Many in Each Group?

The Additional Practice also provides practice you may wish to assign for key skills in this chapter.

ADDITIONAL PRACTICE

p. 370 *Show the groups. Use counters. Complete the sentence.*

1. 2 groups of 5
   $2 \times 5 =$ _[10]_

2. 3 groups of 2
   $3 \times 2 =$ _[6]_

3. 4 groups of 3
   $4 \times 3 =$ _[12]_

4. 2 groups of 4
   $2 \times 4 =$ _[8]_

5. 5 groups of 3
   $5 \times 3 =$ _[15]_

6. 5 groups of 4
   $5 \times 4 =$ _[20]_

p. 378 *Show the groups. Use cubes. Then write the answer.*

1. 15 cubes   5 groups
   How many in each group? _[3]_

2. 20 cubes   4 groups
   How many in each group? _[5]_

3. 18 cubes   3 groups
   How many in each group? _[6]_

CHAPTER 12

Language and Mathematics
Choose the correct word.

1. The × sign in 1 × 5 = 5

   means _____ times _____ .

2. 4 _____ groups _____ of 3 equals 12.

3. The = sign in 2 × 4 = 8

   means _____ equals _____ .

| times |
| equals |
| groups |

Concepts and Skills
Complete.

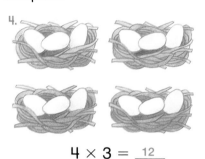

4.

$4 \times 3 =$ __12__

5.

$4 \times 5 =$ __20__

6.

$1 \times 2 =$ __2__

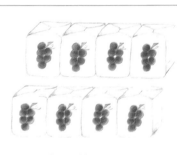

7.

$2 \times 4 =$ __8__

USING THE CHAPTER REVIEW/TEST

The Chapter Review/Test may be used as a review to survey children's knowledge and understanding of the chapter material. Or it may be used as a test to formally assess children's understanding of the concepts and skills taught in the chapter. If used as a test, you may wish to assign one or more of the resources listed in *Reinforcement and Remediation* on p. 386 after reviewing children's test results.

If the Chapter Review/Test is used as a review, you may wish to have children work in pairs to complete it. Have them draw pictures that show 6 x 2 = 12 and use their pictures to talk about how many groups of 2 are in 12. Then, you can use the Chapter Tests—Forms A, B, and C—provided in the *Testing Program Blackline Master and Teacher's Manual* for testing purposes. Any of these forms may be used for pretesting, posttesting, or retesting.

A performance assessment activity for the key concept in this chapter is provided on page 387.

Solve. Use counters to help.

8. Bess had 16 rings.
   She put 4 rings into each jewelry box.
   How many jewelry boxes did she have? ___4___ jewelry boxes

9. 20 players are in the basketball club.
   There are 4 teams.
   Each team has the same number of players.
   How many players are on each team? ___5___ players

Complete.

10.

___6___ birds in all

___2___ groups of 3

Problem Solving

Solve.

11. Judy has 4 pet fish.
    Each fish has 3 stripes on it.
    How many stripes in all?

    ___12___ stripes

12. Scott has 3 gold fish.
    He has 2 black fish.
    How many fish does he
    have altogether?

    ___5___ fish

13. Al, Val, and Sal own fish.
    Each has 5 fish.
    How many fish do they have in all? ___15___ fish

MEETING INDIVIDUAL NEEDS

Reinforcement and Remediation

CHAP. OBJ.	TEST ITEMS	PUPIL'S EDITION pp.			TEACHER'S EDITION pp.	TEACHER RESOURCES	
		Lesson	Extra Practice	Practice Plus	Alt. Teaching Strategy	Reteaching	Practice
12A	1–7	365–370	372	384	366, 368, 370	108, 109, 110	108, 109, 110
12B	8–10	375–378	383	384	376, 378	112, 113	112, 113
12C	11–13	373–374, 379–380	383			111, 114	111, 114

For Students Acquiring English (SAE)

Before beginning the Chapter Review/Test with SAE children, scan the pages for any unfamiliar vocabulary that should be pretaught. You may wish to pair or group SAE children with non-SAE children. You may also wish to repeat some of the activities and techniques for SAE children that were suggested earlier in this chapter.

CHAPTER 12

OBJECTIVE
Assess whether children can apply multiplication and division concepts.

MATERIALS
Manipulatives 36 ○ per child

Teacher Resources
Performance Assessment booklet, pp. 45–47

For Students Acquiring English (SAE)

Before beginning the performance assessment with SAE children, scan the page for any unfamiliar vocabulary that should be pretaught. You may wish to pair or group SAE children with non-SAE children. You may also wish to repeat some of the activities and techniques for SAE children that were suggested earlier in this chapter.

Name _____

Performance Assessment

Work with a partner.

You have 12 apples.
You want to pack the apples into bags.
Each bag should have the same number of apples.

Use ⬤ . Show how many apples are in each bag.
Write a sentence or draw a picture.

A friend gives you 2 more of
these bags of apples.
How many apples are in the 2 bags?
Write a sentence or draw a picture.

You may put this page in your Portfolio

Macmillan/McGraw-Hill

USING PERFORMANCE ASSESSMENT
The Performance Assessment activity may be used to informally assess children's understanding of the key concept(s) of the chapter. Additional assessment activities and Math Journal Options are provided in the *Performance Assessment* booklet.

Performing the Activity
Assign children to work in pairs. Have children model and record how to pack the apples into bags with an equal number in each bag. Children should then draw a picture showing how to determine the number of apples in two of these bags.

Evaluation Guidelines
Use these criteria to help determine the holistic score for each child. The holistic scoring scale can be found in the Teacher's Reference Section.

- How do children determine the number of bags needed?
- Can children create a model showing how to group 12 apples in equal numbers?
- Does the child understand how to use grouping to illustrate division and multiplication concepts?

[Example Response: 4 groups of 3; 3 groups of 4]

If children do not have a full understanding of the key concept(s), you may wish to use the Alternative Teaching Strategies or the MAC Activities within the chapter.

You may wish to have children put their final revised work in their portfolios.

A formal assessment of the concepts and skills taught in this chapter is provided on pages 385–386.

Enrichment For All

Informal Algebra: Division Number Sentences

Jack has 10 marbles.
He can divide them into groups.

2 groups
5 in each group

$10 \div 2 = 5$

10 divided by 2 equals 5.

5 groups
2 in each group

$10 \div 5 = 2$

10 divided by 5 equals 2.

Ring to show equal groups.
Then complete the number sentence.

1. Ring to show 2 groups.

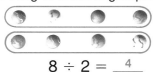

$8 \div 2 = \underline{4}$

2. Ring to show 4 groups.

$8 \div 4 = \underline{2}$

3. Ring to show 3 groups.

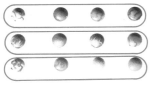

$12 \div 3 = \underline{4}$

4. Ring to show 4 groups.

$12 \div 4 = \underline{3}$

A T · A · G L A N C E p. 388

OBJECTIVE
Identify and describe equal groups.

ASSIGNMENT GUIDE

COURSE	EXERCISES
Basic	p. 388: 1–4
Average	p. 388: 1–4
Challenge	p. 388: 1–4

MATERIALS
Manipulatives 12 ○ (or punchouts) per child

For Students Acquiring English (SAE)

Read the page aloud to SAE children, explaining and demonstrating key vocabulary. Have children point to aspects of the visuals in the textbook as you explain concepts presented. To check comprehension of the directions, ask SAE children to restate them. Pair SAE and non-SAE children to complete ex. 1–4 together. Review the exercises orally, encouraging SAE children to read the complete number sentences aloud.

---

1 PREPARE **WARM-UP** To prepare children for writing division sentences, give each child a set of 12 counters. Have them group the counters into two equal groups of 6 counters, three equal groups of 4 counters, and four equal groups of 3 counters.

2 TEACH **MODELING** Have a volunteer read the sentences at the top of the page. Have children use ten counters to model the groups shown. Then have children read the number sentences aloud.

■ **What does the first number show?** [how many marbles in all]

■ **What does the second number show?** [how many groups]

■ **What does the third number show?** [how many in each group]

3 PRACTICE·APPLY Have children complete ex. 1–4. Call on volunteers to read their completed number sentences and answers.

CLOSE Guide children to summarize the lesson:

■ **What number sentence describes 6 marbles divided into 3 equal groups?** [6 ÷ 3 = 2]

CHAPTER 12

AT·A·GLANCE p. 389

OBJECTIVE
Review and maintain previously learned concepts and skills.

Fill in the ◯ to answer each question.

1. Compare.

$$28 \bigcirc 136$$

<	>	+	=
●	◯	◯	◯

2.

$$\begin{array}{r} 34 \\ + 49 \\ \hline \end{array}$$

72	73	82	83
◯	◯	◯	●

3.

$$\begin{array}{r} 74 \\ - 26 \\ \hline \end{array}$$

48	52	58	100
●	◯	◯	◯

4. Complete.

$$433, 434, \underline{\ ?\ }$$

435	436	445	450
●	◯	◯	◯

5. Find the perimeter.

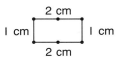

2 cm	3 cm	4 cm	6 cm
◯	◯	◯	●

6. What part is shaded?

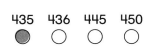

$\frac{1}{2}$	$\frac{1}{3}$	$\frac{1}{4}$	$\frac{1}{8}$
◯	◯	●	◯

7. Michael has 2 backpacks.
He put 4 books into each backpack.
How many books does he have altogether?

- ◯ 6
- ◯ 4
- ◯ 2
- ● 8

Macmillan/McGraw-Hill

USING THE CUMULATIVE REVIEW

The Cumulative Review is presented in a multiple-choice format to provide practice in taking a standardized test. It gives children an opportunity to review previously learned skills. An answer sheet, similar to those used when taking standardized tests, can be found in the *Testing Program Blackline Masters and Teacher's Manual*.

The table that follows correlates the review items to the lesson pages on which the skills are taught.

Review Items	Text Pages	Review Items	Text Pages
1	75–76	5	316
2	191–195, 234	6	340–342
3	221–225, 234	7	379–380
4	287–288		

Testing Program Blackline Masters

In addition to the Cumulative Review in the Pupil's Edition, there are quarterly Cumulative Tests and an End-Year Test. These tests are multiple choice and provide additional opportunities for children to practice taking standardized tests.

Cumulative Tests measure children's performance on major skills and concepts taught during the previous quarters. The **End-Year Test** measures children's performance on major skills and concepts taught throughout the year.

Home Activity

Your child has been learning to multiply. Here is an activity that will strengthen understanding of this skill.

Materials:
25 small objects
5 paper or opaque plastic cups
shallow dish or tray
pencils

Directions:

1. Set out 1 to 5 paper cups, and have your child pick a number from 1 to 5 and count that number of objects into each of the cups. Record your actions in the table.

2. Ask your child to guess how many objects are in all the cups. Record the guess.

3. Then have your child test his or her guess by pouring the objects onto the dish and counting them. Write the product and compare it with your child's guess.

Number of Cups	Number in each	Guess in all	Count in all
5	2	10	10

AT·A·GLANCE p. 390

OBJECTIVE
Give family members an opportunity to share in their child's mathematics learning.

For Students Acquiring English (SAE)

Before assigning this Home Activity to SAE children, find out if someone at home will be able to work with them in English. If not, prepare them to complete the activity independently at home. Explain the directions of the activity and ask SAE children to restate them so you can check comprehension. Scan the page and preteach any difficult vocabulary or phrases that they may not know. If you feel that an SAE child will need extra help with the activity, you might assign that child a non-SAE partner and arrange a time for them to work on the activity in or out of school.

USING THE ACTIVITY

Have children look at the page. Explain that the page has an activity that an adult in the family can help them complete. Read the page with the children, making sure that they understand what needs to be done. Tell children that they will do this page at home.

EXPLORE ADDING and SUBTRACTING 3-DIGIT NUMBERS

66 IN CHAPTER 13, you will be introducing your children to adding and subtracting 3-digit numbers. You will also have the opportunity to explore regrouping. 99

Notes
FROM THE AUTHOR

Here are some notes on the concepts presented in this chapter and how your children can apply them to solve problems.

ADDING 3-DIGIT NUMBERS

Help your children extend their understanding of adding 2-digit numbers with regrouping to adding 3-digit numbers with regrouping. Encourage children to apply their knowledge of place value to the hundreds.

$$\begin{array}{r} 57 \\ + 25 \end{array} \qquad \begin{array}{r} 257 \\ + 525 \end{array} \qquad \begin{array}{r} 49 \\ + 16 \end{array} \qquad \begin{array}{r} 349 \\ + 216 \end{array}$$

Children should begin by combining sets of models to find a total. They then model adding 3-digit numbers with one regrouping and with two regroupings.

Since this topic will be covered in Grade 3, mastery is not expected at this level.

Martin L. Johnson

SUBTRACTING 3-DIGIT NUMBERS

Again help children extend their subtraction skills to subtracting 3-digit numbers with regrouping.

$$\begin{array}{r} 85 \\ -\ 48 \end{array} \qquad \begin{array}{r} 985 \\ -\ 748 \end{array} \qquad \begin{array}{r} 42 \\ -\ 23 \end{array} \qquad \begin{array}{r} 642 \\ -\ 423 \end{array}$$

Your children should model taking away part of a set to find a difference. They then model subtraction of 3-digit numbers but with only one regrouping.

Mastery of this topic is not expected at this level.

PROBLEM SOLVING

In **Problem Solving** your children (1) solve a two-step problem and (2) use number sense to solve a problem.

In **Thinking Mathematically** children use logical reasoning to solve problems. In "Puzzling Pets," children read clues to determine which animal is being described.

In **Decision Making** your children read and use information and then apply their addition skills to decide how many tickets they need to make for a class play.

Mathematics and Literature

To use literature in the application of mathematics.

- Children are introduced to a story in the K–2 *Math Anthology* on page 200. By reading "Bit by Bit," children build addition and subtraction skills and explore the concept of money.

CHAPTER 13 • ORGANIZER

CHAPTER PLANNING GUIDE

CHAPTER OBJECTIVES WITH STANDARDIZED TEST CORRELATIONS

A. Add 3-digit numbers with and without regrouping — CAT, SAT, ITBS, CTBS
B. Subtract 3-digit numbers with and without regrouping — CAT, SAT, ITBS, CTBS
C. Solve problems including those that involve two steps and using number sense — ITBS

SUGGESTED PACING–11 DAYS

LESSONS	NCTM STANDARDS	ASSIGNMENTS Basic/Average/Challenge	STUDENT EDITION Extra Practice/ Practice Plus	Manip. Plus	Reteach	Practice	Enrich	MAC Activities
Chapter Opener: *Too Many Books!* page 391	1, 2, 3, 4, 8	p. 391: All						
✔ 1 Adding 3-Digit Numbers page 392 👥	1, 2, 3, 7, 8	p. 392: All						
✔ 2 Regrouping Tens for Addition pages 393–394 👥	1, 2, 3, 7, 8	p. 393: 1–4; p. 394: 1–4		73				
✔ 3 Adding Ones, Tens, and Hundreds pages 395–396	1, 2, 3, 8	p. 396: 1–6, Mental Math			115	115	115	229, 230
4 3-Digit Addition pages 397–398	1, 2, 3, 8	p. 397: All; p. 398: 1–7	pp. 402, 414	74	116	116	116	231, 232
5 PS: Solving a Two-Step Problem pages 399–400	1, 2, 3, 7, 8	p. 400: 1–5	p. 402		117	117	117	233, 234
✔ 6 PS: Thinking Mathematically page 401 👥	1, 2, 3	p. 401: 1–3						
✔ 7 Regrouping Hundreds for Subtraction pages 403–404 👥	1, 2, 3, 7, 8	p. 403: 1–3; p. 404: 2–5		75				
✔ 8 Subtracting Ones, Tens, and Hundreds pages 405–406	1, 2, 3, 8	p. 406: 1–6, Estimation			118	118	118	235, 236
9 3-Digit Subtraction pages 407–408	1, 2, 3, 8	p. 408: 1–7	pp. 413, 414	76	119	119	119	237, 238
10 PS: Using Number Sense pages 409–410	1, 2, 3, 5, 6	p. 409: 1–2; p. 410: 1–3	p. 413		120	120	120	239, 240
11 PS: Decision Making page 411 👥	1, 2, 3, 6, 8	p. 411: 1–4						

Technology: Calculator page 412

Chapter Review/Test pages 415–416

Performance Assessment page 417

Cumulative Review page 419

Enrichment for All/Home Activity pages 418, 420

NATIONAL COUNCIL OF TEACHERS OF MATHEMATICS Grades K–4

1. Problem Solving
2. Communication
3. Reasoning
4. Connections
5. Estimation
6. Number Sense and Numeration
7. Concepts of Whole Number Operations
8. Whole Number Computation
9. Geometry and Spatial Sense
10. Measurement
11. Statistics and Probability
12. Fractions and Decimals
13. Patterns and Relationships

✔ Activity   👥 Cooperative Learning

MEETING the NCTM STANDARDS

Problem Solving

Strategies and Skills	• solving a two-step problem pp. 399–400 • using number sense pp. 409–410
Applications	• **Decision Making** lesson p. 411 • **Problem of the Day** TE pp. 392, 394, 396B, 398B, 400B, 404, 406B, 408B, 410B
Mathematical Investigations	• **Thinking Mathematically** lesson p. 401

Communication

Language	• using the language of mathematics TE pp. 395–396, 397–398, 403–404, 405–406
Oral/Written	• using cooperative learning activities pp. 390I–390L, 392, 393–394, 401, 403–404 • **Journal Writing** opportunities TE pp. 392, 396, 404, 406, 408, 410

Reasoning

Critical Thinking	• answering questions that analyze and extend concepts pp. 391, 411

Connections

To other subject areas	• Literature p. 391; Literature TE pp. 391–392

Concept Development

Concepts of Whole Number Operations	• regrouping 1 hundred for 10 tens or 10 tens for 1 hundred pp. 392, 393–394, 403–404; TE pp. 390I–390K
Whole Number Computation	• using models to add 3-digit numbers with and without regrouping pp. 395–396, 397–398; TE p. 390J • using models to subtract 3-digit numbers with and without regrouping pp. 405–406, 407–408; TE p. 390L

ASSESSMENT OPTIONS

PERFORMANCE ASSESSMENT

Preassessment Activity

Before beginning Chapter 13, write the examples on the board. Before having children do any computation, discuss how the examples differ from what children have done before. Have children speculate on how 3-digit addition and subtraction might differ from or be similar to 2-digit operations. Have children attempt the problems shown.

$$\begin{array}{cccc} 67 & 367 & 63 & 638 \\ +54 & +554 & -37 & -379 \end{array}$$

Ongoing Assessment

The Ongoing Assessment cards under MEETING INDI-VIDUAL NEEDS on TE pp. 396 and 404 provide criteria and questions for assessing children's understanding of the key mathematical concepts developed in the chapter.

Journal Writing opportunities encourage children to write about mathematics. Their responses can be recorded either pictorially or in words. The journal writing opportunities on the Ongoing Assessment cards also allow you to assess children's understanding of the lessons.

In addition to the Ongoing Assessment cards, other assessment and journal writing opportunities in this chapter include:

• **CLOSE** TE pp. 392, 396, 406, 408, 410

Performance Assessment Activity

The Performance Assessment activity on p. 417 provides an alternative to formal assessment. This activity assesses children's understanding of the key concepts of the chapter.

For performance assessment activities that are keyed to individual chapter objectives, see the *Performance Assessment* booklet.

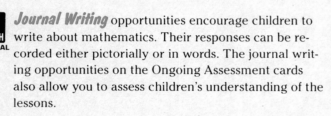

BUILDING A PORTFOLIO

Children should be encouraged to keep a selection of their best work in portfolios. The portfolios provide a way of documenting children's growth in understanding mathematical concepts. Portfolio opportunities in this chapter include:

• **Performance Assessment** p. 417
• **Class Project** TE p. 411A

If you wish to provide additional opportunities for portfolio work, you may choose to use:

• **MAC Activities** 229, 230, 232, 238

You may also wish to have children include their journal writing from the Ongoing Assessment on TE pp. 396 and 404 in their portfolio.

Formal Assessment

The **Chapter Review/Test** assesses children's understanding of the concepts and skills developed in the chapter. The **Cumulative Review** assesses children's understanding of the concepts and skills developed from the beginning of the year.

You can use **Form A** or **Form B** of the **Chapter Test** found in the *Testing Program Blackline Masters and Teacher's Manual* if you wish to use a multiple-choice

format to assess children's understanding of the chapter concepts and skills. You can use **Form C** if you wish to use a free-response format. Any of the forms may be used as a pretest, posttest, or for retesting.

The **COMPUTER MANAGEMENT SYSTEM**, or **CMS**, enables you to score **Forms A** and **B** of the **Chapter Test** quickly and automatically. It also prescribes learning activities based on children's test results.

For more information about Assessment, see the *Professional Handbook*.

Common Error and Remediation

The Teacher's Edition notes for each Develop/Understand (Transitional/Abstract) lesson provide a common error analysis and a remediation activity. Some errors defy quick analysis and can only be identified by interviewing the child.

ALTERNATIVE TEACHING STRATEGY

Alternative Teaching Strategies appear frequently in the chapter. These strategies provide other presentations of the lessons for children who might benefit from instruction in different learning modalities: kinesthetic, visual, and/or auditory.

For Students Acquiring English (SAE)

Review the vocabulary associated with addition, subtraction, and regrouping before starting the chapter.

SAE notes appear periodically in the chapter. These notes provide suggestions for how to work with children to improve comprehension and build vocabulary.

MANIPULATIVES WORKSHOP

Hundreds, tens, and ones models are used in this chapter to examine addition and subtraction of larger numbers. They provide concrete representations of regrouping for either operation.

USING MANIPULATIVES

Here a child models 253 + 141, using hundreds, tens, and ones models to show both addends.

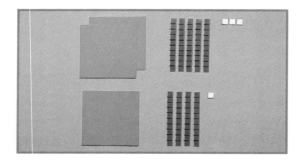

The child combines, ones, tens, and hundreds to find that the sum of 253 and 141 is 394.

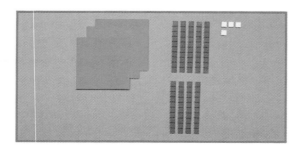

Here a child models 348 − 126.

The child builds the number 348 with hundreds, tens, and ones models.

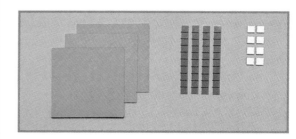

The child takes away 6 ones, 2 tens, and 1 hundred to show the subtraction of 126. The model shows that 348 − 126 = 222.

MAKING MANIPULATIVES See the Manipulatives section of the *Professional Handbook* for materials that can be used as a substitute for hundreds, tens, and ones models.

COOPERATIVE LEARNING WORKSHOP

GETTING STARTED

Saying Goodbye: When you have done a good job at learning to cooperate, it's hard to realize that the community must end. Now's the time to acknowledge each child's contribution to the small groups they have worked with and to the community. Review the successes of the year, the skills learned, the unity experiences, the nostalgia corner, the scrapbook, and/or the photos of major events.

Children can collaborate to prepare an end-of-year ceremony and party to which family members are invited. Souvenirs, such as letters of appreciation in the community mailbox, signature albums, and photos of the celebration are very much in order. Children will enjoy a **remember forever brainstorm:** All children write letters about something that happened this year that they want to remember forever, that they shared within the small group, and then members brainstorm ways never to forget. The ideas and letters are then sealed in self-addressed envelopes, and six months later you mail them.

IDEAS TO TRY

Let's Celebrate! The lessons named below can assist children in planning an end-of-year celebration. Committees can find the best prices for their party foods and decide on a selection of cooperative sports and games. The celebration should include acknowledging the planning skills and problem-solving accomplishments of each committee.

You can apply the above end-of-year celebration ideas in these lessons:
13-1 *Adding 3-Digit Numbers* p. 392
13-2 *Regrouping Tens for Addition* pp. 393–394
13-3 *Adding Ones, Tens, and Hundreds* pp. 395–396

Family Day: Children like to demonstrate their group skills in mathematics for their family members. Small groups can **huddle** to discuss a program that would show their problem-solving strategies. Each group's ideas are brought to a community meeting and a general program is agreed upon. To help family members understand how coop-

erative skills improve group work, assign one skill the class has learned well, and encourage reflection at the end of the program. A **circle of appreciation** is a good wind-up to the event: Children and family members together circle to the left with sideways steps until somone calls "Stop!" to voice appreciation of some person or group. Then they move on again until the next person calls "Stop."

You can apply the above cooperative-demonstration ideas in these lessons:
13-7 *Regrouping Hundreds for Subtraction* pp. 403–404
13-8 *Subtracting Ones, Tens, and Hundreds* pp. 405–406
13-9 *3-Digit Subtraction* pp. 407–408

SEE ALSO

Cooperative Learning Tip for lessons 13-5 Problem Solving p. 400; 13-10 Problem Solving p. 410; 13-11 Decision Making p. 411A

The Cooperative Learning section of the *Professional Handbook* for additional information

ACTIVITY

INTERACTIVE BULLETIN BOARD

SETUP Use oaktag to make a telephone pattern. Cut out enough telephones to give one to each child. Write a different 3-digit number on each telephone. Give each child a sheet of white paper with answer blanks for *hundreds, tens,* and *ones,* as shown in the illustration. Cover the bulletin board with black background paper.

PROCEDURE 👯 Have children fill in the blanks on their sheets and then color their telephones using colored chalk.

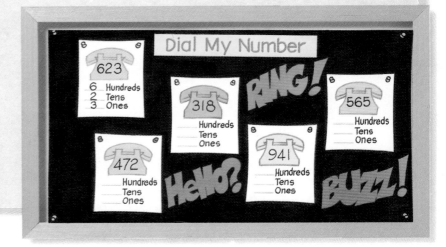

For use before
LESSON 13.2,
pp. 393-394

73

EXPLORE ADDING 3-DIGIT NUMBERS

OBJECTIVE
Explore adding 3-digit numbers.

MATERIALS
Manipulatives 4 H, 15 T, and 15 O models (or punchouts) per child

WHOLE GROUP ACTIVITY

Give each child 4 hundreds, 15 tens, and 15 ones models and Workmat 3. Read the following problem.

■ **The children collected 187 cans for recycling. Then they collected 26 more. How many cans were collected?**

Tell children to model 187 on their workmats. Then have them add another 6 ones to the models. Review the rules for regrouping.

■ **How many ones are there in all?** [13]
■ **How many ones can there be in the ones column?** [0 to 9]
■ **What should be done with the 13 ones?** [Regroup 13 ones as 1 ten 3 ones.]

After regrouping, have a child read the number of hundreds, tens, and ones. [1 hundred 9 tens 3 ones]

Continue the activity similarly to add 2 tens and regroup tens.

Repeat the activity with the following numbers.

1. Show 346. Add 4 ones. Add 6 tens.
2. Show 273. Add 9 ones. Add 2 tens.
3. Show 199. Add 1 one.

EXTENDING THE ACTIVITY

Read aloud examples and challenge children to each try to mentally solve the problems. Have individuals share and discuss their strategies.

ONGOING ASSESSMENT

✓ Are children able to model separating sets and regrouping?

MANIPULATIVES *plus* **ACTIVITY**

For use before LESSON 13.4, pp. 397-398

74

ADDING ON A CALCULATOR

OBJECTIVE
Add on a calculator.

MATERIALS
Calculator

WHOLE GROUP ACTIVITY

Give each child a calculator. Demonstrate the process of adding 3-digit numbers.

Remind children that one reason people use calculators is to add large numbers. Have children enter 285 on the calculator. Then tell them to press the + key and enter 179. Next have them press the = key and read the sum. [464]

Write the following problems on the chalkboard. Have children use their calculators to solve them.

1. Gregory sold 497 tickets on Friday. He sold 341 tickets on Saturday and 381 tickets on Sunday. On which two days did he sell 878 tickets in all? [Friday and Sunday]
2. Suzy sold 353 glasses of lemonade on Friday. She sold 427 glasses on Saturday and 333 glasses on Sunday. On which two days did she sell 760 glasses of lemonade? [Saturday and Sunday]
3. Betty and Bob sold popcorn. They sold 284 bags of popcorn on Friday, 276 bags on Saturday, and 265 bags on Sunday. How many bags of popcorn did they sell in the three days? [825]

EXTENDING THE ACTIVITY

Have children use calculators, if they wish, and work backward from a sum to find two addends. First allow children the opportunity to find any two addends that can be added to make the target sum.

Then provide them with clues to find the two addends you have in mind, as in the following:

■ **I am thinking of two numbers that have a sum of 408. What two numbers am I thinking of?** [Answers will vary. Possible answers: 200 and 208; 104 and 304]

■ **Of the two numbers I am thinking of, both numbers have 2 in the hundreds place.** [Possible answers: 200 and 208; 201 and 207; 202 and 206; 203 and 205; 204 and 204]
One number has the same digit in both the tens place and the ones place. [200 and 208]

ONGOING ASSESSMENT

✓ Are children able to use calculators to add two 3-digit numbers?

75

EXPLORE SUBTRACTING 3-DIGIT NUMBERS

OBJECTIVE
Explore subtracting 3-digit numbers.

MATERIALS
Manipulatives 5 H, 19 T, and 19 O models (or punchouts) per child

WHOLE GROUP ACTIVITY

Give each child 5 hundreds, 19 tens, and 19 ones models and Workmat 3. Read the following problem.

■ **The children made 342 tickets for their class play. They gave out 64 tickets. How many tickets were left?**

Tell children to model 342 on their workmats. Then have them take away 4 ones from the models. Review the rules for regrouping.

■ **How many ones are there?** [2]
■ **How can you get enough ones to take away 4?** [Regroup 1 ten as 10 ones]

After regrouping, have a child read the number of hundreds, tens, and ones. [3 hundreds 3 tens 12 ones] Then have children take away 4 ones.

■ **How many ones are left?** [8]

Have a child read the number of hundreds, tens, and ones. [3 hundreds 3 tens 8 ones]

Continue the activity similarly to take away 6 tens and regroup tens.

Repeat the activity with other numbers.

EXTENDING THE ACTIVITY

Read aloud examples and challenge children to each try to solve the problems mentally. Have individuals share and discuss their strategies.

ONGOING ASSESSMENT

✓ Are children able to model separating sets and regrouping?

For use before LESSON 13.9, pp. 407-408

76

SUBTRACTING ON A CALCULATOR

OBJECTIVE
Subtract on a calculator.

MATERIALS
Calculator

WHOLE GROUP ACTIVITY

Give each child a calculator. Demonstrate the process of subtracting 3-digit numbers.

Remind children that one reason people use calculators is to subtract large numbers. Have children enter 572 on the calculator. Then tell them to press the − key and enter 359. Next have them press the = key and read the difference. [213]

Write the following problems on the chalkboard. Have children use their calculators to solve them.

1. Jane had 256 books to sell at the book fair. She sold 139 books the first day. How many books did she have left? [117]
2. Carlos had 370 marbles to sell at the hobby show. He sold 156 marbles. How many marbles did he have left? [214]
3. Sherry had 849 buttons to sell at the crafts fair. She sold 257 buttons the first day. How many did she have left? [592] She sold 389 buttons the second day. Then how many buttons did she have left? [203]

EXTENDING THE ACTIVITY

Write the following sets of numbers on the chalkboard. Challenge children to find the two numbers in each row that when subtracted equal the difference in the box. Have children guess before testing.

110 101 321 280 ☐211 [321 − 110]
272 564 481 505 ☐59 [564 − 505]

ONGOING ASSESSMENT

✓ Are children able to use calculators to subtract two 3-digit numbers?

READ ALOUD

TOO MANY BOOKS
By Caroline Feller Bauer

Mathematics and Literature

Listening and Speaking

The Read-Aloud selection can be used
with the Chapter 13 Opener and Lesson 13-1
on pages 391-392.

Tape 2, Side 2
Selection 4

▪ TOO MANY ▪
BOOKS!

BY CAROLINE FELLER BAUER

Maralou loved books, even as a baby. When Maralou learned
to read, she read all of the time.
   She read at the breakfast table.
   She read on the bus to school.
   She read in the bathtub.
   She read while she jumped rope
                            . . . or tried to.
   Every week, Maralou took her wagon to the library to borrow
books. The following week, Maralou brought the books back and
borrowed more.

One day during Book Week, Maralou's Aunt Molly *gave* her a book. Fantastic! Now that she owned her own book, she could read it over and over again.

Maralou wanted more books. She asked for books whenever someone wanted to give her a present.

She was given books for her birthday,

For Halloween,

...and even for the Fourth of July.

Maralou also earned money so she could buy books.

She cat sat.

She sold lemonade.

She had a garage sale.

She tried to sell her little brother

...but that didn't work.

After a while, Maralou had a lot of books. Mom and Dad built shelves for the books but there still wasn't enough room.

There were books in the bathtub,

on every table,

all over the floor,

...and even in the refrigerator.

Maralou had too many books! Mom couldn't get out the front door. Dad couldn't get in the back door. But Maralou still loved books and wanted more to read.

How could she make room?

Then Maralou had an idea. Maybe other people would love books too! So she decided to give some books away.

She gave a book to a little boy on his way to school.

She gave a book to the mail carrier.

She left books at the doctor's office

...and at the playground.

Soon the whole town was reading all the time. People bought books, borrowed books, and traded books. The town was bulging with books.

The mayor called the librarian in the next town to see if they would like to have some books. They did, and it wasn't long before *all* the nearby towns were borrowing and trading and reading and sharing books.

But Maralou didn't notice.

She sat in front of the library

...reading a book.

Explore Adding and Subtracting 3-Digit Numbers

AT·A·GLANCE pp. 391-392

LESSON OBJECTIVES

Explore mathematical concepts through literature.
Explore adding larger numbers.

ASSIGNMENT GUIDE

COURSE	EXERCISES
Basic	p. 391: All; p. 392: All
Average	p. 391: All; p. 392: All
Challenge	p. 391: All; p. 392: All

MATERIALS

Classroom Materials math, reading, science, and social studies textbooks
Manipulatives 1H, 10 T, 10 O models (or punchouts) per child

Teacher Resources
Math Anthology, pp. 198–199
Read-Aloud Cassette 2, Side 2, Selection 4

SKILLS TRACE
3-DIGIT ADDITION

Explore (Concrete) 392, 393–394	Develop/Understand (Transitional/Abstract) 395–396, 397–398
Practice 402, 414, 415–416, 419	**Apply** 412, 418

READ ALOUD
TOO MANY BOOKS
By Caroline Feller Bauer

Listen to the story Too Many Books.

Guess how many books you have in your home. Talk about how you made your guess. Possible answer: I added the number of books in each room.

391

---

① PREPARE **WARM-UP** To review hundreds, tens, and ones, give pairs of children 5 hundreds models, 9 tens models, and 9 ones models, and have them model the following:

243 [2 hundreds 4 tens 3 ones]
109 [1 hundreds 0 tens 9 ones]
444 [4 hundreds 4 tens 4 ones]
368 [3 hundreds 6 tens 8 ones]
400 [4 hundreds 0 tens 0 ones]

② TEACH **DISCUSSING** Before reading *Too Many Books,* write this question on the chalkboard: *Where can you find a book to read?* Have volunteers answer this question. List their responses on the chalkboard. [bookstores, libraries, home] Discuss the differences between libraries and bookstores. Then ask chil-

dren where they think libraries get the books they lend. Explain that while most are purchased, some are given to the library by people who love books.

Mathematics and Literature

PUPIL'S EDITION pp. 391-392

Page 391 Read *Too Many Books* found on pages 390M–390N or in *Math Anthology* to children, or play Read-Aloud Cassette 2, Side 2, Selection 4 for them.

Discuss the directive on the page.

Page 392 Discuss the picture with the children. Read the problem aloud.

WORKING TOGETHER Assign children to work in groups of seven. Read the directions aloud.

Name _____

Adding 3-Digit Numbers

Guess how many textbooks are

in your classroom. _Answers will vary._

Working Together

Use ◘ to show each book.

Count the kinds of books.
Record the numbers in the table.

Trade 10 ones for 1 ten.
Count tens and ones.

Books in Our Room	
Kinds of Books	**Number**
Math	
Reading	
Science	
Social Studies	

Find how many books in all.

Put 10 tens together
to make 100.
Count hundreds,
tens, and ones.

Think of other ways to find how
many books there are in all. Answers will
vary. Possible answers: by counting or adding.

Was your guess close? Answers will vary.

MEETING INDIVIDUAL NEEDS

ALTERNATIVE TEACHING STRATEGY

MATERIALS 1 H, 10 T, 10 O models (or punchouts) per child

VISUAL Work with children to find the total number of books in the class. Begin by counting the children's math books. Have each child use a ones model to represent his or her math book. Have them bring their ones models forward. When there are 10 or more ones, regroup 10 ones for 1 ten. Repeat with other books, regrouping ones for tens, and tens for hundreds. When each type of book has been counted, count the models to find the total number.

Check for Understanding

■ **How can models help you find how many books in all?** [Put ones models into groups of 10; put ten groups together to make 100. Count hundreds, tens, ones.]

GUIDED PRACTICE Give each child a specific type of book to count. Stack the books to be counted on table tops. Have each child enter his or her total in the chart. Then have the children in each group combine their models to find the total.

For reteaching, use Alternative Strategy.

3 PRACTICE·APPLY **PRACTICE** Have children complete the page.

C L O S E Guide children to summarize the lesson:
■ **How did you find the total number of books in the classroom?** [Possible response: by counting each type of book and then finding the total number of books]

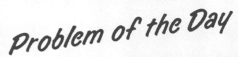

Problem of the Day

The library has 234 animal books and 142 mystery books. How many animal and mystery books does it have in all? [376 books]

AT·A·GLANCE pp. 393-394

LESSON OBJECTIVE
Explore regrouping tens for addition.

ASSIGNMENT GUIDE

COURSE	EXERCISES
Basic	p. 393: 1–4; p. 394: 1–4
Average	p. 393: 1–4; p. 394: 1–4
Challenge	p. 393: 1–4; p. 394: 1–4

MATERIALS
Manipulatives 5 H, 15 T, and 9 O models (or punchouts), Workmat 3* per child

Teacher Resources
*Teacher Aid 15

SKILLS TRACE
3-DIGIT ADDITION

Explore (Concrete) 392, 393–394	Develop/Understand (Transitional/Abstract) 395–396, 397–398
Practice 402, 414, 415–416, 419	Apply 412, 418

See **MANIPULATIVES PLUS 73**, p. 390I.

---

1 PREPARE **WARM-UP** To prepare children to regroup tens for addition, write the following on the chalkboard. Have children identify the number of hundreds, tens, and ones in each number.

1. 123 [1 hundred 2 tens 3 ones]
2. 148 [1 hundred 4 tens 8 ones]
3. 205 [2 hundreds 0 tens 5 ones]
4. 687 [6 hundreds 8 tens 7 ones]
5. 772 [7 hundreds 7 tens 2 ones]
6. 451 [4 hundreds 5 tens 1 ones]

2 TEACH **MODELING** Using Workmat 3 and hundreds, tens, and ones models, review regrouping ones as tens. Display 13 ones.

Name _____

Regrouping Tens for Addition

Holly had 120 books. She used 12 tens to show the books.

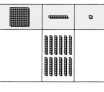

hundreds	tens	ones
0	12	0

She regrouped 10 tens as 1 hundred.

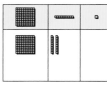

hundreds	tens	ones
1	2	0

Write how many Holly has now.

___1___ hundred ___2___ tens ___0___ ones

Use Workmat 3. Use 15 [ten], 4 [ones], and 1 [hundred].
Show the number.
Regroup 10 tens as 1 hundred.
Write the number.

1.

hundreds	tens	ones
0	13	0

hundreds	tens	ones
1	3	0

2.

hundreds	tens	ones
0	14	0

hundreds	tens	ones
1	4	0

3.

hundreds	tens	ones
0	15	2

hundreds	tens	ones
1	5	2

4.

hundreds	tens	ones
0	10	4

hundreds	tens	ones
1	0	4

Macmillan/McGraw-Hill

Chapter 13   Explore Adding and Subtracting 3-Digit Numbers   three hundred ninety-three **393**

■ **How many ones equal 1 ten?** [10]
■ **Are there enough ones to regroup as 1 ten?** [Yes.]
■ **How many tens and ones are there?** [1 ten 3 ones]

Then display 13 tens models and have children count by tens as you hold up each model.

■ **Are there enough tens to regroup as 1 hundred?** [Yes.]

Regroup 10 tens as 1 hundred and have children identify the number of hundreds and tens. [1 hundred 3 tens]

PUPIL'S EDITION pp. 393-394

Page 393 Work through the example at the top of the page with the children.

Working Together

Use Workmat 3. Use 15 ▭ , 9 ◦ , and 5 ▦ .

Show the two numbers. Combine the numbers.　　　**Regroup. Write the number.**

1.

hundreds	tens	ones
1	6	5

hundreds	tens	ones
3	7	4

hundreds	tens	ones
5	3	9

2.

hundreds	tens	ones
	7	4

hundreds	tens	ones
1	8	3

hundreds	tens	ones
2	5	7

3.

hundreds	tens	ones
1	8	3

hundreds	tens	ones
2	4	6

hundreds	tens	ones
4	2	9

4.

hundreds	tens	ones
	5	7

hundreds	tens	ones
2	9	1

hundreds	tens	ones
3	4	8

For Students Acquiring English (SAE)

Review the names and quantities of **ones, tens,** and **hundreds** models before beginning the lesson. If SAE children need extra assistance, work through ex. 1–4 on page 393 with them orally. As heterogeneous pairs complete Working Together on page 394, circulate and ask them to show and describe their workmats.

ALTERNATIVE TEACHING STRATEGY

ACTIVITY

MATERIALS Teacher Aids Transparency 11, 5 H, 16 T, and 9 O models (or Manipulatives Kit Transparencies 8, 9); overhead projector

VISUAL Place Teacher Aids Transparency 11 on an overhead projector. Model 16 tens on it. Ask children what is the greatest number of tens in the tens column before they must be regrouped. [9 tens] Have a volunteer count the tens and tell if they can be regrouped. [Yes.] Have the child regroup 10 tens as 1 hundred and read the models as 1 hundred 6 tens. Repeat the activity with other numbers.

Check for Understanding

■ **How many hundreds and tens would you have if you regrouped 17 tens?** [1 hundred 7 tens]

GUIDED PRACTICE　ex. 1–4: Provide children with the following: 4 ones models, 15 tens models, 1 hundreds model, and Workmat 3.

For reteaching, use Alternative Strategy.

Page 394 ■ Working Together　Assign children to work in pairs. Tell children to use 9 ones models, 15 tens models, 5 hundreds models, and Workmat 3 for the activity. Have them model each number in a row, one below the other, on the workmat.

PRACTICE·APPLY　**PRACTICE**　ex. 1–4

CLOSE　Guide children to summarize the lesson:
■ **What do you get when you regroup 3 hundreds 18 tens 4 ones?** [484] **8 hundreds 10 tens 7 ones?** [907]

Problem of the Day

Norman has 3 booklets of 100 stamps, 18 booklets of 10 stamps, and 7 single stamps. How many stamps does Norman have? [487]

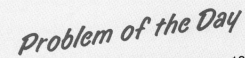

AT·A·GLANCE pp. 395-396

LESSON OBJECTIVE
Add 3-digit numbers, regrouping tens to hundreds.

ASSIGNMENT GUIDE

COURSE	EXERCISES
Basic	p. 396: 1–6, Mental Math
Average	p. 396: 1–6, Mental Math
Challenge	p. 396: 1–6, Mental Math

MATERIALS
Manipulatives 7 H, 17 T, 9 O models (or punchouts), Work-mat 3 per child

Teacher Resources
Reteaching 115
MAC Act. 229, 230
Practice 115
Teacher Aid 15
Enrichment 115

SKILLS TRACE
3-DIGIT ADDITION

Explore (Concrete)	Develop/Understand (Transitional/Abstract)
392, 393–394	395–396, 397–398
Practice	Apply
402, 414, 415–416, 419	412, 418

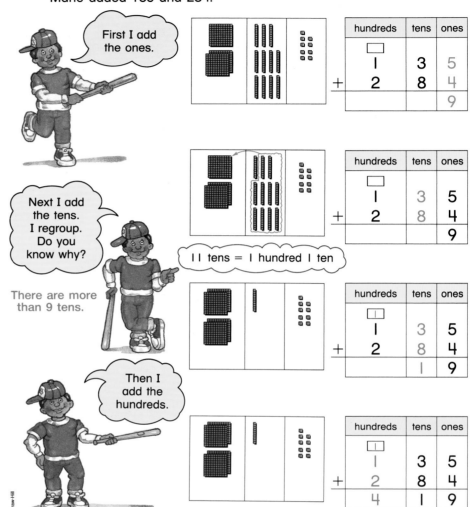

Adding Ones, Tens, and Hundreds

Mario added 135 and 284.

First I add the ones.

Next I add the tens. I regroup. Do you know why?

There are more than 9 tens.

11 tens = 1 hundred 1 ten

Then I add the hundreds.

What is the sum? 135 + 284 = ___419___

Chapter 13   Explore Adding and Subtracting 3-Digit Numbers   three hundred ninety-five   **395**

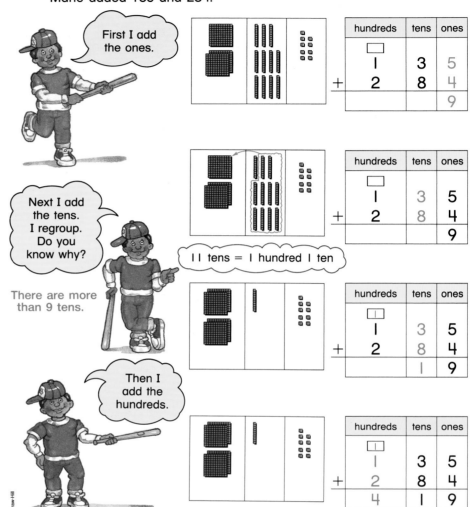

PREPARE

WARM-UP To review regrouping tens, write the following hundreds, tens, and ones in place-value charts on the board. Have children regroup the tens for hundreds.

1. 0 hundreds 17 tens 3 ones   [1 hundred 7 tens 3 ones]
2. 1 hundred 11 tens 9 ones   [2 hundreds 1 ten 9 ones]

2 TEACH

MODELING Provide children with hundreds, tens, and ones models and Workmat 3. Tell them to model the number 153, then 385 below 153. Show the following place-value box on the chalkboard or on an overhead transparency.

Explain this is a way to write an addition for the models on their mats. Emphasize that when adding 3-digit numbers, they must begin with the ones. Have children combine the ones models.

	hundreds	tens	ones
	1	5	3
+	3	8	5

■ **How many ones do you have?** [8]

■ **Do you need to regroup the ones?** [No.]

Write 8 in the sum of the ones column of the place-value box.

Direct children's attention to the tens column and have them combine the tens.

■ **How many tens do you have?** [13]

■ **Is this more than 9 tens?** [Yes.]

Use Workmat 3. Use 17 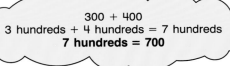 , 9 ▫ , and 7 ▦ .
Find the sum.

1.

hundreds	tens	ones
⊡		
3	7	2
+ 1	4	6
5	1	8

2.

hundreds	tens	ones
1		
2	5	6
+ 1	7	3
4	2	9

3.

hundreds	tens	ones
1		
6	8	3
+	9	4
7	7	7

4.

hundreds	tens	ones
1		
2	8	1
+ 3	4	7
6	2	8

5.

hundreds	tens	ones
1		
4	6	1
+ 2	5	8
7	1	9

6.

hundreds	tens	ones
1		
	7	4
+ 6	7	1
7	4	5

···· *Mental Math* ··

You can add 300 and 400
without using any models.

> 300 + 400
> 3 hundreds + 4 hundreds = 7 hundreds
> **7 hundreds = 700**

Write the sum.

1. 400 + 100   500

2. 200 + 500   700

3. 600 + 300   900

Tell children to regroup 13 tens as 1 hundred 3 tens and put the three tens in the tens column and the hundred in the hundreds column of the workmat. Record 3 in the tens column and 1 at the top of the hundreds column. Have children add the hundreds by combining the models. Record 5 in the hundreds column. Read the addition as 153 plus 385 equals 538.

PUPIL'S EDITION pp. 395-396

Page 395 Work through the page with children.

Check for Understanding

■ **When adding, how can you tell if you need to regroup the tens?** [If there are more than 9 tens, you must regroup.]

Page 396 Tell children to model each exercise, then do addition.

MEETING INDIVIDUAL NEEDS

ONGOING ASSESSMENT

INTERVIEW (1) How would you add 125 + 282? **(2)** Would you have to regroup to find the answer to 244 + 260? Tell why. **(3)** How would you find the answer to 372 + 185?

JOURNAL WRITING You may wish to have children record their responses in their math journals.

ACTIVITY *Common Error and Remediation*

MATERIALS hundreds, tens, and ones models; Workmat 3

When adding 3-digit numbers, some children may forget to add the regrouped hundred. Work individually with each child. Have the child model 47 + 71. After combining the ones, have the child combine the tens and talk about the regrouping process. After several 2-digit exercises, move on to 3-digit exercises that require regrouping tens to hundreds.

ACTIVITY ALTERNATIVE TEACHING STRATEGY

MATERIALS 5 H, 13 T, 9 O models, place-value workmat (Teacher Aid 15), Teacher Aids Transparency 11, Manipulatives Kit Transparencies 8, 9; overhead projector

VISUAL/AUDITORY Write the addition fact 342 + 197 in a place-value box on the chalkboard. Distribute Teacher Aid 15 to each child and place Teacher Aids Transparency 11 on an overhead projector. First, model the exercise on the transparency workmat. Then, have children combine the ones models, combine tens models and regroup, and then combine hundreds models. Make sure children understand each step.

GUIDED PRACTICE ex. 1: For reteaching, use Common Error and Remediation or Alternative Strategy.

3 PRACTICE•APPLY   **PRACTICE** ex. 2–6

MENTAL MATH Discuss the example with the children, pointing out they can think of 300 as 3 hundreds and so on.

CLOSE Guide children to summarize the lesson:

■ **How do you add 235 and 491? Explain each step.** [Add the ones. Add the tens. Regroup 12 tens. Add the hundreds to get 726.]

Chapter 13 • Lesson 3   **396**

MAC Activity 229

SPEAKING MATHEMATICALLY ■ SENTENCE FILL IN

On Your Own   Pair and Share   In a Group

Read the following statements about adding 3-digit numbers. Have children repeat the sentence, filling in the blank with the missing word. Suggested responses are provided, but accept all reasonable answers.

1. When adding 2 digits or more, I begin with the _____. [ones]
2. After adding the ones, I add the _____. [tens]
3. If there are more than 9 tens, I know I need to _____. [regroup]
4. If I have 8 tens, I know that I _____ [do not need to regroup]
5. When adding 3-digit numbers, I add the _____ after the tens. [hundreds]
6. When I add, my answer is called the _____. [sum]

**MAC Activity 229:
Basic-to-Average** ▶

MAC Activity 230

MANIPULATIVES ■ WHAT'S THE PROBLEM?

hundreds	tens	ones
4	8	3
2	7	1

[754]

hundreds	tens	ones
2	8	9
3	9	0

[679]

hundreds	tens	ones
4	2	7
1	9	1

[618]

hundreds	tens	ones
6	6	3
2	8	4

[947]

On Your Own   Pair and Share   In a Group

Materials   hundreds, tens, and ones models or punchouts; punchout Workmat 3

Assign children to work in pairs. Give each pair of children hundreds, tens, and ones models and Workmat 3. Write the following exercises in place-value boxes on the chalkboard.

Tell children that they are to model the numbers and then write a problem to go with the numbers, such as the following:

Nancy had 483 stamps.
Mark had 271 stamps.
How many stamps did they have in all? [754]

Have children solve each other's word problems.

▲
**MAC Activity 230:
Average-to-Challenge**

RETEACHING

RETEACHING-115

Name _____

ADDING ONES, TENS, AND HUNDREDS

Study

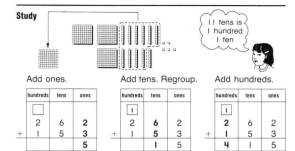

> 11 tens is 1 hundred 1 ten

Add ones.

hundreds	tens	ones
☐		
2	6	**2**
+ 1	5	**3**
		5

Add tens. Regroup.

hundreds	tens	ones
1		
2	**6**	2
+ 1	**5**	3
	1	5

Add hundreds.

hundreds	tens	ones
1		
2	6	2
+ **1**	5	3
4	1	5

Check

Use models and Workmat 4. Add.

1.

hundreds	tens	ones
1		
3	5	4
+ 2	7	2
6	2	6

hundreds	tens	ones
1		
1	7	1
+ 3	7	5
5	4	6

2.

hundreds	tens	ones
1		
6	9	3
+ 1	5	4
8	4	7

hundreds	tens	ones
4	6	2
+ 2	7	1
7	3	3

Reteaching-115

Macmillan/McGraw-Hill, MATHEMATICS IN ACTION
Grade 2, Chapter 13, Lesson 3, pages 395–396

PRACTICE

PRACTICE-115

Name _____

ADDING ONES, TENS, AND HUNDREDS

Use Workmat 3. Use 18 ▭, 9 ▱, and 9 ▦ .
Find the sum.

1.

hundreds	tens	ones
1		
1	4	6
+ 5	8	1
7	2	7

2.

hundreds	tens	ones
1		
2	6	3
+ 2	6	2
5	2	5

3.

hundreds	tens	ones
1		
7	9	1
+	6	4
8	5	5

4.

hundreds	tens	ones
3	8	7
+ 4	5	2
8	3	9

5.

hundreds	tens	ones
1		
8	4	3
+	9	4
9	3	7

6.

hundreds	tens	ones
1		
6	3	8
+ 2	8	1
9	1	9

7.

hundreds	tens	ones
1		
5	6	4
+ 1	5	4
7	1	8

8.

hundreds	tens	ones
1		
1	9	6
+ 4	9	3
6	8	9

Practice-115

Macmillan/McGraw-Hill, MATHEMATICS IN ACTION
Grade 2, Chapter 13, Lesson 3, pages 395–396

ENRICHMENT

ENRICHMENT-115

Name _____

ADDING ONES, TENS, AND HUNDREDS

On Your Own Pair and Share In a Group

HOW FAR AROUND?

Look at the length of each side of the figure. Ring the better estimate of the distance around the figure.

1.

< 500   (> 500)

2.
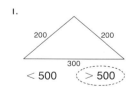
(< 900)   > 900

3.
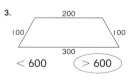
< 600   (> 600)

4.
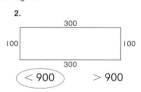
(< 1,000)   > 1,000

5.
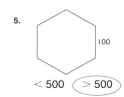
< 500   (> 500)

6.
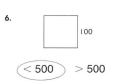
(< 500)   > 500

Enrichment-115

Macmillan/McGraw-Hill, MATHEMATICS IN ACTION
Grade 2, Chapter 13, Lesson 3, pages 395–396

Problem of the Day

The lunchroom sold 173 apples on Monday and 265 apples on Tuesday. Were there more than 500 apples sold on both days? [No; 173 + 265 = 438; 438 < 500.]

AT·A·GLANCE pp. 397-398

LESSON OBJECTIVE
Add 3-digit numbers, regrouping twice.

ASSIGNMENT GUIDE

COURSE	EXERCISES
Basic	p. 397: All; p. 398: 1–7
Average	p. 397: All; p. 398: 1–7
Challenge	p. 397: All; p. 398: 1–7
Extra Practice, p. 402	Practice Plus, p. 414

MATERIALS
Manipulatives 9 H, 22 T, 19 O models (or punchouts), Work-mat 3* per child

Teacher Resources
Reteaching 116
Prob. Solv. 61
Calculator 11
Practice 116
MAC Act. 231, 232
Enrichment 116
*Teacher Aid 15

SKILLS TRACE
3-DIGIT ADDITION

Explore (Concrete) 392, 393–394	Develop/Understand (Transitional/Abstract) 395–396, 397–398
Practice 402, 414, 415–416, 419	**Apply** 412, 418

See **MANIPULATIVES PLUS 74**, p. 390J.

1 PREPARE **WARM-UP** To review regrouping, have children use hundreds, tens, and ones models to regroup the following.
1. 15 tens 8 ones [1 hundred 5 tens 8 ones]
2. 22 tens 6 ones [2 hundreds 2 tens 6 ones]
3. 8 tens 12 ones [9 tens 2 ones]
4. 3 tens 19 ones [4 tens 9 ones]
5. 14 tens 14 ones [1 hundred 5 tens 4 ones]
6. 17 tens 18 ones [1 hundred 8 tens 8 ones]

2 TEACH **MODELING** Write the following exercise in a place-value chart on the chalkboard. Have children use hundreds, tens, and ones models to model the addition on Work-mat 3.

Name _____

3-Digit Addition

Add 275 and 156.

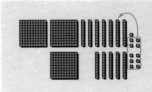

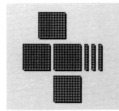

Add the ones.
Regroup if you can.
$$\begin{array}{r} \overset{1}{2}7\,5 \\ +\,1\,5\,6 \\ \hline 1 \end{array}$$

(11 ones = 1 ten 1 one)

Add the tens.
Regroup if you can.
$$\begin{array}{r} \overset{1\,1}{2}7\,5 \\ +\,1\,5\,6 \\ \hline 3\,1 \end{array}$$

(13 tens = 1 hundred 3 tens)

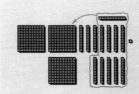

Add the hundreds.
$$\begin{array}{r} \overset{1\,1}{2}7\,5 \\ +\,1\,5\,6 \\ \hline 4\,3\,1 \end{array}$$

Add.

$$\begin{array}{r} \overset{1\,1}{1}9\,7 \\ +\,4\,2\,6 \\ \hline 6\,2\,3 \end{array}$$
$$\begin{array}{r} 5\,3\,6 \\ +\,2\,9\,4 \\ \hline 830 \end{array}$$
$$\begin{array}{r} 6\,0\,4 \\ +\,2\,9\,8 \\ \hline 902 \end{array}$$
$$\begin{array}{r} 2\,4\,1 \\ +\,4\,6\,3 \\ \hline 704 \end{array}$$
$$\begin{array}{r} 4\,9\,5 \\ +\,2\,0\,5 \\ \hline 700 \end{array}$$

Macmillan/McGraw-Hill

$$\begin{array}{r} 1\,8\,3 \\ +\,\ \ 1\,5\,9 \\ \hline \end{array}$$

Have children combine the ones models to add the ones.
■ **Do you need to regroup the ones? Why?** [Yes, because there are more than 9 ones.]
After children model the regrouping, record a 1 under the ones column and a regrouped 1 at the top of the tens column.
■ **Do you need to regroup the tens? Why?** [Yes, because there are more than 9 tens.]
Record the 6 in the tens column and a regrouped 1 at the top of the hundreds column. Have children combine the hundreds models to find the sum. [461]

Add.

1.
$$\begin{array}{r} 379 \\ + 206 \\ \hline 585 \end{array}$$
$$\begin{array}{r} 625 \\ + 173 \\ \hline 798 \end{array}$$
$$\begin{array}{r} 542 \\ + 376 \\ \hline 918 \end{array}$$
$$\begin{array}{r} 495 \\ + 203 \\ \hline 698 \end{array}$$
$$\begin{array}{r} 609 \\ + 294 \\ \hline 903 \end{array}$$

2.
$$\begin{array}{r} 487 \\ + 69 \\ \hline 556 \end{array}$$
$$\begin{array}{r} 289 \\ + 388 \\ \hline 677 \end{array}$$
$$\begin{array}{r} 68 \\ + 293 \\ \hline 361 \end{array}$$
$$\begin{array}{r} 176 \\ + 813 \\ \hline 989 \end{array}$$
$$\begin{array}{r} 280 \\ + 77 \\ \hline 357 \end{array}$$

3.
$$\begin{array}{r} 725 \\ + 189 \\ \hline 914 \end{array}$$
$$\begin{array}{r} 569 \\ + 169 \\ \hline 738 \end{array}$$
$$\begin{array}{r} 290 \\ + 650 \\ \hline 940 \end{array}$$
$$\begin{array}{r} 352 \\ + 6 \\ \hline 358 \end{array}$$
$$\begin{array}{r} 195 \\ + 8 \\ \hline 203 \end{array}$$

Solve.

4. East School collected 123 cans. West School collected 235 cans. How many cans did they collect in all? ___358___ cans

5. West School collected 287 bottles. East School collected 123 cans. How many containers did both schools collect? ___410___ containers

Mixed Review

6. What number is 10 less than 59? ___49___

7. What number is 15 less than 82? ___67___

Extra Practice, page 402 *Practice Plus,* page 414

ACTIVITY Common Error and Remediation

MATERIALS 9 H, 22 T, 19 O models, Workmat 3

Some children may "regroup" when there are fewer than 10 ones or 10 tens. Work individually with each child using hundreds, tens, and ones models and Workmat 3. Give the child exercises in a place-value box format that do and do not require regrouping. Have the child use models, and guide him or her through each exercise. Have the child describe each step of the addition.

For Students Acquiring English (SAE)

As you model 3-digit addition for SAE children, reinforce the right-to-left progression in regrouping. Have SAE children work with non-SAE partners on page 398, using models and verbalizing the steps as they work.

ACTIVITY ALTERNATIVE TEACHING STRATEGY

MATERIALS Manipulatives Kit Transparencies 8, 9 or 8 H, 15 T, 13 O models, Teacher Aids Transparency 11; overhead projector

VISUAL Write 384 + 476 in vertical form on the chalkboard. Model the two numbers on Teacher Aids Transparency 11. Work through each step of the addition, calling on volunteers to tell you what to do next for each step. Repeat the activity with 508 + 295.

Repeat with a similar exercise, without using a place-value box. Discuss that the place-value box is not necessary. Stress the importance of lining up the digits.

Then demonstrate adding with a zero in the tens place; for example, 207 + 498.

PUPIL'S EDITION pp. 397-398

Page 397 Work through the steps of the addition with children. Have them model each step of the exercise.

Check for Understanding

■ If I added 288 + 395, how many times would I need to regroup? [two times]

GUIDED PRACTICE All: Have children use models if they need

help. For reteaching, use Common Error and Remediation or Alternative Strategy.

Page 398 Remind children to use models.

3 PRACTICE•APPLY PRACTICE ex. 1–7

CLOSE Guide children to summarize the lesson:

■ **Do you regroup when you add 238 + 472? What do you regroup?** [Yes; you regroup ones as tens and tens as hundreds.]

■ **Do you regroup when you add 247 + 132? If so, what?** [No.]

■ **Do you regroup when you add 331 + 475? If so, what?** [Yes; you regroup tens as hundreds.]

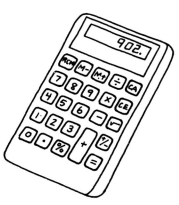

CALCULATOR ■ ADD AND CHECK

MAC Activity 231

On Your Own   Pair and Share   In a Group

$$608 + 294 = 902$$

$$294 + 608 = 902$$

Materials calculator

Assign children to work in pairs. Give each pair of children a calculator. Remind children that they learned that the order of addends could be reversed and the sum would be the same. Further remind them that because of this, the order of addends could be reversed to check addition.

Tell one child to write a 3-digit addition exercise on a piece of paper. Then have the second child perform the addition on a calculator and record the answer. Tell the first child to redo the problem reversing the order of the addends to check the addition. Then have them compare the two sums. Have children alternate roles to continue the activity.

▲
**MAC Activity 231:
Basic-to-Average**

**MAC Activity 232:
Average-to-Challenge**
▼

COMPUTER ■ ADDITION PROGRAM

MAC Activity 232

On Your Own   Pair and Share   In a Group

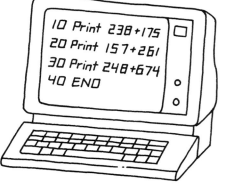

```
10 Print 238+175
20 Print 157+261
30 Print 248+674
40 END
```

Materials ones, tens, and hundreds models or punchouts; computer (optional)

Have children recall that a computer program is a set of instructions that tells a computer what to do. Remind children that without a program, a computer cannot operate. Present the following program and discuss each line. Point to the word *END* and ask children what this command tells the computer. [It tells the computer to stop.]

```
10   Print 238 + 175   [413]
20   Print 157 + 261   [418]
30   Print 248 + 674   [922]
40   END
```

Explain that after command *RUN* is typed in, the computer will print the answer to each addition. Have children use hundreds, tens, and ones models to find each answer and write what the screen would show. If a computer is available, have children write and then execute their own short programs using this sample program as a guide.

RETEACHING

Name _____

3-DIGIT ADDITION

Study

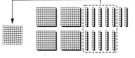

Add ones. Regroup.　Add tens. Regroup.　Add hundreds.

hundreds	tens	ones
	1	
2	7	6
+ 2	5	8
		4

hundreds	tens	ones
1	1	
2	7	6
2	5	8
	3	4

hundreds	tens	ones
1	1	
2	7	6
2	5	8
5	3	4

Check

Use Workmat 4 and models. Add.

1.
hundreds	tens	ones
1	1	
1	7	6
+ 2	4	5
4	2	1

hundreds	tens	ones
2	5	9
+ 2	5	3
5	1	2

2.
hundreds	tens	ones
1	1	
4	3	4
+	8	7
5	2	1

hundreds	tens	ones
1		
3	0	9
+ 1	9	5
5	0	4

Macmillan/McGraw-Hill, MATHEMATICS IN ACTION
Grade 2, Chapter 13, Lesson 4, pages 397–398

Reteaching-116

PRACTICE

Name _____

3-DIGIT ADDITION

Add.

1. 247 + 365 **612**	507 + 369 876	435 + 292 727	182 + 89 271	649 + 214 863
2. 483 + 175 658	364 + 129 493	209 + 428 637	328 + 661 989	745 + 219 964
3. 758 + 87 845	606 + 189 795	452 + 8 460	540 + 118 658	483 + 217 700
4. 214 + 195 409	135 + 383 518	356 + 129 485	469 + 236 705	674 + 96 770
5. 532 + 208 740	765 + 109 874	646 + 328 974	493 + 18 511	542 + 419 961

Solve.

6. Marc unpacked 308 books.
   Kitty unpacked 476 books.
   How many books did they unpack in all?　___784___ books

Macmillan/McGraw-Hill, MATHEMATICS IN ACTION
Grade 2, Chapter 13, Lesson 4, pages 397–398

Practice-116

ENRICHMENT

Name _____

3-DIGIT ADDITION

On Your Own　Pair and Share　In a Group

ADDING MONEY

$1.87
+ 2.56
$4.43

Add.

1. $1.58 + 4.12 $5.70	$4.55 + .25 $4.80	$2.21 + 5.89 $8.10	$1.03 + 2.47 $3.50
2. $5.03 + 2.39 $7.42	$7.88 + 1.56 $9.44	$4.06 + 3.87 $7.93	$2.77 + 4.82 $7.59
3. $5.62 + 1.89 $7.51	$4.77 + 2.18 $6.95	$2.89 + 5.04 $7.93	$5.34 + 2.87 $8.21

4. A plant costs $3.28.
   A flower pot costs $4.06.
   How much money in all?　$7.34

Macmillan/McGraw-Hill, MATHEMATICS IN ACTION
Grade 2, Chapter 13, Lesson 4, pages 397–398

Enrichment-116

Problem of the Day

The sign over the diner has 425 yellow lightbulbs and 285 red lightbulbs. During a storm, all the bulbs blew out. How many bulbs will the diner owner need to buy? [710]

CHAPTER 13 • Lesson 5

AT·A·GLANCE pp. 399-400

LESSON OBJECTIVE
Solve 2-step problems.

ASSIGNMENT GUIDE

COURSE	EXERCISES
Basic	p. 400: 1–4
Average	p. 400: 1–4
Challenge	p. 400: 1–4
Extra Practice, p. 402	

MATERIALS
Manipulatives 8 T, 14 O models (or punchouts), Workmat 2 per child

Teacher Resources
Reteaching 117
Prob. Solv. 62
Practice 117
MAC Act. 233, 234
Enrichment 117

PREPARE   **WARM-UP**   To prepare children for solving 2-step problems, have them give the following sums and differences:

36 + 35 [71]	82 − 71 [11]
41 + 28 [69]	90 − 69 [21]
37 + 14 [51]	73 − 51 [22]

TEACH   **QUESTIONING**   Read the following problem to the children. Have them model the numbers on their workmat.

Tony had 84 stamps. He gave 27 stamps to his sister. He gave 30 stamps to a friend. How many stamps did he have left?

Name _____

Problem Solving

Strategy: Solving a Two-Step Problem

Susan had 90 books.
She gave 35 to the book club and
50 to her friends.
How many books did she have left?

What do I know? What do I need to find out?	Susan had 90 books. She gave away 35 and 50. How many books are left?

What can I do?	Subtract how many she gave away from how many she had.

	How many did she give away in all? Add to find out.

Try the plan.	

Susan had __5__ books left.

What have I learned?	Sometimes there are 2 steps in solving a problem.

Chapter 13   **Explore Adding and Subtracting 3-Digit Numbers**   three hundred ninety-nine   **399**

■ **What do you know?** [Tony had 84 stamps. He gave away 27 and 30.]

■ **What do you need to find out?** [how many stamps Tony has left]

■ **How can you find how many are left?** [Subtract the stamps he gave away from the stamps he had.]

■ **What do you need to find before you can subtract?** [how many stamps in all were given away]

■ **How can you find how many stamps were given away?** [Add; 27 + 30 = 57.]

■ **What do you do next?** [Subtract; 84 − 57 = 27.]

■ **How many stamps did Tony have left?** [27 stamps]

Solve.

1. Wally's booth had 98 books.
   He sold 24 books about animals.
   He sold 31 books about stars.

   How many books were left? __43__ books

2. Kurt had 92¢.
   He bought *Nine Planets* for 28¢.
   He bought *Friends* for 49¢.

   How much money did Kurt have left? __15__ ¢

3. Di took 71 books to the fair.
   She sold 17 books on Saturday.
   She sold 24 books on Sunday.

   How many books did Di have left? __30__ books

4. You have 79¢ to spend.
   Ring two books that you would want to buy.

Horses 41¢

Elephant Jokes 26¢

Number Puzzles 25¢

Sailing 32¢

Rockets 18¢

Dinosaurs 33¢

   How much money would you have left? _____ ¢ Answers will vary.

Extra Practice, page 402

MEETING INDIVIDUAL NEEDS

TEACHER to TEACHER

COOPERATIVE LEARNING TIP  I encourage my children to take turns doing the exercises in pairs. One partner asks appropriate questions to cue the other to use the two steps for solving that were given in the lesson. The other partner reasons aloud, giving explanations for his or her plans. Then they switch roles for the next problem. Partners practice **attentive listening skills** and help each other think things through when one gets stuck. On the review section, they compare answers and agree on a reasonable solution to the problem.

For Students Acquiring English (SAE)

Introduce the word **steps** in the context of doing something in order. Pair SAE children and non-SAE children to work together to complete the exercises on page 400. To review, have partners state how they solved each of the exercises and show the steps of their computations on the chalkboard.

PUPIL'S EDITION pp. 399–400

Page 399   Have a volunteer read the problem at the top of the page. Discuss the questions on the page. Guide children to see that they must first add to find how many books were given away before they can subtract to find how many are left. Have children do the two steps in the problem by tracing the addition and subtraction exercises.

■ **Does the answer 5 make sense?** [Yes; if you add 35 and 50 you get 85. If you subtract 85 from 90 you get 5.]

Discuss the last question. Encourage children to explain other ways to solve this problem.

Check for Understanding

■ **What if Susan had 80 books and gave 27 books to the book club and 30 to her friends? How many books would she have left?** [23]

Page 400   Read the problems with the children as necessary.

GUIDED PRACTICE   ex. 1: Work through problem 1 with the children. Make sure they understand that it is a two-step problem.

3 PRACTICE•APPLY   PRACTICE   ex. 2–4

C L O S E   Guide children to summarize the lesson:

■ **How do you know when two steps are needed to solve a problem?** [Possible response: In some problems you have to find one number first before you can find the answer to the problem.]

MAC Activity 233:
Basic-to-Average

MAC Activity 233

On Your Own   Pair and Share   In a Group

SPEAKING MATHEMATICALLY ▪ FLOWERS FOR SALE

Materials   punchout tens and ones models, punchout Workmat 2

Have children work in groups of three. Give each group of children a set of tens and ones models and Workmat 2. Tell children that you will read them some problems about a person who owns a flower shop. Explain that they are to work together to model the numbers in the problems. Have them write the numbers on paper for reference while they work. Then have children find the answers and explain the steps they followed.

1. Martin has 76 roses in his flower shop. He fills an order for 34 roses. Then he sells 19 more roses. How many roses does he have left to sell? [23; 34 + 19 = 53; 76 − 53 = 23]
2. Martin orders 82 daisies. One day he receives 37 daisies. The next day he receives 27. How many daisies did he not receive? [18; 37 + 27 = 64; 82 − 64 = 18]
3. Tina had 96¢. She spent 58¢ on daffodils. She bought 2 daisies for 23¢. How much money does she have left? [15¢; 58¢ + 23¢ = 81¢; 96¢ − 81¢ = 15¢]

Continue the activity with similar problems.

MAC Activity 234:
Average-to-Challenge ▶

WRITING MATHEMATICS ▪ DEEP SEA RACE

MAC Activity 234

On Your Own   Pair and Share   In a Group

Assign children to groups of four and have them stand in the back of the room. Within the groups, have children work in pairs. Tell the groups to pretend that they are submarine crews in the deep ocean trying to get back to home port, which is the front of the room.

Explain to the children that you will read them some problems. One pair in each group does the first step in the problem and gives the other pair the answer. The second pair does the second step in the problem and announces the answer. Tell children that the first group to give the correct answer advances one table or one row of desks. The group that reaches the front of the room first wins the game.

1. You see a school of 68 dolphins ahead. 42 dolphins swim away. Then 19 dolphins swim away. How many dolphins are left? [7]
2. Your submarine needs to dive 87 feet. First you go down 32 feet. Then you go down another 27 feet. How many more feet do you have to go down? [28]

Continue the activity with similar problems.

Name

PROBLEM SOLVING STRATEGY: SOLVING A TWO-STEP PROBLEM

Study

A store had 74 computers.
39 computers were sold on Monday.
17 computers were sold on Wednesday.
How many computers are left?

Step 1
Add to find how many computers were sold.

$$\begin{array}{r} 39 \\ + 17 \\ \hline 56 \end{array}$$

Step 2
Subtract to find how many computers are left.

$$\begin{array}{r} {}^{6}\!\!\not7{}^{14}\!\!\not4 \\ - 56 \\ \hline 18 \end{array}\ \text{computers left}$$

Check

Solve.
Add first. Then subtract.

1. Naomi had 68 computer games.
She sold 23 games.
She sent 28 games to another store.
How many games are left?

$$\begin{array}{r} 23 \\ + 28 \\ \hline 51 \end{array} \qquad \begin{array}{r} 68 \\ - 51 \\ \hline 17 \end{array}$$

17 games are left

2. A box has 52 computer disks.
Al uses 16 disks.
Jane uses 27 disks.
How many disks are left? **9** disks

3. Greg has 89 computer problems.
He solves 47 problems.
Then he solves 23 problems.
How many problems does Greg have left? **19** problems

Reteaching-117

Macmillan/McGraw-Hill, MATHEMATICS IN ACTION
Grade 2, Chapter 13, Lesson 5, pages 399–400

Name

PROBLEM SOLVING STRATEGY: SOLVING A TWO-STEP PROBLEM

Solve.

1. Blake had 73 fish.
He sold 26 goldfish.
He sold 18 angel fish.
How many fish did he have left? **29** fish

2. Abby had 81 shells.
She gave 32 shells to a friend.
She took 27 shells to school.
How many shells did she have left? **22** shells

3. Jan had 92¢.
She bought a book about fish for 54¢.
She bought a book about the sea for 30¢.
How much money did she have left? **8** ¢

4. Pepe had 65 guppies in a big tank.
He put 17 guppies in a small bowl.
He gave 35 guppies to Mel.
How many guppies are left
in the tank? **13** guppies

5. Pearl had 78 clams in a bucket.
She used 24 clams in the soup.
She steamed 47 clams.
How many clams are left
in the bucket? **7** clams

Practice-117

Macmillan/McGraw-Hill, MATHEMATICS IN ACTION
Grade 2, Chapter 13, Lesson 5, pages 399–400

Name

PROBLEM SOLVING

On Your Own   Pair and Share   In a Group

THE GREAT BEE ROUNDUP

3 beekeepers lost their bees.
Now they have to get the bees back in their hives.
Find how many bees are back in each hive.
Use the clues to solve the problem.

1. In all, 98 bees got away.

2. Erin caught 17 bees.
Then, 14 went back to her hive by themselves.

3. Hector rounded up 7 more bees than Erin has.

4. Dennis got 12 bees back into his hive.
Then he caught 9 more bees.

How many bees are still loose? **8** bees

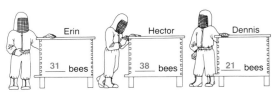

Erin **31** bees   Hector **38** bees   Dennis **21** bees

Enrichment-117

Macmillan/McGraw-Hill, MATHEMATICS IN ACTION
Grade 2, Chapter 13, Lesson 5, pages 399–400

Problem of the Day

Judy had 90¢. She bought four comic books for 54¢. She bought two notebooks for 19¢. She wants to buy a pen for 15¢. Does Judy have enough money left? [Yes; 54¢ + 19¢ = 73¢; 90¢ − 73¢ = 17¢; 17¢ > 15¢.]

AT·A·GLANCE p. 401

LESSON OBJECTIVE
Use logical reasoning.

ASSIGNMENT GUIDE

COURSE	EXERCISES
Basic	p. 401: 1–3
Average	p. 401: 1–3
Challenge	p. 401: 1–3

MATERIALS
Manipulatives 3 ○ (or punchouts) per child (optional)

Teacher Resources
Crit. Think. 25

Name _____

PUZZLING PETS

Strange things are happening at the pet show.
Solve the mystery. Ring the name of the animal.

1. Which dog hid the bone?
   It has spots.
   It does not have a collar.
   It is not lying down.

Sam Rex Ali Kaz

Tom Max Kit Jax

2. Which cat climbed the tree?
   It is not grey.
   It does not have stripes.
   It is not resting.

3. Which animal made a sound?
   It has a beak.
   It is not yellow.
   It is not standing on one leg.

Liz Abe Doc Tip

401

---

1 PLAN **AIMS AND ATTITUDES** This lesson develops logical reasoning involving clues about an animal's physical characteristics. In the lesson, children must eliminate choices only after considering additional clues presented.

You can encourage enthusiasm for doing the activity by stressing its gamelike nature and by encouraging children to pretend that they are detectives who must use each of the clues to determine the "mystery" animal.

MANAGEMENT The activity is intended for all children and has been designed for independent work but is also appropriate for pairs of children. When pairing children, it may be particularly effective to pair a child having strong problem-solving and language skills with one having weaker skills.

2 GUIDE Draw a circle, a square, a rectangle, and a triangle on the chalkboard and have children listen as you give clues about the shapes.

■ **I am thinking of a shape. It has 3 sides. It has 3 corners. Which shape is it?** [triangle]

■ **I am thinking of a shape. It has 4 sides. It has 4 corners. 2 of the sides are shorter than the other 2 sides. Which shape is it?** [rectangle]

Continue the activity by giving clues for the last 2 shapes.

Read the directions on page 401 with the children. Identify the pictures on the page. Have children read each exercise carefully and ring the correct animal. Some children may have difficulty remembering the animals they eliminate. You might suggest that as they read clues, these

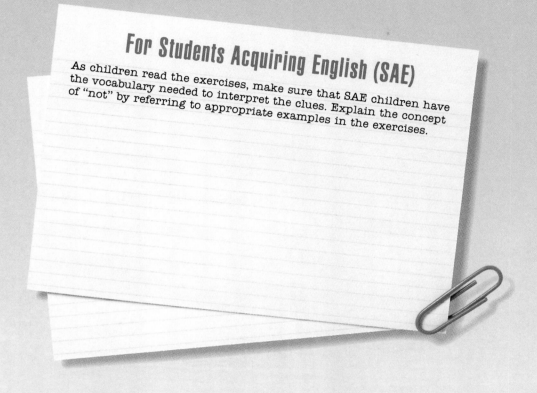

For Students Acquiring English (SAE)

As children read the exercises, make sure that SAE children have the vocabulary needed to interpret the clues. Explain the concept of "not" by referring to appropriate examples in the exercises.

children cover with a counter each animal that does not fit the description.

3 EXTEND Have children repeat the activity on page 401. This time, write on the chalkboard or give children a handout containing the following new clues about the animals:

1. Which dog hid the bone?
   It is standing.
   It has spots.
   It has a collar. [Sam]

2. Which cat climbed the tree?
   It is playing with string.
   It is near the tree.
   It is wearing a collar. [Jax]

3. Which animal made a sound?
   It is not pink.
   It is not yellow.
   It does not have a beak. [Liz]

EXTRA PRACTICE

Extra Practice items are provided so that children may have an opportunity for further practice.

The Additional Practice section also provides practice you may wish to assign.

Extra Practice

EXTRA PRACTICE

3-Digit Addition, pages 397–398 . . . .

Add.

1.
315	528	263	632	883
+192	+219	+277	+189	+104
507	747	540	821	987

2.
461	196	751	393	505
+309	+557	+118	+448	+255
770	753	869	841	760

Problem Solving: 2-Step Problems, pages 399–400 . . . .

Solve.

1. David had 85 flower seeds.
   He gave Harold 42 seeds.
   He gave Marty 29 seeds.
   How many seeds did David have left?

   __14__ seeds

2. Shelly's booth had 97 books.
   She sold 29 storybooks.
   She sold 43 comic books.
   How many books were left?

   __25__ books

ADDITIONAL PRACTICE

p. 397 *Add.*

1.
296	719	392
+413	+267	+107
[709]	[986]	[499]

2.
431	625	346
+216	+147	+552
[647]	[772]	[898]

3.
110	315	517
+268	+449	+316
[378]	[764]	[833]

4.
671	276	775
+243	+293	+192
[914]	[569]	[967]

p. 399 *Solve.*

1. Mary Ann had 86¢. She bought a plant for 35¢. She bought a pen for 39¢. How much money did she have left? [12¢]

2. Seth had 99 baseball cards. He gave Charlie 21 cards. He gave Molly 37 cards. How many cards does Seth have left? [41] cards

AT•A•GLANCE pp. 403-404

LESSON OBJECTIVE
Explore regrouping hundreds for subtraction.

ASSIGNMENT GUIDE

COURSE	EXERCISES
Basic	p. 403: 1–3; p. 404: 2–5
Average	p. 403: 1–3; p. 404: 2–5
Challenge	p. 403: 1–3; p. 404: 2–5

MATERIALS
Manipulatives 8 H, 18 T, 19 O models, spinner for 0–9 (or punchouts) per pair

SKILLS TRACE
3-DIGIT SUBTRACTION

Explore (Concrete) 403–404	Develop/Understand (Transitional/Abstract) 405–406, 407–408
Practice 413, 414, 415–416, 419	Apply 412, 418

See **MANIPULATIVES PLUS 75**, p. 390K.

---

1 PREPARE
WARM-UP To review regrouping tens for ones, have children model the following on Workmat 3 using tens and ones models. For each number, have children tell if it is possible to regroup 1 ten for 10 ones. If so, have them model the regrouping.

1. 5 tens 6 ones   [Yes; 4 tens 16 ones.]
2. 2 tens 9 ones   [Yes; 1 ten 19 ones.]
3. 7 ones   [No.]

2 TEACH
DISCUSSING Write 34 in a place-value chart on the chalkboard. Then use tens and ones models and Workmat 3 to demonstrate regrouping 1 ten as 10 ones so that 3 tens 4 ones becomes 2 tens 14 ones.

Name _____

ACTIVITY

Regrouping Hundreds for Subtraction

Russ had 234 magazines.

He used 2 hundreds, 3 tens, and 4 ones to show the magazines.

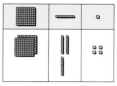

hundreds	tens	ones
2	3	4

He regrouped 1 hundred as 10 tens.

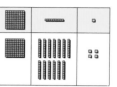

hundreds	tens	ones
1	13	4

Write how many Russ has now.   1 hundred 13 tens 4 ones

Use Workmat 3. Use 18 ▭ , 8 ▫ , and 3 ▦ to show the number.
Regroup 1 hundred as 10 tens.
Write the number.

1.

hundreds	tens	ones
1	6	8

hundreds	tens	ones
	16	8

2.

hundreds	tens	ones
3	8	1

hundreds	tens	ones
2	18	1

3.

hundreds	tens	ones
2	0	5

hundreds	tens	ones
1	10	5

■ **How many ones are equal to 1 ten?** [10 ones]

Write 360 in a place-value box and model 3 hundreds and 6 tens on Workmat 3.

■ **How many hundreds and tens do you see?** [3 hundreds and 6 tens]

■ **Do we have enough hundreds to regroup for 10 tens?** [Yes.]

Do the regrouping and have children count the models to find how many hundreds and tens there are. [2 hundreds 16 tens]

PUPIL'S EDITION pp. 403-404
Page 403 Work through the example at the top of the page.

Write the numbers that the models show.

1.

hundreds	tens	ones
2	3	4

hundreds	tens	ones
1	13	4

2.
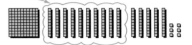

hundreds	tens	ones
2	5	6

hundreds	tens	ones
1	15	6

Working Together

Use Workmat 3. Use 8 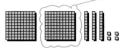, 17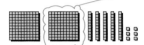
8 □, and a ⊙.

Show	Spin to find how many tens to take away.	Take away the tens. Did you regroup?	Write the number.
Answers will vary. Check students' answers.			
3. 125	_____ tens	yes no	
4. 238	_____ tens	yes no	
5. 874	_____ tens	yes no	

Check for Understanding

■ How many tens are in 1 hundred? [10]

GUIDED PRACTICE ex. 1–3: Provide children with 18 tens, 8 ones, and 3 hundreds models and Workmat 3. For reteaching, use Alternative Strategy.

Page 404 Work through ex. 1.

WORKING TOGETHER Distribute materials to each pair of children. Have children model the number on the chart, spin for the number of tens to take away, regroup the tens if needed, take the tens away, and write the number for the models left.

3 PRACTICE•APPLY

PRACTICE ex. 2–5

MEETING INDIVIDUAL NEEDS

ONGOING ASSESSMENT

OBSERVATION Determine whether children correctly completed the regrouping table on p. 404.

INTERVIEW (1) How would you find the answer to 152 – 83? (2) Would you have to regroup to solve 306 – 284? Tell why. (3) How would you find the answer to 266 – 175?

JOURNAL WRITING You may wish to have children record their responses in their math journals.

For Students Acquiring English (SAE)

Provide additional modeling for regrouping for subtraction using ex. 1–3 on page 403. Go through the steps orally with SAE children, modeling each exercise. On page 404, pair SAE and non-SAE children to complete ex. 2–5. Encourage pairs to talk about the exercises as they work.

ALTERNATIVE TEACHING STRATEGY

MATERIALS 8 H, 18 T, 19 O models (or punchouts), Workmat 3

VISUAL Display 4 hundreds on Workmat 3. Tell children that you need to take away 7 tens. Discuss that 1 hundreds model could be regrouped for 10 tens. Have a volunteer regroup 1 hundred as 10 tens and identify the number of hundreds and tens. [3 hundreds 10 tens] Take away the 7 tens and have a volunteer tell how many hundreds and tens are left. [3 hundreds 3 tens] Repeat the activity with other numbers.

CLOSE Guide children to summarize the lesson:

■ If you regroup 1 hundred for tens in 3 hundreds 0 tens 7 ones, how many hundreds, tens, and ones would you have? [2 hundreds 10 tens 7 ones]

Problem of the Day

Susan checked the storeroom and counted 6 cases with 100 cans of peaches in each case. She counted 4 boxes with 10 cans of peaches in each box. If Susan opened 1 case and put the cans into boxes of 10, how many cases and boxes would she have in all? [5 cases, 14 boxes]

AT·A·GLANCE pp. 405-406

LESSON OBJECTIVE
Subtract 3-digit numbers, regrouping hundreds to tens.

ASSIGNMENT GUIDE

COURSE	EXERCISES
Basic	p. 406: 1–6, Estimation
Average	p. 406: 1–6, Estimation
Challenge	p. 406: 1–6, Estimation

MATERIALS
Manipulatives 9 H, 18 T, 9 O models (or punchouts), Workmat 3* per child

Teacher Resources
Reteaching 118
MAC Act. 235, 236
Practice 118
Teacher Aids 1, *15
Enrichment 118

SKILLS TRACE
3-DIGIT SUBTRACTION

Explore (Concrete) 403–404	Develop/Understand (Transitional/Abstract) 405–406, 407–408
Practice 413, 414, 415–416, 419	**Apply** 412, 418

ACTIVITY

Subtracting Ones, Tens, and Hundreds

Ellen subtracts 184 from 326.

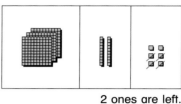

First subtract the ones.

hundreds	tens	ones
□ 3	□ 2	6
1	8	4
		2

2 ones are left.

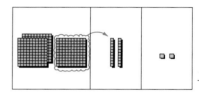

Then look at the tens. Regroup. Do you know why?

There are not enough tens.

hundreds	tens	ones
[2] 3	[12] 2	6
1	8	4
		2

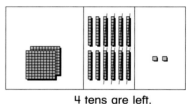

Now subtract the tens.

hundreds	tens	ones
[2] 3	[12] 2	6
1	8	4
	4	2

4 tens are left.

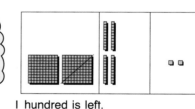

Then subtract the hundreds.

hundreds	tens	ones
[2] 3	[12] 2	6
1	8	4
1	4	2

1 hundred is left.

What is the difference? 326 − 184 = ___142___

Macmillan/McGraw-Hill

Chapter 13   Explore Adding and Subtracting 3-Digit Numbers   four hundred five   **405**

---

1 PREPARE

WARM-UP To review regrouping hundreds to tens, write the following in place-value boxes on the chalkboard. Have children regroup 1 hundred to tens, using models if needed, and tell how many hundreds, tens, and ones there are.

1. 5 hundreds 7 tens 3 ones
   [4 hundreds 17 tens 3 ones]
2. 2 hundreds 1 ten 6 ones
   [1 hundred 11 tens 6 ones]
3. 4 hundreds 8 tens 9 ones
   [3 hundreds 18 tens 9 ones]
4. 6 hundreds 0 tens 2 ones
   [5 hundreds 10 tens 2 ones]

2 TEACH

DISCUSSING Model the number 358 on Workmat 3 and write the number on the chalkboard in a place-value box. Then write the number 173 directly under 358 in the place-value box. Tell children that you are going to subtract, or take away, 173 from 358.

Using models, guide children through the regrouping process.

■ **Can we take 3 ones away from 8 ones?** [Yes.]

Remove 3 ones models from the workmat. Have children count the remaining ones models as you record the number 5 in the ones column in the place-value box.

Focus attention on the tens models.

■ **Can we take 7 tens away from 5 tens? Why?** [No, because there are not enough tens.]

■ **What can we do to get more tens?** [Regroup 1 hundred as 10 tens.]

Do the regrouping, and then subtract 7 tens from 15 tens. Have children count to find how many are left. [8 tens] Record this number in the tens column in the place-value box. Then have children subtract 1

Use Workmat 3. Use 16 ▭ , 8 ◻ , and 9 ▦ .
Find the difference.

1.

hundreds	tens	ones
[4]	[16]	
5̶	6̶	4
− 1	8	2
3	8	2

2.

hundreds	tens	ones
[5]	[12]	
6̶	2̶	3
− 4	7	1
1	5	2

3.

hundreds	tens	ones
[6]	[13]	
7̶	3̶	8
− 4	5	2
2	8	6

4.

hundreds	tens	ones
[8]	[11]	
9̶	1̶	8
− 2	3	4
6	8	4

5.

hundreds	tens	ones
[2]	[14]	
3̶	4̶	6
−	9	5
2	5	1

6.

hundreds	tens	ones
[7]	[15]	
8̶	5̶	2
−	6	0
7	9	2

···· *Estimation* ····

You can estimate to subtract.
Find the nearest hundred.
Then subtract.

> 531 − 218
> 500 − 200 = 300
> The difference is **about 300**.

1. 328 − 112 (200)

2. 639 − 407 (200)

3. 715 − 240 (500)

---

hundred from 2 hundred and count to find how many are left. [1 hundred] Read the subtraction as 358 minus 173 equals 185.

PUPIL'S EDITION pp. 405-406

Page 405 Work through the example with the children. Point out how regrouping is recorded in small boxes. Have children write the difference.

Check for Understanding

■ **When subtracting, how can you tell if you need to regroup the hundreds?** [If you do not have enough tens to subtract, you must regroup the hundreds.]

Page 406 ■ **GUIDED PRACTICE** ex. 1: For reteaching, use Common Error and Remediation or Alternative Strategy.

MEETING INDIVIDUAL NEEDS

ACTIVITY *Common Error and Remediation*

MATERIALS 9 H, 18 T, 9 O models, Workmat 3 per child

When subtracting 3-digit numbers, some children may forget to add the regrouped tens to the existing tens. Work individually with each child. Have the child model 34 − 17 on Workmat 3. As the child models the subtraction, have him or her talk through each step. Then have the child model 539 − 256. Have the child explain each step in the process as he or she uses models to show the regrouping and subtraction. Repeat activity with other examples.

TEACHER to TEACHER

MANAGEMENT TIP My children benefited from describing each step of the subtraction process as they worked with models.

ACTIVITY **ALTERNATIVE TEACHING STRATEGY**

MATERIALS overhead projector; Teacher Aids Transparency 11; 9 H, 18 T, 9 O models or Manipulatives Kit Transparencies 8, 9

VISUAL/KINESTHETIC Model the subtraction 419 − 146 on Teacher Aids Transparency 11. Describe each step of the subtraction process to children, giving special attention to the regrouping step. Repeat with other examples that require regrouping, having children give oral descriptions of each step in the subtraction.

3 PRACTICE•APPLY **PRACTICE** ex. 2–6

ESTIMATION Discuss the example with the children, pointing out they can round to the nearest hundred.

CLOSE Guide children to summarize the lesson:

■ **How could you use hundreds, tens, and ones models to help you subtract 3-digit numbers?** [Possible response: Model the first number. Then take away the second number, beginning with the ones. If necessary, regroup hundreds as tens, to find the difference.]

MAC Activity 235:
Basic-to-Average ▼

NUMBER SENSE ■ SUBTRACTION RACE

Materials game board (Teacher Aid 1), game markers, number cubes (Teacher Aid 15)

Setup Write 3-digit subtraction problems with and without regrouping hundreds to tens in the squares of the game board on Teacher Aid 1. In several squares, write instructions such as "move a turn," "lose a turn," "move ahead 2 spaces," and so on. Duplicate a copy for each group.

Procedure Assign children to work in groups of three to five. Give each group a game board, a game marker for each player, and a number cube. Tell children they are to take turns rolling the cube and moving their marker that number of spaces. In order to remain on the square, they must correctly find the difference. If the difference is incorrect, the marker is moved back one space.

To Win The first child to reach the end of the board wins the game.

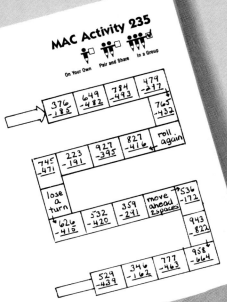

MAC Activity 235

On Your Own · Pair and Share · In a Group

MATH AND SOCIAL STUDIES ■ CITIES NEAR AND FAR

MAC Activity 236

On Your Own · Pair and Share · In a Group

Materials state atlas or road map

Display a map of your state that contains a distance table. With children's assistance, compile a list of cities showing their distance from the state capital or other major city. Using this information, have children work with a partner to write subtraction problems. Have pairs of children exchange problems and solve them. Use the following as examples to help children get started.

1. Laredo is 228 miles from Austin.
   Dallas is 192 miles from Austin.
   How much farther from Austin is Laredo than Dallas?
   [228 − 192 = 36 miles]
2. Abilene is 216 miles from Austin.
   Beaumont is 205 miles from Austin.
   How much farther from Austin is Abilene than Beaumont? [216 − 205 = 11 miles]

▲ **MAC Activity 236:**
Average-to-Challenge

Name

SUBTRACTING ONES, TENS, AND HUNDREDS

Study

Subtract ones.

hundreds	tens	ones
☐	☐	
4	3	**5**
− 1	7	**2**
		3

Regroup.
Subtract tens.

hundreds	tens	ones
3	13	
⁴4̸	₃8̸	5
− 1	7	2
	6	**3**

Subtract hundreds.

hundreds	tens	ones
3	13	
4̸	8̸	5
− 1	7	2
2	**6**	**3**

Check

Use models and Workmat 3. Subtract.

1.

hundreds	tens	ones
2	15	
3̸	5̸	8
− 1	7	2
1	8	6

hundreds	tens	ones
3	12	
4	2̸	9
− 2	7	5
1	5	4

2.

hundreds	tens	ones
5	14	
6̸	4̸	7
− 1	7	6
4	7	1

hundreds	tens	ones
7	16	
8̸	6̸	6
− 2	8	3
5	8	3

Macmillan/McGraw-Hill, MATHEMATICS IN ACTION
Grade 2, Chapter 13, Lesson 8, pages 405–406

Reteaching-118

Name

SUBTRACTING ONES, TENS, AND HUNDREDS

Use Workmat 3. Use 18 ▭ , 9 ▢ , and 9 ▦ .
Find the difference.

1.

hundreds	tens	ones
3	13	
4̸	3̸	6
− 1	7	2
2	6	4

2.

hundreds	tens	ones
4	15	
5̸	5̸	9
− 2	7	3
2	8	6

3.

hundreds	tens	ones
7	12	
8̸	2̸	7
−	3	4
7	9	3

4.

hundreds	tens	ones
8	11	
9̸	1̸	8
−	6	7
2	4	1

5.

hundreds	tens	ones
3	14	
4̸	4̸	5
− 2	5	1
1	9	4

6.

hundreds	tens	ones
2	16	
3̸	6̸	6
−	9	2
2	7	4

7.

hundreds	tens	ones
2	15	
3̸	5̸	4
− 1	8	1
1	7	3

8.

hundreds	tens	ones
5	17	
6̸	7̸	9
− 2	8	5
3	9	4

Macmillan/McGraw-Hill, MATHEMATICS IN ACTION
Grade 2, Chapter 13, Lesson 8, pages 405–406

Practice-118

Name

SUBTRACTING ONES, TENS, AND HUNDREDS

On Your Own   Pair and Share   In a Group

SUBTRACTION PATTERNS
Find the pattern.
Write the next exercise.

1.
999	899	799	699	599
− 100	− 100	− 100	− 100	− 100
899	799	699	599	499

2.
909	808	707	606	505
− 101	− 101	− 101	− 101	− 101
808	707	606	505	404

3.
100	200	300	400	500
− 10	− 20	− 30	− 40	− 50
90	180	270	360	450

4.
101	202	303	404	505
− 100	− 200	− 300	− 400	− 500
1	2	3	4	5

5.
999	888	777	666	555
− 10	− 10	− 10	− 10	− 10
989	878	767	656	545

6.
800	700	600	500	400
− 400	− 350	− 300	− 250	− 200
400	350	300	250	200

Macmillan/McGraw-Hill, MATHEMATICS IN ACTION
Grade 2, Chapter 13, Lesson 8, pages 405–406

Enrichment-118

Problem of the Day

Last year Mrs. Lima saved $538 and spent $284 on car repairs. This year she saved $663 and she spent $321 on repairs. In which year did Mrs. Lima have more money left after paying for car repairs? [this year; possible solution: $538 − $284 = $254; $663 − $321 = $342; $342 > $254]

AT·A·GLANCE pp. 407-408

LESSON OBJECTIVE
Subtract 3-digit numbers, regrouping tens and ones.

ASSIGNMENT GUIDE

COURSE	EXERCISES
Basic	p. 408: 1–7
Average	p. 408: 1–7
Challenge	p. 408: 1–7
Extra Practice, p. 413	Practice Plus, p. 414

MATERIALS
Classroom Materials paper bags
Manipulatives number cards for 1–9*, 8 H, 15 T, 18 O models (or punchouts), Workmat 3* per child

Teacher Resources
Reteaching 119   Practice 119   Enrichment 119
MAC Act. 237, 238   *Teacher Aid 11
Computer Software *Mathematics Skills:* Disk 4 Act. 5, 6

SKILLS TRACE
3-DIGIT SUBTRACTION

Explore (Concrete)	Develop/Understand (Transitional/Abstract)
403–404	405–406, 407–408
Practice 413, 414, 415–416, 419	Apply 412, 418

See **MANIPULATIVES PLUS 76**, p. 390L.

3-Digit Subtraction

Paul collected 362 newspapers.
He gave 145 to the collection drive last week.
How many newspapers does he have left
to give this week?

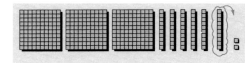

Not enough ones.
Regroup.

$$\begin{array}{r} 362 \\ -145 \\ \hline \end{array}$$

Subtract the ones.

7 ones are left.

$$\begin{array}{r} 3\overset{5\ 12}{\cancel{6}\cancel{2}} \\ -145 \\ \hline 7 \end{array}$$

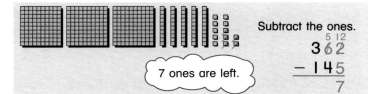

Subtract the tens.

I ten is left.

$$\begin{array}{r} 3\overset{5\ 12}{\cancel{6}\cancel{2}} \\ -145 \\ \hline 17 \end{array}$$

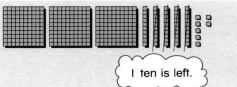

Subtract the hundreds.

2 hundreds are left.

$$\begin{array}{r} 3\overset{5\ 12}{\cancel{6}\cancel{2}} \\ -145 \\ \hline 217 \end{array}$$

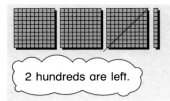

Macmillan/McGraw-Hill

Chapter 13   **Explore Adding and Subtracting 3-Digit Numbers**   four hundred seven   **407**

PREPARE

WARM-UP To prepare children to subtract 3-digit numbers with regrouping of tens to ones, write the following numbers on the chalkboard.

    23   17   8   45   16   31

Put number cards for 1 to 9 in a paper bag and have children take turns selecting a card. Have the child hold the card under each number on the chalkboard. Ask children if they would have to regroup if they subtracted the number on the card from the number on the chalkboard.

TEACH

MODELING Write the following exercise in a place-value box on the chalkboard. Have children use hundreds, tens, and ones models to model the number 574 on Workmat 3.

$$\begin{array}{r} 574 \\ -238 \\ \hline \end{array}$$

■ **Do you have enough ones to subtract 8 ones?** [No.]
■ **What should be done to get enough ones?** [Regroup 1 ten as 10 ones.]

After children model the regrouping and the subtraction of the ones, demonstrate how the regrouping is recorded in the place-value box at the tops of the tens and ones columns. Continue to work through the example, having children model the subtraction on their workmats as you write the numbers in the place-value box.

Write a similar problem without a place-value box, and have children model it on their workmats. Emphasize that the place-value box is not necessary if they remember the value of each digit in the numbers.

Find the difference.

1.
$$\begin{array}{r} ^{6\,18}\\ 4\cancel{7}\cancel{8}\\ -\ 139\\ \hline 339 \end{array}$$
$$\begin{array}{r} 375\\ -\ 249\\ \hline 126 \end{array}$$
$$\begin{array}{r} 582\\ -\ 164\\ \hline 418 \end{array}$$
$$\begin{array}{r} 690\\ -\ 415\\ \hline 275 \end{array}$$
$$\begin{array}{r} 763\\ -\ 247\\ \hline 516 \end{array}$$

2.
$$\begin{array}{r} 295\\ -\ 140\\ \hline 155 \end{array}$$
$$\begin{array}{r} 654\\ -\ 272\\ \hline 382 \end{array}$$
$$\begin{array}{r} 856\\ -\ 813\\ \hline 43 \end{array}$$
$$\begin{array}{r} 261\\ -\ 228\\ \hline 33 \end{array}$$
$$\begin{array}{r} 935\\ -\ 83\\ \hline 852 \end{array}$$

Add or subtract.

3.
$$\begin{array}{r} 214\\ +\ 129\\ \hline 343 \end{array}$$
$$\begin{array}{r} 276\\ -\ 127\\ \hline 149 \end{array}$$
$$\begin{array}{r} 614\\ -\ 423\\ \hline 191 \end{array}$$
$$\begin{array}{r} 396\\ +\ 178\\ \hline 574 \end{array}$$

Solve.

4. Fran collected 235 cans this week.
She collected 124 last week.
How many more did she collect this week?

___111___ cans

5. Pedro collected 218 bottles.
His sister collected 125 bottles.
How many did they collect in all?

___343___ bottles

Mixed Review

6. Moira has 3 wagons.
Each wagon has 4 wheels.
How many wheels in all?

___12___ wheels

7. Kim has 45¢.
Mel has 15¢ more than Kim.
How much money does Mel have?

___60¢___

Extra Practice, page 413 *Practice Plus,* page 414

Stress the importance of keeping the digits lined up as you demonstrate subtracting with zero. Use examples such as 420 − 18 and 500 − 130.

PUPIL'S EDITION pp. 407-408

Page 407 Work through the steps of the subtraction with the children. Have them model each step of the exercise.

Check for Understanding

■ **How can you tell if you need to regroup 1 ten for 10 ones when subtracting a 3-digit number?** [Look at the ones. If there are not enough ones to subtract, you must regroup 1 ten for 10 ones.]

Page 408 ■ GUIDED PRACTICE ex 1: Remind children that they can use models if they need help.

MEETING INDIVIDUAL NEEDS

ALTERNATIVE TEACHING STRATEGY

MATERIALS overhead projector; Teacher Aids Transparency 11; 6 H, 7 T, 9 O models or Manipulatives Kit Transparencies 8, 9

VISUAL Write 671 − 358 in vertical form on the chalkboard. Model 671 on the workmat transparency. Work through each step of the subtraction calling on volunteers to tell you what to do for each step. Record these steps in the exercise on the chalkboard. Repeat the activity with 460 − 229.

For Students Acquiring English (SAE)

Assist SAE children in completing the first example. Read the story problems aloud for less-capable SAE children; explain unfamiliar vocabulary using synonyms and gestures. Pair SAE children with non-SAE children to do Mixed Review.

ACTIVITY Common Error and Remediation

MATERIALS 8 H, 15 T, 18 O models (or punchouts), Workmat 3 per child

Some children may consistently subtract the greater digit from the smaller digit. Work individually with each child using hundreds, tens, and ones models and Workmat 3. Give the child exercises, with and without regrouping, that have been written in place-value boxes. Have the child use models, as you guide him or her through each exercise. Tell the child to describe each step of the subtraction.

For reteaching, use Common Error and Remediation or Alternative Strategy.

3 PRACTICE•APPLY PRACTICE ex. 2–7

CLOSE Guide children to summarize the lesson:

■ **What steps do you follow when subtracting 157 from 383?** [Check to see if there are enough ones; regroup; subtract the ones; subtract the tens; subtract the hundreds.]

MAC ACTIVITY CENTER

MAC Activity 238

On Your Own   Pair and Share   In a Group

CALCULATOR ■ WHAT'S THE RULE?

Materials calculator

Draw the following function tables on the chalkboard. Have children work with a partner. Give each pair a calculator and ask children to find the rule that applies to each. Work through the first table with the children. Guide them to see that by finding the difference between each beginning and ending number they will find the rule.

Extend the activity by having pairs of children make up their own tables using the same format. Then have children exchange tables with other pairs of children to complete.

Rule:___	
Begin with	End with
357	249
624	516
789	681

[-108]

Rule:___	
Begin with	End with
523	308
974	759
638	423

[-215]

Rule:___	
Begin with	End with
319	48
501	230
690	419

[-271]

Rule:___	
Begin with	End with
608	151
872	415
790	333

[-457]

▲ **MAC Activity 238:**
Average-to-Challenge

NUMBER SENSE ■ SPIN, WRITE, AND SUBTRACT

MAC Activity 237

On Your Own   Pair and Share   In a Group

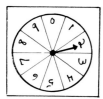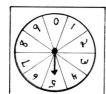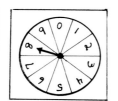

258

Materials 3 punchout spinners for 0–9

Assign children to work in pairs. Have children line up the spinners. Identify them as the hundreds, the tens, and the ones spinners. Have one child spin to get two 3-digit numbers and record each number on a sheet of paper. The other child should then use these numbers to write a subtraction exercise with the larger number on top and the smaller number on the bottom. Have children work together to do the subtraction. Repeat the activity by having children reverse roles.

▲ **MAC Activity 237:**
Basic-to-Average

RETEACHING-119

Name _____

3-DIGIT SUBTRACTION

Study

Regroup. Subtract ones.	Subtract tens.	Subtract hundreds.

hundreds	tens	ones
	6	14
3	7̸	4̸
− 1	2	8
		6

hundreds	tens	ones
	6	14
3	7̸	4̸
− 1	2	8
	4	6

hundreds	tens	ones
	6	14
3	7̸	4̸
− 1	2	8
2	4	6

Check

Use Workmat 3 and models. Subtract.

1.

hundreds	tens	ones
	7	15
6	8̸	5̸
− 2	3	7
4	4	8

hundreds	tens	ones
	4	14
4	5̸	4̸
− 1	2	6
3	2	8

2.

hundreds	tens	ones
	5	12
5	6̸	2̸
− 3	1	5
2	4	7

hundreds	tens	ones
	3	17
7	4̸	7̸
−	1	9
7	2	8

Reteaching-119

Macmillan/McGraw-Hill, MATHEMATICS IN ACTION
Grade 2, Chapter 13, Lesson 9, pages 407–408

PRACTICE-119

Name _____

3-DIGIT SUBTRACTION

Subtract.

1.
```
  7 17
  787      376      694      229      571
 −249     −138     −347     −153     −228
  538      238      347       76      343
```

2.
```
  319      648      736      546      822
 − 48     −152     −271     −319     −517
  271      496      465      227      305
```

3.
```
  673      851      762      239      443
 −252     −691     −148     − 65     −216
  421      160      614      174      227
```

4.
```
  862      582      654      771      591
 −325     − 18     −525     − 57     −257
  537      564      129      714      334
```

Add or Subtract.

5.
```
  583       46      456      182      658
 +209     +358     −193     +345     −294
  792      404      263      527      364
```

6.
```
  215      746      641      542      734
 −192     −273     +172     −381     + 99
   23      473      813      161      833
```

Practice-119

Macmillan/McGraw-Hill, MATHEMATICS IN ACTION
Grade 2, Chapter 13, Lesson 9, pages 407–408

ENRICHMENT-119

Name _____

3-DIGIT SUBTRACTION

On Your Own   Pair and Share   In a Group

SUBTRACTING MONEY

```
      2 12
    $2.3̸2̸
   − 1.17
    $1.15
```

Subtract.

1.
```
  $2.20     $5.43     $2.51     $9.86
 − 1.06    − 1.61    − 1.38    − 5.92
  $1.14     $3.82     $1.13     $3.94
```

2.
```
  $4.70     $6.34     $4.85     $5.19
 − 1.52    −  .92    − 1.37    − 2.36
  $3.18     $5.42     $3.48     $2.83
```

3.
```
  $7.65     $8.67     $3.54     $6.27
 − 4.38    − 5.31    − 1.37    − 3.54
  $3.27     $3.36     $2.17     $2.73
```

4.
```
  $5.30     $5.52     $8.16     $5.07
 − 2.15    − 2.28    − 2.32    −  .32
  $3.15     $3.24     $5.84     $4.75
```

Enrichment-119

Macmillan/McGraw-Hill, MATHEMATICS IN ACTION
Grade 2, Chapter 13, Lesson 9, pages 407–408

Problem of the Day

The Little Theatre has 685 seats. The box office sold tickets for 667 seats. An hour before the show, Mr. Jones called to see if he could buy 20 tickets. Were there enough seats left? [No. Possible solution: 685 − 667 = 18; 18 < 20.]

CHAPTER 13 • Lesson 10

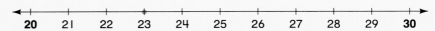

Problem Solving

UNDERSTAND / PLAN / TRY / CHECK / EXTEND

Strategy: Using Number Sense

Sometimes you do not need an exact number.

The class met for play practice 23 times.
Did the class meet nearer to 20 or 30 times?

```
◄──┼────┼────┼────┼────┼────┼────┼────┼────┼────┼──►
   20   21   22   23   24   25   26   27   28   29   30
```

Is 23 nearer to 20 or 30? How do you know?

The class met nearer to __20__ times.

> The numbers nearer to 20 are 21, 22, 23, and 24.

> The numbers nearer to 30 are 26, 27, 28, and 29.

> 25 is halfway between 20 and 30. We make it 30.

Ring about how many.

```
◄──┼──┼──┼──┼──┼──┼──┼──┼──┼──┼──┼──┼──┼──┼──┼──┼──┼──┼──┼──►
  30 31 32 33 34 35 36 37 38 39 40 41 42 43 44 45 46 47 48 49 50
```

1. 42 children went to see the play.
   About how many children went? **(about 40)**   about 50

2. 36 children sang in the chorus.
   About how many children sang?   about 30   **(about 40)**

Chapter 13   Explore Adding and Subtracting 3-Digit Numbers   four hundred nine   **409**

---

409 Chapter 13 • Lesson 10

126 parents went to see the play.
About how many parents went?

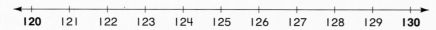

| 120 | 121 | 122 | 123 | 124 | 125 | 126 | 127 | 128 | 129 | **130** |

About 130 parents went to see the play.

> 126 is nearer to 130 than 120.

Ring about how many.

| **200** | 201 | 202 | 203 | 204 | 205 | 206 | 207 | 208 | 209 | **210** |

1. The children made 203 tickets for the play.
   About how many tickets did they make?

   (about 200)   about 210

| **420** | 421 | 422 | 423 | 424 | 425 | 426 | 427 | 428 | 429 | **430** |

2. There are 428 seats in the auditorium.
   About how many seats are there?

   about 420   (about 430)

| **380** | 381 | 382 | 383 | 384 | 385 | 386 | 387 | 388 | 389 | **390** |

3. The children made 384 programs for the play.
   About how many programs did they make?

   (about 380)   about 390

Extra Practice, page 413

■ **How can you use the number line to find if 23 is nearer to 20 or 30?** [Find 23; then look at 20 and 30 to see which number is nearer.]

Have children put their finger on 23 on the number line and count the numbers to 30 and the numbers to 20. Have them do the same for the other numbers. Then have them put their finger on 25 and count forward to 30.

■ **Is 20 a sensible answer to the problem?** [Yes, because 23 is nearer to 20.]

Encourage children to explain other ways to solve this problem.

Check for Understanding

■ **What if the class met for play practice 25 times? About how many times did the class meet?** [30]

MEETING INDIVIDUAL NEEDS

GUIDED PRACTICE ex. 1–2: Work through problem 1 with the children. Make sure they understand how to solve the problem using number sense.

Page 410 Have a volunteer read the problem at the top of the page. Have children find 126 on the number line. Discuss whether 126 is nearer to 120 or 130.

3 PRACTICE•APPLY   PRACTICE ex. 1–3

C L O S E Guide children to summarize the lesson:

■ **How do you know when you do not need an exact answer to solve a problem?** [Possible response: When the problem asks about how many, you can give an estimate.]

MAC Activity 239:
Basic-to-Average
▼

MAC Activity 239

MATH AND SCIENCE ▪ TOUR OF THE PLANETS

On Your Own   Pair and Share   In a Group

Materials   number line

Setup   Draw a number line from 110 to 160 on a long sheet of paper. At the tens, write the names of the planets as shown.

Procedure   Tape the number line to the floor. Have children stand around it as you read the names of the planets. Explain that you will read them several problems. Have children take turns standing on or pointing to the number in the problem, moving up or down to the nearest ten, and naming the planet on which they land. Have children tell you which ten is nearer as they move up or down.

1. You are traveling in your spaceship. You see 139 asteroids, so you go to the nearest planet. About how many asteroids do you see? [140, Mars]
2. You count 153 bright stars outside your spaceship window and head to the nearest planet. About how many bright stars do you see? [150, Jupiter]

Continue the activity with similar problems using numbers from 110 to 160.

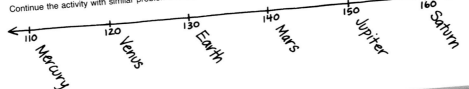

110 Mercury   120 Venus   130 Earth   140 Mars   150 Jupiter   160 Saturn

MAC Activity 240:
Average-to-Challenge
▼

SPEAKING MATHEMATICALLY ▪ I HAVE

MAC Activity 240

On Your Own   Pair and Share   In a Group

Materials   number lines, index cards

Setup   Prepare seven number lines on a sheet of paper, using the following numbers: 50 to 60, 80 to 90, 110 to 120, 170 to 180, 230 to 240, 260 to 270, 320 to 330. Duplicate a copy for each child in the class. Write each of the following numbers on index cards: 52, 55, 57, 84, 86, 89, 111, 115, 118, 172, 176, 178, 233, 235, 239, 261, 266, 322, 324, 325, 327.

Procedure   Have children play in small groups. Give each child a sheet of number lines and each group a set of number cards. The first player will mix the number cards and place them facedown. He or she then draws a number and makes up a problem beginning with "I have" for the person on the left. For example, if the player draws 233, a problem might be: "I have 233 goldfish. About how many fish do I have?" The second player then locates 233 on one of the number lines and moves to the nearest ten. If the nearest ten is greater than the number, the player gains two points. If the nearest ten is less than the number, the player gains one point. The player who made the move then takes the number cards and makes up a problem for the person on his or her left.

To Win   The child with the most points at the end of play is the winner.

I have 233 goldfish.

RETEACHING

Name

PROBLEM SOLVING STRATEGY: USING NUMBER SENSE

Study

The band practiced their songs 37 times.
Did the band practice about 30 times or about 40 times?

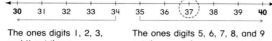

30 31 32 33 34 35 36 37 38 39 40

The ones digits 1, 2, 3, and 4 put these numbers nearer to 30.

The ones digits 5, 6, 7, 8, and 9 put these numbers nearer to 40.
The band practiced about 40 times.

Check

Ring about how many.

40 41 42 43 44 45 46 47 48 49 50

1. There are 44 children in the band.
   About how many children are there?   (40)   50

20 21 22 23 24 25 26 27 28 29 30

2. 28 children play different horns.
   About how many children play horns?   20   (30)

110 111 112 113 114 115 116 117 118 119 120

3. 112 people came to the band concert.
   About how many people came?   (110)   120

Macmillan/McGraw-Hill, MATHEMATICS IN ACTION
Grade 2, Chapter 13, Lesson 10, pages 409–410

Reteaching-120

PRACTICE

Name

PROBLEM SOLVING STRATEGY: USING NUMBER SENSE

Ring about how many.

20 21 22 23 24 25 26 27 28 29 30 31 32 33 34 35 36 37 38 39 40

1. There are 36 children on the racing team.
   About how many children are on the team?

   30   (40)

2. 23 children will be running in the relay race.
   About how many children will be in the race?

   (20)   30

340 341 342 343 344 345 346 347 348 349 350

3. 342 people came to see the race.
   About how many people were there?

   (340)   350

270 271 272 273 274 275 276 277 278 279 280

4. The Brown School team made 275 points.
   About how many points did they make?

   270   (280)

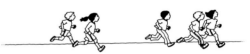

Macmillan/McGraw-Hill, MATHEMATICS IN ACTION
Grade 2, Chapter 13, Lesson 10, pages 409–410

Practice-120

ENRICHMENT

Name

PROBLEM SOLVING

On Your Own   Pair and Share   In a Group

HOW MANY MILES TO GO?

The Greens visited friends in Texas.
About how many miles did they drive each day?
Write the nearest 10.

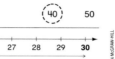

1. Monday—Abilene to Fort Worth
   154 miles

   About __150__ miles

2. Tuesday—
   Fort Worth to Dallas

   About __30__ miles

3. Wednesday—Dallas to Houston

   About __240__ miles

4. Thursday—Houston to Austin

   About __160__ miles

5. Friday—Austin to San Antonio

   About __100__ miles

On what day did they drive the most miles? __Wednesday__

Macmillan/McGraw-Hill, MATHEMATICS IN ACTION
Grade 2, Chapter 13, Lesson 10, pages 409–410

Enrichment-120

Problem of the Day

For the play to be a success, the theater needed to sell about 400 tickets. After the performance, the cashier counted 395 tickets sold. Was the play a success? [Yes; 395 is close to 400.]

AT·A·GLANCE p. 411

LESSON OBJECTIVE
Make decisions using information.

ASSIGNMENT GUIDE

COURSE	EXERCISES
Basic	p. 411: 1–4
Average	p. 411: 1–4
Challenge	p. 411: 1–4

MATERIALS
Classroom Materials drawing paper, crayons, blunt scissors

Teacher Resources
Crit. Think. 26   Prob. Solv. 64

Name _____

Decision Making

Problem Solving: Planning Tickets

Your class is putting on a play.
You are in charge of making the tickets.

On Friday, the first grade and second grade
classes of your school will come.

On Saturday, each student in your class can
invite 3 guests.

1. How can you find out how many tickets
   you need? Write your plan. Answers will vary.

   _____

   _____

   _____

2. Now try your plan.
   About how many tickets will you need? _____

3. What information should you put on
   the tickets? Make a list.

Use your own paper.

 4. Compare your list with a partner's list.
   What information is the same?
   What information is different?

Macmillan/McGraw-Hill

Chapter 13   Explore Adding and Subtracting 3-Digit Numbers   four hundred eleven   **411**

PREPARE   **WARM-UP** To review adding and subtracting
3-digit numbers, write the following numbers on the
chalkboard.

344	589	672	812	376
+237	+387	−173	−777	+99
[581]	[976]	[499]	[35]	[475]

Have children find the sums or differences.

TEACH   **DISCUSSING** Have children name times when
they needed a ticket to do something. List children's
responses on the chalkboard. [Possible responses: see a movie, play,
puppet show, circus] Read the completed list for the children, and discuss each event.

PUPIL'S EDITION p. 411
Discuss the picture at the top of the page with the children.

Check for Understanding
■ **What do you have to make?** [tickets]
■ **Who will be attending the play?** [first and second graders and
their guests]

PRACTICE·APPLY   Have children complete ex. 1–4. Call
on volunteers to tell how they would
find the number of tickets that are needed and the information that
must be written on the tickets.

TEACHER to TEACHER

COOPERATIVE LEARNING TIP In my classroom, children often work in three **rotating sets of pairs** within a group. I ask the first set of pairs to do the warm up section, the second set to do the planning list, and the third set to do the summary question together. Between each shift of partners, the members of the group confer on the problem and compare summaries.

For Students Acquiring English (SAE)

To carry out the Project activity, have children work in heterogeneous pairs.

CLOSE Guide children to summarize the lesson:

■ **What should you do before you plan to make tickets?** [Decide what information must be written on each ticket and how many people will need tickets.]

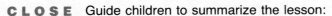
Portfolio

CLASS PROJECT

Materials drawing paper, pencils, crayons, scissors

Have each child use a set of materials to make two tickets. Remind children to think of an event and the information that is needed on a ticket before designing their tickets.

When children have completed the project, have volunteers display and tell about their tickets. Then have children give one of their tickets to a classmate.

Technology

Calculator: Problem Solving

1. 353 people are at Reed School's picnic. 359 people are at Scott School's picnic. How many people are at both picnics?

You can use a calculator to help you solve the problem.

Press [ON/C] 353 [+] 359 [=] ___712___ people

2. How many more people were at Scott School's picnic than at Reed School's picnic?

I can use a calculator.

I can use mental math.
359 − 353 = 6

Solve. Use mental math, 🖩 paper and pencil, or a 🖩.

3. David brings 275 hamburgers and 215 hot dogs to the picnic. How many hamburgers and hot dogs are there? ___490___ in all

4. How many more hamburgers than hot dogs did David bring? ___60___ hamburgers

---

Doris sold 137 tickets.
Bob sold 258 tickets.
How many tickets did they sell in all?
[395 tickets]

Have children discuss the procedures they used to solve the problem. Discuss which was faster or easier for them. Then have children reverse roles and solve the following problem.

Bill made 200 cookies.
Len made 300 cookies.
How many more cookies did Len make than Bill? [100 cookies]

Discuss the procedures again. Guide children to see that the problem could have been done mentally more quickly.

For Students Acquiring English (SAE)

Help SAE children identify the operation they should use to solve each problem by emphasizing key words **both picnics, in all,** and **how many more . . . than.**

3 PRACTICE•APPLY Have a volunteer read the sample problem at the top of the page. Work through the solution with children. Have children check each other's calculators to verify the answers.

CLOSE Guide children to summarize the lesson:

■ **When you add 367 + 246 which is faster or easier, a calculator or pencil and paper?** [Responses will vary.]

CHAPTER 13

EXTRA PRACTICE

Extra Practice items are provided so that children may have an opportunity for further practice.

The *Additional Practice* section also provides practice you may wish to assign.

Extra Practice

3-Digit Subtraction, pages 407–408 . . . .

Subtract.

1.
409	239	768	595	847
− 118	− 135	− 429	− 246	− 397
291	104	339	349	450

2.
627	954	514	827	774
− 584	− 139	− 374	− 603	− 226
43	815	140	224	548

3.
574	393	689	453	918
− 366	− 245	− 195	− 381	− 128
208	148	494	72	790

Problem Solving: Using Number Sense, pages 409–410 . . . .

Ring about how many.

```
30  31  32  33  34  35  36  37  38  39  40
```

1. Sandy picked 36 carrots.
   About how many carrots did she pick?

   about 30   (about 40)

```
50  51  52  53  54  55  56  57  58  59  60
```

2. Larry picked 54 beets.
   About how many beets did he pick?

   (about 50)   about 60

Macmillan/McGraw-Hill

ADDITIONAL PRACTICE

p. 407 *Subtract.*

1.
396	793	679
− 145	− 438	− 299
[251]	[355]	[380]

2.
952	572	431
− 538	− 246	− 218
[414]	[326]	[213]

3.
647	890	296
− 319	− 375	− 111
[328]	[515]	[185]

p. 409 *Ring about how many.*

1. 32 children went to see the circus. About how many children went?

   40   [30]

2. The parents mailed 158 letters. About how many letters were mailed?

   150   [160]

3. We saw 69 birds in one day. About how many birds did we see?

   [70]   60

4. 236 people visited the zoo on Sunday. About how many people visited?

   230   [240]

Practice Plus

Key Skill: 3-Digit Addition, page 398 . . . .

Add.

1.
195	674	409	856
+ 519	+ 297	+ 523	+ 118
714	971	932	974

2.
248	705	527	243	389
+ 414	+ 162	+ 329	+ 476	+ 389
662	867	856	719	778

3.
843	104	399	78	265
+ 27	+ 8	+ 41	+ 625	+ 573
870	112	440	703	838

Key Skill: 3-Digit Subtraction, page 408 . . . .

Subtract.

1.
626	371	583	846	917
− 145	− 209	− 237	− 576	− 654
481	162	346	270	263

2.
795	488	956	675	999
− 179	− 315	− 428	− 567	− 111
616	173	528	108	888

3.
700	847	345	590	694
− 120	− 145	− 18	− 9	− 108
580	702	327	581	586

414 four hundred fourteen

CHAPTER 13

PRACTICE *PLUS*

Practice Plus is provided to supply additional practice for the two key skills in this chapter.

Key Skills
Page 398: 3-Digit Addition
Page 408: 3-Digit Subtraction

The *Additional Practice* also provides practice you may wish to assign for key skills in this chapter.

ADDITIONAL PRACTICE

p. 398 *Add.*

1.
427	639	345	449
+ 291	+ 146	+ 285	+ 296
[718]	[785]	[630]	[745]

2.
117	751	371	270
+ 523	+ 214	+ 386	+ 345
[640]	[965]	[757]	[615]

3.
810	530	236
+ 127	+ 416	+ 547
[937]	[946]	[783]

4.
118	391	654
+ 349	+ 406	+ 186
[467]	[797]	[840]

5.
367	708	535
+ 271	+ 101	+ 380
[638]	[809]	[915]

p. 408 *Subtract.*

1.
419	879	980	456
− 213	− 316	− 473	− 191
[206]	[563]	[507]	[265]

2.
621	763	578	397
− 374	− 252	− 292	− 146
[247]	[511]	[286]	[251]

CHAPTER 13

AT·A·GLANCE pp. 415-416

OBJECTIVE
Review/test the concepts and skills presented in Chapter 13.

13A. Add 3-digit numbers with and without regrouping.
13B. Subtract 3-digit numbers with and without regrouping.
13C. Solve problems including those that involve two steps and using number sense.

Teacher Resources
Testing Program, pp. 139–150
Computer Software *Mathematics Skills: Disk 4 Final Checkup*

Language and Mathematics

Choose the correct words.

1. To add 274 and 318, you must ____regroup____.

2. 1 hundred = 10 ____tens____

3. 1 ten = 10 ____ones____

ones
tens
regroup

Concepts and Skills

Add.

4.
hundreds	tens	ones
☐1☐		
3	2	8
+ 2	9	1
6	1	9

5.
hundreds	tens	ones
☐1☐	☐1☐	
3	6	4
+ 1	6	7
5	3	1

Subtract.

6.
hundreds	tens	ones
☐3☐	☐11☐	
4̸	1̸	8
− 1	6	7
2	5	1

7.
hundreds	tens	ones
	☐6☐	☐13☐
5	7̸	3̸
− 2	4	6
3	2	7

Macmillan/McGraw-Hill

USING THE CHAPTER REVIEW/TEST

The Chapter Review/Test may be used as a review to survey children's knowledge and understanding of the chapter material. Or it may be used as a test to formally assess children's understanding of the concepts and skills taught in the chapter. if used as a test, you may wish to assign one or more of the resources listed in *Reinforcement and Remediation* on p. 416 after reviewing children's test results.

If the Chapter Review/Test is used as a review, you may wish to have children work in pairs to complete it. Have them talk about when to regroup in addition and subtraction. Then, you can use the Chapter Tests—Forms A, B, and C—provided in the *Testing Program Blackline Master and Teacher's Manual* for testing purposes. Any of these forms may be used for pretesting, posttesting, or retesting.

A performance assessment activity for the key concept in this chapter is provided on page 417.

Add or subtract.

8.
$$122 + 231 = 353$$
$$273 + 418 = 691$$
$$406 + 259 = 665$$
$$248 + 75 = 323$$
$$365 + 387 = 752$$

9.
$$578 - 245 = 333$$
$$346 - 228 = 118$$
$$625 - 352 = 273$$
$$580 - 426 = 154$$
$$856 - 108 = 748$$

Problem Solving

Solve.

10. Cathy earned 35¢ on Monday.
She earned 25¢ on Tuesday.
Then she spent 49¢ for a whistle.

How much money did she have left? __11¢__

Ring about how many.

80 81 82 83 84 85 86 87 88 89 **90**

11. There are 82 whistles in Mr. Kelly's store.
About how many whistles are there?

(about **80**)   about **90**

12. There are 88 children at King Elementary.
About how many children are there?

about **80**   (about **90**)

Reinforcement and Remediation

CHAP. OBJ.	TEST ITEMS	PUPIL'S EDITION pp.			TEACHER'S EDITION pp.	TEACHER RESOURCES	
		Lesson	Extra Practice	Practice Plus	Alt. Teaching Strategy	Reteaching	Practice
13A	1, 4–5, 8	393–398	402	414	394, 396, 398	115, 116	115, 116
13B	2–3, 6–7, 9	403–408	413	414	404, 406, 408	118, 119	118, 119
13C	10–12	399–400, 409–410	402, 413			117, 120	117, 120

For Students Acquiring English (SAE)

Before beginning the Chapter Review/Test with SAE children, scan the pages for any unfamiliar vocabulary that should be pretaught. You may wish to pair or group SAE children with non-SAE children. You may also wish to repeat some of the activities and techniques for SAE children that were suggested earlier in this chapter.

CHAPTER 13

AT·A·GLANCE p. 417

OBJECTIVE
Assess whether children can apply addition and subtraction concepts (with 3-digit numbers).

Teacher Resources
Performance Assessment booklet, pp. 48–50

For Students Acquiring English (SAE)

Before beginning the performance assessment with SAE children, scan the page for any unfamiliar vocabulary that should be pretaught. You may wish to pair or group SAE children with non-SAE children. You may also wish to repeat some of the activities and techniques for SAE children that were suggested earlier in this chapter.

Performance Assessment

Work with a partner.

Regroup if you can.

Tell a friend how to add
this math example.

$$\begin{array}{r} 245 \\ + 128 \\ \hline \end{array}$$

_____

_____

_____

_____

_____

Tell a friend how to subtract
this math example.

$$\begin{array}{r} 635 \\ - 342 \\ \hline \end{array}$$

_____

_____

_____

_____

_____

Macmillan/McGraw-Hill

You may put this page in your Portfolio

USING PERFORMANCE ASSESSMENT
The Performance Assessment activity may be used to informally assess children's understanding of the key concept(s) of the chapter. Additional assessment activities and Math Journal Options are provided in the *Performance Assessment* booklet.

Performing the Activity
Assign children to work in pairs. Have children work together to explain how to add two 3-digit numbers with regrouping. Allow them to continue with the subtraction problem. Let them record their explanations individually.

Evaluation Guidelines
Use these criteria to help determine the holistic score for each child. The holistic scoring scale can be found in the Teacher's Reference Section.

- Can children explain how to add and subtract 3-digit numbers?
- Can children regroup in addition?
- Can children regroup in subtraction?

[Example Response: $\begin{array}{r} 245 \\ +128 \\ \hline 373 \end{array}$]

If children do not have a full understanding of the key concept(s), you may wish to use the Alternative Teaching Strategies or the MAC Activities within the chapter.

You may wish to have children put their final revised work in their portfolios.

A formal assessment of the concepts and skills taught in this chapter is provided on pages 415–416.

Enrichment For All

Adding Money

$$\begin{array}{r} \$4.97 \\ +\quad 4.39 \\ \hline \$9.36 \end{array}$$

Remember to write the dollar sign and cents point.

$4.97

$2.99

$ .89

$3.77

$4.49

Add to find the total cost.

1.
$2.99	$3.77	$4.97	$4.49	$3.77
+ 4.97	+ 4.49	+ .89	+ 2.99	+ 3.77
$7.96	$8.26	$5.86	$7.48	$7.54

2. Which 2 toys would you choose? _____ Answers will vary.

What is the total cost? _____ Verify children's answers.

A T · A · G L A N C E p. 418

OBJECTIVE
Add money amounts.

ASSIGNMENT GUIDE

COURSE	EXERCISES
Basic	p. 418: 1–2
Average	p. 418: 1–2
Challenge	p. 418: 1–2

MATERIALS
Manipulatives   8 $1 bills, 4 Q, 8 T, 2 N, 10 P per pair

For Students Acquiring English (SAE)

Read the page aloud to SAE children, explaining and demonstrating key vocabulary. Have children point to the visuals in the textbook as you explain them. To check comprehension of the directions, ask SAE children to restate them. Review the children's answers to ex. 1–2 aloud. If time permits, direct children to choose two other toys and have another child find their total cost.

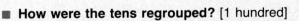

1 PREPARE

WARM-UP   To prepare children for adding money, have them give the following sums.

1. 349 + 263 = _____ [612]
2. 132 + 494 = _____ [626]
3. 571 + 78 = _____ [649]
4. 256 + 487 = _____ [743]

2 TEACH

DISCUSSING   Have children work in pairs. Give each pair eight dollar bills and two dollars in coins. Tell children to count out and add $4.97 and $4.39. Have them study the same amounts added on the page. Explain that adding money is like adding numbers.

■ **How were the ones regrouped?** [1 ten]

■ **How were the tens regrouped?** [1 hundred]

Have children read the total amount. Then discuss the pictures and the prices.

■ **What would you do to find how much two items cost?** [Add the prices.]

3 PRACTICE·APPLY   Have children complete ex. 1–2.

CLOSE   Guide children to summarize the lesson:

■ **What is the total cost of two whistles?** [$1.78]

Cumulative Review

Name _____

Fill in the ◯ to answer each question.

1.

$$\begin{array}{r} 35 \\ + 19 \\ \hline \end{array}$$

44　45　54　55
◯　◯　●　◯

2.

$12 + 33 + 5 = \underline{\ ?\ }$

40　45　50　55
◯　◯　●　◯

3.

$$\begin{array}{r} 76 \\ - 58 \\ \hline \end{array}$$

12　18　22　38
◯　●　◯　◯

4. Compare.

$476 \bigcirc 582$

<　>　+　=
●　◯　◯　◯

5. How many corners?

▭

2　3　4　5
◯　◯　●　◯

6.

$$\begin{array}{r} 248 \\ + 706 \\ \hline \end{array}$$

954　944　905　844
●　◯　◯　◯

7. Jack had 254 stamps. Derek gave him 26 stamps. How many stamps does Jack have now?

● 280 stamps
◯ 270 stamps
◯ 256 stamps
◯ 232 stamps

Macmillan/McGraw-Hill

Chapter 13　Explore Adding and Subtracting 3-Digit Numbers　　four hundred nineteen　**419**

USING THE CUMULATIVE REVIEW

The Cumulative Review is presented in a multiple-choice format to provide practice in taking a standardized test. It gives children an opportunity to review previously learned skills. An answer sheet, similar to those used when taking standardized tests, can be found in the *Testing Program Blackline Masters and Teacher's Manual.*

The table that follows correlates the review items to the lesson pages on which the skills are taught.

Review Items	Text Pages
1	191–195, 234
2	204
3	221–225, 234
4	290

Review Items	Text Pages
5	309
6	394–398
7	397–398

Testing Program Blackline Masters

In addition to the Cumulative Review in the Pupil's Edition, there are quarterly Cumulative Tests and an End-Year Test. These tests are multiple choice and provide additional opportunities for children to practice taking standardized tests.

Cumulative Tests measure children's performance on major skills and concepts taught during the previous quarters. The **End-Year Test** measures children's performance on major skills and concepts taught throughout the year.

Home Activity

Your child has been learning to add and subtract 3-digit numbers. Here is an activity you can do with your child to practice these skills.

Materials:
paper and pencil

Directions:

1. Each of you chooses 1 grocery item to buy. Add the prices to find the cost.

$$
\begin{array}{r}
\text{Oatmeal } \$1.\overset{1}{0}7 \\
\text{Soap } \underline{+ .58} \\
\$1.65
\end{array}
$$

2. One person chooses another item to buy. Add the price of the item to the first sum. Take turns choosing and adding until you have bought all the items.

3. For subtraction, start with $9.99. One person chooses 1 item to pay for. Subtract the price of the item from $9.99 to find the amount left.

$$
\begin{array}{r}
\$9.99 \\
\text{Soap } \underline{- .58} \\
\$9.41
\end{array}
$$

4. The other person chooses another item to pay for. Subtract the price of the item from the first amount left. Take turns choosing and subtracting until you have paid for all the items.

OBJECTIVE
Give family members an opportunity to share in their child's mathematics learning.

For Students Acquiring English (SAE)

Before assigning this Home Activity to SAE children, find out if someone at home will be able to work with them in English. If not, prepare them to complete the activity independently at home. Explain the directions of the activity and ask SAE children to restate them so you can check comprehension. Scan the page and preteach any difficult vocabulary or phrases that they may not know. If you feel that an SAE child will need extra help with the activity, you might assign that student a non-SAE partner and arrange a time for them to work on the activity in or out of school.

USING THE ACTIVITY

Have children look at the page. Explain that the page has an activity that an adult in the family can help them complete. Read the page with the children, making sure that they understand what needs to be done. Tell children that they will do this page at home.

Picture Glossary

calendar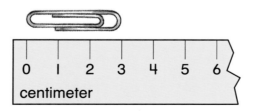

centimeter

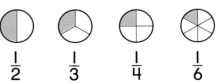

circle

cone

cube

cup

cylinder

difference

$$10 - 4 = \underset{\underset{\text{difference}}{\uparrow}}{6}$$

dime 10¢

dollar  $1.00

fact family

$$5 + 4 = 9 \qquad 9 - 5 = 4$$
$$4 + 5 = 9 \qquad 9 - 4 = 5$$

fraction

$\dfrac{1}{2} \qquad \dfrac{1}{3} \qquad \dfrac{1}{4} \qquad \dfrac{1}{6}$

gallon

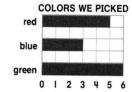

1 quart 1 quart 1 quart 1 quart 1 gallon

graph

COLORS WE PICKED

	red					
blue						
green						

0 1 2 3 4 5 6

greater than

$$71 > 57$$

half dollar 50¢

half hour

2:30
two-thirty

hour

4:00
four o'clock

Macmillan/McGraw-Hill

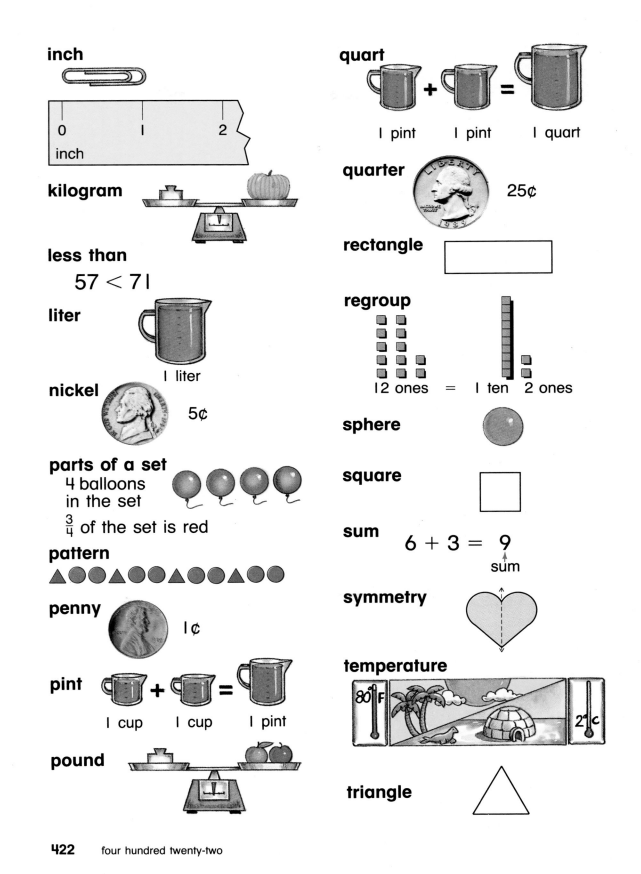

inch

kilogram

less than

$57 < 71$

liter

I liter

nickel

5¢

parts of a set

4 balloons
in the set

$\frac{3}{4}$ of the set is red

pattern

penny

I¢

pint

I cup   I cup   I pint

pound

quart

I pint   I pint   I quart

quarter

25¢

rectangle

regroup

12 ones = I ten   2 ones

sphere

square

sum

$6 + 3 = 9$

sum

symmetry

temperature

80° F   2° C

triangle

422   four hundred twenty-two

SCOPE and SEQUENCE

This section contains the Scope and Sequence for Mathematics in Action. The following mathematical strands are covered:

NUMERATION AND NUMBER THEORY	K	1	2	3	4	5	6	7	8
Count	■	■	■	■					
Skip-count		■	■	■	■				
Ordinal numbers	■	■	■	■					
Place value									
whole numbers		■	■	■	■	■	■	■	■
decimals				■	■	■	■	■	■
Compare and order									
whole numbers	■	■	■	■	■	■	■	■	■
decimals				■	■	■	■	■	■
fractions and mixed numbers				■	■	■	■	■	■
integers							■	■	■
rational numbers								■	■
Round									
whole numbers				■	■	■	■	■	■
decimals					■	■	■	■	■
fractions and mixed numbers						■	■	■	■
Exponents					■	■	■	■	■
Scientific notation							■	■	■
Squares and square roots							■	■	■
Other numeration systems			■	■	■	■	■	■	■
Common factors / greatest common factor (GCF)					■	■	■	■	■
Common multiples / least common multiple (LCM)					■	■	■	■	■
Divisibility rules				■	■	■	■	■	■
Even and odd numbers			■	■	■	■	■	■	■
Prime and composite numbers					■	■	■	■	■
Prime factorization					■	■	■	■	■

DECIMALS	K	1	2	3	4	5	6	7	8
Concepts									
Place value				■	■	■	■	■	■
Equivalent decimals					■	■	■	■	■
Compare and order					■	■	■	■	■
Round					■	■	■	■	■
Convert decimals and fractions					■	■	■	■	■
Convert decimals and percents						■	■	■	■
Terminating and repeating							■	■	■
Nonrepeating								■	■
Scientific notation								■	■
Rational numbers								■	■
Real numbers									■
Computation									
Add decimals					■	■	■	■	■
Subtract decimals					■	■	■	■	■
Estimate sums and differences					■	■	■	■	■
Multiply by whole number						■	■	■	■
Multiply by decimal						■	■	■	■
Estimate products						■	■	■	■
Divide by whole number						■	■	■	■
Divide by decimal						■	■	■	■
Zeros in quotient and dividend						■	■	■	■
Estimate quotients						■	■	■	■
Mental math strategies						■	■	■	■
Compute with rational numbers								■	■
Solve equations								■	■

GRADE 2
NUMERATION AND NUMBER THEORY
Count
  understand numbers
    to 100: 52, 60, 87
    to 1,000: 276, 299
Skip-count
  by 10s, 56, 60, 89
  by 2s, 61-62, 64, 68, 84, 85, 86, 87, 301
  by 5s, 61, 84
  by 3s, 62, 68, 84, 85, 87, 213
  by 4s, 62, 68, 84, 85, 87, 123
Ordinal numbers
  to twentieth, 77-78, 83, 86, 87
Place value
  whole numbers
    expanded form, 88
      tens and ones, 53-54, 55-56, 57-58, 74, 87, 88,
        89, 98, 213, 278
      hundreds, tens, and ones, 277-278, 279-280,
        281-282, 286, 296, 297-299, 331, 361
Compare and order
  whole numbers, using > and <
    to 100: 59, 68, 73-74, 75-76, 83-84, 85-86, 87, 123,
      136, 149, 273, 277-278, 279-280, 286, 297, 298,
      331, 361
    to 1,000: 287-288, 289-290, 295, 296, 298, 299,
      306, 361, 419
Round
  whole numbers, 300
Other numeration systems
  Chinese numerals, 82
  Roman numerals, 48
Even and odd numbers, 63-64, 68, 85

Red type denotes introduction of skill.

WHOLE NUMBER COMPUTATION	K	1	2	3	4	5	6	7	8
Addition									
Meaning of addition		▨	▨	▨	▨				
Properties		▨	▨	▨	▨	▨			
Basic facts		▨	▨	▨	▨	▨	▨		
Fact families		▨	▨	▨	▨	▨			
Missing addends		▨	▨	▨	▨	▨	▨		
Add 2- and 3-digit numbers			▨	▨	▨	▨	▨	▨	
Add greater numbers			▨	▨	▨	▨	▨	▨	▨
Add money amounts			▨	▨	▨	▨	▨	▨	▨
Mental math strategies		▨	▨	▨	▨	▨	▨		
Estimate sums			▨	▨	▨	▨	▨	▨	
Solve equations						▨	▨	▨	▨

GRADE 2
WHOLE NUMBER COMPUTATION
Addition
Meaning of addition, 9, 10
  count on to add, 23, 31-32, 46, 60, 97
  sentences, 11, 17, 19, 21, 23, 25, 28, 31, 33, 35,
    39-40, 43, 46, 47, 49, 93, 95, 101
Properties
  order, zero, 15
  grouping, 31-32, 43, 44, 46, 47, 49
Basic facts
  to 5, 11, 45, 46, 47, 49
  to 6, 19-20, 32, 46, 47, 89
  to 7, 21-22, 28, 32, 44, 45, 46, 47
  to 8, 29-30, 32, 46, 47, 60, 183, 245, 301
  to 9, 33-34, 45, 46, 47, 49, 60, 105, 123
  to 10, 10, 35-36, 38, 43, 44, 46, 47, 60, 89, 102, 111,
    123, 138, 149
  to 11, 93-94, 118, 119, 121, 138, 168, 194
  to 12, 95-96, 119, 121, 138
  to 13, 99-100, 119, 120, 121, 149, 168, 194
  to 14 and 15, 101-102, 118, 119, 120, 121, 168,
    183, 224
  to 16, 17, and 18, 92, 107-108, 117, 118, 119, 121, 123,
    194, 245, 273
  add with doubles, 30, 32, 89, 102, 111, 121, 123, 149,
    168, 224
  add three numbers, 31-32, 43, 44, 46, 47, 49, 111,
    117, 118, 120, 121, 123, 204, 207, 208, 210, 211,
    213, 361, 419
Fact families, 13-14, 20, 22, 28, 30, 34, 36, 43, 44, 45,
  94, 95, 99, 102, 106
Missing addends, 27, 98, 196, 204
Add 2- and 3-digit numbers
  2-digit numbers, 186, 191-192, 193-194, 195, 197-198,
    200, 208, 209, 210, 211, 212, 213, 224, 234,
    235-236, 239, 243, 245, 252, 301, 331, 338, 419
  3-digit numbers, 392, 395-396, 397-398, 402, 414,
    415, 416, 417, 419
Add money amounts, 37, 112, 183, 203, 207, 210, 211,
  213, 245, 418
Mental math strategies, 97, 396
Estimate sums, 36, 108, 201-202, 282, 406

Red type denotes introduction of skill.

WHOLE NUMBER COMPUTATION	K	1	2	3	4	5	6	7	8
Subtraction									
Meaning of subtraction	■	■	■	■					
Properties		■	■	■	■				
Basic facts	■	■	■	■					
Fact families		■	■	■					
Subtract 2- and 3-digit numbers		■	■	■	■	■			
Subtract greater numbers				■	■	■	■	■	■
Subtract money amounts			■	■	■	■	■	■	■
Mental math strategies			■	■	■	■	■	■	■
Estimate differences			■	■	■	■	■	■	■
Solve equations				■	■	■	■	■	■
Multiplication									
Meaning of multiplication			■	■	■	■	■		
Properties			■	■	■	■	■	■	■
Basic facts			■	■	■	■			
Fact families			■	■	■	■			
Missing factors				■	■	■	■	■	■
Multiply 3 factors				■	■	■	■	■	■
Multiply powers of 10					■	■	■	■	■
Multiply by 1-digit multiplier			■	■	■	■	■	■	■
Multiply by 2-digit multiplier					■	■	■	■	■
Multiply greater numbers				■	■	■	■	■	■
Multiply money amounts				■	■	■	■	■	■
Mental math strategies				■	■	■	■	■	■
Estimate products				■	■	■	■	■	■
Solve equations				■	■	■	■	■	■
Division									
Meaning of division			■	■	■	■	■		
Properties				■	■	■	■	■	■
Basic facts				■	■	■	■		
Fact families				■	■	■	■		
Divide powers of 10					■	■	■	■	■
Divide by 1-digit divisor				■	■	■	■	■	■
Divide by 2-digit divisor					■	■	■	■	■
Divide by 3-digit divisor						■	■	■	■
Zeros in quotient					■	■	■	■	■
Short division					■	■	■	■	■
Divide money amounts				■	■	■	■	■	■
Mental math strategies				■	■	■	■	■	■
Estimate quotients				■	■	■	■	■	■
Solve equations							■	■	■

GRADE 2
WHOLE NUMBER COMPUTATION

Subtraction
Meaning of subtraction, 9, 10
  count back to subtract, 24, 60
  sentences, 12, 18, 19, 21, 24, 26, 33, 35, 39-40, 43, 46, 47, 49, 93, 95, 101
  number line, 231-232
Properties
  zero, 16
Basic facts
  to 5: 12, 32, 45, 46, 47, 49
  to 6: 19-20, 46, 47, 49, 102
  to 7: 21-22, 28, 32, 44, 45, 46, 47, 49
  to 8: 29-30, 32, 34, 46, 47, 102, 149
  to 9: 33-34, 45, 46, 47, 60, 89, 102, 105, 183, 194
  to 10: 10, 35-36, 38, 43, 44, 46, 47, 60, 89, 102
  to 11: 93-94, 96, 119, 121
  to 12: 95-96, 119, 121
  to 13: 99-100, 168, 194
  to 14 and 15: 101-102, 119, 121, 123, 128, 138, 149, 168, 213
  to 16, 17, and 18: 92, 107-108, 117, 118, 119, 121, 138, 168, 183, 194, 331
Fact families, 13-14, 20, 22, 28, 30, 34, 36, 43, 44, 45, 94, 95, 99, 102, 106
Subtract 2- and 3-digit numbers
  2-digit numbers, 216, 221-222, 223-224, 225, 230, 234, 235-236, 239, 240, 241-242, 243, 245, 273, 288, 301, 331, 338, 361, 398, 419
  3-digit numbers, 405-406, 407-408, 413, 414, 415, 416, 417
Subtract money amounts, 37, 112, 233, 239, 240, 242, 243, 245
Mental math strategies, 98, 222, 406
Estimate differences, 406

Multiplication
Meaning of multiplication, 363-364
  sentences, 365-366
Properties
  order, zero, one, 369-370
Basic facts
  by 2 and 3: 365-366, 369-370, 372, 385, 386, 387
  by 4 and 5: 367-368, 369-370, 372, 384, 385, 386, 387
  by 0: 370

Multiply by 1-digit multiplier, 365-366, 367-368, 369-370, 372, 379-380, 384, 385, 386, 387, 389

Division
Meaning of division, 364
  equal groups, 375-376, 377-378, 383, 384, 385, 386, 387
  sentences, 388

Red type denotes introduction of skill.

FRACTIONS AND MIXED NUMBERS	K	1	2	3	4	5	6	7	8
Concepts									
Meaning of fractions	X	X	X	X	X	X	X	X	X
Equivalent fractions				X	X	X	X	X	X
Simplest form				X	X	X	X	X	X
Least common denominator (LCD)					X	X	X	X	X
Compare and order				X	X	X	X	X	X
Round					X				
Convert improper fractions and mixed numbers					X	X	X	X	X
Find fraction of a number					X	X	X	X	X
Density property									X
Reciprocals							X	X	X
Computation									
Add fractions				X	X	X	X	X	X
like denominators				X	X	X	X	X	X
unlike denominators					X	X	X	X	X
Add mixed numbers					X	X	X	X	X
Estimate sums						X	X	X	X
Subtract fractions				X	X	X	X	X	X
like denominators				X	X	X	X	X	X
unlike denominators					X	X	X	X	X
Subtract mixed numbers					X	X	X	X	X
Estimate differences						X	X	X	X
Multiply fractions					X	X	X	X	X
Multiply mixed numbers						X	X	X	X
Estimate products						X	X	X	X
Divide fractions						X	X	X	X
Divide mixed numbers							X		X
Estimate quotients							X	X	X
Convert fractions and decimals					X	X	X	X	X
Convert fractions and percents					X	X	X	X	X
Solve equations							X	X	X

GRADE 2
FRACTIONS AND MIXED NUMBERS
Concepts

Meaning of fractions, 334, 337, 342
  halves, 335-336, 343, 345, 356, 357, 358, 359, 376
  fourths, 337-338, 343, 344, 345-346, 354, 356, 357, 358, 359, 376
  thirds, 339-340, 344, 346, 354, 356, 357, 359, 376
  sixths, 341-342, 344, 345-346, 355, 356, 358, 359, 361
  parts of a set, 347-348, 355, 356, 358, 359
  parts of a whole, 334, 335-336, 337-338, 339-340, 341-342
  using half inches, 360

Red type denotes introduction of skill.

MEASUREMENT, TIME, MONEY	K	1	2	3	4	5	6	7	8
Measurement									
Estimate and measure length									
nonstandard units	▓	▓	▓	▓	▓				
metric/customary units		▓	▓	▓	▓	▓	▓	▓	▓
Estimate and measure capacity	▓	▓	▓	▓	▓	▓	▓	▓	▓
metric/customary units		▓	▓	▓	▓	▓	▓	▓	▓
Estimate and measure weight (mass)	▓	▓	▓	▓	▓	▓	▓	▓	▓
metric/customary units		▓	▓	▓	▓	▓	▓	▓	▓
Convert units			▓	▓	▓	▓	▓	▓	▓
Compute with denominate numbers					▓	▓	▓	▓	▓
Temperature		▓	▓	▓	▓	▓	▓	▓	▓
Perimeter			▓	▓	▓	▓	▓	▓	▓
Circumference						▓	▓	▓	▓
Area			▓	▓	▓	▓	▓	▓	▓
Surface area							▓	▓	▓
Volume			▓	▓	▓	▓	▓	▓	▓
Precision							▓	▓	▓
Indirect measurement								▓	▓
Time									
Read a calendar	▓	▓	▓	▓	▓				
Estimate and tell time	▓	▓	▓	▓	▓	▓			
Convert units				▓	▓	▓	▓	▓	▓
Compute with denominate numbers						▓	▓	▓	▓
Find elapsed time		▓	▓	▓	▓	▓	▓	▓	▓
Money									
Find values of coins and bills	▓	▓	▓	▓	▓	▓			
Make change			▓	▓	▓	▓	▓	▓	▓
Compare and order			▓	▓	▓	▓	▓	▓	▓
Round				▓	▓	▓	▓	▓	▓
Estimate and compute with money amounts		▓	▓	▓	▓	▓	▓	▓	▓
See Problem Solving—Consumer Math	▓	▓	▓	▓	▓	▓	▓	▓	▓

GRADE 2
MEASUREMENT, TIME, MONEY

Measurement
Estimate and measure length
  nonstandard units, 152
  metric units, 153-154, 155-156, 164, 178, 179, 180,
    181, 213, 330
  customary units, 5, 152, 165-166, 167-168, 176, 177,
    178, 180, 181, 360
Estimate and measure capacity
  compare: holds more, less, 157
  metric units, 157-158, 164, 179, 181
  customary units, 169-170, 177, 180, 181, 382
Estimate and measure weight (mass)
  metric units, 159, 164, 179, 180, 181
  customary units, 171, 177, 180, 181
Temperature
  Celsius, 160, 164, 180, 181, 245
  Fahrenheit, 172, 177, 180, 181, 301
Perimeter, 315-316, 325, 326, 328, 329
Area, 317, 325, 328, 329
Volume, 318

Time
Read a calendar, 261-262, 266, 267, 270, 271
Estimate and tell time
  hour, 249-250, 254, 269, 271, 308
  half hour, 251-252, 254, 268, 269, 271, 301, 308
  quarter hour, 257-258, 270, 271, 361
  five minutes, 259-260, 267, 268, 269-270, 273, 308
  A.M. and P.M., 272
Find elapsed time, 253, 255-256, 260, 265, 285

Money
Find values of coins and bills
  penny, 7, 126, 127-128, 145, 146, 147, 148, 149, 156,
    183, 273
  nickel, 7, 126, 127-128, 145, 146, 147, 148, 149,
    156, 183
  dime, 7, 126, 127-128, 145, 146, 147, 148, 149, 156,
    183, 273
  quarter, 129-130, 134, 144, 145, 147, 148, 156, 183,
    273
  half dollar, 130
  dollars and cents, 135-136, 137-138, 143, 144,
    145-146, 147, 156, 183, 331
Make change, 148
Estimate and compute with money amounts
  add/subtract, 37, 112, 183, 203, 207, 210, 211, 213,
    233, 238, 239, 240, 242, 243, 245, 418
See Problem Solving—Consumer Math

Red type denotes introduction of skill.

GEOMETRY	K	1	2	3	4	5	6	7	8
Patterns	▪	▪	▪	▪	▪	▪	▪	▪	▪
Points, lines, line segments, rays, angles				▪	▪	▪	▪	▪	▪
Classify angles					▪	▪	▪	▪	▪
Measure and estimate angles					▪	▪	▪	▪	▪
Identify plane figures	▪	▪	▪	▪	▪	▪	▪	▪	▪
Identify space figures	▪	▪	▪	▪	▪	▪	▪	▪	▪
Classify polygons				▪	▪	▪	▪	▪	▪
Classify triangles					▪	▪	▪	▪	▪
Classify quadrilaterals				▪	▪	▪	▪	▪	▪
Similarity					▪	▪	▪	▪	▪
Congruence				▪	▪	▪	▪	▪	▪
Symmetry		▪	▪	▪	▪	▪	▪	▪	▪
Circles					▪	▪	▪	▪	▪
Use geometric formulas					▪	▪	▪	▪	▪
Constructions						▪	▪	▪	▪
Tessellations					▪	▪	▪	▪	▪
Translations, reflections, and rotations					▪	▪	▪	▪	▪
Coordinate geometry						▪	▪	▪	▪
Pythagorean theorem								▪	▪
Special right triangles									▪
Tangent, sine, cosine ratios									▪

GRADE 2
GEOMETRY
Patterns, 3, 142, 313, 321-322
Identify plane figures
   circle, triangle, rectangle, square, 307-308, 309-310,
     314, 326, 327, 329, 419
   open and closed figures, 310
Identify space figures
   cone, cylinder, sphere, rectangular prism, cube,
     305-306, 314, 327, 329
Congruence, 320, 324, 325, 328
Symmetry, 319, 324, 325, 328, 329

Red type denotes introduction of skill.

PROBLEM SOLVING	K	1	2	3	4	5	6	7	8
Strategies and Skills									
Use the five-step process		▪	▪	▪	▪	▪	▪	▪	▪
Use/draw a picture/diagram	▪	▪	▪	▪	▪	▪	▪	▪	▪
Find a pattern	▪	▪	▪	▪	▪	▪	▪	▪	▪
Identify extra information	▪	▪	▪	▪	▪	▪	▪		▪
Find needed information		▪	▪	▪	▪	▪	▪		▪
Make an organized list	▪	▪	▪	▪	▪	▪	▪	▪	▪
Use/make a graph	▪	▪	▪	▪	▪	▪	▪	▪	▪
Choose operation/write a number sentence	▪	▪	▪	▪	▪	▪	▪		▪
Write and solve an equation						▪	▪	▪	▪
Use a physical model	▪	▪	▪	▪	▪	▪	▪	▪	▪
Use/make a chart/table	▪	▪	▪	▪	▪	▪	▪	▪	▪
Guess, test, and revise		▪	▪	▪	▪	▪	▪	▪	▪
Use estimation		▪	▪	▪	▪	▪	▪	▪	▪
Solve a simpler problem			▪	▪	▪	▪	▪	▪	▪
Use number sense	▪	▪	▪	▪	▪	▪	▪	▪	▪
Work backward			▪	▪	▪	▪	▪	▪	▪
Solve two-step problems			▪	▪	▪	▪	▪	▪	▪
Solve multistep problems				▪	▪	▪	▪	▪	▪
Check for a reasonable answer		▪	▪	▪	▪	▪	▪	▪	▪
Conduct an experiment or simulation		▪	▪	▪	▪	▪	▪	▪	▪
Interpret the quotient and remainder				▪	▪	▪	▪		▪
Use a proportion							▪	▪	▪
Use a formula					▪	▪	▪	▪	▪
Use different strategies				▪	▪	▪	▪	▪	▪
Use more than one strategy					▪	▪	▪	▪	▪
Strategies review		▪	▪	▪	▪	▪	▪	▪	▪
Thinking Mathematically									
Investigate patterns		▪	▪	▪	▪	▪	▪	▪	▪
Apply mathematics	▪	▪	▪	▪	▪	▪	▪	▪	▪
Use number concepts	▪	▪	▪	▪	▪	▪	▪	▪	▪
Visual reasoning	▪	▪	▪	▪	▪	▪	▪	▪	▪
Measuring	▪	▪	▪	▪	▪	▪	▪	▪	▪
Collect and interpret data			▪	▪	▪	▪	▪	▪	▪
Logical reasoning	▪	▪	▪	▪	▪	▪	▪	▪	▪
Experiment and predict	▪	▪	▪	▪	▪	▪	▪	▪	▪
Consumer Math									
Interpret consumer information sources	▪	▪	▪	▪	▪	▪	▪	▪	▪
Spend/buy	▪	▪	▪	▪	▪	▪	▪	▪	▪
Save/invest							▪	▪	▪
Percent applications							▪	▪	▪
Misleading statistics								▪	▪
Decision making			▪	▪	▪	▪	▪	▪	▪

GRADE 2
PROBLEM SOLVING
Strategies and Skills
Use the five-step process, 17-18
Use/draw a picture/diagram, 131-132, 134, 311-312, 345-346, 355, 358, 359
Find a pattern, 69-70, 83, 86, 87, 123, 280
Identify extra information, 227-228, 230, 242, 243
Make an organized list, 79-80, 283-284, 286, 298, 299
Use/make a graph, 6, 71, 72, 113-114, 117, 120, 121, 176, 182, 311-312, 314, 328, 329
Choose operation/write a number sentence, 25-26, 28, 39-40, 43, 46, 47, 49, 89, 103-104, 106, 116, 120, 121, 149, 173-174, 177, 180, 181, 235-236, 239, 242, 243, 245, 273, 301, 331, 361, 379-380, 383, 386, 387, 389, 398, 408, 419
Use a physical model, 321-322
Use/make a chart/table, 82, 176, 196, 197-198, 200, 206, 210, 211, 226, 253
Guess, test, and revise, 139-140, 373-374
Use estimation, 201-202, 231-232
Solve a simpler problem, 212
Use number sense, 65-66, 161-162, 263-264, 267, 270, 271, 409-410, 413, 416, 417
Work backward, 255-256
Solve two-step problems, 399-400, 402, 416, 417
Strategies review, 291-292, 351-352

Thinking Mathematically
Investigate patterns, 2, 3, 313, 371
Apply mathematics, 105, 229, 253
Use number concepts, 7, 27, 67, 343
Visual reasoning, 163, 199, 401
Measuring, 5
Collect and interpret data, 6
Logical reasoning, 4, 8, 285
Experiment and predict, 133

Consumer Math
Interpret consumer information sources, 41, 131-132, 139-140, 141, 293, 353, 373-374, 381
Spend/buy, 7, 37, 127-128, 129-130, 131-132, 135-136, 137-138, 139-140, 148, 183, 203, 216, 233, 234, 400, 418
Decision making
  planning a craft, 41
  planning a game, 81
  choosing a classroom pet, 115
  planning a collection, 141
  planning a garden, 175
  planning rides, 205
  choosing a prize, 237
  planning a class trip, 265
  planning a recycling drive, 293
  planning a bulletin board, 323
  planning a pizza order, 353
  planning a catalog order, 381
  planning tickets, 411

Red type denotes introduction of skill.

MATHEMATICAL REASONING	K	1	2	3	4	5	6	7	8
Thinking Mathematically	■	■	■	■	■	■	■	■	■
Decision making	■	■	■	■	■	■	■	■	■
Critical thinking				■	■	■	■	■	■

ESTIMATION	K	1	2	3	4	5	6	7	8
Strategies									
Round				■	■	■	■	■	■
Front-end					■	■	■	■	■
Compatible numbers					■	■	■	■	■
Clustering						■	■	■	■
Computation									
Whole numbers									
sums and differences	■	■	■	■	■	■	■	■	■
products and quotients			■	■	■	■	■	■	■
Decimals									
sums and differences					■	■	■	■	■
products and quotients˙						■	■	■	■
Fractions / mixed numbers									
sums and differences						■	■	■	■
products and quotients							■	■	■
Percents							■	■	■
Measurement									
Length, weight (mass), capacity	■	■	■	■	■	■	■	■	■
Time		■	■	■	■	■	■	■	■
Temperature		■	■	■	■	■	■	■	■
Perimeter, area, volume				■	■	■	■	■	■
Angle measure						■	■	■	■
Problem Solving									
Check for reasonableness				■	■	■	■	■	■
Over- and underestimates				■	■	■	■	■	■

MENTAL MATH	K	1	2	3	4	5	6	7	8
Count on or back	■	■	■	■	■				
Use doubles		■	■	■	■				
Make ten		■	■	■	■				
Skip-count		■	■	■	■				
Work left to right					■	■	■	■	■
Break apart numbers					■	■	■	■	■
Use fact families			■	■	■	■	■		
Use properties		■	■	■	■	■	■	■	■
Use patterns	■	■	■	■	■	■	■	■	■
Use compensation					■	■	■	■	■
Multiply and divide by powers of 10				■	■	■	■	■	■
Scale up or down							■	■	■
Solve equations							■	■	■
Find percent of a number								■	■
Find fraction of a number								■	■

GRADE 2

MATHEMATICAL REASONING

Thinking Mathematically, See Problem Solving
Decision making, See Problem Solving—Consumer Math

ESTIMATION

Strategies
Round, 282, 300, 406

Computation
Whole numbers
   sums and differences, 36, 108, 201-202, 282, 406

Measurement
Length, weight (mass), capacity, 153-154, 155-156,
   157-158, 159, 165-166, 167-168, 169-170, 171, 177, 178,
   179, 180, 181
Time, 248, 260, 267, 270, 271
Temperature, 160

MENTAL MATH

Count on or back, 23-24, 60, 85, 87, 96
Use doubles, 30
Make ten, 35-36, 97-98
Skip-count, 56, 60, 61-62, 64, 68, 84, 85, 86, 87, 89,
   123, 213, 301
Use fact families, 13-14, 20, 22, 28, 30, 34, 36, 43, 44,
   45, 94, 95, 99, 102, 106
Use properties, 15-16, 31-32, 43, 44, 46, 47, 49, 369-370
Use patterns, 15-16, 109-110

Red type denotes introduction of skill.

ALGEBRA	K	1	2	3	4	5	6	7	8
Expressions, Equations, Inequalities									
Patterns, relations, functions	▓	▓	▓	▓	▓	▓	▓	▓	▓
Inverse operations		▓	▓	▓	▓	▓	▓	▓	▓
Properties		▓	▓	▓	▓	▓	▓	▓	▓
Use order of operations					▓	▓	▓	▓	▓
Evaluate algebraic expressions							▓	▓	▓
Write/solve number sentences/equations	▓	▓	▓	▓	▓	▓	▓	▓	▓
Solve 2-step equations								▓	▓
Solve equations in 2 variables								▓	▓
Graph equations								▓	▓
Inequalities							▓	▓	▓
Graph inequalities								▓	▓
Positive/Negative Numbers									
Integers					▓	▓	▓	▓	▓
meaning of					▓	▓	▓	▓	▓
properties							▓	▓	▓
absolute value							▓	▓	▓
compare and order							▓	▓	▓
add and subtract							▓	▓	▓
multiply and divide								▓	▓
graph							▓	▓	▓
Rational numbers									▓
meaning of									▓
properties									▓
compare and order									▓
compute with									▓
Irrational numbers									▓
Real numbers									▓
Negative exponents								▓	▓
Law of exponents								▓	▓

GRADE 2
ALGEBRA

Expressions, Equations, Inequalities

Patterns, relations, functions, See Patterns, Relations, Functions

Inverse operations, 13-14, 27

Properties, 15, 16, 31-32, 43, 44, 46, 47, 49, 109-110, 369-370

Write/solve number sentences/equations, 14, 17-18, 25-26, 27, 98, 101-102, 107-108, 122, 196, 226, 388-389

Inequalities

use >, < symbols, 75-76, 83, 84, 86, 87, 136, 149, 290, 295, 298, 299, 306

Red type denotes introduction of skill.

PROBABILITY AND STATISTICS	K	1	2	3	4	5	6	7	8
Probability									
Meaning			■	■	■	■	■	■	■
Conduct an experiment/simulation			■	■	■	■	■	■	■
Simple events			■	■	■	■	■	■	■
Mutually exclusive events							■	■	■
Independent events							■	■	■
Dependent events							■	■	■
Theoretical/experimental probability						■	■	■	■
List outcomes				■	■	■	■	■	■
Tree diagrams				■	■	■	■	■	■
Counting principle					■	■	■	■	■
Predict outcomes				■	■	■	■	■	■
Sample space						■	■	■	■
Random numbers					■	■	■	■	■
Permutations							■	■	■
Combinations							■	■	■
Statistics									
Collect and organize data	■	■	■	■	■	■	■	■	■
Conduct a survey		■	■	■	■	■	■	■	■
Conduct an experiment or simulation		■	■	■	■	■	■	■	■
Tally	■	■	■	■	■	■	■	■	■
Make a table/graph	■	■	■	■	■	■	■	■	■
Interpret data	■	■	■	■	■	■	■	■	■
Find mean, median, mode, and range				■	■	■	■	■	■
Effects of change on data						■	■	■	■
Misleading statistics/deceptive graphs						■	■	■	■
Use statistical sampling							■	■	■

GRADE 2
PROBABILITY AND STATISTICS

Probability
Meaning, 349-350
Conduct an experiment/simulation, 349-350

Statistics
Collect and organize data
   from a picture, 131-132, 134
   make a list, 79-80, 283-284, 286, 298-299
   from a table, 82, 176, 182, 197-198, 200, 206, 210,
     211, 253
Conduct a survey, 182
Conduct an experiment or simulation, 349-350
Tally, 71, 182
Make a table/graph, 182, 198, 206, See Graphing
Interpret data
   from a map, 42, 330
   from a graph, See Graphing

Red type denotes introduction of skill.

GRAPHING	K	1	2	3	4	5	6	7	8
Pictographs		▪	▪	▪	▪	▪	▪	▪	▪
Bar graphs	▪	▪	▪	▪	▪	▪	▪	▪	▪
Line graphs				▪	▪	▪	▪	▪	▪
Circle graphs					▪	▪	▪	▪	▪
Frequency tables and histograms					▪	▪	▪	▪	▪
Scattergrams								▪	▪
Line plots							▪	▪	▪
Stem-and-leaf plots							▪	▪	▪
Box-and-whisker plots								▪	▪
Deceptive graphs							▪	▪	▪
Coordinate graphing		▪	▪	▪	▪	▪	▪	▪	▪

PATTERNS, RELATIONS, FUNCTIONS	K	1	2	3	4	5	6	7	8
Patterns									
Number patterns	▪	▪	▪	▪	▪	▪	▪	▪	▪
Sequences	▪	▪	▪	▪	▪	▪	▪	▪	▪
Geometric/spatial patterns	▪	▪	▪	▪	▪	▪	▪	▪	▪
Relations									
Graphing and ordered pairs		▪	▪	▪	▪	▪	▪	▪	▪
Functions									
Meaning						▪	▪	▪	▪
Function tables						▪	▪	▪	▪
Graph functions								▪	▪

RATIO, PROPORTION, PERCENT	K	1	2	3	4	5	6	7	8
Ratio									
Meaning					▪	▪	▪	▪	▪
Equal ratios						▪	▪	▪	▪
Rate							▪	▪	▪
Tangent, sine, cosine ratios									▪
Proportion									
Meaning							▪	▪	▪
Solve proportions							▪	▪	▪
Scale drawings						▪	▪	▪	▪
Similar figures							▪	▪	▪
Scale up or down							▪	▪	▪
Indirect measurement							▪	▪	▪
Percent									
Meaning						▪	▪	▪	▪
Convert fractions and percents						▪	▪	▪	▪
Convert decimals and percents						▪	▪	▪	▪
Percents greater than 100% and less than 1%							▪	▪	▪
Percent of a number						▪	▪	▪	▪
Percent one number is of another							▪	▪	▪
Find number when percent of it is known								▪	▪
Estimate percents							▪	▪	▪
Mental math							▪	▪	▪
Percent increase and decrease							▪	▪	▪
Percent applications							▪	▪	▪
circle graphs							▪	▪	▪
simple/compound interest								▪	▪
discount/sale price							▪	▪	▪
commission								▪	▪

GRADE 2

GRAPHING

Pictographs, 72
Bar graphs, 6, 71, 113-114, 117, 120, 121, 176, 182
Coordinate graphing, 311-312, 314, 328, 329

PATTERNS, RELATIONS, FUNCTIONS

Patterns

Number patterns, 56, 61-62, 68, 84, 85, 87, 123, 213
   addition/subtraction, 15-16, 109-110, 244
   multiplication, 369-370
Geometric/spatial patterns, 3, 313, 321-322

Relations

Graphing and ordered pairs, 311-312

Red type denotes introduction of skill.

TECHNOLOGY	K	1	2	3	4	5	6	7	8
Calculator									
Patterns									
Computation									
Choose a calculation method									
Order of operations									
Fractions and decimals									
Special keys									
Computer									
Logo									
Spreadsheets									
Patterns									
Simulations									
Functions									
Graphs									

GRADE 2
TECHNOLOGY

Calculator
Patterns, 294, 368
Computation
    addition/subtraction, 38, 62, 196, 204, 226,
        373-374, 412
    multiplication, 368
Choose a calculation method, 38, 103, 131, 139, 173,
    196, 226, 228, 235, 379, 380
Special keys
    [C], 294

Computer
Logo, 116, 324
Spreadsheets, 238
Patterns, 142
Graphs, 176

Red type denotes introduction of skill.

TEACHER'S REFERENCE SECTION

This section contains the following:

BIBLIOGRAPHY

Books for Teachers

Ashlock Robert B., et al. *Guide Each Child's Learning of Mathematics.* Columbus, OH: Merrill, 1983.

Beaumont, Vern, et al. *How to Teach Perimeter, Area, and Volume.* Reston, VA: National Council of Teachers of Mathematics, 1986.

Beyer, Barry K. *Practical Strategies for the Teaching of Thinking.* Boston: Allyn and Bacon, 1987.

Billstein, R., et al. *A Problem Solving Approach to Mathematics for Elementary School Teachers.* Menlo Park, CA: Benjamin Cummings, 1987.

Brisby, Linda-Sue, et al. *Measurement: A "Hands On" Approach to Teaching.* Solvang, CA: Hands On, Inc., 1968.

————. *Patterns and Functions: A "Hands On" Approach to Teaching.* Solvang, CA: Hands On, Inc., 1990.

Copeland, Richard W. *How Children Learn Mathematics: Teaching Implications of Piaget's Research.* New York: Macmillan, 1984.

Farrell, Margaret A., ed. *Imaginative Ideas for the Teacher of Mathematics.* Reston, VA: National Council of Teachers of Mathematics, 1988.

Feinberg, Miriam M. *Solving Word Problems in the Primary Grades: Addition and Subtraction.* Reston, VA: National Council of Teachers of Mathematics, 1988.

Forseth, Sonia D. *Creative Math-Art Activities for the Primary Grades.* Englewood Cliffs, NJ: Prentice-Hall, 1984.

Graph Paper Masters. Palo Alto, CA: Dale Seymour Publications, 1989.

Grossnickle, Foster E., et al. *Discovering Meanings in Elementary School Mathematics,* 7th ed. New York: Holt, Rinehart and Winston, 1983.

O'Daffer, Phares G., ed. *Problem Solving: Tips for Teachers.* Reston, VA: National Council of Teachers of Mathematics, 1988.

Reys, Robert, Marilyn N. Suydam, and Mary N. Lindquist. *Helping Children Learn Mathematics.* Englewood Cliffs, NJ: Prentice-Hall, 1984.

Skolnick, Joan, Carol Langbort, and Lucille Day. *How To Encourage Girls in Math and Science: Strategies for Parents and Educators.* Englewood Cliffs, NJ: Prentice-Hall, 1982.

Slavin, R., et al., eds. *Learning to Cooperate, Cooperating to Learn.* New York: Plenum Press, 1985.

Worth, Joan, ed. *Preparing Elementary School Mathematics Teachers: Readings from the Arithmetic Teacher.* Reston, VA: National Council of Teachers of Mathematics, 1988.

Grade 2

Books for Students

Chapter 1 — Adding and Subtracting Facts to 10

Grossman, Virginia. *Ten Little Rabbits.* San Francisco: Chronicle, 1991. ISBN 0-87701-552-X. **(Average)**

Peek, Merle. *Roll Over: A Counting Song.* New York: Clarion Books, 1981. ISBN 0-395-29438-X. **(Easy)**

Wolkstein, Diane. *The Banza.* New York: Dial Books for Young Readers, 1981. ISBN 0-8037-0428-3. **(Average)**

Chapter 2 — Understanding Numbers to 100

Cutler, Daniel Solomon. *One Hundred Monkeys.* New York: Simon & Schuster, 1991. ISBN 0-671-73564-0. **(Average)**

MacCarthy, Patricia. *Ocean Parade: A Counting Book.* New York: Dial Books for Young Readers, 1990. ISBN 0-8037-0780-0. **(Easy)**

Moore, Margaret. *Fifty Red Nightcaps.* San Francisco: Chronicle Books, 1988. ISBN 0-87701-520-1. **(Average)**

Mora, Pat. *A Birthday Basket for Tia.* New York: Macmillan Publishing Co., 1992. ISBN 0-02-767400-2. **(Average)**

Sloat, Teri. *From One to One Hundred.* New York: Dutton Children's Books, 1991. ISBN 0-525-44764-4. **(Challenging)**

Chapter 3 — Adding and Subtracting Facts to 18

Carle, Eric. *The Rooster Who Set Out to See the World.* New York: Franklin Watts, Inc., 1972. ISBN 0-88708-042. **(Average)**

Gackenbach, Dick. *A Bag Full of Pups.* New York: Clarion, 1981. ISBN 0-395-30081-9. **(Average)**

Merriam, Eve. *12 Ways to Get to 11.* New York: Simon and Schuster Books for Young Readers, 1992. ISBN 0-671-75544-7. **(Challenging)**

Pittman, Helena Clare. *Miss Hindy's Cats.* Minneapolis: Carolrhoda Books, Inc., 1990. ISBN 0-87614-368-0. **(Average)**

Chapter 4 — Money

Caple, Kathy. *The Purse.* Boston: Houghton Mifflin Company, 1986. ISBN 0-395-4182-6. **(Average)**

Hoban, Russell. *A Brithday for Frances.* New York: Harper & Row, Publishers, 1968. ISBN 0-06-022338-3. **(Challenging)**

Hoban, Tana. *26 Letters and 99 Cents.* New York: Scholastic, Inc., 1987. ISBN 0-688-06361-6. **(Average)**

Schwartz, David. *If You Made a Million.* New York: Lothrop, Lee & Shepard, 1989. 0-688-07017-5. **(Challenging)**

Viorst, Judith. *Alexander, Who Used to be Rich Last Sunday.* New York: Atheneum, 1978. ISBN 0-689-30602-4. **(Average)**

Zaslavsky, Claudia. *Count on Your Fingers African Style.* New York: Thomas Y. Crowell, 1987. ISBN 0-690-03864-X. **(Challenging)**

Chapter 5 — Measurement

Briggs, Raymond. *Jim and the Beanstalk.* New York: Coward-McCann, Inc., 1970. ISBN 0-698-20641-X. **(Average)**

Dahl, Roald. *Esio Trot.* New York: Viking, 1990. ISBN 0-670-83451-3. **(Challenging)**

Gibbons, Gail. *Weather Forecasting.* New York: Macmillan Publishing Company, 1987. ISBN 0-02-737-250-2. **(Challenging)**

Lionni, Leo. *Inch by Inch.* New York: Astor-Honor, Inc., 1960. ISBN 0-8392-3010-9. **(Easy)**

Morimoto, Junko. *The Inch Boy.* New York: Viking Kestrel, 1986. ISBN 0-14-050677-2. **(Challenging)**

Myller, Rolf. *How Big is a Foot?* New York: Atheneum, 1969. **(Challenging)**

Pluckrose, Henry. *Length.* New York: Franklin Watts, 1988. ISBN 0-531-10618-7. **(Average)**

Ziefert, Harriet. *A New Coat for Anna.* New York: Alfred A. Knopf, Inc., 1986. ISBN 0-394-97426-3. **(Average)**

Chapter 6 — Adding 2-Digit Numbers

Hoban, Tana. *26 Letters and 99 Cents.* New York: Scholastic, Inc., 1987. ISBN 0-688-06361-6. **(Average)**

Chapter 7 — Subtracting 2-Digit Numbers

Caple, Kathy. *The Purse.* Boston: Houghton Mifflin Company, 1986. ISBN 0-395-4182-6. **(Average)**

Hoban, Lillian. *Arthur's Funny Money.* New York: Harper & Row, Publishers, 1981. ISBN 0-06-022343-X. **(Average)**

Viorst, Judith. *Alexander, Who Used to be Rich Last Sunday.* New York: Atheneum, 1978. **(Average)**

Chapter 8 — Time

Baden, Robert, reteller. *And Sunday Makes Seven/Y Domingo Siete.* IL: Albert Whitman & Co., 1990. ISBN 0-8075-0356-8. **(Average)**

Gould, Deborah. *Brendan's Best-Timed Birthday.* New York: Bradbury, 1988. ISBN 02-737390-8. **(Challenging)**

Singer, Marilyn. *Nine O'Clock Lullaby.* New York: HarperCollins, 1991. ISBN 0-06-025648-6. **(Average)**

Chapter 9 — Understanding Numbers to 1,000

Anderson, Lonzo, and Adrienne Adams. *Two Hundred Rabbits.* New York: Viking Penguin, 1968. **(Average)**

Birch, David. *The King's Chessboard.* New York: Dial Books, 1988. ISBN 0-8037-0367-8. **(Challenging)**

Gag, Wanda. *Millions of Cats.* New York: Coward-McCann, 1928. ISBN 0-698-20637-1. **(Easy)**

Sharmat, Marjorie Weinman. *The 329th Friend.* New York: Four Winds Press, 1992. ISBN 0-02-782259-1. **(Average)**

Chapter 10 — Geometry

Feldman, Judy. *Shapes in Nature.* Chicago: Children's Press, 1991. ISBN 0-516-05102-4. **(Easy)**

Fisher, Leonard Everett. *Look Around: A Book About Shapes.* New York: Viking Kestrel, 1987. ISBN 0-670-80869-5. **(Easy)**

Grifalconi, Ann. *The Village of Round and Square Houses.* Boston: Little, Brown, 1986. ISBN 0-316-32862-6. **(Average)**

Tompert, Ann. *Grandfather Tang's Story.* New York: Crown Publishers, Inc., 1990. ISBN 0-517-57487-X. Gr. 2, Ch. (10) **(Challenging)**

Tucker, Sian. *The Shapes Game.* New York: Henry Holt and Company, 1989. ISBN 0-8050-1280-X **(Average)**

Chapter 11 — Fractions

Anno, Mitsumasa. *Anno's Math Game III.* New York: Philomel Books, 1989. ISBN 0-399-21615-4. **(Challenging)**

Pomerantz, Charlotte. *The Half-Birthday Party.* Boston: Houghton Mifflin, 1984. ISBN 0-89919-273-4 **(Easy)**

Watson, Clyde. *Tom Fox and the Apple Pie.* New York: Crowell, 1972. **(Challenging)**

Chapter 12 — Explore Multiplication and Division Facts

Anno, Mitsumasa, and Masaichiro Anno. *Anno's Mysterious Multiplying Jar.* New York: Putnam/Philomel, 1983. ISBN 0-399-21615-4. **(Challenging)**

Blia, Xiong. *Nine-in-One-Grrr!: A Folktale from the Hmong People of Laos.* Adapted by Cathy Spagnoli. San Francisco: Children's Book Press, 1989. ISBN 0-89239-048-4 **(Challenging)**

Giganti, Paul, Jr. *Each Orange Had Eight Slices.* New York: Greenwillow Books. 1992. ISBN 0-688-10429-0. **(Challenging)**

Hulme, Joy. *Sea Squares.* **(Challenging)**

Chapter 13 — Explore Adding and Subtracting 3-Digit Numbers

Birch, David. *The King's Chessboard.* New York: Dial Books, 1988. ISBN 0-8037-0367-8. **(Challenging)**

Pittman, Helena Clare. *A Grain of Rice.* New York: Hastings House, 1986. ISBN 0-8038-2728-8. **(Challenging)**

Sharmat, Marjorie Weinman. *The 329th Friend.* New York: Four Winds Press, 1992. ISBN 0-02-782259-1. **(Average)**

HOLISTIC SCORING SCALE

Below is given a general scoring scheme for open-ended activities. The method is called "holistic" because it focuses on all the work that the student does, rather than solely on the correctness of the final solution.

One recommended way to begin holistic scoring is to divide your class's work into three groups:

   ✍ **Superior Work**   (**6** or **5**)

   ✍ **Capable Work**   (**4** or **3**)

   ✍ **Insufficient Work** (**2, 1,** or **0**)

Then each of the three groups can be redivided into subgroups using the scoring scheme described below.

Seven-Point Assessment Scheme

SCORE	EXPLANATION
Superior **6**	**Exemplary Response** - student gives a complete response with a clear, coherent, and unambiguous explanation.
5	**Effective Response** - student gives a fairly complete response with clear explanations.
Capable **4**	**Satisfactory** - student gives a fairly complete response but the explanation may be somewhat unclear or incomplete.
3	**Nearly Satisfactory** - student begins the activity appropriately and shows progress, but fails to complete it or omits significant parts of it. Explanation fails to show full understanding of mathematical ideas involved.
Insufficient **2**	**Begins, But Fails to Carry Through** - student cannot go beyond the early stages of the activity. Explanation is not understandable. Student shows no understanding of problem situation.
1	**Unable to Begin Effectively** - student response does not correspond to the activity. Response indicates complete lack of understanding of mathematical ideas involved.
0	**No Attempt**

INDEX

INDEX

INDEX

ACKNOWLEDGMENTS

CONSULTANTS

MULTICULTURAL AND EDUCATIONAL CONSULTANTS
Rim An
Marcia Ascher
Elsie Babcock
Vicki Chan
Dr. Alejandro Gallard
Zelda Gold
Jerilyn Grignon
Earlene Hall
Susan Lair
Dr. Barbara Merino
Carol Mitchell
James R. Murphy
Gail Lowe Parrino
Yolanda Rodriguez
Claudia Zaslavsky

ASSESSMENT CONSULTANT
Michael Priestley

COOPERATIVE LEARNING CONSULTANT
Liana Nan Graves

ACKNOWLEDGMENTS
The publisher gratefully acknowledges permission to reprint the following copyrighted material:

ARITHMETIC IN VERSE AND RHYME selected by Allan D. Jacobs and Leland B. Jacobs. Drawings by Kelly Oechsli. Copyright © 1971 by Allan D. Jacobs and Leland B. Jacobs. Cover art used by permission of Kelly Oechsli.

THE BANZA by Diane Wolkstein, pictures by Marc Brown. Text, copyright © 1981 by Diane Wolkstein. Pictures, copyright © 1981 by Marc Brown. Reprinted by permission of the publisher, Dial Books for Young Readers.

CLOCKS AND MORE CLOCKS by Pat Hutchins. Reprinted with permission of Macmillan Publishing Company. Copyright © 1970 by Pat Hutchins.

THE DOORBELL RANG by Pat Hutchins. Text copyright © 1986 by Pat Hutchins. By permission of Greenwillow Books (A Division of William Morrow & Co.).

"Homework Machine" from A LIGHT IN THE ATTIC by Shel Silverstein. Copyright © 1981 by Evil Eye Music, Inc. Reprinted by permission of HarperCollins Publishers, Inc.

HOW BIG IS A FOOT? written and illustrated by Rolf Myller. Reprinted with permission of Atheneum Publishers, an imprint of Macmillan Publishing Company. Copyright © 1962 Rolf Myller.

HOW MANY WAYS CAN YOU CUT A PIE? by Jane Belk Moncure. © The Child's World, Inc., Elgin, IL, and used by permission.

NINETY-NINE POCKETS by Jean Myrick. Copyright © 1966 by Jean Myrick. Used by permission of Lantern Press, Inc.

PENELOPE GETS WHEELS by Esther Allen Peterson. Copyright © 1981 by Crown Publishers, Inc. Reprinted by permission of the publishers.

THE RANDOM HOUSE BOOK OF POETRY FOR CHILDREN selected by Jack Prelutsky and illustrated by Arnold Lobel. Copyright © 1983 by Random House, Inc. Cover art used by permission of the publisher.

THE STORY SNAIL by Anne Rockwell. Reprinted with permission of Macmillan Publishing Company. Copyright © 1974 by Anne Rockwell.

"Surprises" by Jean Conder Soule. Used by permission of the author.

TOO MANY BOOKS by Caroline Feller Bauer. Copyright © 1986. Reprinted by permission of Viking Penguin Inc.

TWO HUNDRED RABBITS by Lonzo Anderson and Adrienne Adams. Copyright © 1968. Reprinted by permission of Viking Penguin Inc.

"Using Subtraction" by Lee Blair from ARITHMETIC IN VERSE AND RHYME selected by Allan and Leland Jacobs. Copyright © 1971. Reprinted by permission of Leland B. Jacobs.

COVER DESIGN Designframe Inc. **COVER PHOTOGRAPHY** Pete McArthur

ILLUSTRATION Elizabeth Allen; 11, 12, 233, 234 • Istvan Banyai; 142, 176, 238, 294, 324, 412 • Nina Barbaresi; 87, 101, 147, 154, 181, 329, 387, 399, 400, 407, 408, 409 • Bill Basso; 276, 397, 398 • Christine Beauregard; stickers 2A-D; 19, 20, 46, 96, 230, 231, 232, 239, 254, 257, 258, 266, 267, 286, 291, 292, 373, 374, 385, 386 • Shirley Beckes; 37, 58, 59, 60, 68, 99, 100, 139, 140, 141, 201, 202, 384 • Phillipe Beha; stickers 3B-C; 3, 17, 18, 173, 174, 199 • Patti Boyd; 6 • Stephanie Britt; 23, 24 • Maxi Chambliss; stickers 1A-B; 2, 22, 45, 50, 61, 76, 85, 87, 90, 102, 112, 119, 121, 124, 127, 145, 150, 153, 154, 156, 179, 181, 184, 191, 204, 208, 209, 214, 220, 221, 241, 246, 252, 269, 271, 274, 297, 299, 302, 305, 327, 329, 332, 342, 357, 359, 362, 367, 377, 384, 385, 387, 390, 396, 414, 415, 418 • Lydia Chang; 82 • Luisa D'Augusta; 47 • Fred Daunno; 401 • Jim Deigan; 337, 350 • Suzanne DeMarco; 116, 330 • Susan Dodge; 55, 56, 115, 167, 168 • Kathleen Dunne; 31, 32, 39, 40, 129, 130, 197, 198, 206, 244, 272, 323, 354, 382 • Eldon Doty; 28, 71, 72, 107, 120, 235, 236, 266 • Andrea Eberback; 102, 118, 285 • Lois Ehlert; 52, 92, 126 • Mac Evans; 22, 111, 161, 162, 165, 166, 178, 237, 287, 288, 392, 394, 395, 421, 422 • Don Gambino; 238, 324 • David Garner; 353 • Doreen Gay-Kassel; 7, 27, 61, 62 • Marvin Glass; 203 • Fred Harsh; 122, 148 • Steve Henry; 25, 26, 41, 42, 67, 75, 76, 147, 193, 194, 243, 251, 252, 254, 302, 335, 377, 381, 382, 417 • Chris Hill; 116, 142 • Tom Huffman; 48, 88 • Marilyn Janovitz; stickers 3D, 4A; 216, 277, 278 • Dave Joly; 313 • Brian Karas; 225, 226 • Elliot Kreloff; 69, 70, 134, 143, 314, 325 • Lingta Kung; 253 • Claude Martinot; 15, 16, 86, 133, 146, 175, 179, 180, 200, 242, 255, 256, 263, 264, 269, 270, 300, 330, 359, 416 • Hima Pamoedjo; 354 • Dennis Panek; 13, 14, 17, 18, 95, 169, 170, 192, 227, 228, 279, 280, 296, 341, 348, 356, 411 • Jerry Pavey; 371 • Charles Peale; 135, 136 • Judith Pfeiffer; stickers 4D; 159, 160, 311, 312, 403, 404 • Debbie Pinkney; 28, 43, 82, 103, 104, 113, 176, 345, 346, 372, 379, 380, 383, 402 • Norman Rainock; 33, 34, 44, 79, 80, 223, 224, 305, 306, 307, 308, 318, 319, 320, 321, 322, 327, 351, 352, 360, 388 • Chris Reed; 81 • Tim Robinson; 84, 171, 172, 222, 240, 259, 260, 268, 326 • Doug Roy; 83, 90, 106, 124, 164, 177, 183, 332, 420 • Joanna Roy; 206 • Joshua Schreier; 315, 316 • Bob Shein; stickers 4B-C, 229, 339, 340 • Jerry Smath; 63, 64 • Linda Solovic; punchouts 3, 4, 7, 19; 10, 20, 22, 30, 34, 36, 97, 98, 127, 128, 187, 195, 196, 205, 212, 217, 218, 219, 265, 282, 290, 293 • Dorothy Stott; stickers 1D; 35, 36, 77, 78, 94, 109, 110, 153, 155, 156, 186, 248, 249, 283, 284, 309, 310, 409, 410 • Peggy Tagel; 73, 74, 343 • Arnie Ten; 42, 152, 182 • Randy Verougstraete; 8, 29, 30, 157, 158, 250, 344, 369, 375, 376 • Michael Waldman; 5, 418 • John Wallner; 53, 54 • Vicki Wehrman; punchout 20 • Fred Winkowski; 137, 138, 144, 189, 190, 261, 262, 364 • Leslie Wolf; 4 • Rusty Zabransky; stickers 1C; 64, 76, 116, 266 • Jerry Zimmerman; stickers 3A; 65, 66, 105, 131, 132, 163, 334, 365, 366, 368, 405, 406
CONTENTS: Bob Shein

PHOTOGRAPHY Animals Animals / Mantis Wildlife, 51 • Bruce Coleman Inc. / Jane Burton, 275B, D; Hans Reinhard, 275C; Tom Stack, 9B, C; Norman O. Tomalin, 9D • Ken Cavanaugh, 38 • Bob Cass, 1C-D, 9A, 52, 91, 93, 125, 126, 151, 169, 185, 196, 215, 247, 249, 275A, 303, 333, 363, 391 • Rob Gray, punchouts 3, 4, 5, 6, 9, 10, 11 12; 3, 7, 11, 12, 37, 101, 127, 128, 129, 130, 133, 134, 135, 136, 137, 138, 143, 144, 145, 146, 147, 148, 149, 156, 179, 183, 273, 331, 347, 421, 422 • Scott Harvey; 85, 95, 147, 266 • Richard Hutchings, 1A-B, 11, 12, 21, 65, 92, 153, 154, 188, 226, 289, 304, 307, 317, 336, 347, 349, 368, 369, 370, 378 • The Image Bank / Grant V. Faint, 9 • J. Gerard Smith, 57, 108, 412
CONTENTS: Clara Aich, ivB, v, viT, viB, viiiT, viiiB, ivT, xT • Bob Cass, iiiB, xB • Lillian Gee, ivB • Richard Haynes, iiiT, ivT • Richard Hutchings, viiB

Production: Textart, Inc.
All photographs are by the Macmillan/McGraw-Hill School Division (MMSD) except as noted below.
Manipulative Workshop pages and manipulatives all by Scott Harvey for MMSD. Hand shots and performance assessment pages by Scott Harvey for MMSD; and Ken Karp for MMSD. Author photos all by Ken Karp for MMSD except: Audrey Jackson by James Visser for MMSD.
Setup photography for MAC Activity and Manipulatives Plus pages: Clara Aich
4/C illustration for Problem Solving pages: Deb Troyer Bunnell
Line illustration for MAC Activity and Manipulatives Plus pages: Shirley Beckes, Rick Cooley, Daniel DelValle, Julie Durrell, Judith Fast, Felipe Galindo, G. Brian Karas, Kathie Kelleher, Jane F. Kendall, Vickie Learner, Kathi McCord, Karen Pellaton, Marcy Dunn Ramsey, Dana C. Regan, Joel Synder, Lynn Sweat
Technical illustration: Network Graphics